VECTOR MECHANICS

VECTOR MECHANICS

DAN EDWIN CHRISTIE

PROFESSOR OF MATHEMATICS AND PHYSICS

BOWDOIN COLLEGE

Second Edition

McGraw-Hill Book Company

New York   San Francisco   Toronto   London

VECTOR MECHANICS

PREFACE

A course in unspecialized vector mechanics is a natural meeting place of future physicists, engineers, mathematicians, and teachers of physics or mathematics. The physics student requires the habit of visualizing the phenomena behind symbols, the engineering student learns to analyze complex situations in terms of basic principles, and the mathematics student gains intuitive insights from physical models. Since, at the elementary level, these students and their needs are so often indistinguishable, it is fortunate that a single course contributes directly to professional training in all three fields.

This textbook, like its predecessor, is for undergraduates familiar with the calculus. The introduction of fundamental concepts and principles is very gradual. There are many worked examples and hundreds of problems with answers. Hence the book is well-suited to self-teaching, leaving the professor free to concentrate on difficulties and on points of special interest.

A principal aim of the book is to persuade students to think in terms of vectors. This aim is assisted by the nomenclature: in general, vectors are denoted by boldface capitals and scalars by lowercase italics. The introduction to vector algebra is sufficiently detailed to promote vectorial thinking. The treatment of vector fields emphasizes visualization, leaving rigor for courses in the calculus of several variables. Appendices provide supplementary work on vector spaces and on vector geometry. An appendix on linear transformations and matrices forms a link with courses in linear algebra.

The most conspicuous change in this revision is in the organization. The topics are now arranged to permit a more rapid penetration to the key concepts of energy and momentum. The distribution of material among an increased number of chapters allows the instructor more latitude in putting together either a one-semester or a two-semester course. In this period of changing curricula, such flexibility is a distinct advantage. Numerous chapters are made easy to omit. The four chapters labeled "Applications" are optional, and certain elementary chapters can be omitted by students with strong preparation in physics or calculus. The chapters on stress and strain, wave motion, kinetic theory, and the equations of Lagrange and of Hamilton are optional introductions to topics which the instructor may wish to develop further in lectures.

Clearly a variety of courses of different levels and lengths can be based on this text. For example, in a semester course called *Vector Mechanics of a Particle* the author currently uses Chaps. 1, 2, 3, 5, 6, 7, 8, 9, 12, 13, 14, and the last part of Appendix 4 (as a substitute for Sec. 13.6). A second-semester course on *Mechanics of Bodies and Media* is based on a selection of remaining chapters. It is easy to put together other combinations: *Statics* (Chaps. 1, 2, 3, 4, 9, 10, 11, 15, 19), *Dynamics* (5, 6, 7, 8, 12, 13, 16, 21), *Vectors* (2, 5, 9, 17, 18, Appendices 1, 2, 3, 4). A course on *Physical Mechanics* for students who have done previous work in vectors might review Chaps. 1 to 3, 5 to 9, 17, and 18, and then concentrate on 10, 12, 13, 14, 19, 20, 21, 22, 23.

In this edition more attention is given to the bridges connecting mechanics with physics, mathematics, and engineering.   The teacher wishing to enrich his course will find many kick-off points: satellites, effect of friction on orbits, vector geometry, rockets, neutron moderation, Compton effect, radiation pressure, galaxy dynamics, dual bases for vectors, regular reflection and refraction, resonance, Serret-Frenet formulas, ballistic pendulum, characteristic vectors, center-of-mass coordinates, the strain matrix, speed of efflux of a gas, Stokes' theorem, Michelson-Morley experiment, hodographs, Liouville's theorem, etc.

There are many minor changes in the revision.   There are now over 1,300 problems, some placed as practice exercises at the ends of sections, others as review problems at the ends of chapters.   The treatments of particle orbits, rigid-body kinematics, stress and strain, flux and solid angle, and kinetic theory have major changes or additions.   A short chapter on the equations of Lagrange and Hamilton has been added.   The appendices on vector algebra and geometry are mostly new. Throughout the book there is more careful use of physical motivation for formal definitions.

Inevitably a flexible, multipurpose book is a long book.   From the whole spectrum of topics from *vectors* to *Hamilton's canonical equations* the instructor will select only a fraction.   But the student has the advantage of an integrated treatment of related matters for review or supplementary study, and the teacher, even after the course has begun, can painlessly modify his objectives.

It is impossible to acknowledge adequately sources of assistance in writing this book.   Dozens of books and articles, scores of former students and assistants (many of them now physicists, engineers, and mathematicians of high repute), and numerous colleagues in colleges and universities have lent ideas and criticisms.   A number of distinguished scientists and teachers, engaged by the publisher to make suggestions, have provided for the revision valuable advice on content, nomenclature, organization, etc.   This advice, except for some late arrivals, has been fully heeded.   It could not all be followed because of outright contradictions.   I am very grateful for this assistance and will welcome criticisms of this new edition.

My thanks go to Eleanor W. Christie and Mark E. Christie for tolerant literary criticism and for assistance with typing and proofs; to Marcia J. Putnam for typing most of the manuscript; and to Ruth A. Crosman and Mary K. Damewood for typing.

Dan E. Christie

CONTENTS

CHAPTER 17
FIELDS AND GRADIENTS   428

CHAPTER 18
VECTOR PROPERTIES OF FLUIDS
AND FLOW   448

CHAPTER 19
ELEMENTARY PROPERTIES OF
ELASTICITY   479

CHAPTER 20
VECTOR TREATMENT OF STRESS
AND STRAIN   491

CHAPTER 21
WAVE MOTION IN ONE DIMENSION   513

CHAPTER 22
KINETIC THEORY   529

CHAPTER 23
INTRODUCTION TO METHODS OF
LAGRANGE AND HAMILTON   551

CHAPTER ONE

INTRODUCTION: THE NATURE of MECHANICS

The proper time for seeing a field in perspective is after rather than before studying it.   But the chances are very slight that you have never previously heard of mechanics. Hence, to refresh your memory and to outline our aims before launching into a systematic treatment of vectors and of mechanics, let us stop briefly to consider the nature of the subject.   You may wish to return for more deliberate consideration after you have read Chap. 6.

I.I. SUBJECT MATTER: EXPERIMENT AND CLASSICAL THEORY

In the science of mechanics a study is made of the motions of physical objects.   The revolutions of wheels and planets, the trajectories of baseballs and rockets, the starting and stopping of automobiles, the oscillations of pendulums and pistons, the falling of raindrops and the rising of balloons, and even the nonmotion of bridges and other structures lie in its domain.   There are two main aspects of the subject of mechanics.   One may study motion experimentally by making careful observations and precise measurements of positions, times, and forces, or one may approach the problem from the theoretical point of view by setting up a mathematical model or "theory" whose properties are analogous to observed phenomena.

A mathematical science such as mechanics tends in its early stages to advance in alternating strides, theory and experiment progressing in turn.   Conclusions deduced from the theory suggest experimental tests, while experimental results often necessitate modifications of the theory.   In this course we shall explore a relatively simple theory which has been found to be in remarkably close accord with experiment.   It was at one time thought to be the key to all the secrets of the universe, and the mechanistic point of view became dominant in many fields of thought.   It is now known that the model has distinct limitations: it does not, for instance, represent adequately the phenomena of atomic physics or of motion at speeds close to that of light.   Much less simple theories have been created to handle many such problems. For ordinary objects at ordinary speeds (as in ballistics, mechanical engineering, aerodynamics, etc.), the simpler classical theory is entirely satisfactory.

I

1.2. THE PHYSICAL INGREDIENTS OF THE THEORY

In the theoretical development we shall investigate the behavior of such unnatural objects as material points, called *particles*, absolutely rigid bodies, and entirely nonviscous fluids.   These are the things of mechanics: these are our ideal substitutes for the more complicated entities of physics, astronomy, or engineering.   In mechanics we are concerned with motion in terms of idealized space and time of these ideal objects.   The first two quantitative ingredients of the theory, then, are *length* as a key to position and *time* as the basis for studying change of position.   The physical concepts of length and time are quite sufficient for characterizing motion. In terms of them we can define new concepts such as speed and acceleration.   A third fundamental physical ingredient will be the concept of *force*.   The whole theoretical structure of elementary mechanics will be assembled from these three ingredients, length, time, and force, applied to particles and bodies.   In order that the theory may be strictly pertinent, it is necessary to have unequivocal understanding as to how length, time, and force are to be measured.

The concepts designated as fundamental in a branch of physics may be chosen arbitrarily, although certain choices usually seem more natural.   Very often mass is taken as fundamental, force being defined in terms of mass.   In the organization of this text it is convenient to describe how forces are measured and to define mass in terms of length, time, and force.

1.3. THE STRUCTURE AND USE OF THE THEORY

The theory itself is a mathematical structure whose symbols represent physical concepts: l for length, t for time, f for force, etc.   The starting point, aside from customary geometrical assumptions, will be certain dynamical *laws*, roughly as stated by Sir Isaac Newton.   These basic postulates for the mathematical theory are both suggested and checked by experimental observations.   From these assumed principles one may deduce mathematically conclusions which may be applied with reasonable confidence to physical situations.   These conclusions enable us to predict, as well as to describe, motion.   Results about particles may be applied to problems involving projectiles or planets.   And properties discovered for ideal rigid bodies have significance when applied to the design of practical machinery.   The propositions of classical mechanics usually may be stated as equations, often involving derivatives and integrals.   Hence, along with agreements as to what one means in terms of laboratory operations by such words as length, time, and force, there are also necessarily agreements, implicit if not explicit, concerning the mathematical operations (addition, differentiation, etc.) which may meaningfully be applied to the symbols.

The development of theory and the analysis of applications become, in the context described above, primarily a matter of setting up, solving, and interpreting equations.   In this course the prerequisites from mathematics are taken to be light, so systematic familiarity with differential equations is not assumed.   Most students of this text will have had or be having concurrently work in mathematics.   You should look constantly for ways to carry over insights from one course to the other.

1.4. THE ROLE OF VECTORS

It should be recognized that vector notation is introduced as a natural and economical means of describing physical situations.   The student should resolve to master this technique.   He should not be satisfied until he can carry out vector operations with ease and can see the physical meaning of each vector expression involving forces, velocities, etc. The number of basic principles used in this treatment is extremely small. They should be studied and thought over until they are thoroughly comprehended. It will then be found that the vector equations are merely a precise crystallization of fundamental ideas. If you have had previous experience with vectors, you should study Chap. 2 enough to become acquainted with its nomenclature and to sharpen your vector techniques. If this is your first serious encounter with vectors, you should realize that you are confronted with a typical foreign-language situation. It is not enough to be able to translate roughly and self-consciously from one language to the other. You should give yourself enough practice so that you can think in terms of vector operations. This ability will be of great value to you in physics, mathematics, or engineering.

1.5. PROBLEM SOLVING IN MECHANICS

Mechanics is often described as a "problem-solving course." The solution of many, many problems is indispensable to the achievement of a reasonable mastery of mechanics. Formal manipulations and physical doctrines are appreciated fully only when they have been approached and utilized in many different ways. It should be unnecessary to insist that exercises be done thoughtfully. While technique is of extreme importance, the aim of a problem assignment is not merely a list of correct numerical answers; it is also a fuller understanding of the theory and of the relationships between theoretical principles and specific physical situations. The student should strive to develop power and confidence in analyzing problems. When the fundamentals have been mastered in this way, a reliable basis will exist for future studies in applied mathematics, theoretical physics, and engineering analysis.

In this text most sections have sets of exercises which will assist you in mastering current material and in relating it to previous work. The problems at the ends of chapters offer you a chance to select the methods which strike you as most natural and to carry out a more careful analysis of situation, solution, and interpretation. Try to do problems in more than one way, using different principles or different simplifying assumptions.

1.6. MECHANICS AND OTHER DISCIPLINES

Mechanics is a fundamental branch of physics, having a particularly close affiliation with heat and electricity. An understanding of its concepts and principles is fundamental to the mastery of most physical theory as well as to the design and interpretation of much laboratory apparatus. The historical development of mechanics has been so close to that of mathematical analysis that your beginning courses in calculus have undoubtedly used mechanics examples in abundance. If one were to excise from pure mathematics all the topics which have been inspired by mechanics, the loss would be immense. Mechanics also is a keystone of engineering analysis. Your professional ambitions may alter the emphasis of your study and the focus of your interest, but you may be sure that, in mastering the techniques of vector analysis and in grappling with problems requiring basic mechanics, you are contributing to your development in the fields of physics, mathematics, and engineering.

CHAPTER TWO

DISTANCE, POSITION, and VECTORS

The first concept of mechanics we take to be length. Working with length alone, one can define area and volume, and hence one can systematically develop the geometric properties of space. Classical mechanics is based on euclidean geometry. It will appear that many mathematical devices suitable for geometry have wide application in various parts of mechanics. The subject matter of this chapter is thus doubly important, for it emphasizes the language of vectors in simple geometrical situations. This chapter also has a special tactical significance for the beginning student; in later chapters this same vector language will be used in unfamiliar situations. So here, against the familiar background of everyday geometry, is the place for acquiring a thorough understanding of vectors.

2.1. DISTANCE

In order to describe quantitatively the motion of a body or even of a point, some standard of distance or length is necessary. The metric unit of length, the meter, is defined in terms of marks on a standard meter bar under stated conditions or in terms of the wavelength of a characteristic cadmium or mercury isotope radiation. The English unit of length, the foot, may be taken as approximately 0.305 m. In this course we shall not attempt a full analysis of the philosophical or practical difficulties associated with the problem of measurement. We merely state that from the experimental point of view length is the result of measurement with a suitable instrument: meter stick, micrometer, cathetometer, comparator, etc. From the point of view of our mathematical theory, on the other hand, length is a primitive concept to which numerical values may be assigned and in terms of which other concepts (such as volume and speed) might be defined.

2.2. REFERENCE FRAMES

One aim of this chapter is to provide a language for answering a question such as, Where is the point? This question is fully meaningful only if a specific reference body is understood. The selection of a suitable reference body is in itself an interesting enterprise. We feel intuitively, perhaps, that it should be absolutely at rest, but this requirement is meaningless as reflection will show. In most of our mechanics

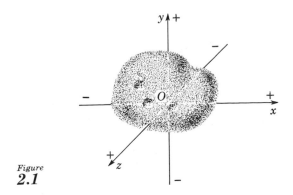

Figure
2.1

problems, the earth, or a somewhat rigid extension of the earth such as a room, will be an adequate reference body. When the effects of the earth's motion are to be taken into account, one may imagine a reference frame which is fixed in our solar system and which does not rotate with respect to the stars fixed in our galaxy.

It is customary and convenient to select in the reference body fixed straight lines known as *axes*. In Fig. 2.1 the shaded space represents the body. A point O fixed in the body is chosen as *origin*; a set of three mutually perpendicular lines through O are chosen as axes. O divides each line into halves, one of which is arbitrarily called positive, the other negative. When the positive x and positive y directions have been chosen, the positive z direction is usually taken so that the $90°$ rotation carrying the positive x axis into the positive y axis will appear counterclockwise to an observer looking back toward O from the positive z axis. This is a right-handed set of axes; the opposite choice of the positive z axis would yield a left-handed set. Why is this frame called "right-handed"? If the thumb, forefinger, and middle finger of the right hand are held at right angles representing the x, y, and z axes, the answer is apparent. Another approach is that the rotation described would cause a z axis which was threaded like an ordinary screw to advance in its positive direction. Such a set of axes is called a *reference frame*. Relative to such a frame we can describe positions and motions of points and bodies.

2.3. RECTANGULAR COORDINATES

Once a standard of length and a reference frame have been adopted, it is in principle easy to specify the position of a point. It is assumed that the student is familiar with rectangular coordinates as used in analytic geometry; therefore the discussion here will be brief. Consider any point P (see Fig. 2.2). A plane through P perpendicular to the x axis cuts the x axis at P_x. The point P_x is the x projection of P. Similarly, the y projection P_y and the z projection P_z are defined. P_x has coordinate x on the x axis, P_y has coordinate y on the y axis, and P_z has coordinate z on the z axis. The coordinates of P then are (x,y,z). This set of three real numbers describes uniquely the position of the point P. In the same sense the origin O, the projections P_x, P_y, P_z, and the projections onto coordinate planes P_{yz}, P_{zx}, P_{xy} have, respectively, coordinates $(0,0,0,)$ $(x,0,0)$, $(0,y,0)$, $(0,0,z)$, $(0,y,z)$, $(x,0,z)$, and $(x,y,0)$.

In dealing with many aspects of vector analysis and mechanics it is exceedingly helpful to be able to visualize geometrical relationships in three dimensions. Good practice is afforded by sketching the position of points of various coordinates, using box diagrams as in Fig. 2.2. For example, the point $P(4,-4,6)$ might be sketched as in Fig. 2.3.

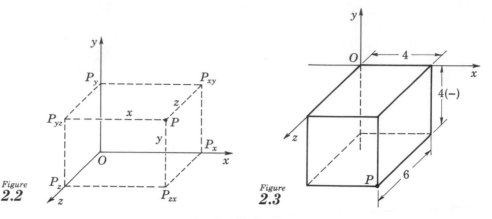

Figure
2.2

Figure
2.3

EXERCISES

1. Use box diagrams to plot the points (5,3,4), (−3,5,4), (−3,0,0).
2. Figure 2.4 represents a rectangular room 24 by 18 by 8 ft. *K* is the center of the wall *ABCD*. *M* and *N* are centers of edges *AE* and *BF*. If *G* is taken as origin, *GF* as the positive *x* axis, *GC* as the positive *y* axis, and *GH* as the negative *z* axis, find the co-ordinates of *A, B, C, D, E, F, H, K, M, N*.

2.4. DISPLACEMENTS AND DIRECTED LINE SEGMENTS

For describing motion the idea of displacement is fundamental. If a particle or point moves from point $P(x,y,z)$ to point $P'(x',y',z')$, the *net* change of position depends only on the *initial point P* and the *final point P'*. Thus a net point displacement may be characterized by an ordered pair of points PP'. If P and P' are the same point, PP' is a *null* displacement. $P'P$ is the displacement *opposite* to PP'. Associated with PP' are various projected displacements. Thus $P_x P'_x$ or $(PP')_x$ is the projection onto the x axis of PP'. Similarly, $P_{xy}P'_{xy}$ or $(PP')_{xy}$ is the projection onto the xy plane of PP'.

The manner in which successive point displacements may be combined is of particular interest for us. A displacement from P to Q followed by a displacement from Q to R clearly has the same net effect as a displacement from P to R. This type of combination is usually called *addition* of displacements, written symbolically by

$$(2.1) \qquad\qquad PQ + QR = PR$$

Since a net point displacement PP' depends only on its initial and final points, it is natural to represent such a displacement by the directed line segment or arrow determined by the same end points. Figure 2.5 shows a typical displacement,

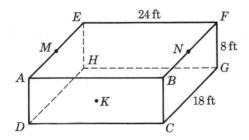

Figure
2.4

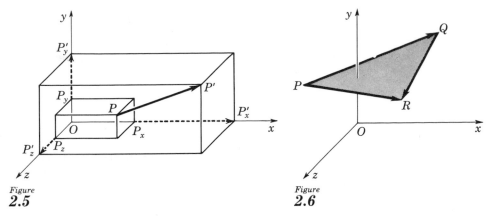

Figure
2.5

Figure
2.6

together with its projections onto the axes. Figure 2.6 shows how directed line segments are "added" according to Eq. (2.1).

The *components* of a displacement or directed line segment are the differences of corresponding coordinates for the initial and final points. Thus, for PP', the x component is $x' - x$ and the y and z components are $y' - y$ and $z' - z$. These components are conveniently indicated by Δx, Δy, Δz, respectively. In mechanics, both the length and the direction of a displacement are of prime interest. Both aspects may be expressed in terms of the components. Figure 2.7 shows a displacement from P to P'. Planes through P and P' perpendicular to the axes form a boxlike region whose sides have lengths equal (except possibly for sign) to the components of the displacement. Using the Pythagorean theorem (see Fig. 2.8), we determine the length d of the displacement. From triangles $PP'Q'$ and PQQ' one has, respectively, $d^2 = c^2 + (\Delta y)^2$ and $c^2 = (\Delta x)^2 + (\Delta z)^2$. Thus the net displacement has magnitude

$$(2.2) \qquad d = [(\Delta x)^2 + (\Delta y)^2 + (\Delta z)^2]^{\frac{1}{2}}$$

The *direction* of the displacement can be specified by stating angles between the displacement and rays parallel to the positive axes. These angles are labeled α, β, and γ in Fig. 2.9. In actual practice it is usually more convenient to state the cosines of these angles.

$$l = \cos \alpha = \frac{\Delta x}{d}$$

$$(2.3) \qquad m = \cos \beta = \frac{\Delta y}{d}$$

$$n = \cos \gamma = \frac{\Delta z}{d}$$

The quantities l, m, n are called *direction cosines*.

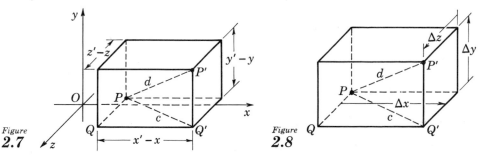

Figure
2.7

Figure
2.8

If both sides of Eq. (2.2) are divided by d, an interesting identity is discovered:

$$\frac{d}{d} = \sqrt{\left(\frac{\Delta x}{d}\right)^2 + \left(\frac{\Delta y}{d}\right)^2 + \left(\frac{\Delta z}{d}\right)^2}$$

or

(2.4) $l^2 + m^2 + n^2 = 1$

Example 1

What is the distance from $P(-1,-4,5)$ to $P'(3,-2,2)$?

Solution

The displacement from P to P' is equal to the result of an x displacement, $\Delta x = 4$; a y displacement, $\Delta y = 2$; and a z displacement, $\Delta z = -3$. The distance then is

$$d = \sqrt{(4)^2 + (2)^2 + (-3)^2} = \sqrt{29} = 5.4$$

Example 2

What are the direction cosines of the directed line segment PP' described in the preceding example?

Solution

$$l = \frac{4}{5.4} = 0.74 \qquad m = \frac{2}{5.4} = 0.37 \qquad n = \frac{-3}{5.4} = -0.56$$

(The angles between PP' and the positive axes are then 42°, 68°, 124°.)

EXERCISES

3. A helicopter flies 500 ft vertically upward, then 700 ft horizontally south, and then 300 ft horizontally east. How far is it from the starting point?

4. P and Q are points with coordinates $(3,-2,1)$, $(-1,1,1)$. (a) What is the distance from P to Q? (b) What are the direction cosines of the directed line segment PQ?

5. The positive x axis is horizontal and east, the positive y axis vertical upward, and the positive z axis horizontal and south. An observer sits on the ground at the origin. The peak of a spire has an angle of elevation above the horizontal of 30° in a direction 50° east of south. What are the direction cosines of the line from the observer to the spire?

6. The point P having coordinates $(2,5,d)$ is at a distance 5 from the point $(-1,1,4)$. Find d.

7. O is the origin, P a second point. The segment OP makes an angle of 60° with the positive x axis, 45° with the positive y axis. What can be said about its angle with the positive z axis?

8. What angle does OP make with the positive axes if P is the point $(3,3,3)$?

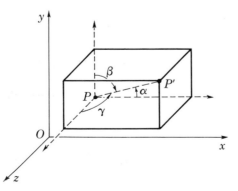

Figure
2.9

2.5. VECTORS

We have already seen how a change in position, i.e., a displacement, can be described by a directed line segment. In mechanics we shall meet many other concepts which similarly have both magnitude and direction. These are called *vector concepts*. Examples are force, velocity, acceleration, momentum, angular velocity, and torque. These concepts have so many significant properties in common that a separate study of this common ground is richly worthwhile. This subject is known as vector analysis. Only the elementary aspects are considered in this course. We shall begin with some definitions.

Vector. *A vector is a directed line segment or arrow having definite length and definite direction.* This reference to direction implies that a reference frame has already been selected. The definite direction might be expressed by giving a unique set of direction cosines. In a given discussion, only one frame will ordinarily be used. Figure 2.10 is a portrait of a vector. The length of the arrow is the *magnitude* of the vector. It is imagined that the arrow in the figure is drawn in the direction of the vector. A vector quantity (i.e., a specific example of a vector concept) may be represented by a vector in an obvious way. The vector in the figure might represent a 100-lb force in the direction shown. A 50-lb force would be represented by an arrow just half as long. The figure might equally well represent a velocity in the indicated direction of 75 miles per hour (mph). In that case an arrow twice as long would represent a velocity of 150 mph. In general, then, the figures are drawn to scale so that lengths are proportional to the magnitudes represented.

Scalar. In this context the word scalar is used to denote ordinary real numbers. Thus a *scalar concept*, in contrast with a vector concept, is one which can be specified by a numerical or scale value (positive, negative, or zero) without requiring any statement about direction. Examples are temperature, time, energy, and mass. We shall use *boldface capital letters* for vector quantities and *italic small letters* for scalar quantities. Thus in Fig. 2.10 the *vector* is labeled **A**. Its *magnitude*, a nonnegative scalar, would be written a or, when more convenient, $|\mathbf{A}|$.

A particular directed segment has a definite initial point and a definite final point. But in the algebra of vectors only direction and magnitude will be important for each vector. Two vectors will be called equal if both their directions and magnitudes are identical regardless of where they are located. This is analogous to calling two scalars equal if they have the same sign and the same magnitude. Thus the scalar -2 is equal to the scalar $-\frac{10}{5}$ regardless of where they are written. In Fig. 2.11 **A** and **B** are equal. **A** and **C** are not equal, for their directions are opposite. Likewise, **A** and **D** are not equal, for their magnitudes differ. Symbolically,

$$\mathbf{A} = \mathbf{B} \qquad \mathbf{A} \neq \mathbf{C} \qquad \mathbf{A} \neq \mathbf{D}$$

Using small letters to denote magnitudes, as suggested above, we may write

$$a = b = c \qquad a \neq d$$

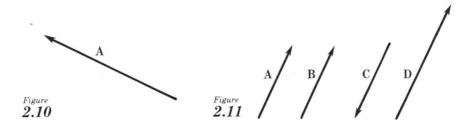

Figure
2.10

Figure
2.11

It should be noticed that equal vectors may represent vector quantities which are not equivalent. For instance, two forces represented by **A** and **B** in Fig. 2.11 are not equivalent, for their lines of action do not agree. This should not, however, disturb us. The scalars 3 and 3 are equal, but this does not mean that three degrees centigrade and three degrees Kelvin are equivalent temperatures. A similar amount of discernment in particular applications will enable us to use the idea of vector equality successfully.

Minus a Vector. If two vectors **A** and **C** have the same magnitudes but opposite directions (as in Fig. 2.11), we shall write

(2.5) $\mathbf{A} = -\mathbf{C}$ or $-\mathbf{A} = \mathbf{C}$

We say that **A** is the *opposite* of **C** and that **C** is the *opposite* of **A**. **A** and **D** are *parallel* vectors; **C** and **D** are *antiparallel*. Note that for any vector **A**, $-(-\mathbf{A}) = \mathbf{A}$. This follows intuitively from the idea of same and opposite directions. Or one might reason thus: If **A** has direction cosines l, m, n, then $-\mathbf{A}$ has direction cosines $-l, -m, -n$. But l, m, n are scalars, so we already know $-(-l) = l$, etc.

EXERCISES

9. A parallelogram is made up of four line segments. If its diagonals are drawn, four more segments (the semidiagonals) are added. Change these eight segments into vectors by indicating directions (*a*) so that no two vectors are equal; (*b*) so that there are four pairs of equal vectors.

10. Four successive straight displacements all of equal magnitude bring a moving point back to the starting point. Show that this may be done in such a way that the vectors representing the displacements satisfy the following statements: (*a*) the vectors form two distinct *opposite* pairs, that is, **A**, $-\mathbf{A}$, **B**, $-\mathbf{B}$, where $\mathbf{B} \neq \mathbf{A} \neq -\mathbf{B}$ (the order need not be as given in this list); (*b*) the vectors form two *equal* pairs; (*c*) no two of the vectors are either *equal* or *opposite*.

2.6. VECTOR ADDITION

An *operation* on vectors is a rule for combining vectors with vectors or vectors with scalars in such a way as to yield new vectors or scalars. Some of these operations may seem at first to be arbitrary and artificial. Their utility for dealing with spatial situations will, however, appear in the exercises. In later parts of the course the elementary relationships of mechanics will be expressed in terms of them.

In this section we define an operation which, for convenience, is called *addition* of vectors. It is based on the method of addition of displacements described in Sec. 2.4. In general, given two vectors **A** and **B**, their sum **A** + **B** is defined to be equal to the third vector obtained by combining **A** and **B** (or vectors equal to them) as if they were successive displacements. This is illustrated in Fig. 2.12. The two

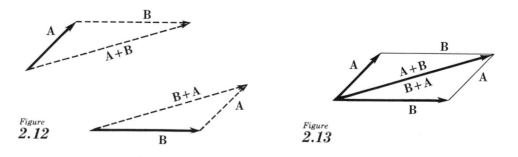

Figure
2.12

Figure
2.13

given vectors are **A** and **B**. To find a vector equal to the sum **A** + **B**, a copy of **B** is drawn adjacent to **A**. Then the vector from the "initial point" of **A** to the "final point" of **B** is drawn. This vector is the desired sum. The roles of **B** and **A** may be interchanged; then the sum **B** + **A** is obtained. These two operations may be combined in a single diagram, as shown in Fig. 2.13. The fact that the diagonal of the parallelogram is the same whether viewed from above or below constitutes an extremely important proposition in vector algebra: *the commutative law for vector addition.* It is restated symbolically in the following equation:

(2.6) $$\mathbf{A} + \mathbf{B} = \mathbf{B} + \mathbf{A}$$

Figure 2.13 illustrates the familiar *parallelogram rule* for vector addition.

The Null Vector. It is highly desirable that an operation *always* be defined. In particular, given *any* two vectors, a unique vector equal to their sum should exist. The sum of a vector and its opposite poses a problem. A displacement **A** followed by the displacement −**A** results in a net effect of no displacement at all. Clearly, a *null* displacement does not satisfy our criterion for a vector quantity: it has no unique direction. Just as a matter of convenience, then, we decide to create a null vector **O** to express the result of all additions such as

(2.7) $$\mathbf{A} + (-\mathbf{A}) = \mathbf{O}$$

Successive Additions. Thus far we have considered sums for pairs of vectors. Figure 2.14 shows how the definition may be extended. To the sum **A** + **B** the vector **C** is added, giving the vector (**A** + **B**) + **C**. This vector can be described as extending from the initial point of **A** to the final point of **C**. It appears, moreover, from Fig. 2.14, that the sum **A** + (**B** + **C**) is precisely the same vector. This fact constitutes a second important proposition of vector algebra, *the associative law of vector addition,*

(2.8) $$(\mathbf{A} + \mathbf{B}) + \mathbf{C} = \mathbf{A} + (\mathbf{B} + \mathbf{C})$$

This, together with the commutative law, ensures that successive additions of several vectors will have a unique result independent of the order in which vectors are combined. As an illustration of the essential simplicity of successive vector additions, a number of vectors are added in Fig. 2.15, which represents the equation

$$\mathbf{A} + \mathbf{B} + \mathbf{C} + \mathbf{D} + \mathbf{E} + \mathbf{F} + \mathbf{G} = \mathbf{H}$$

Vector Subtraction. The difference of two vectors is defined in terms of addition and minus a vector by the following equation:

(2.9) $$\mathbf{A} - \mathbf{B} = \mathbf{A} + (-\mathbf{B})$$

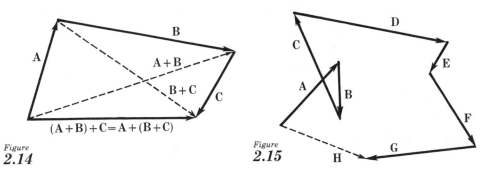

$(A+B)+C = A+(B+C)$

Figure
2.14

Figure
2.15

In Fig. 2.16 this is shown.   From the geometry of the parallelograms in this figure it is clear that

$$\mathbf{A} - \mathbf{B} = -(\mathbf{B} - \mathbf{A})$$

The construction used in Fig. 2.16 involved two steps: the construction of the opposite of one of the vectors and then addition.   The result, however, suggests a shorter construction:

(2.10) *If the vectors are drawn with the same initial point* (as in Fig. 2.17), *then the vector between their final points is the difference.*   This is illustrated in Fig. 2.17. The student should convince himself that the difference $\mathbf{B} - \mathbf{A}$ is the unique solution of the equation

$$\mathbf{A} + \mathbf{X} = \mathbf{B}$$

EXERCISES

11. Draw four vectors **A**, **B**, **C**, **D**, of random length and direction.   Using graphic methods (e.g., constructions with ruler, compass, or protractor), find a fifth vector **E** such that

$$\mathbf{A} + \mathbf{B} + \mathbf{C} + \mathbf{D} + \mathbf{E} = \mathbf{O}$$

12. *M* is the mid-point of a segment *AB*.   Construct graphically, and compare the two vector sums $OA + OB$ and $OM + OM$.

13. *ABC* is a triangle.   *G* is the point of intersection of its medians, and *M* is the mid-point of the side *BC*.   Construct the vector sums

$$OG + OG + OG \qquad OM + OM + OA \qquad OA + OB + OC$$

14. *ABCD* is a square, *M* is its center, and *O* is any other point in its plane.   Construct and compare

$$OA + OB + OC + OD \qquad OM + OM + OM + OM \qquad MA + MB + MC + MD$$

15. Use the definition given for the null vector to show that, for any vector **A**,

$$\mathbf{A} + \mathbf{O} = \mathbf{A}$$

16. For two nonparallel vectors **A** and **B** draw a figure to show that

$$\mathbf{A} + \mathbf{B} - \mathbf{A} - \mathbf{B} = \mathbf{O}$$

17. Prove that the equation $\mathbf{A} + \mathbf{C} = \mathbf{B} + \mathbf{C}$ always implies $\mathbf{A} = \mathbf{B}$.

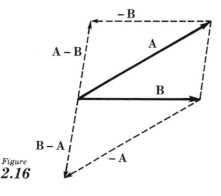

Figure
2.16

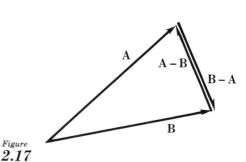

Figure
2.17

2.7. POLAR NOTATION FOR PLANE VECTORS

In many mechanics problems we shall find that coordinate axes may be chosen in such a way that most, if not all, of the vectors under discussion are in or parallel to the xy plane. Such a vector is described uniquely if its magnitude and its angle with the positive x axis are specified. This angle is usually called positive if it is measured counterclockwise from the positive x axis. Thus in Fig. 2.18 the vector shown may be written

(2.11) $$\mathbf{A} = a\underline{/\theta}$$

Some numerical examples are given in Fig. 2.19. Since no analytical methods have been developed thus far in the course, it is assumed that most of the following exercises will be done graphically (measuring angles with a protractor); therefore extreme accuracy is not expected.

EXERCISES

18. Plot to scale the vectors $3\underline{/0°}$, $4\underline{/45°}$, $5\underline{/90°}$, $4.5\underline{/150°}$, $3.8\underline{/-90°}$.
19. Show that, reasonably interpreted, the following are true:
    (a) $a\underline{/\theta°} = a\underline{/\theta° + n360°}$, for any integer n.
    (b) $-a\underline{/\theta°} = a\underline{/\theta° \pm 180°}$.   (c) $a\underline{/\theta°} + b\underline{/\theta°} = (a + b)\underline{/\theta°}$.
20. Compute the following graphically:
    (a) $4\underline{/90°} + 3\underline{/0°}$.   (b) $5\underline{/30°} + 5\underline{/120°}$.
    (c) $10\underline{/60°} - 8.7\underline{/30°}$.   (d) $10\underline{/180°} - 10\underline{/90°}$.
21. Express in polar form displacements of length 5 whose direction cosines are (a) -0.707, $+0.707$, 0; (b) 0.866, -0.500, 0.

2.8. PRODUCTS OF VECTORS BY SCALARS

In the problems following Sec. 2.6, such sums as $OM + OM$, $OM + OM + OM$ occurred. It is a natural and convenient abbreviation to write instead $2OM$, $3OM$. This notation suggests the following definition: For any positive scalar c and any non-null vector $\mathbf{A}$, the product $c\mathbf{A}$ is a vector parallel to $\mathbf{A}$, having magnitude c times the magnitude of $\mathbf{A}$; that is,

(2.12) $$|c\mathbf{A}| = c\,|\mathbf{A}|$$

This definition is extended to the cases where the scalar multiple is zero or negative as follows:

(2.13) $$(-c)\mathbf{A} = -c\mathbf{A}$$

(2.14) $$0\mathbf{A} = \mathbf{O}$$

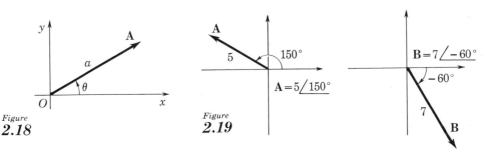

Figure
2.18

Figure
2.19

In this last equation it should be realized that the 0 in the left member is the scalar *zero* but that the **O** in the right member denotes the *null vector*. The three cases may be summarized in a single statement: The product of a scalar c by a vector **A** is a vector whose magnitude is equal to the magnitude of **A** multiplied by the absolute value of the scalar c; it is parallel to **A** if c is positive, opposite to **A** if c is negative. For a converse of this statement, see Exercise 26 below. Illustrations are given in Fig. 2.20. That this operation is associative, distributive with respect to scalar addition, and distributive with respect to vector addition is easily shown. The demonstrations are left as exercises (see Exercises 22a, b, and c below).

It is sometimes convenient to write the factors c and **A** in the opposite order; so we assume the equality

$$(2.15) \qquad\qquad c\mathbf{A} = \mathbf{A}c$$

Since c may be any real number, we can immediately define *division* of a vector by a scalar $c \neq 0$ thus:

$$(2.16) \qquad\qquad \mathbf{A} \div c = \mathbf{A}\frac{1}{c} = \frac{1}{c}\mathbf{A}$$

In applications it is convenient to designate directions by vectors of length 1, that is, by *unit vectors*. If **A** is any non-null vector, a parallel unit vector **E** is given by dividing **A** by its own magnitude thus:

$$(2.17) \qquad\qquad \mathbf{E} = \frac{1}{a}\mathbf{A} = \mathbf{A} \div |\mathbf{A}|$$

This means that any vector **A** can be analyzed as the product of a scalar (the magnitude of **A**) times a unit vector (giving the direction of **A**).

$$(2.18) \qquad\qquad \mathbf{A} = a\mathbf{E} \quad \text{or} \quad \mathbf{A} = |\mathbf{A}|\,\mathbf{E}$$

as is shown in Fig. 2.21. The letter **E** will be used as a generic symbol for unit vectors in any context. In theoretical discussions, then, **E** may be used simply as a symbol for direction. In particular problems it is usual to consider the directions of the axes as preferred directions. Unit vectors parallel to the positive x, y, and z axes will be denoted, respectively, by **I**, **J**, and **K**. In problems confined to the xy plane, the symbol **I** is interchangeable with the symbol $1/\!\underline{0°}$ and the symbol **J** is interchangeable with $1/\!\underline{90°}$. Figure 2.22 shows these unit vectors in the customary setting. In later sections the letters **L**, **M**, **T**, **N**, etc., will be introduced as unit vectors having particular connotations.

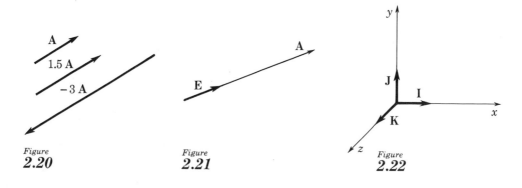

Figure
2.20

Figure
2.21

Figure
2.22

EXERCISES

22. Using the definitions above, prove each of the following for any scalars c, c' and any vectors $\mathbf{A}$, $\mathbf{A}'$:

(a) $c(c'\mathbf{A}) = (cc')\mathbf{A}$.   (b) $(c + c')\mathbf{A} = c\mathbf{A} + c'\mathbf{A}$.

(c) $c(\mathbf{A} + \mathbf{A}') = c\mathbf{A} + c\mathbf{A}'$.   (d) $1\mathbf{A} = \mathbf{A}$.

(e) $(-c)(-\mathbf{A}) = c\mathbf{A}$.

23. Given the two vectors $\mathbf{A} = 10\underline{/0°}$ and $\mathbf{B} = 10\underline{/60°}$, construct graphically each of the following:

$$\mathbf{A} + 2\mathbf{B} \qquad -\mathbf{A} + 2\mathbf{B} \qquad -\mathbf{A} - 2\mathbf{B} \qquad \mathbf{A} - 2\mathbf{B}$$

24. AB is a line segment, and O is a point not on the line. Show that the mid-point M of AB is determined by

$$OM = 0.5\,OA + 0.5\,OB$$

25. Show that any vector $\mathbf{A} = a\underline{/\theta°}$ in the xy plane can be expressed as the sum of multiples of $1\underline{/0°}$ and $1\underline{/90°}$, i.e., that this equation will hold for the correct choice of scalars c and d:

$$a\underline{/\theta°} = c(1\underline{/0°}) + d(1\underline{/90°})$$

Express c and d in terms of a and θ.

26. If $\mathbf{A}$ is parallel to $\mathbf{B}$ (or to its opposite vector), show that for some scalar c this equation holds:

$$\mathbf{A} = c\mathbf{B}$$

27. If $\mathbf{A}$ and $\mathbf{B}$ are nonparallel vectors and $\mathbf{C}$ is parallel to the plane they determine, prove that for some scalars c and d, $\mathbf{C} = c\mathbf{A} + d\mathbf{B}$. Illustrate with several diagrams showing possible arrangements. SUGGESTION: Show that if $\mathbf{C}$ is parallel to neither $\mathbf{A}$ nor $\mathbf{B}$, it is possible to draw a triangle with sides parallel to $\mathbf{A}$, $\mathbf{B}$, and $\mathbf{C}$, so that for suitable scalars a', b', c' one can write

$$a'\mathbf{A} + b'\mathbf{B} + c'\mathbf{C} = \mathbf{O}$$

28. Express in the form $a\underline{/\theta°}$ a unit vector in the direction of (a) $\mathbf{I} + \mathbf{J}$; (b) $2\mathbf{I} - \mathbf{J}$; (c) $5.00\underline{/45°} + 8.66\underline{/135°}$. (Either graphic methods or simple trigonometry may be used.)

29. Solve the equation $a\mathbf{E} = a_x\mathbf{I} + a_y\mathbf{J}$ for a and $\mathbf{E}$ (in polar form) when (a) $a_x = 5$, $a_y = 12$; (b) $a_x = 20$, $a_y = -21$.

30. Solve the equation $\mathbf{A} = a_x\mathbf{I} + a_y\mathbf{J}$ for a_x and a_y when $\mathbf{A}$ is the vector $10\underline{/\theta}$ and θ is (a) $30°$; (b) $90°$; (c) $180°$; (d) $300°$.

31. Show that, if $\mathbf{E}$ is a unit vector parallel to $\mathbf{A} = a\underline{/\theta°}$, then

$$\mathbf{E} = \cos\theta\,\mathbf{I} + \sin\theta\,\mathbf{J}$$

2.9. COMPONENTS AND PROJECTIONS OF A VECTOR

In Sec. 2.4 we discussed particular projections and components of displacements. Equations (2.3) showed that the x component of a displacement is equal to the length of the displacement times the cosine of its angle with the x axis. We shall generalize this idea by defining the *component of a vector* $\mathbf{A}$ *in the direction of a unit vector* $\mathbf{E}$ as the product of the magnitude of $\mathbf{A}$ by the cosine of the angle ϕ between the two vectors. Just what is meant by the angle between any two vectors is apparent if the vectors are drawn as in Fig. 2.23 with a common initial point, and by our definition of equality of two vectors it is clear that we may draw them that way if convenient. The symbol for the scalar component of **A** parallel to **E** will be a_E; thus

(2.19) $$a_E = a \cos \phi$$

In cases where the unit vector determines a coordinate axis, the symbol for that coordinate may be used as the subscript:

$$a_I = a_x \qquad a_J = a_y \qquad a_K = a_z$$

From the definition it follows that equal vectors have equal components in any direction. Observe also that components in opposite directions have opposite signs. Proofs of these remarks are left for Exercises 34 and 35.

We have already seen in Sec. 2.4 how the projection of a directed segment onto a coordinate axis is a new directed segment. More generally, let **A** be a vector with initial point P and terminal point Q and let l be a line or axis whose direction is given by a unit vector **E**, as in Fig. 2.24. Let P' and Q' be the feet of the perpendiculars dropped from P and Q to l. Then the vector $P'Q'$ is the *projection of* **A** *parallel to* **E**. It should be clear that this vector is given by

(2.20) $$P'Q' = (a_E)\mathbf{E}$$

Note that if **E** is replaced by $-\mathbf{E}$ as a means of designating the direction of l, then ϕ is replaced by the supplement of ϕ, so that Eq. (2.20) is still valid.

It should be noted that a_E is a positive scalar when ϕ is an acute angle, that it is zero when ϕ is 90°, and that it is negative when ϕ is obtuse. Of the two angles determined by two vectors, we shall always choose the smaller; therefore ϕ will not exceed 180°. In Fig. 2.25 components are represented as signed lengths of projections upon a line having the direction of a unit vector **E**.

An important proposition concerning projections is that *the projection of the sum of two (or more) vectors is equal to the sum of their projections.* This is illustrated in Fig. 2.26, where it is apparent that the vector sum of the projections $P'Q' + Q'R' + R'S'$ is precisely the vector $P'S'$. But $P'S'$ is the projection of PS, which is equal to the vector sum $PQ + QR + RS$. In terms of the notations which have been described, this equality appears as

(2.21) $$(a_E)\mathbf{E} + (b_E)\mathbf{E} + (c_E)\mathbf{E} = (d_E)\mathbf{E}$$

or, using one of the distributive laws for multiplication of vectors by scalars,

(2.22) $$(a_E + b_E + c_E)\mathbf{E} = (d_E)\mathbf{E}$$

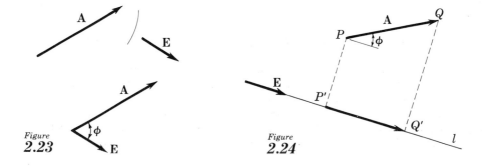

Figure
2.23

Figure
2.24

By the definition of equality of vectors, however, two vectors can be equal only if their magnitudes are equal; hence

(2.23) $$a_E + b_E + c_E = d_E$$

(Of course, the left member may be negative, but only if the right one is, also.) We conclude:

(2.24) *Parallel to any unit vector* **E** *the sum of the components (projections) of a number of vectors is equal to the component (projection) of their sum.*

Example

In discussing a displacement from $P(x,y,z)$ to $P'(x',y',z')$, it was remarked that the whole could be regarded as the result of three displacements parallel to the axes. In terms of the symbols here used this might be stated:

$$PP' = \Delta x \, \mathbf{I} + \Delta y \, \mathbf{J} + \Delta z \, \mathbf{K}$$

EXERCISES

32. Compute the component of **A** in the direction of **E**, and illustrate with a diagram for each of the following cases:

(a) $\mathbf{A} = 10\underline{/-120°}$ and $\mathbf{E} = \mathbf{I}$.   (b) $\mathbf{A} = 10\underline{/-120°}$ and $\mathbf{E} = \mathbf{J}$.

(c) $\mathbf{A} = 10\underline{/-120°}$ and $\mathbf{E} = 1\underline{/30°}$.   (d) $\mathbf{A} = 10\underline{/-120°}$ and $\mathbf{E} = 1\underline{/-150°}$.

(e) $\mathbf{A} = 10\underline{/-120°}$ and $\mathbf{E} = 1\underline{/150°}$.   (f) $\mathbf{A} = 10\underline{/-120°}$ and $\mathbf{E} = 1\underline{/50°}$.

33. Compute the component of $\mathbf{A} = 5\mathbf{I} + 6\mathbf{J}$ parallel to **E** in each of the following cases. (NOTE: Results on components of sums may be used.)

(a) $\mathbf{E} = \mathbf{I}$.   (b) $\mathbf{E} = \mathbf{J}$.

(c) $\mathbf{E} = 1\underline{/30°}$.   (d) $\mathbf{E} = 1\underline{/135°}$.

(e) $\mathbf{E} = 1\underline{/300°}$.   (f) $\mathbf{E} = 1\underline{/-130°}$.

34. Show that $\mathbf{A} = \mathbf{B}$ implies that $a_E = b_E$ for any unit vector **E**.

35. Show that $a_E = -a_{(-E)}$ for any vector **A** and any unit vector **E**.

2.10. x, y, AND z COMPONENTS OF A VECTOR

The concluding equation in the preceding section shows how any displacement, and hence any vector, can be expressed as the vector sum of its projections onto the coordinate axes. Each of these projections, according to Eq. (2.20), may be written as the product of a component by a corresponding unit vector. For any

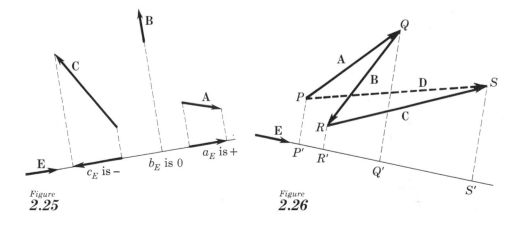

Figure
2.25

Figure
2.26

vector $\mathbf{A}$ we shall frequently write

(2.25) $$\mathbf{A} = a_x\mathbf{I} + a_y\mathbf{J} + a_z\mathbf{K}$$

This addition is illustrated by Fig. 2.27. The expression of vectors in terms of components leads to numerous working formulas for actual numerical computations.

It follows from Eq. (2.2) that the magnitude of $\mathbf{A}$ is given by

(2.26) $$|\mathbf{A}| = a = \sqrt{a_x^2 + a_y^2 + a_z^2}$$

If $\mathbf{A}$ is given as above and $\mathbf{B}$ by the equation

$$\mathbf{B} = b_x\mathbf{I} + b_y\mathbf{J} + b_z\mathbf{K}$$

then, using the associative and commutative laws for addition and the distributive laws for products by scalars, we may write

(2.27) $$\mathbf{A} + \mathbf{B} = (a_x + b_x)\mathbf{I} + (a_y + b_y)\mathbf{J} + (a_z + b_z)\mathbf{K}$$

Since this is an assertion that *the x component of* $\mathbf{A} + \mathbf{B}$ *is the x component of* $\mathbf{A}$ *plus the x component of* $\mathbf{B}$, etc., it may be regarded as corroborating the statements made earlier in the preceding section about sums of projections and sums of components. From the equations

(2.28) $$c\mathbf{A} = c(a_x\mathbf{I} + a_y\mathbf{J} + a_z\mathbf{K}) = ca_x\mathbf{I} + ca_y\mathbf{J} + ca_z\mathbf{K}$$

we may similarly conclude that *the x component of the product of a vector by a scalar is equal to the product of the x component of the vector by the scalar*, and similarly for components in other directions.

If it is given that two vectors are equal,

$$\mathbf{A} = \mathbf{B}$$

it follows that

$$\mathbf{A} - \mathbf{B} = \mathbf{O} = (a_x - b_x)\mathbf{I} + (a_y - b_y)\mathbf{J} + (a_z - b_z)\mathbf{K}$$

Since the component in any direction of a null vector is zero, we have as a consequence

(2.29) $$a_x = b_x \qquad a_y = b_y \qquad a_z = b_z$$

Conversely, equal components require equal vectors. Thus *two vectors are equal if and only if their x, y, and z components are, respectively, equal.*

In Sec. 2.4 the direction cosines l, m, and n of a segment were derived by multiplying the x, y, and z components of the displacement by the reciprocal of the length

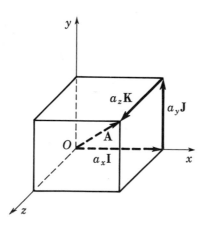

Figure
2.27

of the displacement. It follows that the vector having l, m, and n as components parallel to the axes is a unit vector parallel to the displacement:

$$(2.30) \qquad \mathbf{E} = l\mathbf{I} + m\mathbf{J} + n\mathbf{K} = \cos\alpha\,\mathbf{I} + \cos\beta\,\mathbf{J} + \cos\gamma\,\mathbf{K}$$

This fact ties together two of our devices for describing direction: *the x, y, and z components of any unit vector are its direction cosines.*

EXERCISES

36. Express in the form $e_x\mathbf{I} + e_y\mathbf{J} + e_z\mathbf{K}$ a unit vector in each of the following directions:
    (a) Parallel to $\mathbf{I} + \mathbf{J}$.
    (b) Parallel to $10/150°$.
    (c) Parallel to $4\mathbf{I} - 3\mathbf{J}$.
    (d) Parallel to $6\mathbf{J} + 8\mathbf{K}$.
    (e) Parallel to $6\mathbf{I} - 3\mathbf{J} - 6\mathbf{K}$,
    (f) Parallel to a displacement from the point with coordinates $(5,0,3)$ to the point with coordinates $(-7,0,8)$.
    (g) Parallel to a displacement from the point with coordinates $(5,0,3)$ to the point with coordinates $(3,4,-1)$.
37. Express in the form $a_x\mathbf{I} + a_y\mathbf{J} + a_z\mathbf{K}$ each of the following vectors:
    (a) $15/140°$.
    (b) $5/-90°$.
    (c) The magnitude is 100, and the direction is parallel to the unit vector $0.8\mathbf{J} - 0.6\mathbf{K}$.
    (d) The magnitude is 70, and the direction is parallel to the vector $2\mathbf{I} + 3\mathbf{J} - 6\mathbf{K}$.
    (e) The magnitude is 50, and the angles with the positive x, y, and z axes are 60°, 45°, 120°.
38. Find the magnitude and direction cosines of each of the following vectors:
    (a) $-33\mathbf{I} + 56\mathbf{K}$.   (b) $-14\mathbf{I} + 7\mathbf{J} + 14\mathbf{K}$.
    (c) $-30\mathbf{K}$.   (d) $8\mathbf{I} - 7\mathbf{J} - 6\mathbf{K}$.
39. Find the magnitude of each of the following sums and express in the form $e_x\mathbf{I} + e_y\mathbf{J} + e_z\mathbf{K}$ a unit vector parallel to the sum:
    (a) $\mathbf{I} + \mathbf{J} + \mathbf{K}$.   (b) $(\mathbf{I} + \mathbf{J}) + (-\mathbf{J} + \mathbf{K})$.
    (c) $(2\mathbf{I} - 3\mathbf{K}) + (\mathbf{I} + 6\mathbf{J} - 3\mathbf{K})$.   (d) $10/120° + 10/45°$.
    (e) $7/30° + 7/150°$.
40. Any vector $\mathbf{A}$ in the xy plane can be expressed as a linear combination of two independent vectors such as $(\mathbf{I} + \mathbf{J})$ and $(2\mathbf{I} - \mathbf{J})$; that is, $\mathbf{A} = m(\mathbf{I} + \mathbf{J}) + n(2\mathbf{I} - \mathbf{J})$ for suitable scalars m and n. Find the correct values of m and n for the following cases:
    (a) $\mathbf{A} = \mathbf{I}$.   (b) $\mathbf{A} = \mathbf{J}$.
    (c) $\mathbf{A} = \mathbf{O}$.   (d) $\mathbf{A} = \mathbf{I} + 2\mathbf{J}$.
41. Starting at the point with coordinates $(1,2,3)$, a displacement of length 6 is made in a direction whose direction cosines are -0.81, 0.32, -0.49. What are the coordinates of the stopping point?

2.11. POSITION VECTORS

It has already been remarked that in our study of mechanics we shall require concise and lucid means of describing motion. We ask the question, Where is the point? The answer can be given by stating the coordinates of the point with respect to an established frame of reference. This point of view, developed in Sec. 2.3, is very efficient when specific numerical information is needed, but it is unnecessarily clumsy and obscure in theoretical or qualitative discussions. Vector notation affords a means of stating position, which is equivalent to coordinate notation in numerical work but which is simpler and more intuitive for general discourse. Given a point (x,y,z), we call the vector drawn from the origin to that point its *position vector*. The most frequently used symbol will be $\mathbf{R}$. It is presumably obvious that the components of $\mathbf{R}$ (see Fig. 2.28) parallel to the axes are precisely the coordinates x, y, and z. Thus we may write

(2.31) $$\mathbf{R} = x\mathbf{I} + y\mathbf{J} + z\mathbf{K}$$

The magnitude of $\mathbf{R}$ will usually be denoted by r, and the unit vector parallel to it by $\mathbf{L}$; thus we write the equation

(2.32) $$\mathbf{R} = r\mathbf{L}$$

The position vector $\mathbf{R}$ and the unit radial vector $\mathbf{L}$ are easily visualized as means of describing position. Imagine that you are studying the motion of an airplane by following its course with a monocular. Regard your eye as the origin and the airplane as a moving point. Then the line of sight from your eye to the airplane serves as the position vector of the point. The length of this position vector is continually varying, but the monocular represents a parallel vector of fixed length always pointing at the airplane. Regard the monocular, then, as a model of the unit vector $\mathbf{L}$ which designates the direction to the moving point but ignores the distance. Some such intuitive feeling for vector notation must be deliberately cultivated by the student if he is to reap the full benefit of its use.

Since every point has a unique position vector and every vector starting at the origin determines a specific point, it will be convenient and economical to use the same symbol for both point and vector, as in Fig. 2.29. Thus $\mathbf{R}$ will be called the position vector of the point $\mathbf{R}$. Similarly, if $\mathbf{P}$ is a point, $\mathbf{P}$ will be the name of its position vector. The letter $\mathbf{O}$ now has two meanings: name of the origin and null vector. Since the position vector of the origin with respect to itself is assuredly a null vector, no serious ambiguity results. A displacement PP' will now be written $\mathbf{PP'}$.

Motion means change of position; therefore it is exceedingly gratifying to discover that displacements are easily described in terms of position vectors. Consider the displacement $\mathbf{PP'}$ from the point $\mathbf{P}$ (and hence with position vector $\mathbf{P}$) to the point $\mathbf{P'}$. Since position vectors have by definition the same initial points, it follows that a displacement is equal to a difference of position vectors (see rule for subtraction in Sec. 2.6). Thus a displacement is, as it should be, a change in position.

(2.33) $$\mathbf{PP'} = \mathbf{P'} - \mathbf{P} = \Delta\mathbf{P}$$

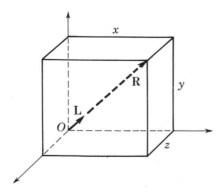

Figure
2.28

This is illustrated in Fig. 2.30.   This symbolism may be compared with corresponding expressions for change of coordinate in a displacement:

$$\Delta x = x' - x \qquad \Delta y = y' - y \qquad \Delta z = z' - z$$

Example 1

Find the magnitude and direction cosines of the displacement from $(-1, 4, 2)$ to $(3, 2, -2)$.

Solution

In terms of position vectors the displacement is from $\mathbf{P} = -\mathbf{I} + 4\mathbf{J} + 2\mathbf{K}$ to $\mathbf{P}' = 3\mathbf{I} + 2\mathbf{J} - 2\mathbf{K}$.   The displacement $\Delta \mathbf{P}$ is thus given by $\Delta \mathbf{P} = \mathbf{P}' - \mathbf{P} = 4\mathbf{I} - 2\mathbf{J} - 4\mathbf{K}$.   The magnitude is $\sqrt{4^2 + (-2)^2 + (-4)^2} = 6$.   A unit vector parallel to the displacement is obtained by dividing $\Delta \mathbf{P}$ by 6.   Its components $0.667, -0.333, -0.667$ are the direction cosines.

Example 2. Mid-point of a Segment

Let $\mathbf{M}$ be the mid-point of the segment $\mathbf{PQ}$.   This means that the vector $\mathbf{PM}$ is in magnitude one-half as long as the vector $\mathbf{PQ}$:

$$\mathbf{PM} = 0.5\mathbf{PQ}$$

Using Eq. (2.33), we may write

$$\mathbf{M} - \mathbf{P} = 0.5(\mathbf{Q} - \mathbf{P})$$

Solving for $\mathbf{M}$, we get

(2.34) $$\mathbf{M} = 0.5\mathbf{P} + 0.5\mathbf{Q} = 0.5(\mathbf{P} + \mathbf{Q})$$

In solving for $\mathbf{M}$ one actually uses a considerable number of the algebraic properties which we have derived for vector operations: properties of minus a vector and of the null vector, the commutative and associative laws for addition, and the various properties of multiplication by scalars.   You will find it instructive to fill in the missing steps, making sure that you can justify each of them.

Equation (2.34) summarizes in vivid fashion facts about the location of a mid-point.   It asserts that the point $\mathbf{M}$ may be found by constructing, by the parallelo-gram rule, the vector sum of $0.5\mathbf{P}$ and $0.5\mathbf{Q}$.   It also is identified as the mid-point of the diagonal vector $\mathbf{P} + \mathbf{Q}$ of the parallelogram determined by $\mathbf{P}$ and $\mathbf{Q}$.   You can draw instructive figures for these configurations, taking the origin $\mathbf{O}$ for the position vectors $\mathbf{P}, \mathbf{Q}$ and $\mathbf{M}$ as any point *not* on the line through the points $\mathbf{P}$ and $\mathbf{Q}$.   Next you may wish to draw figures for the special cases where $\mathbf{O}$ is on the segment $\mathbf{PQ}$ or on an extension of the segment.

Equation (2.34) was easy to derive and also easy to interpret geometrically. For actual numerical evaluation in mechanics it is often expedient to shift from the vector formulation to a component formulation.   In the case of the mid-point formula, this shift is readily accomplished.   Denote by (x_1,y_1,z_1), (x_2,y_2,z_2), and

Figure 2.29

Figure 2.30

$(\bar{x},\bar{y},\bar{z})$ the coordinates of **P**, **Q**, and **M** in that order.   Now put each vector in Eq. (2.34) in **IJK** form:

$$\bar{x}\mathbf{I} + \bar{y}\mathbf{J} + \bar{z}\mathbf{K} = 0.5(x_1\mathbf{I} + y_1\mathbf{J} + z_1\mathbf{K}) + 0.5(x_2\mathbf{I} + y_2\mathbf{J} + z_2\mathbf{K})$$
$$= 0.5(x_1 + x_2)\mathbf{I} + 0.5(y_1 + y_2)\mathbf{J} + 0.5(z_1 + z_2)\mathbf{K}$$

Using the result that two vectors are equal if and only if their x, y, and z components are equal, we have, in place of the one vector equation (2.34), the three scalar equations

(2.35)
$$\bar{x} = 0.5(x_1 + x_2)$$
$$\bar{y} = 0.5(y_1 + y_2)$$
$$\bar{z} = 0.5(z_1 + z_2)$$

This transition from one vector equation to three equivalent scalar equations is representative of what may be done at any stage of a development in vector mechanics. It illustrates the remarkable conciseness and simplicity of vector notations, and at the same time it shows that the vector equations are equivalent to suitable sets of scalar equations.   For further geometric uses of vectors, see Appendix 2.

EXERCISES

42. Evaluate the components parallel to the axes of the unit radial vector **L** associated with each of the following points: (a) (1,0,1); (b) (1, −1, 1); (c) (−10, 12, −8).
43. Find the magnitude and direction cosines of the displacement from **P** to **P′** when (a) **P** = (−5, 0, 5) and **P′** = (0,0,0); (b) **P** = (−5, 0, 5) and **P′** = (2,8,14).
44. Find the position vectors of the two points five units from **P** on a line through **P** having direction cosines 0.500, −0.707, 0.500.   **P** is the point (1,1,1).
45. Assuming that $(\bar{x},\bar{y},\bar{z})$ are the coordinates of $\bar{\mathbf{R}}$, (x_1,y_1,z_1) of $\mathbf{R}_1$, etc., write three scalar equations equivalent to the vector equation

$$10\bar{\mathbf{R}} = 2\mathbf{R}_1 + 5\mathbf{R}_2 + 3\mathbf{R}_3$$

2.12. INNER PRODUCT OF TWO VECTORS

Two operations have already been discussed for vectors: addition, in which two vectors are combined to give a third vector, and multiplication by scalars, in which a vector and a scalar are combined to give a new vector.   In this section an operation is defined by which two vectors are combined to give a scalar.   This scalar is the *scalar product* or the *inner product* of the two vectors.   This new product grows naturally out of our discussion of components.   In Eq. (2.19) we wrote

$$a_E = a \cos \theta$$

where θ is the angle between the vector **A** and the unit vector **E**.   We now shall regard the **E** component of **A** as a product of **A** by **E**:

$$a_E = \mathbf{A} \cdot \mathbf{E} = a \cos \theta$$

More generally, let **A** and **B** denote any two vectors and θ the angle between them as

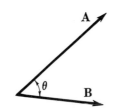

Figure
2.31

in Fig. 2.31.   Then the scalar product of **A** and **B**, denoted by $\mathbf{A} \cdot \mathbf{B}$ (and hence often called a *dot product*), is defined as the product of the magnitudes of the two vectors by the cosine of the angle:

(2.36) $$\mathbf{A} \cdot \mathbf{B} = ab \cos \theta$$

$\mathbf{A} \cdot \mathbf{B}$ may be interpreted as "*b* times the **B** component of **A**," or symmetrically, as "*a* times the **A** component of **B**."

Example I

Consider $\mathbf{A} \cdot \mathbf{B}$, where $\mathbf{A} = 5\underline{/40°}$ and $\mathbf{B} = 2\underline{/-20°}$.   Then
$$\theta = 40° - (-20°) = 60°$$
$$\mathbf{A} \cdot \mathbf{B} = (5)(2) \cos 60° = 5$$

Example 2

Consider $\mathbf{A} \cdot \mathbf{B}$, where $\mathbf{A} = 5\underline{/40°}$ and $\mathbf{B} = 2\underline{/160°}$.   Then
$$\theta = 160° - 40° = 120°$$
$$\mathbf{A} \cdot \mathbf{B} = (5)(2) \cos 120° = -5$$

Special Conclusions

1. Note that for any vector **A**

(2.37) $$\mathbf{A} \cdot \mathbf{A} = |\mathbf{A}|^2 = a^2$$

since in this case $\theta = 0°$. $\mathbf{A} \cdot \mathbf{A}$ is often written as $\mathbf{A}^2$.

2. *Criterion for perpendicularity.*   Consider the cases in which $\mathbf{A} \cdot \mathbf{B} = 0$. From the definition it is apparent that this is true whenever one of the vectors is a null vector.   *Aside from this special case, it is apparent that*

$$\mathbf{A} \cdot \mathbf{B} = 0$$

means that **A** *and* **B** *are perpendicular.*

3.   Note that

$$\mathbf{I} \cdot \mathbf{I} = \mathbf{J} \cdot \mathbf{J} = \mathbf{K} \cdot \mathbf{K} = 1$$
(2.38) $$\mathbf{I} \cdot \mathbf{J} = \mathbf{J} \cdot \mathbf{I} = \mathbf{J} \cdot \mathbf{K} = \mathbf{K} \cdot \mathbf{J} = \mathbf{K} \cdot \mathbf{I} = \mathbf{I} \cdot \mathbf{K} = 0$$

4. Note that for any two unit vectors **E** and **F**, having between them an angle θ,

(2.39) $$\mathbf{E} \cdot \mathbf{F} = \cos \theta$$

Similarly, the angle between any two vectors **A** and **B** has a cosine given by

(2.40) $$\cos \theta = \frac{\mathbf{A}}{a} \cdot \frac{\mathbf{B}}{b} = \frac{\mathbf{A} \cdot \mathbf{B}}{ab}$$

5. The scalar product of a vector **A** by a unit vector **E** has the special significance pointed out at the beginning of this section:

(2.41) $$\mathbf{A} \cdot \mathbf{E} = (a)(1) \cos \theta = a \cos \theta = a_E$$

That is, the scalar product of a vector by a unit vector is equal to the component of the vector in the direction of the unit vector.   For instance,

$$a_x = \mathbf{A} \cdot \mathbf{I}, \qquad a_y = \mathbf{A} \cdot \mathbf{J}, \qquad \cdots$$

This property will be used frequently; therefore the student should take care to fix firmly in his mind the equivalence just described.   It may be noted further that the projection of **A** parallel to **E** is simply $(\mathbf{A} \cdot \mathbf{E})\mathbf{E}$.

Algebraic Properties.   From the symmetry of the definition and the fact that

$$ab = ba$$

it follows that *scalar multiplication of vectors is commutative*:

(2.42) $\mathbf{A} \cdot \mathbf{B} = \mathbf{B} \cdot \mathbf{A}$

It is easy to show that scalar factors may be factored out of a scalar product:

(2.43) $(c\mathbf{A}) \cdot (d\mathbf{B}) = cd(\mathbf{A} \cdot \mathbf{B})$

The proof is listed as Exercise 73.

We have seen how this new operation may be combined with multiplication by scalars. We now consider its use in conjunction with the operation of addition. Consider the product $(\mathbf{A} + \mathbf{B}) \cdot \mathbf{C}$.   Let us write $\mathbf{C}$ as $c\mathbf{E}$, where as usual $\mathbf{E}$ represents a unit vector in the desired direction.   Factoring out the scalar multiple c, we are left with c times $(\mathbf{A} + \mathbf{B}) \cdot \mathbf{E}$, which we have just seen to be equal to the component $(\mathbf{A} + \mathbf{B})$ parallel to $\mathbf{E}$.   But in Sec. 2.9 it was shown that such a component of a sum is equal to the sum of the components in the same direction of the vectors being added; that is,

$$(\mathbf{A} + \mathbf{B}) \cdot \mathbf{E} = \mathbf{A} \cdot \mathbf{E} + \mathbf{B} \cdot \mathbf{E}$$

If both sides of this equation are multiplied by c, we have

$$(\mathbf{A} + \mathbf{B}) \cdot \mathbf{C} = c(\mathbf{A} + \mathbf{B}) \cdot \mathbf{E} = c(\mathbf{A} \cdot \mathbf{E}) + c(\mathbf{B} \cdot \mathbf{E})$$

or, using the rule for scalar factors,

(2.44) $(\mathbf{A} + \mathbf{B}) \cdot \mathbf{C} = (\mathbf{A} \cdot c\mathbf{E}) + (\mathbf{B} \cdot c\mathbf{E}) = (\mathbf{A} \cdot \mathbf{C}) + (\mathbf{B} \cdot \mathbf{C})$

This shows that *scalar multiplication of vectors is distributive with respect to vector addition*.   Using this result together with the commutative law, one may derive a second form of the distributive law:

(2.45) $\mathbf{A} \cdot (\mathbf{B} + \mathbf{C}) = \mathbf{A} \cdot \mathbf{B} + \mathbf{A} \cdot \mathbf{C}$

By successive application of the commutative and distributive laws it is possible to justify free manipulation of the operations thus far defined according to the rules of elementary algebra.   Of course, one must keep in mind that a scalar is not a vector, so that, for instance, it is meaningless to write $(\mathbf{A} \cdot \mathbf{B}) \cdot \mathbf{C}$ unless one understands that this must mean the same as $(\mathbf{A} \cdot \mathbf{B})\mathbf{C}$.

Working Formula for Inner Products.   As an example of such manipulations as the above, we shall compute a working formula for scalar products in terms of components.   Let us evaluate

$$\mathbf{A} \cdot \mathbf{B} = (a_x\mathbf{I} + a_y\mathbf{J} + a_z\mathbf{K}) \cdot (b_x\mathbf{I} + b_y\mathbf{J} + b_z\mathbf{K})$$

Expanding the right member, using the distributive property, we get nine terms such as

$$(a_x\mathbf{I} \cdot b_x\mathbf{I}), \qquad (a_y\mathbf{J} \cdot b_z\mathbf{K}), \qquad \ldots$$

By the rule for factoring out scalar factors, they may be rewritten as

$$a_x b_x(\mathbf{I} \cdot \mathbf{I}), \qquad a_y b_z(\mathbf{J} \cdot \mathbf{K}), \qquad \ldots$$

It is now apparent that six of the nine terms are equal to zero.

$$(\mathbf{J} \cdot \mathbf{K} = 0, \ldots)$$

Hence, if we replace $(\mathbf{I} \cdot \mathbf{I})$ by its value one (and similarly for $\mathbf{J} \cdot \mathbf{J}$ and $\mathbf{K} \cdot \mathbf{K}$), we shall have as an end result

$$(2.46) \qquad\qquad \mathbf{A} \cdot \mathbf{B} = a_x b_x + a_y b_y + a_z b_z$$

This is a formula of great utility.

Example 3

Find the component of $\mathbf{A} = 9\mathbf{I} - 3\mathbf{J} + 6\mathbf{K}$ parallel to the unit vector $\mathbf{E} = (\tfrac{2}{3})\mathbf{I} - (\tfrac{1}{3})\mathbf{J} + (\tfrac{2}{3})\mathbf{K}$.

Solution

$$a_E = \mathbf{A} \cdot \mathbf{E} = (9)(\tfrac{2}{3}) + (-3)(-\tfrac{1}{3}) + (6)(\tfrac{2}{3}) = 11$$

Example 4

Find the angle subtended at the origin by the points with coordinates $(3,4,0)$ and $(0,-8,6)$.

Solution

The vectors from the origin to these points are

$$\mathbf{A} = 3\mathbf{I} + 4\mathbf{J} \qquad \text{and} \qquad \mathbf{B} = -8\mathbf{J} + 6\mathbf{K}$$

Then

$$\cos \theta = \frac{\mathbf{A} \cdot \mathbf{B}}{ab} = \frac{-32}{5 \times 10} = -0.64$$

whence

$$\theta = 129.8°$$

Example 5

Determine the vector obtained by projecting a vector $\mathbf{A}$ onto a plane which is normal to a unit vector $\mathbf{N}$.

Solution

Denote this vector by $\mathbf{A}'$. Since lines drawn from the ends of $\mathbf{A}'$ to the corresponding ends of $\mathbf{A}$ are parallel to $\mathbf{N}$, it is apparent (see Fig. 2.32) that $\mathbf{A}$ is equal to the vector sum of $\mathbf{A}'$ and the projection of $\mathbf{A}$ parallel to $\mathbf{N}$:

$$\mathbf{A} = \mathbf{A}' + (\mathbf{A} \cdot \mathbf{N})\mathbf{N}$$

Thus $\mathbf{A}'$ is expressible by the equation

$$(2.47) \qquad\qquad \mathbf{A}' = \mathbf{A} - (\mathbf{A} \cdot \mathbf{N})\mathbf{N}$$

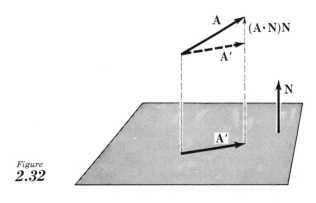

Figure
2.32

Example 6. Plane through the Origin

Let $\mathbf{P}$ be position vector of any point in the plane through the origin normal to the constant vector $\mathbf{A}$. Since $\mathbf{A}$ is perpendicular to $\mathbf{P}$, it follows that $\mathbf{P}$ must satisfy the simple equation $\mathbf{A} \cdot \mathbf{P} = 0$. This vector equation expresses eloquently the idea of a plane as a locus of lines normal to a fixed line. From this vector equation one may derive a more conventional scalar equation. Let $\mathbf{A}$ and $\mathbf{P}$ be given by $\mathbf{A} = a_x\mathbf{I} + a_y\mathbf{J} + a_z\mathbf{K}$ and $\mathbf{P} = x\mathbf{I} + y\mathbf{J} + z\mathbf{K}$. Then

$$\mathbf{A} \cdot \mathbf{P} = a_x x + a_y y + a_z z = 0$$

Any specific equation of a plane through the origin, such as $6x - 3y - 2z = 0$, is at once identifiable as the equation of the plane normal to the vector $6\mathbf{I} - 3\mathbf{J} - 2\mathbf{K}$.

EXERCISES

46. Find the scalar product of each of the following pairs of vectors:
  (a) $25\underline{/0°}$ and $10\underline{/110°}$.   (b) $5\underline{/-50°}$ and $6\underline{/40°}$.
  (c) $1\underline{/70°}$ and $1\underline{/130°}$.   (d) $1\underline{/30°}$ and $1\underline{/210°}$.
  (e) $15\underline{/155°}$ and $\mathbf{J}$.   (f) $2\mathbf{I} + \mathbf{J}$ and $2\mathbf{I} - \mathbf{J}$.
  (g) $\mathbf{I} - 2\mathbf{J} + 3\mathbf{K}$ and $\mathbf{J} - \mathbf{K}$.   (h) $2\mathbf{I} - \mathbf{J} - 3\mathbf{K}$ and $4\mathbf{I} + 5\mathbf{J} + \mathbf{K}$.

47. Find the angle between (a) the vectors $2\mathbf{I} - 2\mathbf{J} + \mathbf{K}$ and $4\mathbf{I} - 3\mathbf{K}$; (b) the position vectors of the points with coordinates $(2,0,5)$ and $(3, -6, -6)$; (c) the lines AB and AC where A, B, and C are points with coordinates $(3, -2, 6)$, $(5, -2, 7)$, and $(1, -1, 6)$, respectively; (d) the directions having direction cosines $(\frac{2}{3})$, $(\frac{1}{3})$, $(-\frac{2}{3})$ and $(\frac{1}{3})$, $(\frac{2}{3})$, $(\frac{2}{3})$.

48. The vector $a\mathbf{I} - 2\mathbf{J} + \mathbf{K}$ is perpendicular to the vector $\mathbf{I} - 2\mathbf{J} - 3\mathbf{K}$. Find a.

49. The vectors $\mathbf{A} + \mathbf{B}$ and $\mathbf{A} - \mathbf{B}$ are perpendicular. Use the scalar product as a means of arriving at a conclusion concerning the magnitudes of $\mathbf{A}$ and of $\mathbf{B}$.

50. Find the component of the vector $2\mathbf{I} - 3\mathbf{J} + 6\mathbf{K}$ parallel to (a) the unit vector $0.33\mathbf{I} - 0.67\mathbf{J} + 0.67\mathbf{K}$; (b) the z axis; (c) the vector $3\mathbf{I} - 9\mathbf{J} - 2\mathbf{K}$; (d) the vector $3\mathbf{I} + 2\mathbf{J}$.

51. Find the projection of $6\mathbf{I} - 6\mathbf{J} - 7\mathbf{K}$ (a) parallel to the y axis; (b) parallel to $3\mathbf{I} - 4\mathbf{K}$.

52. A unit vector $\mathbf{E}$ makes angles of $45°$, $60°$, and $120°$, respectively, with the coordinate axes. Find the component parallel to $\mathbf{E}$ of the vector $\mathbf{I} - \mathbf{J} - \mathbf{K}$.

53. A vector $\mathbf{V}$ has magnitude 10 and direction cosines 0.5, 0.707, and -0.5. Find the component of $\mathbf{V}$ parallel to the z axis; parallel to the vector $4\mathbf{I} - 3\mathbf{K}$.

54. $\mathbf{E}$ and $\mathbf{F}$ are unit vectors. Under what conditions can the sum $\mathbf{E} + \mathbf{F}$ be a unit vector? (HINT: Expand the scalar product of $\mathbf{E} + \mathbf{F}$ with itself.)

55. Given two nonperpendicular vectors $\mathbf{A}$ and $\mathbf{B}$. For some scalar k, the vector $k\mathbf{B}$ has a projection in the direction of $\mathbf{A}$ which is exactly equal to $\mathbf{A}$. Prove that

$$k = \frac{\mathbf{A} \cdot \mathbf{A}}{\mathbf{A} \cdot \mathbf{B}}$$

2.13. TWO SUGGESTIONS FOR SUPPLEMENTARY STUDY

In this chapter you have seen how, studying physical displacements in the context of analytic geometry, it is natural to introduce vectors as a new mathematical tool. Vector addition and multiplication by a scalar are completely natural generalizations of operations on displacements. The final operation of inner product turned out to be a device for describing and computing components. Instead of starting with the intuitive displacement model, we could start with a set of axioms. Next, supplementary properties would be deduced and applications made. In Appendix 1 such a list of axioms is given. If your present grasp of the formal properties of vectors is vague, you might profit from a perusal of this Appendix.

Some students at first have difficulty in the visualization of spatial situations common to mechanics and vector analysis. With this in mind you may wish to study some of the additional elementary geometric uses of vectors given in Appendix 2.

REVIEW EXERCISES

56. The top of Mt. Dome (4,815 ft above sea level) is northeast of Acton (1,265 ft above sea level). From Beckton (1,265 ft above sea level, east of Acton), the peak of Mt. Dome is seen 30° west of north at an angle of 22° above the horizontal. Taking right-handed axes with Acton as origin, the horizontal easterly line as z axis, and the horizontal northerly line as x axis:
    (a) What are the coordinates of Beckton?
    (b) What are the direction cosines of the line of sight from Acton to the top of Mt. Dome?
    (c) A straight road runs from Acton to Beckton. How close does the road come to the peak?

57. Taking the center of the earth as origin, the radial line in the equatorial plane to the Greenwich meridian as positive x axis, the radial line to the North Pole as positive y axis, and the z axis so as to form a right-handed system, and using miles as units, what are the coordinates of:
    (a) Brunswick, Maine: latitude 44°N, longitude 70°W?
    (b) Reno, Nevada: latitude 40°N, longitude 120°W?
    (c) Canberra, Australia: latitude 35°S, longitude 149°E?
    Treat the earth as a sphere of radius 4,000 miles.

58. Using the information of Exercise 57, compute the distance from Brunswick to Canberra.

59. Using the axes of Exercise 57, find the direction cosines of the segment from Brunswick to Canberra.

60. A and B are nonparallel vectors. Draw with a common initial point the four vectors A, −A, B, −B. Now construct the two vectors A − (−B) and B − (−A). Use a geometrical argument to show that these two vectors are equal.

61. This problem involves a geometric construction of the approximate location of the centroid of a semicircle. Divide the semicircle into 2^n equal arcs. Draw correspondingly 2^n vectors from the center of the circle to the mid-points of the arcs. Form the vector sum of these 2^n vectors. Multiply this result by the scalar $1/2^n$. Do this for $n = 1, 2, 3$.

    Compare your result with the following fact. Let the distance to the centroid from the center of the given circle be denoted by $\bar{r}$. Then a semicircle of radius $\bar{r}$ has total arc length equal to the diameter of the given semicircle.

62. A and B are any two vectors. Discuss critically the two inequalities:
    (a) $|A| - |B| \leq |A + B|$.   (b) $|A + B| \leq |A| + |B|$.

63. The vector A has x component -8, y component $+12$, and z component -9. Find in the form $e_x I + e_y J + e_z K$ the unit vector parallel to A.

64. The vectors A and B in the xy plane are given by $A = 10/30°$, $B = 20/135°$.
    (a) Find in polar form the unit vector parallel to the vector $A + B$.
    (b) Compute in the form $c_x I + c_y J + c_z K$ the vector $A - B$. Check graphically on the fact that $c_x = a_x - b_x$, $c_y = a_y - b_y$.

65. Let R_0 be any position vector in the xy plane. Let $A = 5/\!-30°$, $B = 3/\!45°$. Then the position vectors R_1, R_2, R_3, R_4 are defined, respectively, by

$$R_1 = R_0 + A \qquad R_2 = R_0 + B \qquad R_3 = R_0 - A \qquad R_4 = R_0 - B$$

Express in polar form unit vectors parallel to R_1R_2, R_2R_3, R_3R_4, R_4R_1.

66. Show that the point P dividing the segment $P'P''$ in the ratio $r:(1 - r)$ is given by $P = (1 - r)P' + rP''$.

67. The four points having position vectors A, B, C, D form a quadrilateral $ABCD$. The mid-points of the four sides AB, BC, CD, DA are, respectively, K, L, M, N. Use the ratio formula derived in Exercise 66 to prove that $KLMN$ is a parallelogram.

68. If P, Q, and R are position vectors while a, b, and c are nonzero scalars, what geometric conclusions about the vectors can be concluded from the two relations

$$aP + bQ + cR = O$$
$$a + b + c = 0$$

69. Suppose that T_E is a projection operator so that, in Fig. 2.26,

$$T_E(A) = T_E(PQ) = P'Q'$$

Verify that, for any unit vector E and any vector A, $T_E[T_E(A)] = T_E(A)$.

70. Use the dot product to verify, using the terminology of the preceding problem, that

$$T_{-E}(A) = T_E(A)$$

71. *Cylindrical coordinates.* In cylindrical coordinates, each position vector R is expressed as the sum of a vector zK parallel to the axis of the system plus the projection R' onto a plane normal to that axis.

$$R = zK + R'$$

R' is expressible in polar coordinates:

$$R' = r'/\!\theta$$

Thus the cylindrical coordinates (z,r',θ) are related to the unit vectors K, L', M', as shown in Fig. 2.33.

$$R = zK + r'L'$$

(a) Express in IJK form the position vector of the point with coordinates $(-6°,10°,60°)$.
(b) Find cylindrical coordinates for the point with position vector $6I - 6J + 3K$.

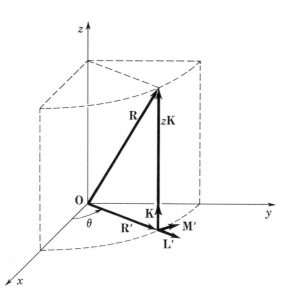

Figure
2.33

72. *Spherical coordinates.* In spherical coordinates the magnitude of the position vector is given, together with two angles specifying the direction of this vector. One of these angles is the polar coordinate θ of the projected vector $\mathbf{R}'$ (as in Exercise 71); the other angle is the direction angle γ (as in Sec. 2.4). These spherical coordinates (r,θ,γ) are related to the unit vectors $\mathbf{L}$, $\mathbf{M}'$, $\mathbf{N}$ shown in Fig. 2.34. (In each case the unit vector shows the way $\mathbf{R}$ would start to move if one coordinate grew while the other two remained fixed.)

(*a*) Express in **IJK** form the position vector of the point with spherical coordinates $(10,300°,60°)$.

(*b*) Find spherical coordinates for the point with position vector $6\mathbf{I} - 6\mathbf{J} - 3\mathbf{K}$.

(*c*) Express $\mathbf{R} = (r,\theta,\gamma)$ in **IJK** form.

73. For vectors $\mathbf{A}$, $\mathbf{B}$ and scalars c, d prove that the following identity is valid:

$$(c\mathbf{A}) \cdot (d\mathbf{B}) = cd(\mathbf{A} \cdot \mathbf{B})$$

74. $\mathbf{E}$ and $\mathbf{F}$ are unit vectors. $\mathbf{E} - \mathbf{F}$ is also a unit vector. Use scalar products to draw a further conclusion about $\mathbf{E}$ and $\mathbf{F}$.

75. $\mathbf{E}$ and $\mathbf{F}$ are unit vectors. $\mathbf{E} - 2\mathbf{F}$ has magnitude 2. Use scalar products to draw a further conclusion about $\mathbf{E}$ and $\mathbf{F}$.

76. If $\mathbf{A} = (\mathbf{A} \cdot \mathbf{B})\mathbf{B}$, prove that $\mathbf{B}$ is a unit vector.

77. Under what conditions if any is cancellation of the common factor $\mathbf{C}$ valid in an equation such as $\mathbf{A} \cdot \mathbf{C} = \mathbf{B} \cdot \mathbf{C}$? Prove your answer carefully.

78. Use scalar products to prove that any vector which is perpendicular to both $\mathbf{A}$ and $\mathbf{B}$,

$$\mathbf{A} = a_x\mathbf{I} + a_y\mathbf{J} + a_z\mathbf{K} \qquad \mathbf{B} = b_x\mathbf{I} + b_y\mathbf{J} + b_z\mathbf{K}$$

is a scalar multiple of the vector

$$\mathbf{C} = (a_yb_z - a_zb_y)\mathbf{I} + (a_zb_x - a_xb_z)\mathbf{J} + (a_xb_y - a_yb_x)\mathbf{K}$$

79. Show how the law of cosines of trigonometry can be derived from an expansion of the scalar product

$$(\mathbf{A} + \mathbf{B}) \cdot (\mathbf{A} + \mathbf{B})$$

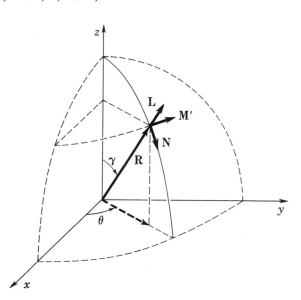

Figure
2.34

80. The projections of **A** parallel and perpendicular to a unit vector **E** have been shown to be, respectively, equal to $(\mathbf{A} \cdot \mathbf{E})\mathbf{E}$ and $\mathbf{A} - (\mathbf{A} \cdot \mathbf{E})\mathbf{E}$. Use the rules for scalar multiplication to show that these two components are perpendicular to each other.

81. Find the component of the vector $2\mathbf{I} - 3\mathbf{J} + 6\mathbf{K}$ parallel to the xy plane.

82. Find the projection of $6\mathbf{I} - 6\mathbf{J} - 7\mathbf{K}$ (*a*) parallel to the plane $x - 2y - 2z = 0$; (*b*) perpendicular to the vector $\mathbf{I} + \mathbf{J}$ (that is, parallel to a plane normal to this vector); (*c*) perpendicular to the vector $3\mathbf{I} + \mathbf{K}$.

83. Write an equation for the plane through the origin and perpendicular to the vector $\mathbf{I} - 2\mathbf{J} - 3\mathbf{K}$.

84. The vertices of a triangle have position vectors **A**, **B**, and **C**. Show that the angle of the triangle at **C** has cosine equal to

$$\frac{(\mathbf{A} - \mathbf{C}) \cdot (\mathbf{B} - \mathbf{C})}{[(\mathbf{A} - \mathbf{C}) \cdot (\mathbf{A} - \mathbf{C})(\mathbf{B} - \mathbf{C}) \cdot (\mathbf{B} - \mathbf{C})]^{\frac{1}{2}}}$$

85. **A**, **B**, **C**, and **D** are position vectors relative to an arbitrary origin of the vertices in cyclic order of a rectangle. Show that

$$\mathbf{A} \cdot \mathbf{C} = \mathbf{B} \cdot \mathbf{D}$$

CHAPTER THREE

FORCES

In our approach to the science of mechanics, *force*, along with distance and time, will be a basic ingredient. The concept of distance is the only such ingredient to be treated so far, for the geometry of position uses distances as coordinates. The vector language of the preceding chapter will be as useful in the study of forces as it was in the study of position.

3.1. THE NATURE OF A FORCE

We shall first review some of the intuitive aspects of force by considering examples. (*a*) When an object falls freely, we say that a gravitational force called the weight is pulling it down. This is an example of a *body force*: the weight of the whole object depends on the weights of all its parts. (*b*) If a drawer sticks, we apply a force to close it. (*c*) If an object hangs in equilibrium at the end of a string, we say that it is prevented from falling by a force called the tension exerted by the string. (*d*) When an automobile skids to a stop, we say that a frictional force caused it to stop. The last three are examples of *contact* or *surface forces*: the force in each case is transmitted to the objects in question across surfaces of contact with other objects. In each of the examples cited, the force had a *direction*. The gravitational force was down; the tension in the string was up; the push on the drawer was deliberately directed as the need required; the frictional force was in a direction opposed to the motion.

Forces also have *magnitudes*. We continually distinguish between large and small forces, and we are accustomed to assigning numerical values to forces. The magnitude of a force may be measured directly by counterbalancing it with a calibrated spring or by removing it and then producing identical effects with such a spring, or it may be measured indirectly by observing its effects when it is left unbalanced. The study of effects of unbalanced forces is deferred until Chap. 6. The metric unit of force, the newton, may be defined in terms of a reference object, the *standard kilogram*, prototypes of which are preserved in bureaus of standards. Such a definition could be based on the character of the motion of the standard object when subjected to an unbalanced force. A more convenient approach for us at this juncture is contained in the statement: The apparent gravitational force or weight in a standard locality on a standard kilogram is 9.80665 newtons. A precise statement of just what constitutes a "standard locality" would drive us back to the indirect

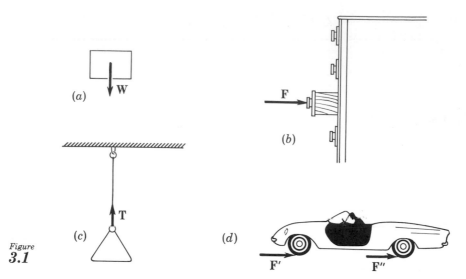

Figure
3.1

approach (cf. Sec. 6.1), but let it be said that any locality on the surface of the earth is nearly a standard locality, the deviation seldom being as much as one-quarter of one per cent. For the exercises in this treatment we shall round off the value to 9.81 newtons/kg and shall regard all surface situations as standard unless otherwise specified. The English unit of force, the pound, is equal to 4.4482 newtons. Here it may be assumed that the conversion factor is 4.45. Other units of force will be mentioned later.

Since forces have direction and magnitude, it is natural that they should be represented by *vectors*. In Fig. 3.1, the vectors **W, F, T, F'**, and **F"** represent the weight, push, tension, and frictional forces which were described in the examples listed above.

Actually, it is not enough to say that forces can be represented as vectors. More will be said about this in Sec. 3.4. For the present let it merely be stated that a force is completely specified if we know its magnitude, its direction, *and* the point at which it is applied. In representing a force, then, we specify a vector and a point of application. These together determine the *line of action* of the force. In diagrams such as those of Fig. 3.1 we usually take the point of application as being an end of the vector. In Fig. 3.1*a* and *c* the point of application is the initial point of the vector; in Fig. 3.1*b* and *d*, the terminal point. This choice is arbitrary, although in some cases one choice may seem more natural than the other. In these first simple analyses we shall assume outright that when two bodies touch, the contact forces act at the point or points of contact. We shall also assume that the weight of a body may be thought of as acting at its center if it is symmetrical and homogeneous; otherwise it may act as some other intermediate point.

3.2. PARTICLES AND RIGID BODIES

Even in the early part of this course we shall envisage forces as acting on objects in great variety. Yet we cannot investigate separately the behavior of automobiles, balls, doors, satellites, bridges, and people. Our theory must be general enough to apply to many such things. This theory in its simplest form will deal with forces as applied to particles. *Particle* is for us a technical term denoting an idealized physical object whose extent is negligible.   The same word is used in other contexts to denote objects of atomic physics.   These objects may sometimes be treated as particles in our sense of the word.   A particle is sometimes called a *mass point*. The mechanics of particles closely resembles that of many real objects.   For instance, a falling stone may act as if all forces influencing it were directed through its center. In such a circumstance it is treated as a particle.   A boy on a sled may be considered a particle as he slides smoothly downhill.   The moon may be treated as a particle for some investigations.   Whenever we apply our theory of particles to a practical problem involving a physical object, we must remember that we implicitly assume that the object acts like a particle, and hence that our results involve an approximation of a basic sort.

Any investigator will of course discover that even in simple situations an object may not behave like a single particle.   In that case we often shall try to regard it as a set of interacting particles.   This approach extends the coverage of our theory tremendously.   An object like a tree blowing in the wind could be studied in this manner.   One would rightly guess, however, that complexity of structure would make the problem difficult.   Much of our work will, in the interest of simplicity, be limited to collections of particles whose relative positions are fixed.   This notion will be elaborated in Chap. 13.   Essentially, a *rigid body* is a collection of particles in firm association: distances between pairs of particles do not change.   Wheels, automobiles, and ladders are examples of objects which it is often advantageous to treat as rigid bodies.   Modern machinery abounds in moving parts, each of which acts very nearly like a rigid body.   While we expect in the laboratory to meet no perfect portrayals of the roles of particle and rigid body, it will be found that adequate accuracy is attained by assuming that many objects behave like a member of one of these elemental categories.

3.3. NEWTON'S LAW OF REACTION AND THE CONCEPT OF ISOLATION

Much of the theory presented in this course is based on *laws of motion* enunciated by Sir Isaac Newton.   His third law stated in effect that every action is paired with an equal and opposite reaction.   This has been abundantly verified experimentally for a wide variety of forces.   This claim leads to no difficulties when the forces of interaction between two particles act along the line joining them.   We shall *assume* it as a postulate, restating it as follows:

(3.1) *Forces act in pairs, equal in magnitude, along the same line, but opposite in direction.*

To see the significance of this postulate, let us reexamine the examples of Sec. 3.1.   In example *a* we accepted the idea of a gravitational force acting on a body and causing it to fall.   The reaction postulate reminds us that an equal force was simultaneously pulling up on the earth.   Because of the disparity of the objects involved, only the effect of one of the two objects is observable; but Newton's theory of gravitation is perfectly symmetrical.   This theory will be studied in Secs. 12.4 and 17.6.   If the sun attracts the earth, so does the earth attract the sun.   In example *b* the push exerted on the drawer gives rise to a force of opposition acting on the pusher.   In example *c* the suspended object pulls down on the cord just as hard as the cord pulls up on it.   In example *d* the tires push ahead on the road surface with exactly the same intensity that the road surface pushes back on the tires.   If the road were not anchored firmly, this force might displace it, just as an unanchored rug slips when a running person suddenly stops on it.

Since forces occur in pairs, it is important to decide for each pair which of the two will be of interest in a given problem. If an object under consideration has n distinct interactions with other objects, then $2n$ forces are involved. But of these $2n$ forces we shall invariably interest ourselves in the n forces acting *on* the object. The process of focusing one's attention on a single object and of sifting out all the forces acting on it from the outside is called *isolating* the object. The isolation process is aided by diagrams. First draw an outline of the isolated object. Then at each point of interaction draw vectors to represent the forces acting on the body from without. Such a diagram is often called a *free-body diagram*. It can be of crucial usefulness in the solution of problems. It should be drawn neatly and carefully at a scale which can be easily studied. In each example first imagine the object or portion of an object to be studied as suspended in space. Then draw a vector to represent its weight, in most local problems a force vertically down. Then for each additional object touching or otherwise affecting the given one, draw one or more vectors to represent the forces of interaction which act on the isolated objects. It is usually convenient to use a small number of such vectors. For instance, in isolating a fakir reclining on a bed of spikes, instead of using a force for each spike, we might use a single upward force representing the resultant of all the individual forces.

A number of illustrations are listed. Note that gravitational forces are drawn as acting at the center of uniform bodies. Justification will be given later. Note also that forces acting at a smooth surface are normal to the plane of contact. This also will be given more attention later.

Example I

Ball on string (as in Fig. 3.2). **T** is the tension of the string; **W** is weight of the ball.

Example 2

Picture hung by wire (as in Fig. 3.3). $\mathbf{T}_1$ and $\mathbf{T}_2$ are the forces exerted by the wire; **W** is the weight of the picture.

Example 3

Sled on a smooth hill (as in Fig. 3.4). **W** is the weight of the sled; **N** is the normal reaction force of the hill on the sled. (This is a single representation of all the contact forces acting on the runners of the sled.)

Example 4

Sled on slightly rough hill (as in Fig. 3.5). **W** is the weight of the sled; **C** is the contact reaction of the hill on the sled (no longer normal).

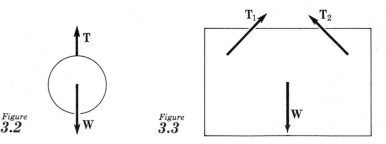

Figure
3.2

Figure
3.3

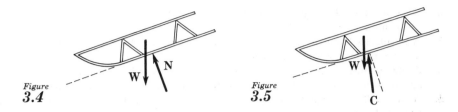

Figure
3.4

Figure
3.5

Example 5

A uniform ladder on rough ground against a smooth wall (as in Fig. 3.6). **W** is the weight of the ladder; **C** is the reaction of the ground on the ladder (not normal); **N** is the reaction of smooth wall on the ladder (normal).

Example 6

To show that Postulate (3.1) may not necessarily apply to physical situations involving transverse forces, consider the magnetic forces between two moving charged particles. The following example is based on the Ampère configuration as usually presented in elementary physics. In Fig. 3.7 two positively charged particles are moving in the plane of the figure in the directions shown by the dashed arrows. First let us isolate A. The magnetic flux at A due to the motion of B vanishes for the instant shown since A is on the line of B's motion. Hence a free-body diagram for A shows no magnetic forces. Now let us isolate B. The flux at B due to the motion of A is normal to the page, and hence B is subject to a transverse force F as shown in the diagram. In this course we shall not ordinarily be concerned with situations of this kind. We shall usually assume that the forces between interacting particles are directed along the line between them. This is the case, for instance, for the coulomb (electrostatic) forces between particles A and B in Fig. 3.7.

The following exercises require, for perfect execution, knowledge of mechanics as yet not introduced. The student should concentrate on two aspects: representation of known forces by suitable vectors and qualitatively correct isolation of bodies. Common sense and previous contact with forces will aid the student in getting reasonable results.

EXERCISES

1. Using a scale of 100 lb/in., draw a free-body diagram of yourself sitting in a chair, feet on floor, with 75 per cent of your weight resting on the chair, the rest through feet on floor.

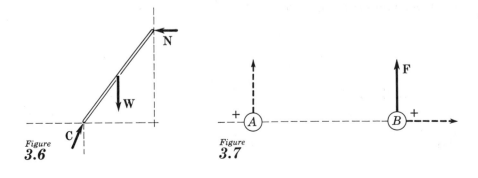

Figure
3.6

Figure
3.7

2. Draw a free-body diagram of an automobile ascending a grade inclined at 20° with the horizontal.

3. An athlete's hammer is swung in a vertical circle. Draw a free-body diagram for it in three of its positions: top, side, bottom.

4. A man stands on the ladder which was used in Example 5 above. (a) Isolate the man, and draw a free-body diagram. (b) Isolate the ladder, and draw a free-body diagram.

5. A boy pulls a horizontal loaded cart by a rope inclined at 15°. Isolate the cart, and draw a diagram.

6. Two boys, weighing 70 and 100 lb, balance on a seesaw. Draw three diagrams, isolating each of the boys and the seesaw separately.

3.4. EQUIVALENCE OF FORCES

We have seen that it is natural and convenient to represent forces by vectors. We must, however, use caution in applying the results of vector algebra developed in Chap. 2. For instance, two vectors are equal if they have the same magnitude and the same direction. But two forces having equal vectors may have quite different mechanical effects on a physical object. In Fig. 3.8, for example, the forces represented by vectors F and F' produce quite dissimilar effects: F causes rotation of the propeller, but F' merely causes a reaction at the bearing. Yet F and F' are equal vectors.

Since vector equality is by itself an unsatisfactory concept when applied to forces, we shall introduce a narrower notion based on the empirical effects of forces. Two sets of forces will be called *equivalent* if their instantaneous effects on a particle or a rigid body would necessarily be the same. As in Sec. 3.3, significant experimental results will serve as working postulates for the further development of the theory. The first conclusion is this: The effects on an essentially rigid body of two equal and parallel forces having the same line of action are indistinguishable. Consequently, a force may be displaced along its line of action without changing its effect, assuming that it still acts on the specified object. In Fig. 3.9 equivalent forces are shown acting on identical carts. Equivalent forces need not be equally easy to apply or to maintain, but as far as effect on a rigid body or particle is concerned, a push is as good as a pull. This property is often called the *principle of transmissibility of forces*. For future reference, we state our postulate thus:

(3.2) *Two forces are equivalent if and only if (a) they are represented by equal vectors and (b) their lines of action coincide.*

A third noteworthy experimental fact about forces is that concurrent forces may be combined according to the rules of vector addition. This too will be stated as a postulate in terms of the notion of equivalence:

(3.3) *If F and F' are vectors representing two forces whose lines of action have a common point, then the vector F + F' represents an equivalent single force whose line of action passes through the same point.*

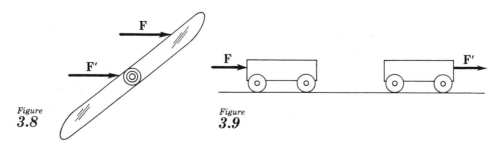

Figure
3.8

Figure
3.9

This is illustrated in Fig. 3.10. (In what follows the same symbol will be used for a force and for the vector representing it.) Postulate (3.3) is often called the *parallelogram law of composition*. It is an extremely useful tool. It justifies replacing a number of concurrent forces by one force. This one force is unique, of course, for the order in which vectors are added is immaterial. It also justifies replacing any one force by a convenient selection of equivalent forces. The equivalence shown in Fig. 3.10 can be represented symbolically by

$$\{\mathbf{F},\mathbf{F'}\} \equiv \{\mathbf{F} + \mathbf{F'}\}$$

Example 1

Any force $\mathbf{F}$ may be replaced by the three concurrent forces whose vectors are $f_x\mathbf{I}, f_y\mathbf{J},$ and $f_z\mathbf{K}$.

Example 2

Two equal and opposite forces having the same line of action are equivalent to a null force. Hence, any family of forces may be augmented by two such forces without changing the effect of the family.

Example 3

If the forces $a_x\mathbf{I} + a_y\mathbf{J} + a_z\mathbf{K}$ and $b_x\mathbf{I} + b_y\mathbf{J} + b_z\mathbf{K}$ are concurrent, they are equivalent to the single force

$$(a_x + b_x)\mathbf{I} + (a_y + b_y)\mathbf{J} + (a_z + b_z)\mathbf{K}$$

EXERCISES

7. (a) Plot to scale the forces $\mathbf{F} = 4/65°$ and $\mathbf{F'} = 6/20°$, where $\mathbf{F}$ acts at the point $(5, -2)$ and $\mathbf{F'}$ at $(0,0)$.

   (b) Use Postulates (3.2) and (3.3) to construct graphically a single force equivalent to $\mathbf{F}$ and $\mathbf{F'}$ in combination.

   (c) Measure from the result of part (b) the magnitude and the angle of this force.

   (d) Using analytical methods, compute from the data the angle and magnitude of $\mathbf{F} + \mathbf{F'}$.

8. Given two forces $\mathbf{A}$ and $\mathbf{B}$ acting at the origin $5/-20°$ and $3/50°$. (a) Plot the vectors to scale. (b) Construct graphically the projections $a_x, b_x, a_x + b_x, a_y, b_y,$ and $a_y + b_y$. (c) From the results of (b) construct $\mathbf{A} + \mathbf{B}$. (d) Check your results analytically.

9. The following forces act at one point:

   A: 10 lb, parallel to the vector $\mathbf{I} + \mathbf{J}$

   B: 15 lb, with direction cosines 0.0, -0.8, 0.6

   C: $3\mathbf{I} + 15\mathbf{J} + \mathbf{K}$ lb

   D: 5 lb, parallel to the negative x axis

   E: 5 lb, making angles of 90°, 135°, and 135° with the positive coordinate axes

   Find the magnitude and direction cosines of a single vector equivalent to the family of five forces.

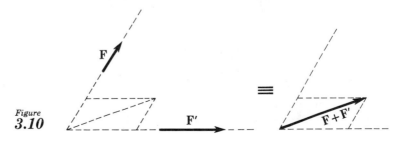

Figure
3.10   F'   F+F'

3.5. RESULTANTS

If a set of forces is equivalent to a single force $\bar{\mathbf{F}}$, then $\bar{\mathbf{F}}$ is called a *resultant* of the set. Any two resultants of a given set of forces are equivalent and, by (3.2), have the same line of action; so it is often convenient to say *the* resultant. A generalization of this term will appear in Chap. 11. In terms of this concept the principal fact of the preceding section may be restated as follows:

(3.4) *If* $\mathbf{F}$ *and* $\mathbf{F}'$ *are forces whose lines of action meet in a common point, then they have as a resultant the force* $\mathbf{F} + \mathbf{F}'$ *acting through the point of intersection.*

This statement may obviously be extended to cover any number of *concurrent forces*, i.e., forces whose lines of action have a common point.

(3.5) *The resultant of a collection of concurrent forces* $\mathbf{F}_1, \mathbf{F}_2, \ldots, \mathbf{F}_n$ *is a single force* $\mathbf{F}_1 + \mathbf{F}_2 + \cdots + \mathbf{F}_n$ *through the point of concurrence.*

Such a vector summation we shall usually abbreviate as $\Sigma\,\mathbf{F}$, the Σ indicating that the vectors in question are to be added. Sometimes a more specific use of the symbol may be required; for instance, $\Sigma_2^5\,\mathbf{F}_i$ indicates the sum of $\mathbf{F}_2, \mathbf{F}_3, \mathbf{F}_4, \mathbf{F}_5$ only.

Example 1

A small particle is subject to forces expressed by the following vectors: $\mathbf{F}_1 = 3\mathbf{I} - 7\mathbf{K}$, $\mathbf{F}_2 = -12\mathbf{J}$, $\mathbf{F}_3 = \mathbf{I} + 4\mathbf{J}$. Compute the resultant.

Solution

Since the forces all act on a small particle, we may consider them as concurrent. Hence the resultant is a single force acting on the particle:

$$\bar{\mathbf{F}} = \mathbf{F}_1 + \mathbf{F}_2 + \mathbf{F}_3 = 4\mathbf{I} - 8\mathbf{J} - 7\mathbf{K}$$

Example 2

Find graphically the resultant of the three forces shown in Fig. 3.11.

Solution

In Fig. 3.11 the solution is effected by first forming $\mathbf{F}_1 + \mathbf{F}_2$ and then $(\mathbf{F}_1 + \mathbf{F}_2) + \mathbf{F}_3$.

Example 3

Construct graphically the resultant of the two forces $\mathbf{F}$ and $\mathbf{F}'$ shown in Fig. 3.12.

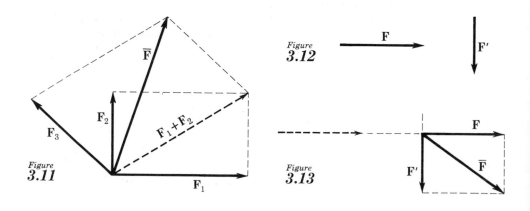

Figure
3.11

Figure
3.12

Figure
3.13

Solution

Here we use both of the techniques of Sec. 3.4. First slide the forces along their lines of action until they both act on the point of concurrence. Then use the parallelogram law for combining them. The result appears in Fig. 3.13.

Resultants of Parallel Forces. Although *parallel forces* have lines of action which do not intersect, their resultants also may often be determined by repeated use of Postulate (3.4). Consider two forces **A** and **B** such that for some scalar k

$$\mathbf{A} = k\mathbf{B}$$

Introduce at right angles (a graphical convenience, but skew angles will do) in the plane of **A** and **B** a pair of equal and opposite forces **C** and $-\mathbf{C}$ having a common line of action. As has been pointed out before, this enlarged set is equivalent to the original one. By Postulate (3.4) **A** and **C** have a resultant $\mathbf{A} + \mathbf{C}$ while **B** and $-\mathbf{C}$ have a resultant $\mathbf{B} - \mathbf{C}$. But these two forces will usually be concurrent; thus they will have a resultant $\bar{\mathbf{F}}$ passing through the point of concurrence. The vector $\bar{\mathbf{F}}$ is given by

$$\bar{\mathbf{F}} = (\mathbf{A} + \mathbf{C}) + (\mathbf{B} - \mathbf{C}) = \mathbf{A} + \mathbf{B}$$

In Fig. 3.14 the construction is shown for the case where **A** and **B** point in the same direction. The success of this construction hinges on the nonparallelism of $\mathbf{A} + \mathbf{C}$ and $\mathbf{B} - \mathbf{C}$. In Fig. 3.14 it seems quite obvious that they are not parallel. It may be much less obvious in the antiparallel case diagramed in Fig. 3.15, even though the steps of the construction are identical. Let us examine this point more critically. If the two vectors happen to be parallel, then for some scalar h we may write

$$\mathbf{A} + \mathbf{C} = h(\mathbf{B} - \mathbf{C})$$

or, since $\mathbf{A} = k\mathbf{B}$,

$$(h - k)\mathbf{B} = (h + 1)\mathbf{C}$$

If $h \neq k$, we have **B** equal to a scalar multiple of **C** and hence parallel to **C**. Since **B** and **C** are not parallel, it follows that the scalar coefficients vanish and that

$$k = h = -1$$

or that

$$\mathbf{A} = -\mathbf{B}$$

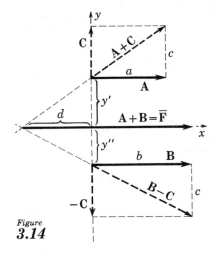

Figure
3.14

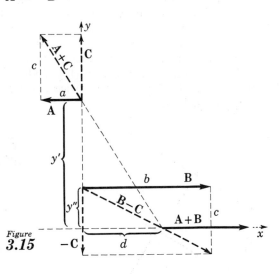

Figure
3.15

Thus this reduction of two parallel forces to a single resultant force is valid except for the case where the given forces are equal in magnitude, opposite in direction, and with different lines of action.   Such a pair of forces constitutes a *couple*.   Figure 3.16 is a portrait of a couple.   Special properties of couples will be investigated later.

In each of the cases considered (parallel and antiparallel), the resultant force is given by the vector $\mathbf{A} + \mathbf{B}$.   The line of action of this force was found to lie between the two given forces (and nearer to the larger) in the parallel case.   In the antiparallel case it was outside but nearer to the larger force, as one would expect.   From the geometry of Figs. 3.14 and 3.15 one can quickly arrive at quantitative conclusions concerning this line of action.   Let y' and y'' be the positive distances from the line of the resultant to $\mathbf{A}$ and $\mathbf{B}$, respectively.   Then, from similar triangles, one may write

$$(3.6) \qquad \frac{c}{a} = \frac{y'}{d} \quad \text{and} \quad \frac{c}{b} = \frac{y''}{d} \quad \text{whence} \quad \frac{y'}{y''} = \frac{b}{a}$$

Thus the resultant is separated from the two given parallel forces by distances inversely proportional to the magnitudes of the forces.

Example 4

The resultant of a set of forces will often be zero.   In each of the diagrams in Fig. 3.17 that is the case.   When the resultant of a family of forces is zero, each force in the family is equal but opposite to the resultant of the remaining forces in the family. The student should convince himself of the truth of this assertion.

Example 5

Four equal forces act along the sides of a square as shown in Fig. 3.18a.   Construct their resultant.

Solution

However we may proceed to combine the forces, we know in advance that the resultant, as a vector, is equal to the vector sum of the four given vectors.   Let a denote the magnitude of each of the forces.   Then the resultant has magnitude $2.828a$, for $\mathbf{A} + \mathbf{D} = \mathbf{B} + \mathbf{C}$, and each of these sums is equal in magnitude to $1.414a$.

The direction of the resultant and its line of action may be arrived at in various ways.   Let us carry out the construction in different orders.   First combine $\mathbf{A}$ and $\mathbf{B}$, then $\mathbf{C}$ and $\mathbf{D}$.   Since $\mathbf{A} + \mathbf{B} = \mathbf{C} + \mathbf{D}$, this resultant lies halfway between and is twice as large (Fig. 3.18b).   As an alternative construction, first form $\mathbf{A} + \mathbf{D}$, then $\mathbf{B} + \mathbf{C}$.   Since these two vectors have the same line of action, their resultant also has this same line of action (Fig. 3.18c).   Finally, as a third approach, let us combine $\mathbf{A}$ and $\mathbf{C}$ to get a vector twice as large halfway between; then treat $\mathbf{B}$ and $\mathbf{D}$ similarly (Fig. 3.18d).

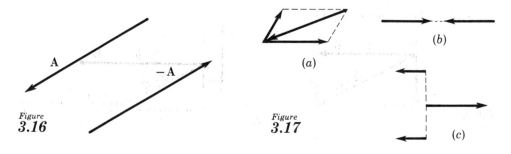

$\mathbf{A}$

$-\mathbf{A}$

Figure
3.16

Figure
3.17

(a)

(b)

(c)

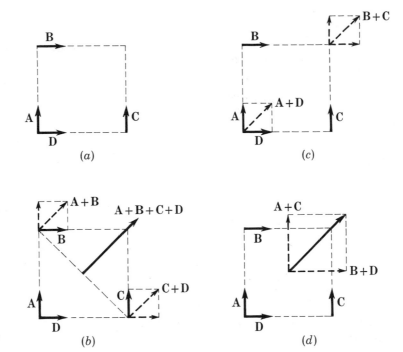

Figure
3.18

(a)   (b)   (c)   (d)

EXERCISES

10. Four equal forces of equal magnitude act along the edges of a square in the directions shown in Fig. 3.19.   Use careful graphical constructions to find their resultant.   Measure the length of your resultant vector to be sure that it is twice as long as the given vectors.

11. Three equal forces act along the edges of an equilateral triangle in the senses shown in Fig. 3.20.   Construct their resultant in three distinct ways (i.e., vary the order in which you combine the forces).

12. Given two nonparallel forces in a diagram such that their point of intersection lies off the paper.   Devise and execute a graphical procedure such that the line of action of the resultant can be found all on the given sheet.   In Fig. 3.21 the dotted lines indicate the boundaries of the paper.

13. Find the resultant of the forces shown in Fig. 3.22.

14. Forces **F**, **2F**, and **3F** are equally spaced as is shown in Fig. 3.23.   Find their resultant.

15. Find by graphical construction the magnitude and line of action of a single force which together with the forces shown in Fig. 3.24 will have a zero resultant.

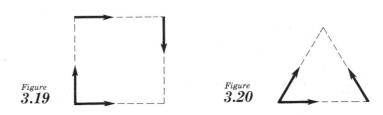

Figure
3.19

Figure
3.20

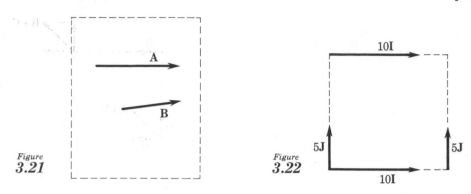

Figure
3.21

Figure
3.22

3.6. NEWTON'S LAWS OF INERTIA AND STATIC EQUILIBRIUM

Forces exist only as they are exerted on *things*. In the preceding sections it was understood that the forces were acting on objects even though these objects were not always specified. The heart of mechanics is the study of the behavior of objects when forces are applied. The first two laws of Newton, properly interpreted, provide a useful summary of experience in such matters. In substance they are:

(3.7)   *First law: A particle or body subject to no forces must remain at rest or in continued uniform motion.*

(3.8)   *Second law: A particle or body subject to unbalanced forces experiences a rate of change of momentum proportional to the vector sum of these forces.*

One aspect of these laws requires some scrutiny. Terms like "at rest" and "in uniform motion" can have significance only with respect to well-defined reference frames. Consequently, it is not surprising to learn that Newton's laws are valid in some reference frames and invalid in others. Elementary mechanics usually deals only with frames of reference for which these laws are assumed to hold. Such frames are sometimes called *inertial frames*. Reference frames such as were described in Sec. 2.2 are to a high degree of accuracy inertial frames. Frames rotating with respect to inertial frames lose this character to a degree dependent on the rate of rotation. Accelerated frames likewise are not inertial.

A body is at rest when its position within the reference frame is constant. It is in uniform motion when the character of its motion does not vary with time in either direction or magnitude. Thus if a pitched baseball could be freed from the effects of gravity and of frictional forces, it would travel at a constant rate in a straight line with a uniform rate of spin about an axis of fixed orientation. Bodies behaving in this way are said to be *in equilibrium*. The case of actual rest is especially important. Much structural engineering—design of bridges, buildings, etc.—depends on the science of *statics*, i.e., the science of *static equilibrium*.

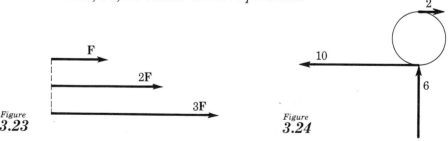

Figure
3.23

Figure
3.24

The concept *momentum* is an aspect of mechanical behavior to be studied later. For the moment we conclude from the definition of equivalence and the second law:

(3.9)   *If two sets of forces are equivalent, then their vector sums are equal.*

And from the first law:

(3.10)   *A family of forces acting on a particle or rigid body will produce equilibrium if and only if it is equivalent to no forces (i.e., a vacuous set of forces).*

As a working rule for equilibrium, we may use the following corollary to (3.10):

(3.11)   *For a particle or body to be in equilibrium, it is necessary that the vector sum of the forces acting on it vanish.*

The state of affairs described in this corollary is not enough to *ensure* equilibrium for a rigid body. A couple, for example, is a set of forces satisfying this condition, but a body subject to an unbalanced couple is not in equilibrium. This is intuitively obvious and will later be deduced from the second law. For the present it is assumed:

(3.12)   *A couple is not equivalent to no forces.*

3.7. EQUILIBRIUM OF A PARTICLE

Let us apply the conclusions of the preceding sections to the problem of equilibrium of a particle. Since forces acting on a particle are concurrent, they always, by (3.5), have as resultant a single force. For equilibrium, by (3.10), we have, then,

(3.13)   *A particle is in equilibrium if and only if the vector sum of the forces acting on it is null.*

We are now in a position to solve problems concerning the equilibrium of a particle. First we isolate the particle. Then we make whatever use seems convenient of the condition

(3.14) $$\Sigma \mathbf{F} = \mathbf{F}_1 + \mathbf{F}_2 + \cdots + \mathbf{F}_n = \mathbf{O}$$

This is equivalent to a set of three scalar equations:

(3.15)
$$\Sigma f_x = f_{x_1} + f_{x_2} + \cdots + f_{x_n} = 0$$
$$\Sigma f_y = f_{y_1} + f_{y_2} + \cdots + f_{y_n} = 0$$
$$\Sigma f_z = f_{z_1} + f_{z_2} + \cdots + f_{z_n} = 0$$

The graphical interpretation of Proposition (3.13) is also often useful, especially when the forces are all parallel to a plane, for it says that if the vectors representing the forces are arranged in tandem, head to tail as in Fig. 3.25, then the figure must be

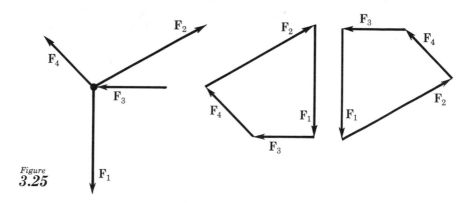

Figure **3.25**

a *closed polygon*.   In this figure, four forces act on a particle.   If the particle is in equilibrium, the four vectors arranged head to tail in any order must form a closed quadrilateral.   Two possible force polygons are shown.   Others are, of course, possible, depending on the order in which the forces happen to be portrayed.   Note that the force polygon represents merely the vector addition of Eq. (3.14); it takes no account of lines of action of forces.

Example 1

Suppose a particle is subjected to two forces **F** and **F′**.   The condition for the particle to be in equilibrium is then

$$\mathbf{F} + \mathbf{F}' = \mathbf{O}$$

Using the rules of vector algebra, this tells us that

$$\mathbf{F} = -\mathbf{F}'$$

In other terms, a particle is in equilibrium under two forces only if the forces are equal but opposite.   These forces cannot constitute a couple since they are concurrent.

Example 2

Suppose a particle is subjected to three nonparallel forces **F**, **F′**, and **F″**.   The force polygon, if there is equilibrium in this case, is a triangle.   Hence, if the particle is in equilibrium under three forces, the forces all lie in the same plane and their vectors form a closed triangle.   We shall now consider a numerical illustration.

Example 3

A 1-ton load is supported by two cables, making angles with the horizontal equal, respectively, to 60° and 30°.   Find the tensions in the two cables.

In any solution of such a problem a useful first step is to draw a figure showing the essential data of the problem (Fig. 3.26).   The first real step is to *isolate something*, as described in Sec. 3.3.   In this case let us isolate the load, assuming that the forces are concurrent.   Let **T** and **T′** denote the unknown tensions; *t* and *t′* will denote their magnitudes.   The result of the isolation appears in Fig. 3.27.   From now on different procedures are possible.   Let us consider both an analytical and a graphical solution.

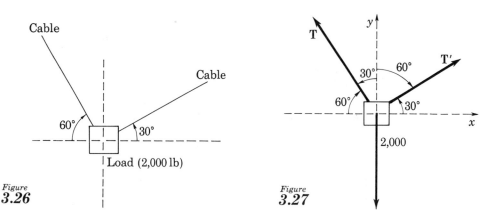

Figure
3.26

Figure
3.27

Analytical Solution

In applying Eqs. (3.15), we are free to choose axes as we please.   Let us take them as horizontal and vertical, as shown in the figure.   Now following the first equation of (3.15), we put the sum of the scalar x components of the isolating forces equal to zero:

$$-t \cos 60° + t' \cos 30° = 0$$

Treating the y components similarly, we have

$$t \cos 30° + t' \cos 60° - 2,000 = 0$$

It is a simple algebraic problem to solve these equations simultaneously and to arrive at the solutions:

$$t = 1,732 \text{ lb} \qquad t' = 1,000 \text{ lb}$$

Graphical Solution

Let us plot the vector polygon to scale, using all the given data (see Fig. 3.28). The unknowns may be measured from the diagram, or they may be computed with the aid of the figure.   Here we have given the direction and magnitude of the weight, the direction of **T**, and the direction of **T'**.

This is a simple problem, but the methods of attack are typical.   In using the analytical approach, one merely chooses axes as cannily as possible; then one writes down the conditions of equilibrium and pushes through an algebraic solution.   The equations are simpler if the axes are chosen so that as many forces as possible are parallel to them: then scalar components tend either to be zero or to be equal to the magnitude of the force.   In using the graphical approach, one should use graph paper, choose a suitable scale for as large a figure as practical, draw with a fine line the vectors which are completely specified, and then construct the loci corresponding to the vectors specified only partly.   Thus if the magnitude of a vector is known, the locus is a circle; if the direction is known, the locus is a line (as in the example just worked).   When the diagram is complete, magnitudes may be read with a ruler; angles may be read roughly with a protractor or more accurately by use of linear measurements and trigonometric tables.   The details in special cases are left to the student's ingenuity and to class discussions.   Additional applications appear in Chap. 4.

It is often desirable to isolate part of an object.   Suppose, for instance, that a 10-lb shot is in equilibrium at the bottom of a 5-ft cable weighing 5 lb.   If we isolate the ball alone, the isolating forces are the gravitational force of 10 lb downward and a counterbalancing tension exerted by the cable of 10 lb upward.   Let us now isolate the weight, together with the bottom half of the cable.   Now the downward force on the isolated object is 12.5 lb; so, for equilibrium, the tension at the middle of the cable is 12.5 lb upward.

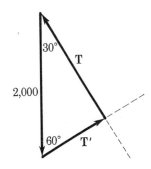

Figure
3.28

EXERCISES

16. A particle is subject to forces whose vectors (in pounds) are given by $\mathbf{F_1} = 8\mathbf{I} + 6\mathbf{J}$, $\mathbf{F_2} = 10\underline{/100°}$, and $\mathbf{F_3} = 10\underline{/-45°}$. Use graph paper to plot to scale a polygon of forces. From this figure, find the force $\mathbf{F} = f\underline{/\theta°}$, which must be added to ensure equilibrium for the particle. Check your result analytically.

17. Show how a 2-lb force and a 4-lb force together can be used to hold a 3-lb force in equilibrium.

18. A 100-lb chandelier is supported by three chains symmetrically arranged, each making an angle of 30° with the vertical. Find the tension sustained by each of the chains.

19. A steel ball bearing weighing 1 lb rests in a V-shaped trough one side of which is vertical and the other side of which makes an angle of 30° with the vertical. Both sides are smooth; therefore reaction forces may be considered as perpendicular to the sides. How great are these forces?

3.8. CONTACT FORCES

In isolating an object we must take account of body forces (usually of gravitational, electric, or magnetic origin) and of surface forces resulting from contacts with neighboring objects. When two objects touch, the pair of equal and opposite contact forces may or may not be normal to the plane of contact. In Fig. 3.29 body *a* is in contact with body *b* at **Q**. Isolate *a*. Then **C** is the effective contact force exerted on *a* by *b*. Let us resolve **C** into components **F** and **N**, respectively, tangential and normal to the contact surface, as in Fig. 3.30. **F** is called the *frictional force*, **N** the *normal reaction force*. As an example, consider a sled resting on bare horizontal ground. If no effort is made to move the sled, **F** is zero. If one tries to slide the sled, an opposing force **F** is generated. If the effort is gradually increased, **F** also will gradually increase up to a maximum at which actual sliding takes place. During sliding, **F** remains nearly constant at a magnitude nearly equal to the maximum. The ratio of this maximum magnitude for **F** to the corresponding magnitude for **N** is called the coefficient of friction, denoted by μ.

$$(3.16) \qquad\qquad \mu = \frac{f_{max}}{n}$$

The coefficient of sliding friction usually differs from the coefficient of starting friction. The relationships are complicated, depending on the nature and history of the materials and even on the speed of motion. Here it will merely be assumed that the coefficient is a constant, depending on the nature but not the size of the surfaces in contact. From the context the student will judge which kind of coefficient is intended. The angle ϕ between the resultant reaction **C** and the normal

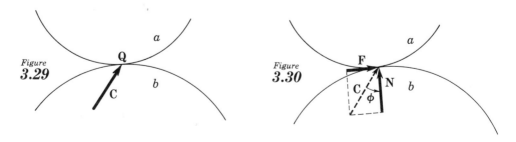

Figure **3.29**

Figure **3.30**

is often called the *angle of friction:*

(3.17) $\tan \phi = \mu$

Example

A 100-lb box resting on a horizontal floor barely starts to slide when pulled by a 25-lb tug directed 30° above the horizontal. What is the coefficient of friction?

Analytical Solution

Choose axes horizontal and vertical. The isolating forces are shown in Fig. 3.31. Use the conditions of equilibrium:

$$\Sigma f_x = 0 = 25 \cos 30° - f \quad \text{or} \quad f = 21.7 \text{ lb}$$
$$\Sigma f_y = 0 = n - 100 + 25 \sin 30° \quad \text{or} \quad n = 87.5 \text{ lb}$$

Consequently,

$$\mu = \frac{f}{n} = \frac{21.7}{87.5} = 0.247$$

Graphical Solution

Draw a force triangle as in Fig. 3.32. The angle between **C** and **W** is the angle of friction. One may use trigonometric techniques or direct measurement to determine this angle. Then its tangent may be looked up to evaluate the coefficient of friction.

EXERCISES

20. A loaded sled weighs 75 lb. The coefficient of friction with a sanded sidewalk is 0.5. If the sled is to slip, how great a force must be exerted along the sled's rope inclined at an angle of 20° with the horizontal?

21. What is the least force that will suffice to drag a 50-lb box up a plane inclined at 40° if the coefficient of friction is 0.4? How must this minimum force be directed?

22. A block of weight w' rests on a plane inclined at an angle θ with the horizontal. The coefficient of friction may be taken as μ. A light strong cord runs from this block, over a pulley of negligible mass and friction, to a hanging object of weight w. For what range of values of w is the system in equilibrium? Express answer in terms of w', μ, θ.

23. A block of weight w can be dragged along a horizontal plane by a horizontal force μw, where μ is the coefficient of friction. Show that, by using a different direction for the force, it is always possible to attain the same result with a force as small as $w \sin \phi$, where ϕ is the angle of friction.

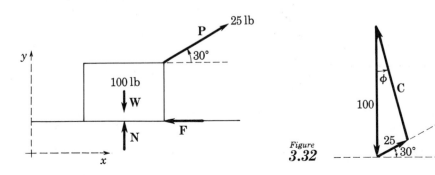

Figure
3.31

Figure
3.32

24. According to Newton's third law, every force has an equal and opposite reaction force. Describe the reaction force (in the sense of the third law) for each of the following forces:

(*a*) The force exerted by the sun on Earth's moon.

(*b*) Your weight.

(*c*) The force exerted by wire on sphere of a trackman's hammer.

REVIEW EXERCISES

25. A particle is subject to three forces **A**, **B**, and **C** making angles of α, β, and γ with each other as shown in Fig. 3.33. If the particle is in equilibrium, show that (*Lamy's theorem*)

$$\frac{a}{\sin \alpha} = \frac{b}{\sin \beta} = \frac{c}{\sin \gamma}$$

Does this condition, conversely, ensure equilibrium?

26. The ends of a rope 77 ft long are attached to hooks 63 ft apart on a horizontal girder. A 200-lb load is attached to the rope 25 ft from one end so that the load and the hooks form a triangle of sides 25, 52, and 63 ft. Find the tensions in the rope on either side of the load.

27. A 500-lb load *W* (see Fig. 3.34) is suspended by a cable *WRP* which passes over a pulley *P*. The cable is to be displaced to one side by a strut *GR* which is to sustain a compression along its length of 300 lb, so that *RP* makes an angle of 60° with the horizontal.

(*a*) Find two possible angles θ which the strut (*GR*) may make with the horizontal.

(*b*) Compute the corresponding tensions in the cable *RP*.

28. A boulder is lifted by three ropes all in one vertical plane. One rope inclined at 150° with the horizontal has a tension of 300 lb; the second at 135° has a tension of 200 lb; the third is inclined at 30°. Find the weight of the boulder and the tension in the third rope.

29. A 100-kg cylinder rests between two smooth planes forming an acute angle whose inclinations are, respectively, 30° and 60°. The planes meet in a horizontal line. Find in newtons the reaction forces between the cylinder and each of the planes.

30. A particle is in equilibrium when subjected to forces as shown in Fig. 3.35. Find the magnitude of the weight **W** and of the force **F**.

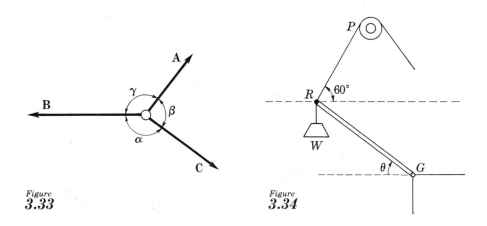

Figure
3.33

Figure
3.34

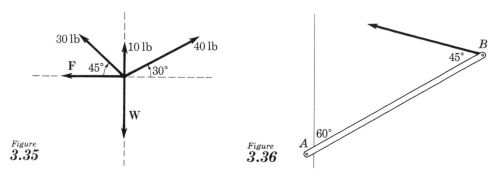

Figure
3.35

Figure
3.36

31. Given: a disk and a force **F** in the plane of the disk but with its line of action not meeting the disk. Show that two forces with lines of action intersecting the disk can always be found such that this set of two forces is equivalent to the given force **F**.

32. It is shown in Sec. 3.5 that any two parallel forces are equivalent to a single force or to a "couple." Show that any two couples both made up of forces in the same given plane are together equivalent to a single couple. HINT: Consider first the special case of two couples composed of forces all of which are parallel (and antiparallel).

33. Given a force **F** with a definite line of action. Let **P** be any point not on the line of action of **F**. Show that **F** is equivalent to a force acting on **P** together with a couple.

34. A chalkboard is supported by two cables passing over pulleys to two separate equal counterweights. When partially mounted it is found that a 5-lb force will prevent the board from descending but that a 25-lb force is required to lift it. Assuming constant friction, how much weight should be added to each counterweight?

35. A 1-ton uniform beam AB is pivoted freely at A and supported by a rope at B with angles as shown in Fig. 3.36. Without using moments, find the direction and magnitude of the force at A and also the tension at B.

36. Show that any set of forces lying in a given plane is equivalent either to a force or to a couple.

37. The rectangular rigid plane object is in equilibrium under the six forces shown (not to scale) in Fig. 3.37. Determine the ratio $|V|/|H|$. Justify briefly steps taken.

38. Set up and derive a formula for the tension in the cord used to hoist a venetian blind. Express the force in terms of the weight of the bottom member, the weight of each slat, the separation of the slats, and the elevation of the bottom member from its lowest position.

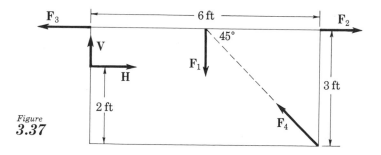

Figure
3.37

39. Neglecting pulley friction, for what range of weights w'' can equilibrium exist if the coefficient of friction between blocks w and w' and between w and the table in Fig. 3.38 is μ?

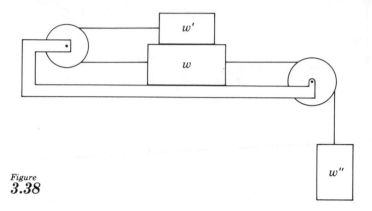

Figure
3.38

APPLICATIONS: STATICS of CONCURRENT and COPLANAR FORCES

The preceding chapter introduced the subject of the properties of forces. In summary, each force is specified by a vector together with a line of action parallel to this vector. A set of forces may be transformed into an equivalent set either by sliding any force along its line of action or by use of vector addition for forces having concurrent lines of action. A particle or rigid body is in equilibrium if the system of applied forces is equivalent to a null force. In this chapter these basic properties of forces are applied to special types of equilibrium problems. No new theory is developed. General and explicit consideration of moments is deferred to Chaps. 10 and 11. This is a chapter for practice in applications.

4.1. THE USE OF FORCE POLYGONS

For the forces acting on a particle to be equivalent to a null force, their vector sum must vanish. This means that if the vectors representing the isolating forces are arranged in order (ignoring points of application), a closed polygon results, as described in Sec. 3.7. For problems where forces are all parallel to a plane, the corresponding plane polygon often provides the basis for the use of geometry in calculations.

Example 1. Minimum Sufficient Force

A block of weight w is dragged along a rough horizontal plane surface by a cord inclined at a variable angle θ above the surface. If the angle of friction is ϕ, for what angle θ is the tension p which the cord must sustain a minimum?

Geometric Solution

The isolating forces for the block are shown in Fig. 4.1a. Now construct the polygon of forces as in Fig. 4.1b. First draw a vector AB representing w to scale: it is fixed in magnitude and direction. Then draw CA parallel to the line of action of the reaction force: its direction is determined. It is clear that the vector BD representing the minimum possible tension must be drawn at right angles to CA since the shortest distance from B to CA is along the perpendicular. The inclination θ of the chord then must equal ϕ for p to be minimum, and this minimum tension is equal to $w \sin \phi$. The use of the force polygon makes it possible to see a whole family of possible solutions: here, for each reasonable θ, a corresponding segment for p is determined. For instance, for $\theta = 0°$, it is immediate from the diagram that the tension, now represented by the vector BE, has magnitude $w \tan \phi$.

Analytic Solution

Using horizontal and vertical components of the forces in Fig. 4.1a,

$$p \cos \theta - r \sin \phi = 0$$
$$p \sin \theta + r \cos \phi - w = 0$$

Eliminating r, we get

$$p \cos \theta \cos \phi + p \sin \theta \sin \phi - w \sin \phi = 0$$

or

$$p \cos (\theta - \phi) = w \sin \phi$$

We could use calculus to determine the condition for a minimum, but this is not necessary. The right-hand member is a positive constant; so p is smallest when $\cos (\theta - \phi)$ is largest. But the largest value, 1, for a cosine occurs when the argument (angle) is 0. So we set $\theta - \phi$ equal to zero.

Example 2. Cable or Belt Friction

Both the graphical and analytical procedures are useful in deriving a formula for the accumulated frictional force on a flexible belt or cable wound around a fixed cylinder. The physical situation is commonplace. By wrapping the cord around a stationary rough post one can exploit the friction to generate a large difference in magnitude of tension between the free ends of the cord. In Fig. 4.2a the cord is represented as having a contact angle θ between points of tangency. This angle could, of course, be several hundred degrees. $\mathbf{F_0}$ and $\mathbf{F}$ can be unequal in magnitude even though the cord is in equilibrium. Let us work for a maximum tension difference and thus assume that the cord is about to slip. Then we take for a typical isolated element the segment subtending angle $\Delta\theta$. This segment may be regarded as a particle. The contact forces aside from the tension are Δn and $\mu\Delta n$.

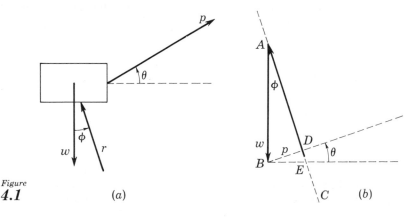

Figure 4.1   (a)   (b)

The forces of tension acting on the isolated piece (shaded in Fig. 4.2b) are $\mathbf{F} + \Delta\mathbf{F}$ and $\mathbf{F}'$, where $|\mathbf{F}| = f = |\mathbf{F}'|$, so that $|\Delta\mathbf{F}|$ is the excess tension due to friction. Figure 4.2b shows the isolating forces for the segment of cord. Figure 4.2c is the vector polygon. For convenience in using the geometry of this polygon, the force $\mathbf{F} + \Delta\mathbf{F}$ is drawn as two parallel forces $\mathbf{F}$ and $\Delta\mathbf{F}$. Note that the polygon has two parts: a right triangle with small acute angle $\Delta\theta/2$ and an isosceles triangle with vertex angle $\Delta\theta$.

Graphical Method

Working directly from the force polygon and writing trigonometric relationships between magnitudes, $\mu\Delta n = \Delta f \cos \Delta\theta/2$ from the right triangle, $\Delta n - \Delta f \sin \Delta\theta/2 = 2f \sin \Delta\theta/2$ from the isosceles triangle (the left member is the length of the base of the isosceles triangle). Multiply the second equation by μ and substitute the first:

$$\Delta f \cos \frac{\Delta\theta}{2} = (\Delta f + 2f)\mu \sin \frac{\Delta\theta}{2}$$

Divide by $\Delta\theta/2$ and take the limit as $\Delta\theta$ approaches 0 to get

$$2\frac{df}{d\theta} = 2f\mu$$

Integrating,

$$\ln f = \mu\theta + \ln f_0$$

where f_0 is the small tension. The desired formula then is

(4.1)
$$f = f_0 e^{\mu\theta}$$

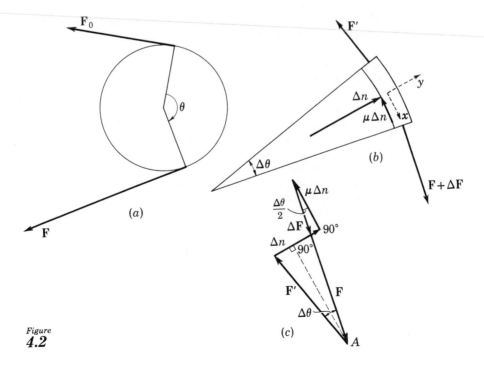

Figure
4.2

(a)

(b)

(c)

Analytical Method

Taking axes as radial and tangential at the middle of the isolated piece, one can write component equations for equilibrium:

$$\Sigma f_x = 0 = \Delta f \cos \frac{\Delta\theta}{2} - \mu \Delta n$$

$$\Sigma f_y = 0 = \Delta n - 2f \sin \frac{\Delta\theta}{2} - \Delta f \sin \frac{\Delta\theta}{2}$$

These equations are identical with those which we read from the vector polygon in the other approach.

Intuitive Check

It is interesting that an informal estimate of limits yields the correct result once a good diagram is drawn. Since $\Delta \mathbf{F}$ is small in comparison with $\mathbf{F}$, it can be seen that, in Fig. 4.2c, the base of the isosceles triangle is approximately Δn, and since $\Delta\theta$ is small, this base differs but slightly from the circular arc with A as center. So, approximately, $\Delta n = f\Delta\theta$. But in the right triangle it appears that approximately $\mu\Delta n = \Delta f$, so we have $\mu f \Delta\theta = \Delta f$ as desired.

EXERCISES

1. A load of weight 700 lb hangs at the end of a cable. A force of magnitude f applied to the middle of the cable at an angle α with the horizontal holds the cable in equilibrium so that its upper section makes an angle of 20° with the vertical. Neglecting the weight of the cable, find the value of α for which f is minimum. Compute this minimum force.

2. The coefficient of friction between a block of weight w and a horizontal plane surface is 0.3. Show how a force equal to half the weight of the block may be directed so as to cause the block just to slide. Show that the answer is not unique.

3. Work Example 1 of the preceding section for the more general case where the plane surface is inclined at a fixed angle α. Is your result valid for the downhill as well as the uphill case?

4. A cable wrapped several times around a fixed rough cylinder (where the coefficient of friction is 0.4) has tensions at the ends of f_1 and f_2. Assuming that the ends of the cable have equal length, what is the tension at the middle of the cable?

4.2. EQUILIBRIUM OF A RIGID BODY SUBJECT TO PARALLEL FORCES IN A PLANE

In Sec. 3.5 we used the postulates about transmissibility of forces and composition of concurrent forces by vector addition to determine resultants for parallel or antiparallel forces. To recapitulate in a form useful for applications, consider two forces $f_1\mathbf{J}$ and $f_2\mathbf{J}$ acting at points on the x axis as shown in Fig. 4.3. Using the result of Sec. 3.5, in all cases except where $f_1 + f_2 = 0$, a resultant $\bar{f}\mathbf{J}$ equal to $(f_1 + f_2)\mathbf{J}$ is determined by

$$(\bar{x} - x_1)f_1 = (x_2 - \bar{x})f_2$$

which leads to the useful result

(4.2) $$\bar{f} = f_1 + f_2$$

(4.3) $$\bar{x}\bar{f} = x_1 f_1 + x_2 f_2$$

If several parallel forces $f_1\mathbf{J}, f_2\mathbf{J}, \ldots, f_n\mathbf{J}$ act at $x_1, x_2, \ldots, x_n$, then the magnitude of the resultant $\bar{f}\mathbf{J}$ is equal to the sum

$$(4.4) \qquad \bar{f} = f_1 + f_2 + \cdots + f_n$$

and is located at the weighted mean position

$$(4.5) \qquad \bar{x}\bar{f} = x_1 f_1 + \cdots + x_n f_n$$

To establish (4.4) and (4.5), one merely needs to apply (4.2) and (4.3) repeatedly to the n forces taken two at a time. A proof by mathematical induction is very simple. We know that (4.4) and (4.5) are valid for $n = 2$. Assume that they hold for k forces. Then if we have a set of $k + 1$ parallel or antiparallel forces, we can replace the first k of them by a single force $\bar{f} = f_1 + f_2 + \cdots + f_k$ acting at $\bar{x}$ determined by $\bar{x}\bar{f} = x_1 f_1 + \cdots + x_k f_k$. This replaces the set of $k + 1$ forces by an equivalent pair of forces $\bar{f}$ and f_{k+1} acting at $\bar{x}$ and x_{k+1}. Applying (4.2) and (4.3), we get

$$\bar{\bar{f}} = \bar{f} + f_{k+1} = (f_1 + f_2 + \cdots + f_k) + f_{k+1}$$

and

$$\bar{\bar{x}}\bar{\bar{f}} = \bar{x}\bar{f} + x_{k+1}f_{k+1} = (x_1 f_1 + x_2 f_2 + \cdots + x_k f_k) + x_{k+1}f_{k+1}$$

which are equivalent to (4.4) and (4.5) for $n = k + 1$.

For a system of plane parallel forces to be in equilibrium, the resultant $\bar{f}$ vanishes, which requires that

$$(4.6) \qquad \bar{f} = \sum_{i=1}^{n} f_i = 0$$

Then (4.5) gives the additional requirement

$$(4.7) \qquad \bar{x}\bar{f} = 0 = \sum_{i=1}^{n} x_i f_i$$

Note that a couple satisfies Eq. (4.6) but not Eq. (4.7). The results of this section are common to most elementary physics textbooks. They are included here to open up a class of simple practice problems just as an application of our force postulates. Later on, in a systematic study of moments, these results will appear as very special cases.

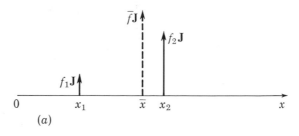

(a)

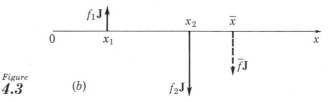

Figure
4.3   (b)

Example I

A uniform rigid 300-lb beam 40 ft long is subjected to forces as shown in Fig. 4.4. Find the bearing reactions f and f'.

Solution

Draw a free-body diagram including weight at center and bearing reactions at supports. Taking origin at left end and **J** upward, we have, for equilibrium corresponding to Eq. (4.6),

$$-400 - 200 + f - 700 - 300 + 200 + f' = 0$$

whence $f + f' = 1,400$ lb; and corresponding to Eq. (4.7), $0(-400) + 10(-200 + f) + 20(-700 - 300) + 30(200) + 40f' = 0$; whence $f + 4f' = 1,600$ lb. Solving, we get $f = 1,333$ lb, $f' = 67$ lb.

4.3. IDEAL THRUSTS AND TENSIONS

In many problems involving structures, beams are assumed to have negligible weight. This assumption is often justified in view of the loads sustained by the beams. Such an assumption makes for a simple solution of an important class of problems. Consider the light strut with forces applied only at the ends, in Fig. 4.5. This may be attained by fastening the strut to other members of the structure by frictionless pins, one at each end of the beam. The condition for equilibrium, in view of Propositions (3.10) and (3.12), is that the forces at the two ends are equal but opposite and directed along the beam, as in Fig. 4.6. Thus a *light* beam with forces acting only at its ends can transmit forces only in its own direction.

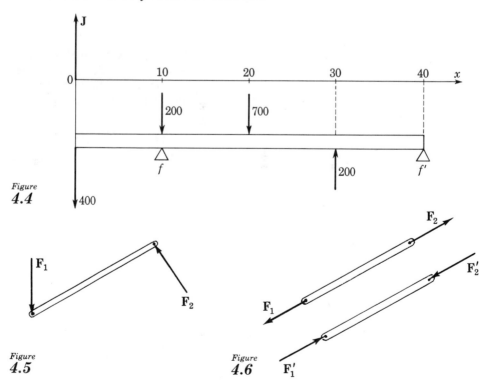

Figure
4.4

Figure
4.5

Figure
4.6

Example 2

A 1,000-lb load is attached to the end of a light beam, making an angle of 60° with the vertical and hinged freely at the lower end. The beam is supported by a cable making an angle of 45° with it. Find the tension in the cable and the thrust provided by the beam.

Solution

Isolate the tip of the beam to which cable and load are attached (Fig. 4.7). Since we know that the thrust of the beam is directed along the beam, we can easily draw a force triangle or apply Lamy's theorem (Chap. 3, Exercise 25), using the third diagram in Fig. 4.7. Let us also consider a routine analytical solution. Take axes parallel and perpendicular to the beam:

$$\Sigma f_x = 0 = t' - t \cos 45° - 1,000 \cos 60°$$
$$\Sigma f_y = 0 = t \cos 45° - 1,000 \cos 30°$$

From these equations we easily compute $t' = 1,366$ lb, $t = 1,225$ lb.

4.4. INTERACTIONS AND COMPLEX STRUCTURES

In each of the problems studied thus far, a single thing has been isolated. In problems involving several parts, we can make direct use of our first assumption (3.1) about forces. By isolating parts in succession and using the fact that interaction forces occur in equal but opposite pairs, we can write successive sets of equilibrium equations using the same unknowns. Similarly, the force polygons for adjacent members of a structure will have equal but opposite sides; therefore they may be drawn in juxtaposition.

Example I

Two blocks weighing, respectively, 10 and 5 newtons rest side by side on a plane inclined at 30°, as in Fig. 4.8. The coefficients of friction are, respectively, 0.2 and 0.1. What horizontal force is necessary to prevent slipping? The contact between the two blocks is smooth.

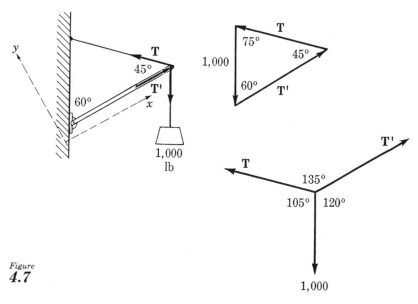

Figure
4.7

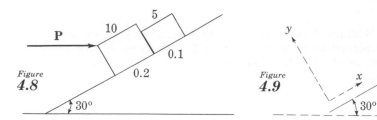

Figure
4.8

Figure
4.9

Solution

Draw axes parallel and perpendicular to the plane as shown.   First isolate the smaller uphill block (Fig. 4.9).

$$\Sigma f_x = 0 = r - 5\cos 60° + f_2$$
$$\Sigma f_y = 0 = n_2 - 5\cos 30°$$

From these equations we conclude that $n_2 = 4.33$ newtons and hence, since slipping is imminent, that $f_2 = 0.433$ newton.   Then we can compute r as $2.5 - 0.43$, or 2.07 newtons.   Now isolate the other block (Fig. 4.10).

$$\Sigma f_x = 0 = p\cos 30° + f_1 - 2.07 - 10\cos 60°$$
$$\Sigma f_y = 0 = -p\cos 60° + n_1 - 10\cos 30°$$

Using the fact that $f_1 = 0.2n_1$, we may solve this pair of equations for p, getting $p = 5.32$ newtons.

A graphical solution is quite possible.   Figure 4.11 shows such a solution. Starting with the small block, draw the vector triangle for the forces: weight $\mathbf{W}_2$ known in direction and magnitude; reaction $\mathbf{R}$ with other block, known in direction; and contact reaction $\mathbf{C}_2$ with plane, known in direction, at angle ϕ_2 whose tangent is 0.1, by Eq. (3.17).   Now reverse $\mathbf{R}$ and draw for the first block the weight $\mathbf{W}_1$ known in direction and magnitude and the contact reaction force at an angle ϕ_1 with the normal.   The force $\mathbf{P}$ is known in direction; thus, with its line, the figure may be completed.   The length of the arrow $\mathbf{P}$ may be measured directly from the figure, or trigonometric computations may be used.

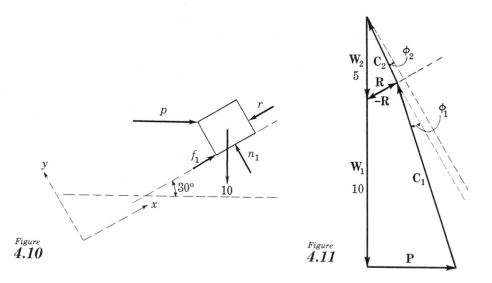

Figure
4.10

Figure
4.11

Example 2

The methods of this section are particularly applicable to problems concerning simple trusses, i.e., frames whose members are light beams freely pinned at the ends. In Fig. 4.12 such a structure is shown subjected to a 100-lb load at B. The bearing reactions at A and C are assumed to be vertical. Using the method of Sec. 4.2, we can determine these bearing reactions, which we denote by f and f'. Taking A as origin and AC as horizontal,

$$f + f' - 100 = 0$$

$$0(f) + 3.6(100) - 10(f') = 0$$

These equations yield $f = 64$ lb, $f' = 36$ lb, as shown in the figure. To find the internal forces in the frame, isolate, say, the vertex pin A. The bearing reaction of 64 lb is known already in both direction and magnitude. Since the structure is a simple truss, the forces exerted by the struts on pin A are parallel to their own directions. A graphical solution is easily obtained by drawing the known 64-lb vector and then completing a triangle with sides parallel to the corresponding struts (see Fig. 4.13). Once such a triangle has been drawn, one can use trigonometry or the geometry of similar triangles to compute the remaining forces. Then one may proceed similarly to other vertices. Note in the vector diagrams that each simple strut has a single thrust or tension associated with it. Thus the member AB is in a state of compression: it thrusts down on pin A but up on pin B. This fact is reflected in Fig. 4.13 by the two opposite vectors, each of magnitude 80, in the vector triangles corresponding to A and B, respectively.

Example 3

A wedge of weight w on a plane inclined at 30° with the horizontal is used to lift a block of weight w' as shown in Fig. 4.14a. Find the applied horizontal force p if at each surface of contact the angle of friction is ϕ.

Solution

Figure 4.14b is a free-body diagram for the block. Note that both reactions n' and r are tilted from the normal by an angle ϕ. Figure 4.14c is a free-body diagram for the wedge. The force of interaction r is merely the opposite of the force labeled r in Fig. 4.14b. Equations of equilibrium for these two isolated objects are easily

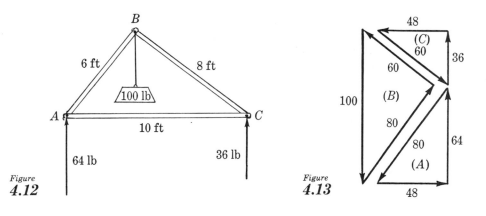

Figure
4.12

Figure
4.13

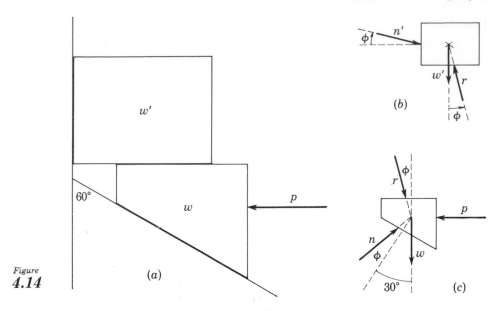

Figure 4.14   (a)   (b)   (c)

written down.   For horizontal and vertical components we get

$$n' \cos \phi - r \sin \phi = 0$$
$$-n' \sin \phi + r \cos \phi - w' = 0$$
$$r \sin \phi + n \sin (30° + \phi) - p = 0$$
$$-r \cos \phi + n \cos (30° + \phi) - w = 0$$

Eliminating n' between the first two equations, we get

$$r = \frac{w' \cos \phi}{\cos 2\phi}$$

Substituting this value in the fourth equation and solving for n, we get $n = (w' \cos^2 \phi \sec 2\phi + w) \sec (\phi + 30°)$.   Finally, substituting the expressions for n and r in the third equation, we get

$$p = \tfrac{1}{2}w' \tan 2\phi + (w' \cos^2 \phi \sec 2\phi + w) \tan (\phi + 30°)$$

Although the use of components is not difficult, it is often more satisfying, if not actually easier, to work with force polygons in a problem such as this.   Such diagrams are shown in Fig. 4.15.   The triangular figure based on the block forces is easy to construct.   The weight is known in both magnitude and direction, while the inter-action forces are known in direction at an angle ϕ from horizontal and vertical, respectively.   From this triangle of forces, by the law of sines, we may write

$$\frac{w'}{\sin (90 - 2\phi)} = \frac{r}{\sin (90° + \phi)} = \frac{n'}{\sin \phi}$$

Hence

$$r = w' \frac{\cos \phi}{\cos 2\phi} \qquad n' = w' \frac{\sin \phi}{\cos 2\phi}$$

Turning to the quadrilateral of forces for the wedge, we can now regard r and w as

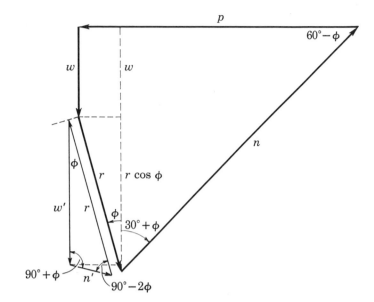

Figure
4.15

known entirely while p and n are known in direction.   To read off relations from the figure, the dotted vertical construction line is useful.   The length of this vertical segment is equal to the sum of the vertical components of w and r: $w + r \cos \phi$. The magnitude of n may be expressed in terms of this result:

$$n = (w + r \cos \phi) \sec (30° + \phi)$$

And then p is equal to the sum of horizontal components of r and n.   After a little rearranging this is seen to be equal to our first answer.

EXERCISES

5. Two blocks weighing, respectively, 10 and 5 newtons rest side by side on a plane inclined at 30° as in Fig. 4.16.   The coefficients of friction between blocks and plane are, respectively, 0.3 and 0.0.   Draw force polygons for both blocks, and determine the magnitude p of a horizontal force sufficient to cause the blocks to slide up the plane.

6. Two blocks are pulled slowly and at constant speed up a plane inclined at 40° by a cord exerting a tension **T**.   The blocks are joined by a cord of tension **T′**, as shown in Fig. 4.17.   If the upper block weighs 10 newtons and has a coefficient of friction 0.3 while the lower block weighs 5 newtons and has a coefficient 0.1, what are the magnitudes of **T** and **T′**?

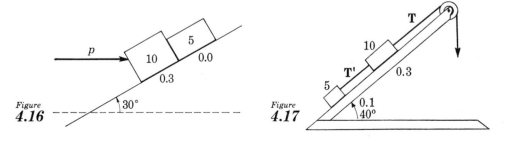

Figure
4.16

Figure
4.17

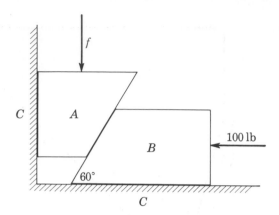

Figure
4.18

7. How large a vertical force f acting on the wedge A will cause block B to move to the right in spite of the 100-lb force shown in Fig. 4.18 and the friction? (The angle shown is 60°; the friction between A and B, B and C, and C and A has a uniform coefficient: $\mu = \tan 15°$.) Neglect weights of A and B.

8. Find the force in each of the three members of the truss shown in Fig. 4.19. State whether it is a tension or a compression. Three external forces are shown.

9. Figure 4.20 represents a simple equiangular truss in equilibrium. External forces act at pins A, B, and C. Member CD is under a tension of 3,000 lb. Member FD is under a compression of 1,000 lb.
(a) What force is transmitted by DE?
(b) What force is transmitted by BD?

4.5. PLANE SETS OF FORCES

If a set of forces $\{F_1, F_2, \ldots, F_n\}$ all lie in a plane, then, as you may have proved in Chap. 3, Exercise 36, the set is equivalent to either a single force or to a couple [this result will also appear as a special case of a more general proposition (10.19) in Chap. 10]. If the n coplanar forces are in equilibrium, then they are equivalent to no forces, so in one case the equivalent single force must be null and in the other case the couple must be degenerate; i.e., the separation of the equal and opposite forces is zero. In particular, if a body is in equilibrium under three nonparallel

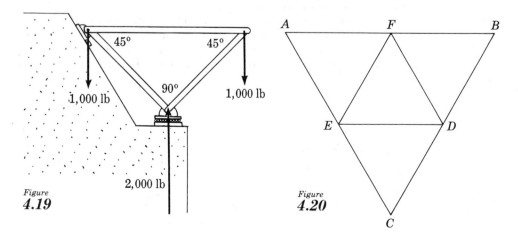

Figure
4.19

Figure
4.20

coplanar forces, the forces are concurrent. Otherwise, if $\mathbf{A} + \mathbf{B} + \mathbf{C} = \mathbf{O}$, the force $\mathbf{A}$ and the force $\mathbf{B} + \mathbf{C}$ formed by combining $\mathbf{B}$ and $\mathbf{C}$ will constitute a couple. This informal discussion suggests a useful approach to numerous simple statics problems involving coplanar forces. Other methods appear in Chaps. 10 and 11.

Example 1

Consider the standard problem of the equilibrium of a uniform ladder about to slip on a rough floor when leaning against a smooth wall. Suppose that the angle of friction is ϕ. The directions of the wall reaction $\mathbf{M}$ and the weight $\mathbf{W}$ are fixed. These two forces, then, are equivalent to a single force acting at P (see Fig. 4.21), directly above the center D of the ladder. This force $\mathbf{R}'$ is, for equilibrium, equal and opposite to $\mathbf{R}$. But $\mathbf{R}$ and $\mathbf{R}'$ must not form a couple, so $\mathbf{R}$ goes through P. We conclude at once that $\tan \phi = AC/CP$ while $\cot \theta = AC/CD$, or $\cot \theta = 2 \tan \phi$.

Example 2

A uniformly loaded crate of weight w, height h, and width b is pushed at uniform speed up a plane surface inclined at angle θ (see Fig. 4.22) by a force of magnitude p parallel to the incline. If the angle of friction is ϕ and if no tipping takes place, find a minimum possible value for b.

Solution

The reaction force $\mathbf{R}$, for equilibrium, must pass through the intersection C of $\mathbf{P}$ and $\mathbf{W}$. Tipping will be imminent when $\mathbf{R}$ acts through the uphill edge of the bottom of the crate. Thus $b/2$ must be at least as large as the sum $DA + AB$. But $DA = (h/2) \tan \theta$ and $AB = h \tan \phi$. Hence we have $b \geq h(2 \tan \phi + \tan \theta)$.

EXERCISES

10. In Example 2 how large is the force $\mathbf{P}$?
11. Solve Example 2 for the case where the crate is being pushed in equilibrium downhill, the force $\mathbf{P}$ being reversed in direction.

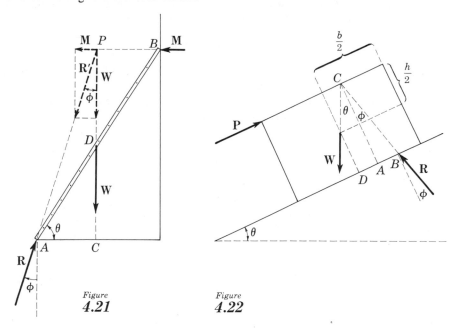

Figure
4.21

Figure
4.22

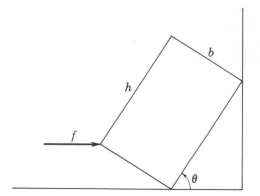

Figure
4.23

12. A uniformly loaded box of dimensions h by b as shown in Fig. 4.23 has weight w. It leans against a wall at angle θ as shown. If wall and floor are both smooth, how large must the horizontal force f be for equilibrium?

4.6. FUNICULAR POLYGONS

In this section a further graphic method for dealing with forces will be presented briefly. In Sec. 3.5 the resultant of two parallel forces was found graphically by introducing equal and opposite forces C and $-C$. This method will now be extended. Suppose that we have given, say, three forces F_1, F_2, F_3, not necessarily parallel, as shown in Fig. 4.24. It is desired to find the resultant $\bar{F}$. The magnitude and direction of $\bar{F}$ are easily found just by forming the vector sum $\bar{F} = F_1 + F_2 + F_3$, as graphed in Fig. 4.25. It remains to determine the line of action of the resultant. To do this, we draw a line l in any convenient direction cutting the line of action of F_1 at P_1. Along this line introduce equal but opposite forces C and $-C$. To see how C combines with F_1, draw a copy of C in Fig. 4.25, as shown. Since C and F_1 are concurrent at P_1, they are equivalent to a single force

$$C + F_1 = C_1$$

through the same point. Now through P_1 draw a line parallel to C_1 cutting the line of action of F_2 at P_2. P_2P_1 is then the line of action of C_1. Now C_1 and F_2 are concurrent at P_2; therefore they are equivalent to a single force $C_2 = C_1 + F_2$ through P_2. In the second diagram we now draw the force C_2 as shown. Now

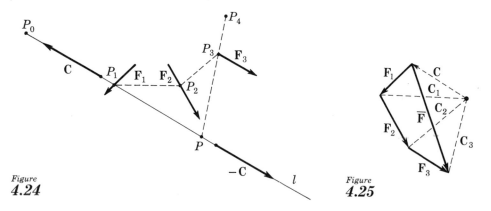

Figure
4.24

Figure
4.25

through P_2 we can draw the line of action of C_2 parallel to C_2 in the auxiliary diagram and cutting the line of F_3 at P_3. Since F_3 and C_2 are concurrent, their resultant is a single force $C_3 = C_2 + F_3$ through P_3. Through P_3 we finally draw a line of action for C_3 (parallel to C_3 in the auxiliary diagram) cutting l at P.

We have so far shown that the original set of forces, together with C and $-C$, are equivalent to the single force C_3 acting along P_3P together with $-C$ acting along l. These two forces are concurrent at P; therefore they are equivalent to a single force $C_3 - C$ through P. But from the auxiliary diagram it is apparent that the following vector equation holds:

$$C_3 - C = \bar{F}$$

Therefore the original system is equivalent to $\bar{F}$ acting at P. To complete the graphical solution, we need merely draw a vector $\bar{F}$ through P. This construction could have been carried out similarly for any number of forces. Special cases will be assigned as exercises.

The polygon $P_0P_1P_2P_3P_4$ is called a *funicular polygon* or *string polygon* for the set of forces. (P_0 is a point on l and P_4 a point on PP_3 selected suitably as in Fig. 4.24.) It is so named because a light string $P_0P_1P_2P_3P_4$ fastened at P_0 and P_4 would be in equilibrium under applied forces F_1, F_2, F_3.

Example 1

A rigid horizontal structure supported at the ends is subjected to vertical forces of 2 and 3 tons as shown in Fig. 4.26. Find the resultant of the five forces shown.

Solution

The auxiliary vector diagram is sketched in Fig. 4.27. The construction of a point P on the 12-ton resultant is shown in Fig. 4.26.

Example 2

The ends of a string are pegged firmly at A and B. Subject to two parallel forces F and F' making an angle of 60° with AB the string assumes the shape of Fig. 4.28. Find the ratio of the magnitudes of F and F'.

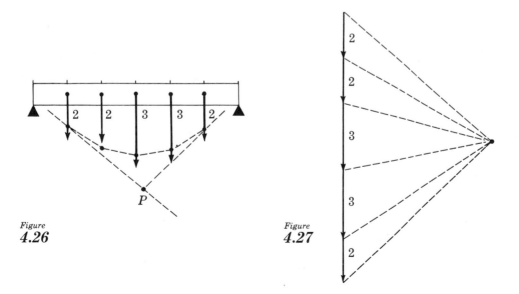

Figure
4.26

Figure
4.27

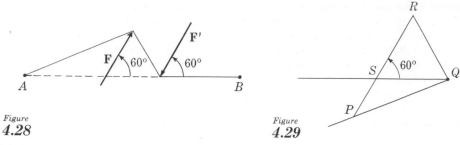

Figure
4.28

Figure
4.29

Solution

The string itself is the funicular polygon for the forces **F** and **F'**; therefore let us draw the associated auxiliary polygon by constructing concentric lines parallel to the string segments, as in Fig. 4.29.   Now draw a line at 60° with the middle ray.   In this figure *PR* represents **F** and *RS* represents **F'**.   The ratio may be determined by direct measurement in the figure.

Continuous Loads.   In the case of a continuous or distributed load, for example, an irregular heavy beam where the weight is part of the load, the funicular polygon becomes a *funicular curve*.   Considering only downward parallel forces, let $q(x)$ denote force per length at a point where the coordinate is x.   This is illustrated in Fig. 4.30. At x a short segment Δx is subject to a downward force Δf.   Thus

(4.8) $$\Delta f = q(x) \, \Delta x$$

Now, to find the funicular curve, we may ask, What shape would a flexible string assume if it were subject to such a load?   The answer is not unique, for different horizontal tensions are possible with the same vertical loads, but we can find conditions which must be satisfied.   Let Fig. 4.31 represent a segment Δx of such a string. Since it is in equilibrium, we may write

$$(t + \Delta t) \sin (\theta + \Delta\theta) - t \sin \theta = q(x) \, \Delta x$$

or

$$\Delta(t \sin \theta) = q(x) \, \Delta x$$

and

$$(t + \Delta t) \cos (\theta + \Delta\theta) = t \cos \theta = h$$

where h is the uniform horizontal component of the tension.   Dividing the second

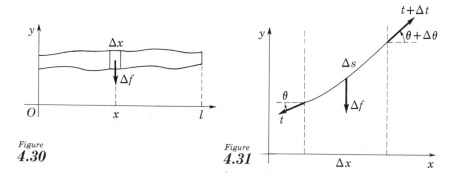

Figure
4.30

Figure
4.31

equation by the last two members of the preceding, we get

$$\Delta(\tan \theta) = \frac{1}{h} q(x) \, \Delta x$$

Replacing $\tan \theta$ by dy/dx, dividing by Δx, and taking the limit as Δx becomes small, we arrive at

(4.9) $$\frac{d^2 y}{dx^2} = \frac{dy'}{dx} = \frac{1}{h} q(x)$$

If there is a point of zero slope on the string, it makes a convenient origin. Then (4.9), integrated, yields

(4.10) $$\frac{dy}{dx} = y' = \frac{1}{h} \int_0^x q(x) \, dx$$

In the case of a suspension bridge, the load of the roadbed may be much in excess of that of the cables themselves. In that case $q(x)$ is a constant q. Then

$$\frac{dy}{dx} = \frac{q}{h} x$$

and for the choice of axes suggested above,

$$y = \frac{q}{2h} x^2$$

which is a *parabola*.

The curve for a cable having no load in addition to its own weight is called a *catenary* and has the shape of a hyperbolic cosine curve. This conclusion follows when we observe that now the vertical force in Fig. 4.31 is proportional to the arc length Δs:

$$\Delta f = \frac{w}{l} \Delta s$$

so that

$$q(x) = \frac{w}{l} \frac{ds}{dx} = \frac{w}{l} (1 + y'^2)^{\frac{1}{2}}$$

Now (4.9) becomes

$$\frac{dy'}{dx} = \frac{w}{hl} (1 + y'^2)^{\frac{1}{2}}$$

This equation may be integrated by separating variables. Again let us take $x = 0$ when $y' = 0$:

$$\int_0^{y'} (1 + y'^2)^{-\frac{1}{2}} \, dy' = \frac{w}{hl} \int_0^x dx$$

or $\log [y' + (1 + y'^2)^{\frac{1}{2}}] = wx/hl$, which can be written

$$y' + (1 + y'^2)^{\frac{1}{2}} = e^{wx/hl}$$

When the radical is eliminated, we can solve for y':

$$\frac{dy}{dx} = y' = \tfrac{1}{2}(e^{wx/hl} - e^{-wx/hl})$$

Another integration yields

(4.11) $$y = \frac{hl}{2w} (e^{wx/hl} + e^{-wx/hl}) + c$$

The constant of integration, taking $y = 0$ when $x = 0$, is $-lh/w$. This last equation is usually written in terms of a hyperbolic cosine:

(4.12)
$$y = \frac{hl}{w} \left[\cosh \left(\frac{wx}{hl} \right) - 1 \right]$$

Very often the x axis is shifted, so that the equation becomes

(4.13)
$$y = \frac{hl}{w} \cosh \frac{wx}{hl}$$

EXERCISES

13. Five forces in the negative y direction act on the x axis as follows: 20 lb at $x = 0$, 15 lb at $x = 10$, 10 lb at $x = 20$, 25 lb at $x = 30$, 10 lb at $x = 40$. Find the resultant by funicular polygon and also by the method of Sec. 4.2.

14. Draw three concurrent forces, and verify by a funicular polygon that the resultant passes through the common point.

15. Use the funicular polygon to find the resultant of three parallel forces, equally spaced, having magnitudes 10, −20, 30.

16. A string $ABCDE$ carries at B, C, and D, respectively, loads of 1, 2, and 3 lb. A and B are made fast. AB is inclined at 45°, while CD is horizontal. Find the tensions in each segment and the inclinations of BC and DE.

17. Three forces act along the sides of a triangle. They are proportional to the corresponding sides and are all directed so as to produce counterclockwise rotation. Carry out a funicular polygon construction and draw what conclusions you can.

18. Derive a formula in terms of x for arc length of a catenary measured from the point where the curve is horizontal.

19. Derive for the catenary with Eq. (4.13) the identity

$$y^2 = s^2 + \frac{h^2 l^2}{w^2}$$

REVIEW EXERCISES

20. Show that a block of weight w can be dragged up a plane inclined at an angle θ by a force of $w \sin (\theta + \phi)$, where ϕ is the angle of friction.

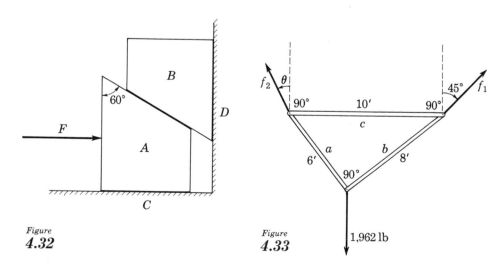

Figure
4.32

Figure
4.33

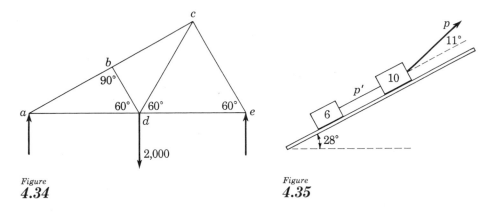

Figure
4.34

Figure
4.35

21. A block of weight w is kept from slipping on a plane inclined at an angle θ by a horizontal force **P**. If the coefficient of friction is μ, how large and how small can **P** be?

22. A block of weight w is kept on a plane inclined at 30° by a horizontal force. **P** is the smallest such force which will prevent downhill slipping. If the horizontal push is increased until the block is about to slip uphill, the magnitude of the force is $p + w$. Compute the coefficient of friction between block and plane.

23. In Fig. 4.32, wedges A and B weigh 200 lb each. The horizontal floor C and the vertical wall D may be regarded as rigid and fixed. The angle of friction between A and C and also between A and B is 15°. But the contact between B and D is smooth. Determine analytically (as well as graphically) the force **F** required to cause B to be raised at uniform speed.

24. A triangular frame of negligible weight is supported by two cords making angles of 45° and θ with the vertical (as shown in Fig. 4.33). A load of 1,962 lb is attached to the lowest joint. Without using moments find:
   (a) The tension in each cord.
   (b) The angle θ.
   (c) The force carried by each member of the frame.

25. Figure 4.34 represents a simple truss supported at its ends a and e and subject to a load at d. Find the force sustained by each of the seven members of the truss. In each case state whether the force is a compression or tension.

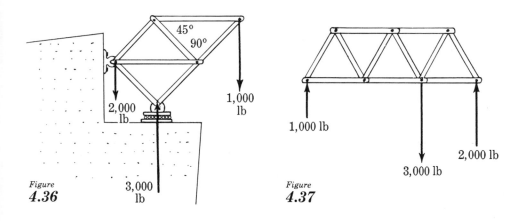

Figure
4.36

Figure
4.37

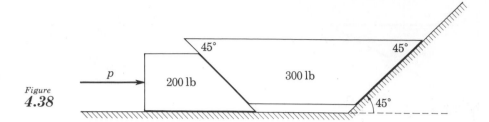

Figure
4.38

26. Two blocks weighing 6 and 10 lb are connected by a cord and placed on a plane inclined at 28°. A second cord attached to the 10-lb block is pulled, as shown in Fig. 4.35, with a tension p. When $p = 14.5$ lb, the blocks slide up the plane at uniform speed. The tension p' in the cord between the blocks is then 5.4 lb. Find the coefficients of friction between the blocks and the plane.

27. Find the tension or compression in each of the seven members of the truss shown in Fig. 4.36.

28. Find the force in each of the 11 members of the loaded truss shown in Fig. 4.37. For each member state whether it is under compression or tension.

29. The 300-lb load in Fig. 4.38 is lifted at uniform speed by the 200-lb wedge to which a horizontal force p is applied. If the angle of friction for each pair of surfaces is 15°, how large is p?

CHAPTER FIVE

SCALAR CALCULUS
of VECTORS
and PARTICLE MOTION

Distance and *force* have already been introduced as logical building blocks to be used in assembling the theory of mechanics. We have reflected briefly on how numbers are assigned to these two quantities. This required both an operational procedure and an agreement on units for our measurements. As long as we were concerned with distance alone, we necessarily studied geometrical examples. In that study we implicitly accepted the postulates of euclidean geometry, but our methods were the novel procedures of vector algebra. In our study of forces acting in space, an explicit statement of basic propositions seemed advisable. Limiting ourselves to objects no more complicated than rigid bodies, we accepted the parallelogram rule for combining concurrent forces, the principle of transmissibility, and also from Newton's famous laws certain ideas about isolation and equilibrium.

Now we shall consider a final primitive concept.

5.1. TIME

The third basic ingredient of mechanics is time. Time intervals are measured by observing coincidences with some cyclic mechanism such as a clock or pendulum. Our standard unit of time, the *second*, is a specified fraction of the mean solar day. It could be defined also in terms of atomic or mechanical frequencies. In the problems which we shall consider we shall assume that time intervals are measured accurately and that such determinations are independent of the observer, no account being taken of the proper times of observers in relative motion as in relativity theory. We shall not delve into philosophical speculations concerning the nature of time, nor shall we be concerned with techniques for standardizing time measurements, despite the fact that such occupations are significant and challenging. As with length, we shall not deem it expedient to set up formal postulates for our use of this concept. Without any such machinery being exhibited, the reader probably would assume that we here conceive of time as smoothly flowing, uniform and irreversible, absolute and impartial.   We shall denote time by the small letter t, since time is to be measured by ordinary numbers and hence is a scalar.   It is convenient to think of our time measurements as being made with a stop watch which is started at the beginning of or during an experiment.   Thus it will be natural to talk about $t = 0$.   Such a designation will have local and temporary significance and will usually not have any such connotation as "midnight," "noon," or "dawn of history."

Chapter 2 initiated the study of the question, Where is the point?   This question now becomes a function of time; we shall expect that the answer may vary moment by moment.   A *point* is merely a geometrical position in a reference frame, a set of coordinates such as (x,y,z), or a position vector such as **R**.   When we talk about a *moving point*, we shall have in mind a continuous succession of positions, in other words, a variable point whose coordinates are functions of time.   It will often be convenient to use the word *particle* instead of point.   Then we shall imagine not merely changing positions, but also *something* whose size is to be ignored in the discussion occupying those positions.   Thus sometimes we might treat a moving baseball as a particle, its position being denoted by the position vector of its center. Under other circumstances the spin of our baseball might make a very essential contribution to its behavior.   Then the particle representation would be inadequate. When we deal with the motion of a body whose physical extent is important for us, we shall regard the body as composed of many particles.   These particles will not be the particles of atomic physics, but rather the arbitrarily small subdivisions, as in integral calculus, of a medium treated as continuous.   The motions of these particles are interrelated.   We shall discover that in important special cases the interrelationships are direct and simple.

5.2. EFFECTIVE VELOCITY

The position vector of a moving particle or point varying with time may be considered as a vector function of the scalar time and hence may be represented thus:

$$(5.1) \qquad\qquad \mathbf{R} = \mathbf{R}(t)$$

This means that, for each value of t in the range of t under consideration, there is a value of the vector **R**.   Usually the vector **R** will be a *continuous* vector function of the scalar variable t.   This merely means, for each time t, that when t_1 is sufficiently close to t, the corresponding position vectors $\mathbf{R}(t)$ and $\mathbf{R}(t_1)$ are arbitrarily close in direction and magnitude.   More precisely, the vector difference $\mathbf{R}(t_1) - \mathbf{R}(t)$ has an arbitrarily small magnitude for a sufficiently small time interval $t_1 - t$.   The functional relationship given in (5.1) is a symbolic representation of the history of the moving particle during the time interval in question.   It also has important geometric significance: it is in the form of a parametric equation for the curve traced out by the moving particle, with t serving as parameter.   As a special case take

$$(5.2) \qquad\qquad \mathbf{R} = \mathbf{R}(t) = 2t\mathbf{I} + (t^2 - 4)\mathbf{J}$$

The path traced out by the moving point described in (5.2) and a number of typical values of **R** are shown in Fig. 5.1.   From the spacing of these vectors it is apparent that the motion speeds up as time passes.   One of our aims in this chapter will be to make a careful study of the rate of such movements.   First, in general terms, we shall define the *effective velocity* over a given time interval.

Suppose that **R** has the value $\mathbf{R}_0$ at time $t = t_0$ and that **R** has the value $\mathbf{R} = \mathbf{R}_0 + \Delta\mathbf{R}$ at the time $t = t_0 + \Delta t$, as in Fig. 5.2.   Then the effective time rate of

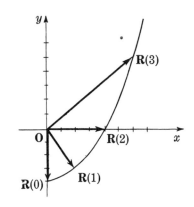

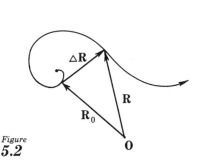

Figure
5.1

Figure
5.2

displacement is given by the ratio of $\Delta\mathbf{R}$ to Δt. This rather crude concept is what we shall term the *effective velocity over the time interval* Δt.

$$(5.3) \qquad\qquad \mathbf{V}_{\text{eff}} = \frac{\Delta\mathbf{R}}{\Delta t}$$

Clearly, $\mathbf{V}_{\text{eff}}$ is a vector concept to be measured in units such as meters per second. It obviously tells nothing about what in detail has happened during the interval. Only the net result is expressed. If Δt is short and if the motion is reasonably regular, then effective velocity is a more reliable and useful concept. In Fig. 5.3 a vector $\mathbf{V}_{\text{eff}}$ is drawn for each of three time intervals. $\mathbf{V}_{\text{eff}}$ is the effective velocity for the interval $\Delta t = t$. Since this evaluation takes no account of the arcwise nature of the displacement from $\mathbf{R}_0$ to $\mathbf{R}$, it is only mildly significant. $\mathbf{V}'_{\text{eff}}$ is a more per-tinent value, for over the time interval t_0 to $t_0 + t/2$ the direction of the net displace-ment is more nearly that of the actual instantaneous motion. $\mathbf{V}''_{\text{eff}}$, over the interval t_0 to $t_0 + t/4$, has practically the direction of the trajectory. The limiting position $\mathbf{V}$ shown in the figure will be discussed in the next section.

Example I

Using again

$$\mathbf{R}(t) = 2t\mathbf{I} + (t^2 - 4)\mathbf{J}$$

investigate the effective velocity near $t = 2$.

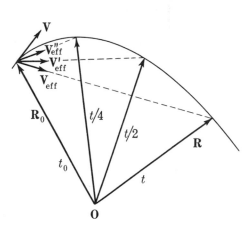

Figure
5.3

Solution

Let us use the time intervals 2 to t', where t' has successively the values 3, 2.5, 2.1, and $2 + \Delta t$.

$$\frac{\Delta \mathbf{R}}{\Delta t} = \frac{\mathbf{R}(3) - \mathbf{R}(2)}{1} = 2\mathbf{I} + 5\mathbf{J}$$

$$\frac{\Delta \mathbf{R}}{\Delta t} = \frac{\mathbf{R}(2.5) - \mathbf{R}(2)}{0.5} = \frac{1.0\mathbf{I} + 2.25\mathbf{J}}{0.5} = 2\mathbf{I} + 4.5\mathbf{J}$$

$$\frac{\Delta \mathbf{R}}{\Delta t} = \frac{\mathbf{R}(2.1) - \mathbf{R}(2)}{0.1} = \frac{0.2\mathbf{I} + 0.41\mathbf{J}}{0.1} = 2\mathbf{I} + 4.1\mathbf{J}$$

$$\frac{\Delta \mathbf{R}}{\Delta t} = \frac{\mathbf{R}(t + \Delta t) - \mathbf{R}(t)}{\Delta t} = \frac{2\Delta t\mathbf{I} + (2t\,\Delta t + \Delta t^2)\mathbf{J}}{\Delta t}$$

$$= 2\mathbf{I} + (2t + \Delta t)\mathbf{J}$$

Example 2

The position of a point moving on the x axis is given by

$$\mathbf{R} = (t - 2t^2)\mathbf{I}$$

What is the effective velocity for the intervals 0 to 0.25, 0.5, 1.0?

Solution

$\mathbf{R}(0) = 0\mathbf{I}$; therefore $\Delta \mathbf{R} = \mathbf{R} = 0.125\mathbf{I}$, $0\mathbf{I}$, $-1.0\mathbf{I}$. Dividing by Δt in each case, we have $\mathbf{V}_{\text{eff}} = 0.5\mathbf{I}$, $0\mathbf{I}$, $-1.0\mathbf{I}$.

EXERCISES

1. A particle $\mathbf{R}$ travels in such a way that $\mathbf{V}_{\text{eff}}$ is constant. What is the nature of the trajectory?
2. At time t, the position of a particle $\mathbf{R}$ is given by

$$\mathbf{R} = \mathbf{R}_0 + s(t)\mathbf{E}$$

where $\mathbf{E}$ is a constant unit vector. If $\mathbf{V}_{\text{eff}}$ is to be constant, what can be said about the scalar function of time $s(t)$?
3. A particle moving counterclockwise in the circle $r = 5$ ft at a uniform speed of 10 ft/sec travels from $5/15°$ to $5/-15°$. What is the effective velocity for this transfer?
4. The position of a particle moving in the xy plane is, at time t, given by $\mathbf{R} = 6/(20t)°$ ft. Plot a graph showing the variation with time of the magnitude of the effective velocity.
5. The position of a moving particle is given by

$$\mathbf{R} = t^2\mathbf{I} + (t - 2t^2)\mathbf{J}$$

Derive a formula for the effective velocity for the time interval from t to $t + \Delta t$.

5.3. VELOCITY AND DERIVATIVE OF A VECTOR

The discussion in Sec. 5.2 concerning effective velocity for diminishing time intervals suggests defining *instantaneous velocity* as the limiting value of effective velocity as the time interval approaches zero. To say that $\mathbf{V}$ is the *limit* of $\mathbf{V}_{\text{eff}}$ means that the *magnitude* and the *direction* of $\mathbf{V}_{\text{eff}}$ approach the magnitude and direction of $\mathbf{V}$ as

Δt is taken continually smaller. This double convergence process is illustrated in Fig. 5.4. Here $\mathbf{V}_{\text{eff1}}$, $\mathbf{V}_{\text{eff2}}$, $\mathbf{V}_{\text{eff3}}$, ... are a sequence of values of $\mathbf{V}_{\text{eff}}$ approaching $\mathbf{V}$. Students of the calculus will immediately discern the appropriateness of calling velocity (i.e., instantaneous velocity) a derivative.

$$(5.4) \qquad\qquad \mathbf{V} = \lim_{\Delta t \to 0} \mathbf{V}_{\text{eff}}$$

$$= \lim_{\Delta t \to 0} \frac{\Delta \mathbf{R}}{\Delta t} = \frac{d\mathbf{R}}{dt}$$

Other nomenclatures for derivatives are common in mathematics. In dealing with motion it is customary to indicate a *derivative with respect to time* by a superior dot:

$$\frac{d\mathbf{R}}{dt} = \dot{\mathbf{R}} \qquad \frac{d^2\mathbf{R}}{dt^2} = \ddot{\mathbf{R}}$$

Thus we may write

$$\mathbf{V} = \dot{\mathbf{R}}$$

Example

Uniform circular motion of period 8 sec is the basis for the following diagrams (see Fig. 5.5) in which the same scale is used for meters and meters per second.

We shall in this section study some of the general properties of derivatives of vectors. Let us assume that $\mathbf{R}$ is a varying vector. It might, for instance, represent a velocity, a force, or a position. Suppose that $\mathbf{R}$ is a function of a scalar variable t. Usually for us this independent scalar variable will be time, but occasionally an angle or a distance will be more convenient. For any value of t, we shall define a new vector function of t, *the derivative of* $\mathbf{R}$ *with respect to* t. A defining equation has already been given in (5.4), but now our treatment is to be quite general; therefore we shall give the equation again without any reference to effective velocity:

$$(5.5) \qquad\qquad \frac{d\mathbf{R}}{dt} = \lim_{\Delta t \to 0} \frac{\mathbf{R}(t + \Delta t) - \mathbf{R}(t)}{\Delta t} = \lim_{\Delta t \to 0} \frac{\Delta \mathbf{R}}{\Delta t}$$

Of course, this new vector is defined only for those values of t for which this limit exists. In our work in elementary mechanics we deal with vector functions whose derivatives exist everywhere that we need them.

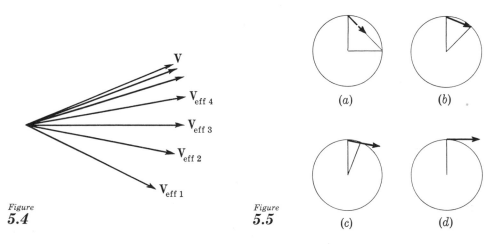

Figure
5.4

Figure
5.5

(a)   (b)

(c)   (d)

In ordinary scalar calculus a derivative is readily illustrated as the slope of a smooth curve. The derivative of a vector function of a scalar variable is not so easily portrayed. A path diagram is, however, helpful. Let each vector $\mathbf{R}(t)$ be drawn with its initial point at an origin $\mathbf{O}$. Then the terminal point of the vector traces out a curve as in Fig. 5.6. It should be apparent that the limit of $\Delta \mathbf{R}/\Delta t$ as Δt gets smaller and smaller is always a vector tangent to this curve at the point designated $\mathbf{R}(t)$. In summary:

(5.6) *If* $\mathbf{R} = \mathbf{R}(t)$, *then* $d\mathbf{R}/dt$ *is a vector function of t having the direction of the tangent to the curve traced out by* $\mathbf{R}(t)$.

The standard rules of reckoning of scalar calculus have their counterparts in vector calculus. Such rules are justified by derivations based on theorems concerning limits such as *limit of sum equals sum of limits*, etc. These theorems may be carried over immediately from the scalar theory of real variables since each vector function is expressible in terms of three scalar functions. The details will not be included here. Only skeleton derivations of the rules will be presented.

Derivative of a Sum.   Let $\mathbf{R}$ and $\mathbf{S}$ be two vector functions of t.   Then

$$\frac{d}{dt}(\mathbf{R} + \mathbf{S}) = \lim_{\Delta t \to 0}\left[\frac{\mathbf{R}(t + \Delta t) + \mathbf{S}(t + \Delta t) - \mathbf{R}(t) - \mathbf{S}(t)}{\Delta t}\right]$$

$$= \lim_{\Delta t \to 0}\left[\frac{\mathbf{R}(t + \Delta t) - \mathbf{R}(t)}{\Delta t}\right] + \lim_{\Delta t \to 0}\left[\frac{\mathbf{S}(t + \Delta t) - \mathbf{S}(t)}{\Delta t}\right]$$

or, using the defining equation (5.5),

(5.7)
$$\frac{d}{dt}(\mathbf{R} + \mathbf{S}) = \frac{d\mathbf{R}}{dt} + \frac{d\mathbf{S}}{dt}$$

Derivative of Product by Scalar Function.   Let $\mathbf{R}$ and c be functions of t.   Then

$$\frac{d(c\mathbf{R})}{dt} = \lim_{\Delta t \to 0}\left[\frac{(c + \Delta c)(\mathbf{R} + \Delta \mathbf{R}) - c\mathbf{R}}{\Delta t}\right]$$

$$= \lim_{\Delta t \to 0}\left[\frac{\Delta c}{\Delta t}\mathbf{R} + c\frac{\Delta \mathbf{R}}{\Delta t} + \Delta c\frac{\Delta \mathbf{R}}{\Delta t}\right]$$

or

(5.8)
$$\frac{d(c\mathbf{R})}{dt} = \frac{dc}{dt}\mathbf{R} + c\frac{d\mathbf{R}}{dt}$$

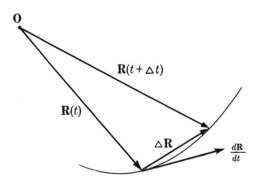

Figure
5.6

Derivatives of Inner Product of Vectors.   Let **R** and **S** be functions of t.   The derivation is left for Exercise 8.

$$(5.9) \qquad \frac{d(\mathbf{R} \cdot \mathbf{S})}{dt} = \frac{d\mathbf{R}}{dt} \cdot \mathbf{S} + \mathbf{R} \cdot \frac{d\mathbf{S}}{dt}$$

Components of Derivatives.   Let $U(t)$ be a vector function of the scalar t.   Then, as a consequence of the rules of vector algebra and the rules of calculus just derived, we may write, assuming that **I**, **J**, and **K** are constant vectors,

$$(5.10) \qquad \frac{d\mathbf{U}}{dt} = \frac{du_x}{dt}\mathbf{I} + \frac{du_y}{dt}\mathbf{J} + \frac{du_z}{dt}\mathbf{K}$$

Applied to the case where the vector in question is a position vector, the result is

$$(5.11) \qquad \mathbf{V} = \frac{dx}{dt}\mathbf{I} + \frac{dy}{dt}\mathbf{J} + \frac{dz}{dt}\mathbf{K}$$

or

$$(5.12) \qquad \dot{\mathbf{R}} = \dot{x}\mathbf{I} + \dot{y}\mathbf{J} + \dot{z}\mathbf{K}$$

This equation throws considerable light on the nature of the velocity vector **V** of a moving point.   Its x projection is merely the velocity of the x projection of the point, and so on for the y and z projections.   This same principle holds for directions other than these three favored ones.

Special Conclusions

Any vector, we have seen, has direction and magnitude.   As an illustration of the new ideas of this section, let us look into the nature of the derivative of the following:

1. A vector whose direction does not change.
2. A vector whose magnitude does not change.

1. A variable vector of constant direction may be represented by

$$\mathbf{R} = r\mathbf{E}$$

where **E** is a constant unit vector.   If **E** does not vary, then

$$\Delta\mathbf{R} = \Delta r\mathbf{E}$$

Therefore

(5.13) *If* **R** *is constant in direction, then* $d\mathbf{R}/dt$ *is parallel to* **R**.

This may be seen too as a quick formal conclusion from (5.8):

$$\frac{d\mathbf{R}}{dt} = \frac{dr}{dt}\mathbf{E} + r\frac{d\mathbf{E}}{dt} = \frac{dr}{dt}\mathbf{E}$$

This follows at once from the assumptions

$$\mathbf{R} = r\mathbf{E}, \qquad \frac{d\mathbf{E}}{dt} = \mathbf{O}$$

2. A variable vector of constant magnitude may be represented by

$$\mathbf{R} = a\mathbf{L}$$

where a is a constant scalar and $\mathbf{L}$ a varying unit vector (see Fig. 5.7). In this interesting case the only possible path diagrams of $\mathbf{R}$ must lie on a sphere of radius a. But for any curve on a sphere, the tangent is perpendicular to the radius and hence to $\mathbf{R}$; thus $\mathbf{R}$ and $d\mathbf{R}/dt$ are at right angles. This too may be deduced formally. First let us note, since a is constant, that

$$\frac{d(\mathbf{R} \cdot \mathbf{R})}{dt} = \frac{d(a^2)}{dt} = 0$$

Now, using (5.9) and the commutative law for scalar products,

$$\frac{d(\mathbf{R} \cdot \mathbf{R})}{dt} = \frac{d\mathbf{R}}{dt} \cdot \mathbf{R} + \mathbf{R} \cdot \frac{d\mathbf{R}}{dt} = 2\frac{d\mathbf{R}}{dt} \cdot \mathbf{R}$$

Combining this with the previous equation, we have (*for a vector* $\mathbf{R}$ *of constant magnitude*)

(5.14)
$$\frac{d\mathbf{R}}{dt} \cdot \mathbf{R} = 0$$

In this case, then, $\mathbf{R}$ *and its derivative are perpendicular.*

EXERCISES

6. $\mathbf{L}$ and $\mathbf{M}$ are unit vectors in the xy plane given by

$$\mathbf{L} = 1\underline{/\theta} \qquad \mathbf{M} = 1\underline{/\theta + 90°}$$

Write each in $\mathbf{IJ}$ form. Then differentiate term by term with respect to time to show that $\dot{\mathbf{L}} = \dot{\theta}\mathbf{M}$ and $\dot{\mathbf{M}} = -\dot{\theta}\mathbf{L}$. Note that $\dot{\theta}$ is measured in radians per second or similar units.

7. In Exercise 6, verify that, when $\dot{\theta} = \omega$ is constant, one has

$$\ddot{\mathbf{L}} = -\omega^2\mathbf{L} \qquad \ddot{\mathbf{M}} = -\omega^2\mathbf{M}$$

8. Use the Δ method [used for establishing (5.7) and (5.8)] to prove (5.9).

9. Prove that the component in the direction of a unit vector $\mathbf{E}$ of a variable vector $\mathbf{R}$ has derivative equal to the $\mathbf{E}$ component of $d\mathbf{R}/dt$.

10. Compute in $\mathbf{IJK}$ form the derivative with respect to t of each of the following vector expressions:
    (a) $(t\mathbf{J}) \cdot t^3(\mathbf{I} + \mathbf{J})$.   (b) $(\sin t\mathbf{I}) \cdot (\cos t\mathbf{J})$.
    (c) $(2t\mathbf{J} - t^3\mathbf{K}) \cdot (t^2\mathbf{I} + 2t\mathbf{J})$.

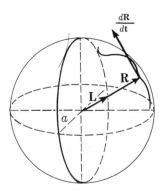

Figure
5.7

11. Find expressions for the velocity of each of the following points. (At time t sec, $\sin t$ equals the sine of t rad.)
   (a) $\mathbf{R} = 2t^2\mathbf{I} + 4t\mathbf{J} + 8\mathbf{K}$.
   (b) $\mathbf{R} = 4 \sin t\mathbf{I} + 4 \cos t\mathbf{J} + t^2\mathbf{K}$.
12. The position vector of a moving particle at time t is given by

$$\mathbf{R} = \cos t\mathbf{I} + \sin t\mathbf{J} + t\mathbf{K}$$

   (at time t sec, $\cos t$ equals the cosine of t rad). Find the magnitude and the direction cosines of the velocity vector at time $t = 1.0472$ sec.
13. The position of a point (x,y) ft, moving in the xy plane, is at time t given by

$$x = 4t^2 \qquad y = 6t$$

   Find analytically the direction and the magnitude of the velocity vector $\mathbf{V} = v\underline{/\theta}$ at $t = 1.0$.
14. The path of a projectile is given by

$$\mathbf{R} = v_0 t \cos \theta \mathbf{I} + (v_0 t \sin \theta - 16t^2)\mathbf{J}$$

   where $\mathbf{V_0} = v_0\underline{/\theta}$ is the muzzle velocity. If $v_0 = 4,000$ ft/sec and $\theta = 30°$, find the speed and direction of the projectile at $t = 1, 5$, and 20 sec.
15. If $\mathbf{L}$ is the unit vector in the xy plane given by $\mathbf{L} = 1\underline{/\theta}$, where θ is a function of t, then $\mathbf{L} \cdot \mathbf{I} = \cos \theta$, $\mathbf{L} \cdot \mathbf{J} = \sin \theta$. Differentiate each of these equations with respect to t to show that

$$\dot{\mathbf{L}} = \dot{\theta}\mathbf{M}$$

   where $\mathbf{M}$ is the variable unit vector $1\underline{/\theta + 90°}$.

5.4. RELATIVE VELOCITY

In our discussions of *time* and *length* it was assumed that two careful experimenters would agree in measuring either quantity. It is perhaps interesting to point out that in the theory of relativity no such assumptions are made. Even from the elementary point of view which we entertain in this course, *velocity* may appear quite different to different observers. The nature of the velocity vector depends on the reference frame with respect to which displacements are measured. A ball tossed back and forth between two people on opposite sides of a train coach appears to retrace the same path over and over again. For an observer on the ground the trajectories form a zigzag pattern. A passenger in an automobile taking a curve feels pushed to the side of the vehicle. From an outside point of view, however, he is merely tending to follow a straight path instead of the sharply curved one dictated by the path of the car. We are so accustomed to considering motion relative to the surface of the earth that we seldom take account even of the diurnal rotation of our planet.

We shall now consider how apparent motions as observed with respect to different reference frames can be compared. We shall limit ourselves at present to the case where one frame does not rotate with respect to the other. Let $\mathbf{O}$ be the origin of the "fixed" reference frame, while $\mathbf{O'}$ is origin of a second frame moving with respect to the first. Since no rotation takes place, we shall assume that the corresponding axes are always, respectively, parallel. At time t, let a particle have position vector $\mathbf{R_1}$ with respect to $\mathbf{O}$ and $\mathbf{R_1'}$ with respect to $\mathbf{O'}$. After a time elapse Δt, the position vector with respect to $\mathbf{O}$ is $\mathbf{R_2}$, the displacement $\Delta \mathbf{R}$ being $\mathbf{R_2} - \mathbf{R_1}$, as shown in

Fig. 5.8. But during the time interval Δt the frame $\mathbf{O}'$ has moved. This means that if our particle had remained at $\mathbf{R}_1'$ (as viewed from $\mathbf{O}'$), it would have undergone a displacement $\Delta \mathbf{R}_f$ (as viewed from $\mathbf{O}$). Since no rotation of the moving frame has taken place, $\Delta \mathbf{R}_f$ is also the displacement of any other point fixed in the frame, for example, of $\mathbf{O}'$. Actually, our particle need not merely have taken a ride on the moving frame. In Fig. 5.8 it is apparent that the new position vector $\mathbf{R}_2'$ is quite different from $\mathbf{R}_1'$. An observer at $\mathbf{O}'$ would report a displacement $\Delta \mathbf{R}' = \mathbf{R}_2' - \mathbf{R}_1'$. This is the "relative displacement" seen from the moving frame. Figure 5.8 makes it clear that the "absolute displacement" is equal to the vector sum of the "frame displacement" and the "relative displacement."

In symbols, we have, then,

$$(5.15) \qquad\qquad \Delta \mathbf{R} = \Delta \mathbf{R}_f + \Delta \mathbf{R}'$$

Since we are considering parallel sets of axes, $\Delta \mathbf{R}'$ has the same x, y, and z components in either frame. The three displacements entering Eq. (5.15) occurred during the same interval Δt. If we divide both members of this equation by Δt and take the limit as Δt is allowed to approach zero, we have an equation involving derivatives:

$$(5.16) \qquad\qquad \frac{d\mathbf{R}}{dt} = \frac{d\mathbf{R}_f}{dt} + \frac{d\mathbf{R}'}{dt}$$

Each of these is a velocity; therefore we rewrite (5.16) as

$$(5.17) \qquad\qquad \mathbf{V} = \mathbf{V}_f + \mathbf{V}'$$

In words, we may say that the absolute velocity of the particle is equal to the vector sum of two other velocities: the velocity which the particle would share with the moving frame if it remained rigidly fixed in it and the velocity which it has relative to the moving frame. In a general case, this second vector, the relative velocity, might be described differently by observers in the two systems. As long as we limit ourselves to reference frames with parallel axes, no such ambiguity arises.

The principal vector equation (5.17) is perhaps more easily believed if it is rewritten in the form

$$(5.18) \qquad\qquad \mathbf{V}' = \mathbf{V} + (-\mathbf{V}_f)$$

Imagine that you are on the deck of a ship during a complete calm. Your most natural reference frame is then attached to the ship. Let $\mathbf{V}$ represent the wind velocity. In a complete calm, $\mathbf{V}$ is a null vector, but you actually feel $\mathbf{V}'$ as a head wind, exactly opposite to the ship's own velocity $\mathbf{V}_f$. In this case Eq. (5.18) becomes $\mathbf{V}' = \mathbf{O} + (-\mathbf{V}_f)$. Now imagine the ship at anchor with a wind blowing. In

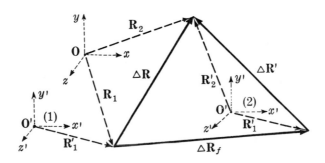

Figure
5.8

this case there is no distinction between the actual and apparent wind velocities $\mathbf{V'} = \mathbf{V} + \mathbf{O}$. Finally, suppose the ship sails north while the wind blows from the west. The apparent velocity of the air particles which you encounter is the vector sum of the wind velocity, together with the artificial head-wind velocity generated by the motion of the ship.

Example 1

The expanding trail of smoke left by a steamer moving due north at 15 mph appears to an airplane pilot like a narrow wedge pointing 30° west of north. If the true velocity of the wind is also 15 mph, what is its true direction?

Solution

Take the steamer as a moving frame with velocity $\mathbf{V}_f$ north at 15 mph. The apparent velocity of the wind as seen from the steamer, $\mathbf{V'}$, has the direction of the line of smoke (i.e., the wind blows toward 30° east of south). Since the absolute velocity $\mathbf{V}$ of the wind has magnitude 15 mph, the vector triangle (Fig. 5.9) relating the three velocities is isosceles; therefore the odd angle is 120°. The wind then actually blows 60° east of south (or from a point 60° west of north).

Example 2

An airplane points due north with an air speed of 80 mph. Because of a north-west wind the airplane's actual course is northeast. Find the actual speed of the airplane and also the speed of the wind.

Solution

Of the three velocities, only $\mathbf{V'}$ is known in both direction and magnitude. (It is the velocity of the airplane relative to the air: due north at 80 mph.) $\mathbf{V}_f$ is the velocity of the air mass, and it is known in direction only (a northwest wind blows southeast, as shown in Fig. 5.10). The absolute velocity $\mathbf{V}$ is known in direction only (northeast). A suitable vector diagram is in the figure. From it, it is clear that

$$v = v_f = 80 \sin 45° = 56.6 \text{ mph}$$

Example 3

A warship sailing at 20 mph sights a target ship 20 miles ahead crossing its path at right angles at 15 mph. In how long a time will their separation be a minimum if their velocities are unchanged?

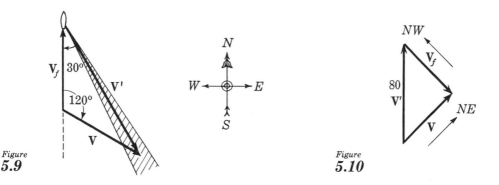

Figure
5.9

Figure
5.10

Solution

It is quite possible to work the problem with little reference to the methods of this section.   Choosing axes, as shown in Fig. 5.11, the positions at time t are, respectively, $20t\mathbf{I}$ and $20\mathbf{I} + 15t\mathbf{J}$.   The distance between them is the magnitude of the vector difference

$$20(1 - t)\mathbf{I} + 15t\mathbf{J}$$

namely,

$$\sqrt{400(1 - t)^2 + 225t^2}$$

If the derivative of this is set equal to zero, one finds that the minimum value occurs at $t = 0.64$ hr.

A more interesting approach is afforded by the concept of relative velocity.   As seen from the ship, the target has velocity

$$\mathbf{V}' = 15\mathbf{J} - 20\mathbf{I} \qquad v' = 25 \text{ mph}$$

Regarding the ship as at the origin, then, the question is, Where does the course come closest to the origin?   The nearest point (see Fig. 5.12) is determined by dropping a perpendicular from $\mathbf{O}'$ to the course.   The minimum distance is at once seen to be 12 miles after a relative displacement of 16 miles at 25 mph, or

$$t = \tfrac{16}{25} = 0.64 \text{ hr}$$

Example 4

A river flows with uniform speed u.   Two rafts a distance l apart are released and allowed to drift with the current downstream.   A boy swims from raft A to raft B and back to A, always at absolute speed c.   Find the time required (*a*) if the line joining A and B is perpendicular to the current and (*b*) if it is parallel to the current. (This situation is analogous to the Michelson-Morley experiment to detect motion relative to an ether.)

Solution

a.   For the first experiment the two velocity diagrams based on Eq. (5.17) are as shown in Fig. 5.13.   The time elapsed is $t = 2l/v'$, where $v' = (c^2 - u^2)^{\frac{1}{2}}$; so

$$t = \frac{2l(c^2 - u^2)^{\frac{1}{2}}}{c^2 - u^2}$$

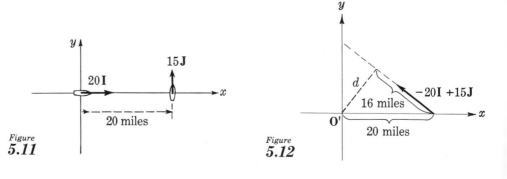

Figure
5.11

Figure
5.12

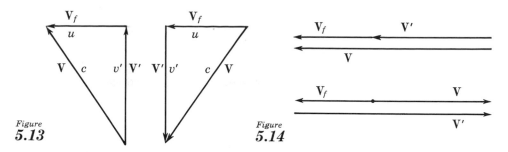

Figure
5.13

Figure
5.14

b.   For the second experiment the two velocity patterns are as shown in Fig. 5.14.   The time elapsed is now

$$t' = \frac{l}{c+u} + \frac{l}{c-u} = \frac{2lc}{c^2 - u^2}$$

Since $(c^2 - u^2)^{\frac{1}{2}}$ is less than c, it is clear that $t' > t$.

If $c \gg u$ (as presumably in the Michelson-Morley experiment), we may use binomial approximations:

$$t = \frac{2l}{c}\left(1 - \frac{u^2}{c^2}\right)^{-\frac{1}{2}} \simeq \frac{2l}{c}\left(1 + \frac{u^2}{2c^2}\right)$$

$$t' = \frac{2l}{c}\left(1 - \frac{u^2}{c^2}\right)^{-1} \simeq \frac{2l}{c}\left(1 + \frac{u^2}{c^2}\right)$$

The difference $t' - t \simeq (2l/c)(u^2/2c^2)$, which is an exceedingly small quantity.

How would the results of this example be changed if the effort of the swimmer were always uniform so that v' was a constant?   (See Exercise 77.)

Example 5

A target vessel T maintains a uniform course of 120° (clockwise from north) at 20 knots.   A pursuit vessel P which travels at 40 knots is initially due south of T. The problem is to determine the course direction for P in order for (*a*) T to be overtaken as soon as possible; (*b*) the speed of T relative to P to be minimum.

Solution

a.   Take a reference frame attached to P as origin, and then apply Eq. (5.18). The velocity $\mathbf{V'}$ of T in this moving frame is the vector sum of the completely specified vector $\mathbf{V}$ and a vector of length 40 in the plane of the motion.   In Fig. 5.15, then, $\mathbf{V'}$ can be any vector starting at T and ending on the circle of radius 40 with the tip of $\mathbf{V}$ as center.   The point A, for instance, is such a point corresponding to the velocity vector $\mathbf{V}_f$ for P.   By choosing the correct A on the circle the pursuer can impress on T the desired relative velocity $\mathbf{V'}$.   For quickest overhauling of T, let $\mathbf{V}_f$ be so chosen that $\mathbf{V'}$ is due south, directly toward P.   This corresponds to point B on the circle in Fig. 5.16.   Using the law of sines for the vector triangle, we find that the distance between T and P diminishes at 46.1 knots when the pursuit course is given by $\phi = 25.6°$.   Note that the easterly components of $\mathbf{V}$ and $\mathbf{V}_f$ are equal, so that the bearing of T from B remains north throughout.

b.   The vector $\mathbf{V'}$ is minimum for the choice of point C on the circle, corresponding to a course for P parallel to the given course for T.

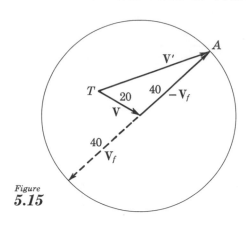

Figure
5.15

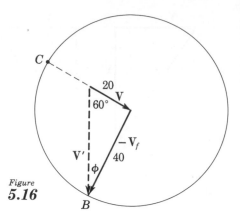

Figure
5.16

EXERCISES

16. An airplane is going northeast at 100 mph. It is observed by a motorcyclist going south at 90 mph. Neglecting the difference in altitude, how fast is the distance between them increasing?

17. A bomber takes off from a base and follows a straight course to a target. Since there is a wind from the southeast, the nose of the airplane is pointed northeast instead of toward the target. It takes the bomber 1 hr to reach the target which is 200 miles from the base. Its average air speed is 195 mph. How many degrees east of the course was the airplane pointed? What was the speed of the wind?

18. A lunch box is lost from a canoe going upstream. Fifteen minutes later the canoe reverses direction and heads downstream, the effort at paddling being uniform and undiminished. The box is overtaken a mile downstream from the spot where it was dropped. What is the speed of the river?

19. A swimmer's speed in still water is 150 ft/min and the current of a river is 90 ft/min. If he swims to a point upstream and back in 5 min, what is the total distance he swam?

20. A train travels at 40 mph. How fast (relative to the train) and in what direction must a ball be thrown to travel 30 mph on a horizontal path perpendicular to the train?

21. An airplane flies north with an air speed of 129 mph and after an hour lands 75 miles due west of the starting point. Describe the wind.

22. Airplane A travels west at a speed of 150 mph. Airplane B, traveling at 250 mph, is nearest to A when it crosses A's path directly ahead of A. In what direction does B travel?

23. For a boy riding a bicycle north at 15 mph, the wind apparently comes from the northwest also at 15 mph. Find in direction and magnitude the true wind velocity.

24. A man in a boat with maximum speed 20 mph sees a speedboat 10 miles away traveling 30 mph at right angles to his line of sight. By traveling at full speed how close can he get to the speedboat? What course should he choose?

25. A transport airplane traveling northeast at 150 mph is spotted 100 miles due north of a fighter which can travel 300 mph. What course should the fighter pilot be directed to take in order to overtake the transport as soon as possible and, assuming constant velocities, how long will it take him to reach the transport?

26. When a motorboat heads north at 20 mph, the apparent wind is from 30° east of north. When it turns west, the apparent wind is from 60° west of south. Find the true wind velocity in direction and magnitude.

27. A motorboat heading northwest experiences an apparent wind from the west; when it

heads northeast at the same speed, the apparent wind is from the east and twice as brisk as before. Find the true wind direction.

28. A rotating wheel of radius 3 ft moves in the xy plane. Its center moves with velocity 5I ft/sec. The angular speed is 2 rad/sec, clockwise as viewed from the positive z axis. Taking moving axes $x'O'y'$ with O' at the center of the wheel, the x' axis parallel to the x axis, and the y' axis parallel to the y axis, each point on the wheel has a velocity V' relative to the moving frame. Construct a scale drawing showing V', V_f, and V for points

$$(x',y') = (3,0), (-3,0), (0,3), (0,-3), (-2,2), (2,-2)$$

5.5. UNIT TANGENT VECTOR

When a moving point of position vector R traces out a path, its velocity vector is given, as we have seen, by

$$(5.19) \qquad V = \lim_{\Delta t \to 0} \frac{\Delta R}{\Delta t}$$

We shall now consider the derivative of R with respect to a different scalar variable, namely, the *positive* distance s measured along the path from any convenient fixed point on the path (see Fig. 5.17):

$$(5.20) \qquad T = \lim_{\Delta s \to 0} \frac{\Delta R}{\Delta s} = \frac{dR}{ds}$$

The *direction* of T is the limiting direction of ΔR, that is, tangent to the path. T then always points in the direction of the motion along the path. As Δs gets small, the magnitude of ΔR approaches Δs; thus T is a *unit vector*. This unit vector T may be thought of as a course indicator, always pointing out the direction to be traveled. It is a vector whose length is constant but whose direction may vary continually.

Example 1

If a point travels along the x axis in the positive direction, we have $T = I$. In this case it is constant in direction as well as magnitude. If the direction be reversed, $T = -I$.

Example 2

If a point travels counterclockwise around a circle of radius a about the origin as center in the xy plane, then at the point $R = a/\theta$ the corresponding T is given by

$$T = 1/\theta + 90°$$

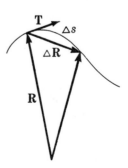

Figure
5.17

We now have two vectors, **V** and **T**, parallel to the path of a moving point at each point of the path. (Some exceptions might be made, for instance, at the point in the first example above where reversal of direction takes place.) Using a "chain rule" for differentiation exactly like that used in scalar calculus, we may write

(5.21) $$\mathbf{V} = \frac{d\mathbf{R}}{dt} = \frac{d\mathbf{R}}{ds}\frac{ds}{dt} = \frac{ds}{dt}\mathbf{T}$$

The quantity ds/dt is the positive scalar rate of travel or *speed*. We shall denote it by v, since it is equal to the magnitude of **V**.

(5.22) $$\mathbf{V} = v\mathbf{T} \qquad v = |\mathbf{V}|$$

Example 3

A moving point has coordinates $(6t,t^2,4)$. Find **T** at time $t = 4$ sec.

Solution

In terms of vectors,
$$\mathbf{R} = 6t\mathbf{I} + t^2\mathbf{J} + 4\mathbf{K}$$

Differentiating with respect to t,
$$\mathbf{V} = 6\mathbf{I} + 2t\mathbf{J}$$

At $t = 4$,
$$\mathbf{V} = 6\mathbf{I} + 8\mathbf{J} \qquad v = 10 \qquad \mathbf{T} = 0.6\mathbf{I} + 0.8\mathbf{J}$$

Let us now see quantitatively how **T** changes in direction as a point moves along a smooth curve. Suppose that the point moves from **P** to **P'** and that **T** meanwhile becomes **T'** (see Fig. 5.18). Let the angle between **T** and **T'**, measured in radians, be $\Delta\psi$. If **P'** is allowed to approach **P**, $\Delta\psi$ will, of course, get small. $\Delta\mathbf{T} = \mathbf{T'} - \mathbf{T}$ can be studied by means of the isosceles triangle determined by the unit vectors **T** and **T'**. From the diagram it is clear that

$$|\Delta\mathbf{T}| = 2\sin\frac{\Delta\psi}{2}$$

Hence

$$\lim_{\Delta\psi\to 0}\frac{|\Delta\mathbf{T}|}{\Delta\psi} = \lim_{\Delta\psi\to 0}\frac{\sin(\Delta\psi/2)}{\Delta\psi/2} = 1$$

Thus $d\mathbf{T}/d\psi$ is a unit vector at right angles to **T** in the direction toward which **T** turns.

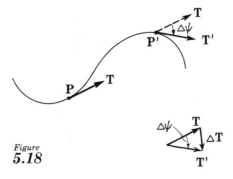

Figure
5.18

This unit vector, normal to the curve and in the plane fitting it most closely (i.e., the *osculating plane*), is called the *unit principal normal vector*. It is denoted by **N**.

$$(5.23) \qquad \mathbf{N} = \frac{d\mathbf{T}}{d\psi}$$

The *unit binormal vector* **B** is normal to both **T** and **N** and hence to the osculating plane. Its sense is chosen to make the triple **T, N, B** determine a right-handed reference frame in the manner of **I, J, K**.

Example 4

If a point travels clockwise around a circle of radius a about the origin as center in the xy plane, then at the point $\mathbf{R} = a\underline{/\theta}$, the corresponding **N** is given by $\mathbf{N} = 1\underline{/\theta + 180°}$ (that is, $\mathbf{R} = -a\mathbf{N}$).

We have seen how **T** varies with respect to the angle measuring its orientation. It is now easy to express the rate of change of **T** with respect to displacement:

$$(5.24) \qquad \frac{d\mathbf{T}}{ds} = \frac{d\mathbf{T}}{d\psi}\frac{d\psi}{ds} = \frac{d\psi}{ds}\mathbf{N}$$

The scalar coefficient of **N** in this expression, the derivative of ψ with respect to s, is the rate with respect to displacement at which the direction of the path is changed. It is called the *curvature* and is denoted by the letter κ. As one drives along a curved road at a fixed speed, the sharper the curve, the faster one's direction changes. Thus κ is large on sharp curves and small on slow ones. In terms of κ, we may write

$$(5.25) \qquad \frac{d\mathbf{T}}{ds} = \kappa\mathbf{N}$$

Example 5

Consider a circle of radius ρ. Since the tangent to a circle is always perpendicular to the radius at the point of tangency, the angle between radii to two neighboring points is equal to the angle $\Delta\psi$ between their tangents (see Fig. 5.19). The displacement or arc length along the curve between these points is then $\rho\,\Delta\psi$. We have, then,

$$(5.26) \qquad \kappa = \frac{d\psi}{ds} = \lim_{\Delta s \to 0}\frac{\Delta\psi}{\rho\,\Delta\psi} = \frac{1}{\rho}$$

We have arrived at the interesting conclusion that the curvature of a circle is merely the reciprocal of its radius. Thus a circle is *the plane curve of constant curvature*

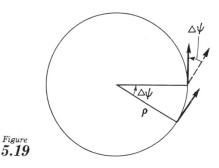

Figure
5.19

(a straight line being considered as part of a circle of infinite radius and hence of zero curvature).   For a random curve at a random point, the reciprocal of the curvature is called the *radius of curvature*.   We shall represent it by the letter ρ.

In terms of the concept described as an extension of the preceding example, Eq. (5.25) may be recast as

(5.27)
$$\frac{d\mathbf{T}}{ds} = \frac{1}{\rho}\mathbf{N}$$

Let us finally compute the time derivative of **T**.

(5.28)
$$\frac{d\mathbf{T}}{dt} = \frac{d\mathbf{T}}{ds}\frac{ds}{dt} = v\kappa\mathbf{N} = \frac{v}{\rho}\mathbf{N}$$

EXERCISES

29. An equation for a point moving along a cycloid is given by

$$\mathbf{R} = 5(3t - \sin 3t)\mathbf{I} + 5(1 - \cos 3t)\mathbf{J}   \text{ft, sec}$$

For what values of t does $\mathbf{T} = \mathbf{I}$?   Compute **V** for these values of t.

30. The coordinates at time t sec of a moving particle are given in meters by

$$x = 48t   y = \tfrac{1}{64}(4 - t^2)^2   z = 4t^2.$$

Find **T** and v at $t = 8$ sec.

31. Any derivative of **T** is a vector parallel to **N**; therefore

$$\frac{d\mathbf{T}}{d\theta} = b\mathbf{N}$$

for any scalar variable θ and some scalar constant b.   For a circle of radius a, pick an origin **O** as any point on the curve.   Let the x axis be a tangent to the circle at **O**. Then the position of any point **R** on the circle can be expressed by giving the angle between **OR** and the x axis.   For this θ, find b for the above formula.

32. Given $\mathbf{R} = 3t\mathbf{I} + \tfrac{1}{3}t^3\mathbf{J} + t^3\mathbf{K}$.   Find **T** and **N** at $t = 2$.

33. The position of a moving particle is given by

$$\mathbf{R} = 3.62t\mathbf{I} + 2.37t^2\mathbf{J} - 1.36t^3\mathbf{K}   \text{m, sec}$$

Find for the time $t = 0.5$ sec the unit tangent vector in **IJK** form and the speed.

5.6. ACCELERATION

Motion in a straight line at uniform speed has a constant velocity vector.   But let either the speed or the direction vary, and the velocity vector may have a nonzero derivative with respect to time.   This derivative is called acceleration, denoted by **A**.

(5.29)
$$\mathbf{A} = \frac{d\mathbf{V}}{dt} = \dot{\mathbf{V}}$$

The most interesting motions in physics are accelerated motions: the motions of falling bodies, of particles traveling in circles, and of vibrating particles.   We shall shortly develop general techniques for computing acceleration.   For the moment let us glance at some simpler special cases, such as the familiar ones just listed.

Example 1

Galileo discovered that in equal successive time intervals a falling body traverses distances which are proportional to the odd integers. What does this imply concerning the acceleration?

Solution

The evidence is first tabulated:

From   0 to Δt distance fallen is 1
From Δt to $2\Delta t$ distance fallen is 3
From $2\Delta t$ to $3\Delta t$ distance fallen is 5, etc.

Now let us express displacements for total elapsed time.

From 0 to Δt total distance fallen is 1
From 0 to $2\Delta t$ total distance fallen is $1 + 3 = 4$
From 0 to $3\Delta t$ total distance fallen is $1 + 3 + 5 = 9$
From 0 to $4\Delta t$ total distance fallen is $1 + 3 + 5 + 7 = 16$

This suggests motion according to an equation of the form

$$y = -bt^2 \qquad \text{or} \qquad \mathbf{R} = -bt^2\mathbf{J}$$

where b is a positive constant and $\mathbf{J}$ a fixed unit vertical vector. From this we may conclude:

$$\mathbf{V} = \dot{\mathbf{R}} = -2bt\mathbf{J} \qquad \text{and} \qquad \mathbf{A} = \dot{\mathbf{V}} = -2b\mathbf{J}$$

Thus the evidence listed is at least consistent with the following:

(5.30)   *The acceleration for a freely falling body is constant.*

Example 2

In uniform circular motion the velocity vector is constant in magnitude but varying in direction. The derivative of such a vector is perpendicular to the vector [see Eq. (5.14)]. We conclude that the acceleration is radial, toward the center of the circle. For this reason it is called *centripetal acceleration*. The magnitude of the acceleration may be easily computed in various ways. Let us do it here by observing (following Fig. 5.20) that the triangles formed by $\mathbf{V}$, $\mathbf{V}'$, $\Delta\mathbf{V}$ and $\mathbf{R}$, $\mathbf{R}'$, $\Delta\mathbf{R}$ are similar. Hence

$$\frac{|\Delta\mathbf{V}|}{v} = \frac{|\Delta\mathbf{R}|}{\rho}$$

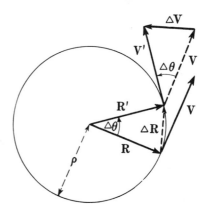

Figure
5.20

and consequently,

$$\left|\frac{\Delta \mathbf{V}}{\Delta t}\right| = \frac{v}{\rho}\left|\frac{\Delta \mathbf{R}}{\Delta t}\right|$$

Taking the limit as $\Delta t \to 0$,

(5.31) $$a = |\mathbf{A}| = \frac{v}{\rho}\left|\frac{d\mathbf{R}}{dt}\right| = \frac{v^2}{\rho}$$

Example 3

Let us consider a special case of oscillation on a straight line:

$$\mathbf{R} = b \cos \omega t \mathbf{I}$$

where b and ω are constants. Compute the acceleration for both the extreme and the neutral positions.

Solution

First we may get a general expression for the acceleration by differentiating twice:

$$\mathbf{A} = \ddot{\mathbf{R}} = -b\omega^2 \cos \omega t \mathbf{I}$$

Note that this expression shows it to be a scalar (negative) multiple of $\mathbf{R}$:

(5.32) $$\mathbf{A} = -\omega^2 \mathbf{R}$$

This may at once be interpreted as a "restoring acceleration proportional to displacement." Now we may evaluate $\mathbf{A}$ for the specific cases required:

$$\mathbf{A} = +b\omega^2\mathbf{I} \qquad \text{when } \mathbf{R} = -b\mathbf{I}$$
$$\mathbf{A} = \mathbf{O} \qquad \text{when } \mathbf{R} = \mathbf{O}$$
$$\mathbf{A} = -b\omega^2\mathbf{I} \qquad \text{when } \mathbf{R} = +b\mathbf{I}$$

Tangential and Normal Components of Acceleration. Having examined these special illustrations, let us return to the general treatment of acceleration. Using the expression $\mathbf{V} = v\mathbf{T}$,

$$\mathbf{A} = \frac{d}{dt}(v\mathbf{T}) = \frac{dv}{dt}\mathbf{T} + v\frac{d\mathbf{T}}{dt}$$

This is a very intuitive expression for the acceleration. Here we discover explicitly that the tangential component of the acceleration vector is the *rate of increase of speed*.

(5.33) $$a_T = \frac{dv}{dt} = \dot{v}$$

A more instructive form of the second term is easily obtained by substituting the value of $d\mathbf{T}/dt$ obtained in (5.28). For the normal component we get

(5.34) $$a_N = v^2\kappa = \frac{v^2}{\rho}$$

Note that this normal component is merely the *centripetal acceleration* which we discovered in the second example. The total acceleration, then, may be written

(5.35) $$\mathbf{A} = a_T\mathbf{T} + a_N\mathbf{N} = \frac{dv}{dt}\mathbf{T} + \frac{v^2}{\rho}\mathbf{N} = \dot{v}\mathbf{T} + v^2\kappa\mathbf{N}$$

This is one of the central equations of kinematics. The student will find it instructive to interpret each of the three examples already studied in terms of this general equation. For straight-line motion, the curvature is zero. For uniform speed, a_T is zero. Let us now examine a problem which will involve somewhat fuller use of (5.35).

Example 4

The position of a moving particle is given by

$$\mathbf{R} = 2t\mathbf{I} - 3t^2\mathbf{J} + 1.5\mathbf{K} \qquad \text{ft, sec}$$

Find v, $\mathbf{T}$, a_T, a_N for $t = 0.25$ sec.

Solution

Differentiating, we obtain

$$\mathbf{V} = 2\mathbf{I} - 6t\mathbf{J} = 2\mathbf{I} - 1.5\mathbf{J}$$

From this we deduce: $v = 2.5$ ft/sec and $\mathbf{T} = 0.8\mathbf{I} - 0.6\mathbf{J}$ at $t = 0.25$. Taking the next derivative, $\mathbf{A} = -6\mathbf{J}$. The normal and tangential accelerations may be computed thus: $a_T = \mathbf{A} \cdot \mathbf{T} = 3.6$ positive, so speed is increasing. $a_N\mathbf{N} = \mathbf{A} - a_T\mathbf{T} = -6\mathbf{J} - 3.6(0.8\mathbf{I} - 0.6\mathbf{J}) = -2.88\mathbf{I} - 3.84\mathbf{J}$. The magnitude of this vector is

$$a_N = 4.8 \text{ ft/sec}^2$$

Note that we can easily devise a kinematic method for computing the radius of curvature of a curve. Applying the method to our example,

(5.36) $$\rho = \frac{v^2}{a_N} = \frac{6.25}{4.8} = 1.3 \text{ ft}$$

EXERCISES

34. The position of a particle traveling along a straight line is given by

$$\mathbf{R} = 5\mathbf{J} + 0.5t^2\mathbf{I}$$

Draw a diagram showing $\mathbf{R}$, $\mathbf{V}$, and $\mathbf{A}$ at $t = 0, 1, 4$ sec

35. The position of a particle in a helical trajectory is given by

$$\mathbf{R} = 4 \cos 2t\mathbf{I} + 4 \sin 2t\mathbf{J} + 6t\mathbf{K} \qquad \text{m, sec}$$

At $t = 0.785$ sec, find v, $\mathbf{T}$, a_T, a_N, ρ.

36. The position of a particle in the xy plane is given by

$$x = 30.0t \qquad y = -10.0t^2 \qquad \text{ft, sec}$$

Find for $t = 2$ the speed and the normal component of acceleration.

37. A particle starts from rest and travels around a circle of radius 10 cm with a speed proportional to the time. If it takes 2 sec for the first complete revolution, what is the magnitude of the normal and tangential components of acceleration after 3 sec?

38. A particle is moving around a circle of radius 2 ft so that the distance s along the arc from a certain point on the circumference t sec after starting is $s = 0.5t^3 + t^2$. Find a_N and a_T for $t = 2$ sec.

39. The position vector of an oscillating particle is given by

$$\mathbf{R} = \sin t\mathbf{I} + t\mathbf{J}$$

Find for $t = 1.571$ sec the normal and tangential components of the acceleration.

40. The distance s in centimeters from a fixed point O measured along a circle of radius 12 cm traveled at time t is given for a particle P by $s = 3t + 0.75t^2$. Compute the magnitude of the acceleration for $t = 2$ sec.

41. Given

$$v = 3s^2 - 12s$$

where s is the distance from a fixed reference point along a curved path. For what s is the tangential component of the acceleration equal to zero?

5.7. RADIAL AND TRANSVERSE COMPONENTS

It might seem that two sets of reference vectors **I**, **J**, **K** and **T**, **N**, **B** would suffice for handling kinematic situations. On the whole this is true. When one is discussing theories of motion, one is likely to favor the *intrinsic vectors* **T**, **N**, and **B**, which depend only on the shape of the path and the sense of motion along *it*. In solving numerical problems the *fixed vectors* **I**, **J**, and **K** are a natural basis for analytical procedures. There are some circumstances, however, that suggest just as naturally the use of unit vectors based on the direction of a position vector, so we shall pause briefly to develop this additional machinery for *motion in the xy plane*. This will require us to study the derivatives of the unit radial vector $\mathbf{L} = 1\underline{/\theta}$. Suppose that, during a time interval t to $t + \Delta t$, **L** changes in direction from **L** to **L**′ as in Fig. 5.21. Then, following the pattern used in evaluating $d\mathbf{T}/d\psi$, we may observe that the quotient of the difference $\mathbf{L}' - \mathbf{L} = \Delta\mathbf{L}$ divided by the angular displacement $\Delta\theta$ is a vector whose length approaches unity as smaller and smaller values of $\Delta\theta$ are considered and whose direction is perpendicular in the limit to **L**. Our conclusion is that the corresponding derivative is a unit vector perpendicular to **L**. For the case where θ is increasing, this is denoted by **M** (otherwise for decreasing θ by $-\mathbf{M}$).

$$(5.37) \qquad \frac{d\mathbf{L}}{d\theta} = \frac{d}{d\theta}(1\underline{/\theta}) = 1\underline{/\theta + 90°} = \mathbf{M}$$

(for increasing θ).

$$(5.38) \qquad \mathbf{M} \cdot \mathbf{M} = 1 \qquad \mathbf{M} \cdot \mathbf{L} = 0$$

Note that as in the other cases we have a right-handed triad of reference unit vectors: **K**, **L**, **M**.

Next we must consider the derivative of **M**. Since $\mathbf{M} = 1\underline{/\theta + 90°}$, it is apparent that, for increasing θ,

$$(5.39) \qquad \frac{d\mathbf{M}}{d\theta} = 1\underline{/\theta + 90° + 90°} = -\mathbf{L}$$

Finally, applying the chain rule for differentiation as in similar cases previously, we get (cf. Exercises 6 and 15)

$$(5.40) \qquad \dot{\mathbf{L}} = \dot{\theta}\mathbf{M} \qquad \dot{\mathbf{M}} = -\dot{\theta}\mathbf{L}$$

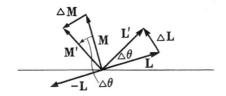

Figure
5.21

We are now in a position to derive expressions for velocity and acceleration in terms of the *radial unit vector* **L** and the *transverse unit vector* **M** for motion in a plane (see Fig. 5.22).   Starting with the familiar relation $\mathbf{R} = r\mathbf{L}$, which we differentiate with respect to t, we obtain

$$(5.41) \qquad\qquad \mathbf{V} = \dot{r}\mathbf{L} + r\dot{\theta}\mathbf{M}$$

A second differentiation yields the acceleration.   Since this affords good practice in routine manipulations, only the result is stated now.   The details are left for Exercise 46.

$$(5.42) \qquad\qquad \mathbf{A} = (\ddot{r} - r\dot{\theta}^2)\mathbf{L} + (2\dot{r}\dot{\theta} + r\ddot{\theta})\mathbf{M}$$

Note that the transverse component is equal to $(1/r)\, d/dt\, (r^2\dot{\theta})$.

Example I

A metal collar slides outward at a uniform radial speed of 50 ft/sec along the spoke of a wheel rotating uniformly at 10 rad/sec.   For the moment when its distance from the center is 4 ft, compute the magnitudes of the acceleration and the velocity.

Solution

First, applying (5.41),

$$\mathbf{V} = 50\mathbf{L} + 4(10)\mathbf{M}$$

This is a vector of magnitude 64 ft/sec.   Next, applying (5.42),

$$\mathbf{A} = -400\mathbf{L} + 1{,}000\mathbf{M}$$

whose magnitude is about 1,080 ft/sec^2.   See Fig. 5.23, and note that different scales may be used in representing **V** and **A**.

Applications.   It is often convenient to combine the use of polar and rectangular formulas for velocity in plane rate problems.   From (5.41) and (5.12) we learn to identify the meanings of certain inner products:

$$(5.43) \qquad \mathbf{V}\cdot\mathbf{L} = \dot{r} \qquad \mathbf{V}\cdot\mathbf{M} = r\dot{\theta} \qquad \mathbf{V}\cdot\mathbf{I} = \dot{x} \qquad \mathbf{V}\cdot\mathbf{J} = \dot{y}$$

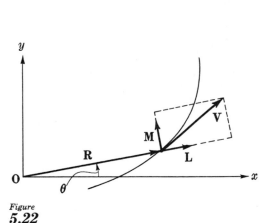

Figure
5.22

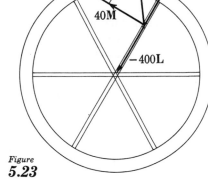

Figure
5.23

Furthermore, in the plane case, it is easy to compute $\mathbf{M}$ if $\mathbf{L}$ is known and if the general direction of the motion is clear, for if $\mathbf{L} = 1\underline{/\theta}$, then $\mathbf{M} = 1\underline{/\theta \pm 90°}$, depending on the sense of the motion. Hence, if $\mathbf{L} = \cos \theta \mathbf{I} + \sin \theta \mathbf{J}$, it follows that

$$\mathbf{M} = \cos (\theta \pm 90°)\mathbf{I} + \sin (\theta \pm 90°)\mathbf{J} = \mp \sin \theta \mathbf{I} \pm \cos \theta \mathbf{J}$$

or

(5.44) $$\pm\mathbf{M} = -\sin \theta \mathbf{I} + \cos \theta \mathbf{J}$$

Example 2

$\mathbf{R} = 4t^2\mathbf{I} - 6t\mathbf{J}$. For $t = 2$, find $\dot{r}$, $\dot{\theta}$.

Solution

Differentiating,
$$\mathbf{V} = 8t\mathbf{I} - 6\mathbf{J}$$

At $t = 2$,

$$\mathbf{R} = 16\mathbf{I} - 12\mathbf{J} \quad \mathbf{L} = 0.8\mathbf{I} - 0.6\mathbf{J} \quad \mathbf{M} = 0.6\mathbf{I} + 0.8\mathbf{J} \quad \mathbf{V} = 16\mathbf{I} - 6\mathbf{J}$$

Hence
$$\mathbf{V} \cdot \mathbf{L} = 12.8 + 3.6 = 16.4 = \dot{r}$$
$$\mathbf{V} \cdot \mathbf{M} = 9.6 - 4.8 = 4.8 = r\dot{\theta} \quad \dot{\theta} = 4.8/20 = 0.24 \text{ rad/sec}$$

Example 3

A telescopic sight which rotates about a vertical axis is used to follow a north-bound airplane which passes in horizontal flight at 120 ft/sec 200 ft directly above a building 600 ft east of an observer. How fast is the distance from observer to plane increasing after one additional second? How fast is the sight being rotated at this moment?

Solution

Let us pick axes as follows: $\mathbf{I}$ is east; $\mathbf{J}$ is north; $\mathbf{K}$ is up. You may wish to make a simple sketch to assist your visualization of this problem.
Then
$$\mathbf{R} = 600\mathbf{I} + 120t\mathbf{J} + 200\mathbf{K} \quad \mathbf{V} = 120\mathbf{J}$$
and at $t = 1$,
$$\mathbf{R} = 600\mathbf{I} + 120\mathbf{J} + 200\mathbf{K} \quad \mathbf{V} = 120\mathbf{J}$$

$$\frac{dr}{dt} = \mathbf{V} \cdot \mathbf{L} = \frac{\mathbf{V} \cdot \mathbf{R}}{r} = \frac{14,400}{644} = 22.5 \text{ ft/sec}$$

The change of line of sight involves the projection into the xy plane of the motion (since the axis is vertical). This means omitting 200$\mathbf{K}$ from the expression for $\mathbf{R}$. Denoting the projected quantities with primes, we have

$$\mathbf{R}' = 600\mathbf{I} + 120t\mathbf{J} \quad \mathbf{V}' = 120\mathbf{J} = \mathbf{V} \quad r' = 612 \text{ ft}$$

At $t = 1$,

$$\mathbf{L}' = \frac{600\mathbf{I} + 120\mathbf{J}}{612} \quad \mathbf{M}' = \frac{-120\mathbf{I} + 600\mathbf{J}}{612}$$

$$\mathbf{V}' \cdot \mathbf{M}' = r'\dot{\theta} = \frac{120 \times 600}{612} \quad \dot{\theta} = \frac{120 \times 600}{612^2} = 0.192 \text{ rad/sec}$$

EXERCISES

42. The angular position of a particle on a circle of radius 5 ft is indicated by $\theta = 3t^2$. For time $t = 0.5$ sec, compute the normal, tangential, and total acceleration of the particle. Use Eqs. (5.41) and (5.42) with the proper correlation of **T** and **N** with **L** and **M**.

43. A point moves along the spoke of a wheel so that its distance from the axis of the wheel is $r = 6 + 4 \cos t$, r in feet, t in seconds. If the wheel rotates at 0.5 rad/sec, what is the maximum speed of the point?

44. An airplane traveling at 200 ft/sec has passed overhead at a height of 100 ft. When the line of sight becomes 30° above the horizontal, how fast is this angle diminishing and how fast is the distance to the plane increasing?

45. A barge is being drawn toward a wharf by a rope which is being wound up on the wharf at the rate of 5 ft/sec. If the surface of the wharf is 20 ft above the barge, how fast is the barge moving when it is 40 ft away from the wharf?

46. Derive in detail Eq. (5.42).

5.8. RECTILINEAR KINEMATICS

The basic concepts for the quantitative study of motion have so far been introduced in a general way. Our displacements, velocities, and accelerations were vectors in widely varying directions. If the motion of a particle is restricted to a straight line, say, the x axis, then, as we have seen previously, **R**, **V**, and **A** may be expressed in terms of the unit vector **I**:

$$(5.45) \qquad \mathbf{R} = x\mathbf{I} \qquad \mathbf{V} = \dot{x}\mathbf{I} = \pm v\mathbf{I} \qquad \mathbf{A} = \ddot{x}\mathbf{I} = \pm a\mathbf{I}$$

The plus or minus alternative is indicated because v and a previously have been magnitudes and hence positive while the derivatives of x may be of either sign. Since this distinction is easily understood, we shall in this section dispense with the minus sign, letting v be negative for motion in the negative x direction. We shall write, for the purposes of this section,

$$(5.46) \qquad v = \frac{dx}{dt} = \dot{x} \qquad a = \frac{dv}{dt} = \dot{v}$$

Direction plays such a limited role in straight-line motion that it is convenient to use these scalar equations instead of the vector ones first given. The chain rule of ordinary calculus yields an alternative expression for a:

$$(5.47) \qquad a = \frac{dv}{dx}\frac{dx}{dt} = v\frac{dv}{dx}$$

The three central scalar equations so far presented are investigated in most calculus courses; so it is perhaps unnecessary to pursue them here. Considering the importance of the topic, a cursory treatment will, however, be given.

Equations (5.46) and (5.47) were presented as expressions involving derivatives. Such expressions may also be regarded as relations between differentials. Either point of view suggests the possibility of carrying out integrations. The nature of the integration depends on whether v and a happen to be regarded as functions of x or t. In the following we shall write $v(t)$ for v if it is expressed explicitly as a function of t; $v(x)$ will be used if v is a function of x. With this understanding it is easy to see that numerous possibilities arise. They are stated both in the form of simple differential equations with variables separated and in the form of definite integrals where corresponding limits of integration are employed. This means merely that at time t_0 the values x_0, v_0, and a_0 apply, while at time t the proper values are x, v, and a. This use of corresponding limits is easily seen to be equivalent to using indefinite integrals and constants of integration to be evaluated with initial or other conditions.

$$(5.48) \qquad dx = v(t)\, dt \qquad \text{or} \qquad \int_{x_0}^{x} dx = \int_{t_0}^{t} v(t)\, dt$$

$$(5.49) \qquad dt = \frac{dx}{v(x)} \qquad \text{or} \qquad \int_{t_0}^{t} dt = \int_{x_0}^{x} \frac{dx}{v(x)}$$

$$(5.50) \qquad dv = a(t)\, dt \qquad \text{or} \qquad \int_{v_0}^{v} dv = \int_{t_0}^{t} a(t)\, dt$$

$$(5.51) \qquad v\, dv = a(x)\, dx \qquad \text{or} \qquad \int_{v_0}^{v} v\, dv = \int_{x_0}^{x} a(x)\, dx$$

$$(5.52) \qquad dt = \frac{dv}{a(v)} \qquad \text{or} \qquad \int_{t_0}^{t} dt = \int_{v_0}^{v} \frac{dv}{a(v)}$$

$$(5.53) \qquad \frac{v\, dv}{a(v)} = dx \qquad \text{or} \qquad \int_{x_0}^{x} dx = \int_{v_0}^{v} \frac{v\, dv}{a(v)}$$

These long expressions assuredly are not to be memorized. The student should rather commit to memory (5.46) and (5.47). Then he should practice manipulating these expressions until he can see how (5.48) to (5.53) can be at once deduced.

Example I

A point moves on the x axis with speed given by $v = 2x^2$. At time $t = 0$, it is at $x = 1$. Find the time required for it to reach $x = 2$ and the acceleration at $x = 2$. Units are feet, seconds, etc.

Solution

$$v = \frac{dx}{dt} = 2x^2 \qquad dt = \frac{dx}{2x^2}$$

$$t = \int_{1}^{2} \frac{dx}{2x^2} \qquad \text{or} \qquad t = 0.25 \text{ sec}$$

$$a = v\frac{dv}{dx} = (2x^2)(4x) = 8x^3 = 64 \text{ ft/sec}^2$$

Example 2. Freely Falling Bodies

Near the surface of the earth objects experience a downward acceleration ranging in this vicinity from 9.78 m/sec² in Central America to 9.82 m/sec² in Alaska. A "standard value," 9.80665 m/sec² or 32.174 ft/sec², rounded off to 9.81 or 32.2 will be used in problems here. At any one locality this acceleration for free fall may be considered as constant, provided that air friction can be neglected. In Exercise 47 the student will derive some formulas analogous to those used in elementary physics.

Phase Spaces. In various parts of physics and allied fields use is often made of *phase space*. In a phase space, velocity (or momentum) components are treated as additional coordinates. Thus coordinates appropriate for studying the motion of a particle in ordinary space would be $(x,y,z,\dot{x},\dot{y},\dot{z})$. The corresponding six-dimensional phase space can be studied as a whole or in terms of projections into the *configuration space* with coordinates (x,y,z) and the *velocity space* with coordinates $(\dot{x},\dot{y},\dot{z})$. Each point in such a phase space represents complete information about an instantaneous state of a particle, for it tells where the particle is and what its velocity is. As a particle traces out its trajectory in the laboratory (which corresponds to part of the configuration space), the representative point in phase space has its own trajectory. Motion of a particle on a single line is especially suitable for study by means of a phase space because only two coordinates $(x,\dot{x})$ are involved.

Example 3

A phase-space representation of Example 1 is shown in Fig. 5.24. Note that the acceleration equals the product of the slope dv/dx by the ordinate v.

EXERCISES

47. Given the following: a is a constant; subscript 0 indicates values at time $t = 0$. Using the methods of this section, verify the following equations:

$$v^2 - v_0^2 = 2a(x - x_0)$$

$$x - x_0 = v_0 t + \tfrac{1}{2}at^2$$

$$\frac{x - x_0}{t} = v_{\text{eff}} = \frac{1}{2}(v + v_0)$$

48. A point moves along the x axis according to the law $v = 2x + 3$ (ft, sec). What is its acceleration when it passes through the origin? How long does it take the point to move from the origin to the point $x = 13.5$?

49. A point moves along the x axis, starting from the origin, according to the equation

$$v = \frac{2}{1 + x} \quad \text{cm, sec}$$

How long does it take the point to reach the position $x = 4$ cm? For what x would the acceleration be -4 cm/sec^2?

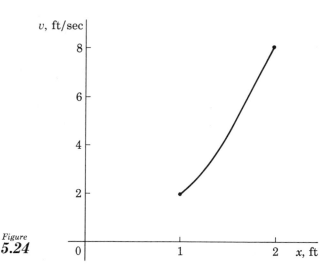

Figure
5.24

50. The acceleration (centimeters per second per second) of a particle falling vertically in a resisting medium is given in terms of the speed (centimeters per second) by

$$a = 5 - 2v$$

If the particle falls from rest, how long in seconds will it take it to acquire a speed of 1.25 cm/sec?

51. The speed of a moving particle sliding along the x axis is given as $v = -x$ (ft, sec). How long does it take to travel from $x = 5$ to $x = 3$? What is the acceleration at $x = 5$?

52. The acceleration of a particle moving along the x axis is given as $a = 6t - 3t^2$. At $t = 0$, the particle is at rest at $x = 1$. Find the speed at $t = 1$.

5.9. SIMPLE HARMONIC MOTION

This section is devoted to a single outstandingly significant example of rectilinear motion. A more general form of the defining equation appeared in an earlier section [see Eq. (5.32)]. Limiting the motion to the x axis, we start with

(5.54) $a = -\omega^2 x$

This equation merely tells us that the motion is characterized by a restoring acceleration proportional to the displacement from the origin. What is the nature of the motion? This is our problem, to be solved by the methods of the preceding section. If you have already studied linear homogeneous second-order differential equations, you may wish to rewrite (5.54) as

$$\frac{d^2x}{dt^2} + \omega^2 x = 0$$

and to use standard procedures to arrive at solutions such as Eq. (5.56). The following details, however, are sufficient for present purposes and require only calculus. Starting with

$$v \, dv = -\omega^2 x \, dx \qquad \text{or} \qquad \int_{v_0}^{v} v \, dv = -\omega^2 \int_{x_0}^{x} x \, dx$$

we get

$$v^2 - v_0^2 = \omega^2 x_0^2 - \omega^2 x^2$$

This implies that

(5.55)   *The quantity $v^2 + \omega^2 x^2$ must be a constant for the motion governed by (5.54).*

Such an assertion immediately suggests that the motion is oscillatory, the maximum speed v_m and the maximum displacement (or amplitude) x_m being related by

$$v_m^2 = \omega^2 x_m^2$$

Since the position of maximum displacement corresponds to zero speed, we have, from (5.55),

$$v^2 + \omega^2 x^2 = 0 + \omega^2 x_m^2$$

or

$$v = \frac{dx}{dt} = \omega(x_m^2 - x^2)^{\frac{1}{2}}$$

Using the method of the preceding section, letting $t = t_0$ for $x = 0$, we get

$$\omega \int_{t_0}^{t} dt = \int_0^x \frac{dx}{(x_m^2 - x^2)^{\frac{1}{2}}}$$

Integrating, we have

$$\omega(t - t_0) = \sin^{-1} \frac{x}{x_m}$$

or

(5.56) $$x = x_m \sin \omega(t - t_0)$$

The angle $-\omega t_0$ is often called the epoch angle, denoted by ϵ, and Eq. (5.56) is written

(5.57) $$x = x_m \sin (\omega t + \epsilon)$$

If ϵ happens to be chosen as $90° + \epsilon'$, the equation becomes

(5.58) $$x = x_m \cos (\omega t + \epsilon')$$

This may be compared with Sec. 5.6, Example 3. Many other equivalent forms are available and often used. In any case, the *period* of an oscillation described by (5.54) is well known:

(5.59) $$\tau = \frac{2\pi}{\omega}$$

It will pay the student to remember something equivalent to the following:

(5.60) *A motion governed by the equation* $a = -\omega^2 x$ *is a simple harmonic oscillation of period* $2\pi/\omega$.

EXERCISES

53. A point moves along the x axis according to the law $a + 4x = 0$. The largest value of x is 10. With what speed does the point go through the origin? How long does it take the point to go from $x = 2$ to $x = 6$?

54. Prove that the projection onto a diameter of a particle traveling at uniform speed around a circle is in simple harmonic motion.

55. A point in simple harmonic motion has a period of 2 sec and an amplitude of 3 ft. What is the maximum speed? What is the maximum acceleration?

56. Discuss as fully as you can the motion of a particle subject to the relation

$$a = -6(x - 4)$$

5.10. INTEGRAL CALCULUS FOR VECTORS

Up to this point we have considered only the differential calculus of vectors. To each vector function $\mathbf{R}$ of a scalar variable t we have seen how to assign, in all but exceptional cases, a new vector function, the derivative of $\mathbf{R}$ with respect to t:

(5.61) $$\mathbf{V}(t) = \frac{d\mathbf{R}(t)}{dt}$$

On the other hand, given a suitable vector function $\mathbf{V}(t)$, one can call $\mathbf{R}(t)$ an integral of $\mathbf{V}(t)$. Such integrals, as in scalar calculus, may differ by a constant (vector) of integration. Copying the usual nomenclature for the indefinite integral, we get

(5.62) $$\mathbf{R}(t) = \int \mathbf{V}(t) \, dt$$

Suppose that another pair of functions $\mathbf{R}'$ and $\mathbf{V}'$ are related similarly. Then we already know that

$$\frac{d}{dt}(\mathbf{R}+\mathbf{R}') = \mathbf{V}+\mathbf{V}'$$

Consequently, omitting constants of integration,

(5.63) $$\int (\mathbf{V}+\mathbf{V}')\,dt = \mathbf{R}+\mathbf{R}' = \int \mathbf{V}\,dt + \int \mathbf{V}'\,dt$$

In a similar manner we may verify for constants c and $\mathbf{C}$ and functions u and $\mathbf{V}$

(5.64) $$\int c\mathbf{V}\,dt = c\int \mathbf{V}\,dt \qquad \int \mathbf{C}u\,dt = \mathbf{C}\int u\,dt$$

$$\int \mathbf{C}\cdot\mathbf{V}\,dt = \mathbf{C}\cdot\int \mathbf{V}\,dt$$

Applying these conclusions, we get

(5.65) $$\int \mathbf{V}\,dt = \mathbf{I}\int v_x\,dt + \mathbf{J}\int v_y\,dt + \mathbf{K}\int v_z\,dt$$

This shows that (5.62) is equivalent to

(5.66) $$x = \int v_x\,dt \qquad y = \int v_y\,dt \qquad z = \int v_z\,dt$$

Proceeding from the point of view of definite integration, we may consider, for a range of the scalar variable t, say, from t_0 to t_1, an expression of the sort

$$\lim_{\Delta t \to 0} \Sigma\, \mathbf{V}(t)\,\Delta t$$

where it is understood that each $\mathbf{V}(t)$ is evaluated for some t in the corresponding Δt (see Fig. 5.25). One way of interpreting this limit is by resolving into components:

$$\lim_{\Delta t \to 0} \Sigma\, \mathbf{V}(t)\,\Delta t = \left[\lim_{\Delta t \to 0} \Sigma\, v_x(t)\,\Delta t\right]\mathbf{I} + \left[\lim_{\Delta t \to 0} \Sigma\, v_y(t)\,\Delta t\right]\mathbf{J} + \left[\lim_{\Delta t \to 0} \Sigma\, v_z(t)\,\Delta t\right]\mathbf{K}$$

The array on the right is immediately interpreted:

(5.67) $$\lim_{\Delta t \to 0} \Sigma\, \mathbf{V}(t)\,\Delta t = \mathbf{I}\int_{t_0}^{t_1} v_x(t)\,dt + \mathbf{J}\int_{t_0}^{t_1} v_y(t)\,dt + \mathbf{K}\int_{t_0}^{t_1} v_z(t)\,dt$$

Here the burden of proof has been shifted to the scalar point of view, but in the interest of brevity this ruse seems desirable. Needless to say, the last expression suggests a symbol for our limit:

(5.68) $$\lim_{\Delta t \to 0} \sum_{t_0}^{t_1} \mathbf{V}(t)\,\Delta t = \int_{t_0}^{t_1} \mathbf{V}(t)\,dt$$

Combining (5.67) and (5.68), one sees that definite integrals of this type must have the usual properties for scalar integrals. In particular, assuming (5.61), we have

(5.69) $$\int_{t_0}^{t_1} \mathbf{V}(t)\,dt = \mathbf{R}(t_1) - \mathbf{R}(t_0)$$

Figure
5.25

Example I.   Projectile Motion

A particle in motion near the earth is, neglecting friction, subject to a constant acceleration which we may express by

$$\mathbf{A} = \frac{d\mathbf{V}}{dt} = -g\mathbf{J}$$

Integrating, we have

$$\mathbf{V} = \int - g\mathbf{J}\, dt + \mathbf{C}$$

or

$$\frac{d\mathbf{R}}{dt} = \mathbf{V} = -gt\mathbf{J} + \mathbf{V_0}$$

where the constant of integration $\mathbf{C}$ is evaluated as the initial velocity $\mathbf{V_0}$.   Integrating again,

(5.70) $$\mathbf{R} = \int (-gt\mathbf{J} + \mathbf{V_0})\, dt + \mathbf{C}'$$

or

$$\mathbf{R} = -\tfrac{1}{2}gt^2\mathbf{J} + \mathbf{V_0}t$$

for if we initiate the motion at the origin, it follows that $\mathbf{C}' = \mathbf{O}$.   The physical interpretation of this equation is very interesting.   The position of the projectile at time t (see Fig. 5.26) coincides with the position to which a particle would have fallen freely from rest if it had been dropped at time $t = 0$ from the corresponding point on the original line of sight (i.e., the point with position vector $t\mathbf{V_0}$).   It is interesting to compare the scalar forms of this equation.   Taking $\mathbf{V_0}$ in the xy plane at an elevation α, we have

(5.71)
$$x = (v_0 \cos \alpha)t$$
$$y = -\tfrac{1}{2}gt^2 + (v_0 \sin \alpha)t$$

These equations are familiar to most students of the calculus.

Example 2

A particle travels from $t = 0$ to $t = 3$ with velocity

$$\mathbf{V} = 4t\mathbf{I} - 3t^2\mathbf{J}$$

What is the net displacement?

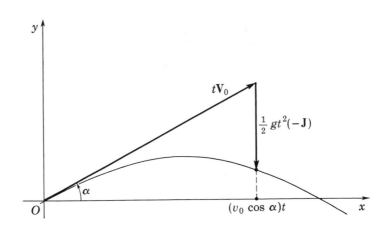

Figure
5.26

Solution

$$\mathbf{R} = \int_0^3 \mathbf{V}\,dt = 2t^2\mathbf{I} - t^3\mathbf{J}\Big|_0^3 = 18\mathbf{I} - 27\mathbf{J}$$

Example 3.   Centroids

A nonkinematic example of definite integration involves the concept of centroid. Suppose that we have given a rigid body and that we divide it up, as in ordinary integral calculus, into convenient volume elements.   Then, from each element, pick a point $\mathbf{R}$.   If we use the volume of the element Δv as a scalar multiplier of $\mathbf{R}$, then add, and divide by a total volume, we get a *weighted mean* of the $\mathbf{R}$'s, where volume is the *weight function*.   Passing to the limit, we have, by (5.68), a definite integral (divided by the volume)

(5.72)
$$\bar{\mathbf{R}} = \frac{1}{\mathrm{vol}}\int_v \mathbf{R}\,dv = \frac{1}{\mathrm{vol}}\lim_{\Delta v \to 0}\sum_v \mathbf{R}\,\Delta v$$

The point $\bar{\mathbf{R}}$ is called the *centroid*.   The limits of the integration must be put in specifically when specific coordinates are chosen and the integration "set up" for actual computation.   We indicate this part of the transaction here merely by the letter v under the integral sign.   This means that, if the integration is actually carried out, the limits shall be so chosen as to cover the whole volume.   For *our* purposes it is more important to understand the *idea* of (5.72) thoroughly than to be able to do heroic feats of integration.   Computational technique is, of course, important and should be acquired in due time.

Scalar forms of (5.72) may already be familiar:

(5.73)
$$\bar{x} = \frac{1}{\mathrm{vol}}\int_v x\,dv \qquad \bar{y} = \frac{1}{\mathrm{vol}}\int_v y\,dv \qquad \bar{z} = \frac{1}{\mathrm{vol}}\int_v z\,dv$$

In all these expressions, $\mathrm{vol} = \int dv$.   The relationship between (5.72) and (5.73) is given by

(5.74)
$$\bar{\mathbf{R}} = \bar{x}\mathbf{I} + \bar{y}\mathbf{J} + \bar{z}\mathbf{K}$$

The process here outlined could be applied to any other scalar function of a volume element.   The mass (to be defined later) is used especially often: there, if Δm is the mass of the element of volume Δv, we should write

(5.75)
$$\bar{\mathbf{R}} = \frac{1}{m}\int_m \mathbf{R}\,dm$$

Now $\bar{\mathbf{R}}$ is called the *center of mass*.   For objects of uniform density, the centroid and the center of mass coincide.   Methods of computation and more emphasis on the physical significance of these concepts will be given in Chap. 15.

Example 4.   Impulse

Another example of vector integration appears in the concept of impulse.   It is defined by expressions of the form

$$\int_{t_0}^{t_1} \mathbf{F}(t)\,dt$$

If $\mathbf{F}$ is a force varying with time, then this definite integral represents the net impulse exerted by $\mathbf{F}$ during the interval t_0 to t_1.   This important concept will figure prominently in Chap. 7.

EXERCISES

57. Plot for values of t from 0 to 4 two possible trajectories for which

$$V(t) = 10I + 2tJ$$

58. Given: $A = (h - t^2)J$ ft/sec^2 and $V_0 = v_0I$ ft/sec. Derive an expression for R at time t for a particle projected from the origin at time $t = 0$. (h is a scalar constant.)

59. (a) Get an approximate value for $\int_0^6 (3I + tJ) \, dt$ by evaluating the corresponding sum, using intervals Δt of length 1. Illustrate with a diagram. (b) Check your value for part (a) by direct integration.

60. At time t a force is given by $F = tI - 10J$ lb. What impulse is exerted between $t = 0$ and $t = 10$ sec?

61. What initial speed must a projectile have in order to attain an altitude of 6,400 ft: (a) When the initial angle of elevation is 90°? (b) When the initial angle of elevation is 30°? (Assume gravity to be constant and friction to be negligible.)

62. Use (5.72) to prove that the centroid of a body symmetrical in a point is its center.

63. If a body has a line or plane of symmetry, show that its centroid lies on this line or plane.

64. An object is composed of two parts: one of centroid $\bar{R}'$ and volume v', the other of centroid $\bar{R}''$ and volume v''. Prove that the centroid of the whole is

$$\bar{R} = \frac{v'\bar{R}' + v''\bar{R}''}{v' + v''}$$

65. Find the centroid of a set of three small identical spheres set each at a vertex of a large triangle. (Use the result of Exercise 64.)

66. A uniform wire 2 ft long is bent to form a circular arc of radius 1 ft. Where is the centroid? (HINT: Take origin at center. $dv = ra \, d\theta$, where a is area of cross section of wire and r is radius of the circle.)

67. A uniform 12-ft wire is bent to form a triangle of sides 3, 4, and 5 ft. Find the centroid.

REVIEW EXERCISES

68. The position of a particle moving on a helical path is given by

$$R = 5 \cos tI + 5 \sin tJ + 4tK$$

(Here it is understood that t is expressed in seconds and that $\cos t$ is the cosine of an angle of t rad. R is expressed in meters.) Show that the particle has uniform speed, and evaluate this speed.

69. The path of a particle is given by

$$R = 3tI - 0.25t^4J + 2t^2K \qquad \text{ft, sec}$$

Evaluate for $t = 1$ sec in IJK form the vectors $\dot{R}$ and $\ddot{R}$. Find in IJK form the unit vector $T = V/|V|$ for $t = 1$.

70. Two media are separated by a plane. P is any point on one side of the plane, and Q any point on the other side. A particle which travels at speed v_1 in the first medium and at speed v_2 in the second medium is to go from P to Q in the shortest possible time. Show that Snell's law (sines of angles with normal to plane are proportional to speeds) is obeyed.

71. An automobile heads due north at 60 mph. A paper streamer on the automobile

points 60° east of south. The actual wind is toward the east. What is the actual wind speed?

72. A boy on a train traveling at 60 ft/sec throws a baseball which travels at right angles to the train (as viewed by a fixed observer on the ground) at 25 ft/sec. How fast would the same effort cause the ball to travel if thrown on a ball diamond?

73. A cargo ship *C* capable of traveling at 26 mph gets a radio report of a low-flying bomber *B* 15 miles away in a direction 60° west of north (see Fig. 5.27). The bomber is taking a course due east at 100 mph.

(*a*) Draw a vector diagram to show the velocity of the bomber *relative to the ship* when the ship flees due south at top speed. Label vectors clearly.

(*b*) Under the conditions described in (*a*), how close does the bomber get to the ship?

(*c*) In what direction should the ship have traveled in order that this distance of closest approach be maximized?

74. A hiker approaching a crossroad sees a friend on a bicycle going 10 mph along the other road. If the bicycle is $\frac{1}{2}$ mile away when it goes through the intersection, if the roads intersect at 90°, and if the hiker can run across country at 8 mph, how close can he get to the cyclist?

75. A motorboat *A* is traveling with speed 10 mph northeast. Eight miles south of *A* is a motorboat *B* capable of 15 mph.

(*a*) How should the course of *B* be directed in order that *A* be overtaken as soon as possible?

(*b*) How long will it take *B* to overtake *A*?

76. An enemy warship traveling uniformly east at 30 mph is initially 7 miles northwest of a freighter. How fast must the freighter go so that the warship's distance will never be less than the original 7 miles? The freighter may sail in the optimum direction.

77. A river flows with uniform speed *u*. Two rafts a distance *l* apart are released and allowed to drift with the current downstream. A boy swims from raft *A* to raft *B* and back to *A*, always at speed *c* relative to the water. Find the time required (*a*) if the line joining *A* and *B* is perpendicular to the current and (*b*) if it is parallel to the current.

78. The center of mass of a system of two particles (one of mass m_1 at $\mathbf{R}_1$, the other of mass m_2 at $\mathbf{R}_2$) has position vector $\bar{\mathbf{R}}$ given by $(m_1 + m_2)\bar{\mathbf{R}} = m_1\mathbf{R}_1 + m_2\mathbf{R}_2$. Show that the two particle velocities *relative to the center of mass* are parallel.

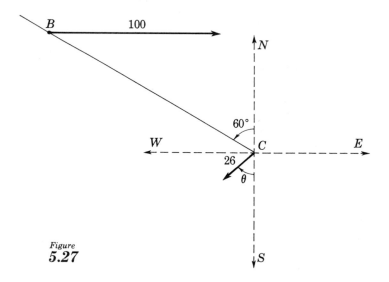

Figure
5.27

79. A particle starts from rest and travels around a circle of radius 8 ft with speed increasing at a uniform rate. At the end of 2 sec the acceleration vector makes an angle of 45° with the tangent. When will this angle be 60°?

80. The position vector of an oscillating particle is given by

$$\mathbf{R} = (2t)\mathbf{I} - \left(\frac{3}{\pi} \sin \pi t\right)\mathbf{J} \quad \text{ft, sec}$$

   For $t = 0.333$ sec, find the normal and tangential components of acceleration.

81. Q is a point on a circle of radius 12 cm. Distances measured counterclockwise around the circle from Q are denoted by s. A particle P travels around this circle with speed proportional to the square of s. At time $t = 0$, P is at the point $s = 18$ cm and is moving with speed 40.5 cm/sec.
   (a) At time $t = 0$, compute a_N, a_T, a.
   (b) For what value of t does P next reach Q?

82. The speed of a particle traveling around a circle of radius 10 cm is given at time t sec by

$$v = 30 - \frac{20}{t} \quad \text{cm/sec}$$

   At time $t = 2$ sec, find:
   (a) The angle between the acceleration $\mathbf{A}$ and the velocity $\mathbf{V}$ of the particle.
   (b) The magnitude of $\mathbf{A}$.

83. The speed with which a particle travels around a circle of radius 100 cm is given by $v = 0.125(160s - s^2)$, where s is the arc length along the circle from a fixed reference point. Find the tangential and normal components of acceleration a_T and a_N for $s = 40$ cm.

84. The position vector (components in feet) at time t (sec) of a moving point is given by

$$\mathbf{R} = 2t^2\mathbf{I} - 3t\mathbf{J} + 7\mathbf{K}$$

   Evaluate at time $t = 1$ sec each of the following (in $\mathbf{IJK}$ form when appropriate):

   (a) $\mathbf{V}$.   (b) v.   (c) $\mathbf{T}$.   (d) $\mathbf{A}$.   (e) dv/dt.

85. The position of a moving particle is given by $\mathbf{R} = 1.50\mathbf{I} - 1.00t\mathbf{J} + 0.75t^2\mathbf{K}$. Units are feet and seconds, etc. Find, for the instant $t = 0.50$ sec, each of the following:
   (a) The speed v.
   (b) The unit tangent vector $\mathbf{T}$ (in $\mathbf{IJK}$ form).
   (c) The tangential acceleration component a_T.
   (d) The normal acceleration component a_N.
   (e) The radius of curvature ρ.

86. A baseball is hit directly over first base so that its position vector (taking first base as origin) is

$$\mathbf{R} = (40t - 90)\mathbf{I} + (96t - 16t^2)\mathbf{J} \quad \text{ft}$$

   (a) What is the initial speed of the ball?
   (b) Evaluate $\mathbf{T}$ for $t = 0$ and $t = 6$ sec.
   (c) How high does the ball go?
   (d) The right fielder catches the ball on the run at a velocity of $15\mathbf{I} + 20\mathbf{K}$ ft/sec. What is the speed of the ball relative to the fielder when he catches it? (Assume that the ball is caught at the level at which it was hit.)

87. Use (5.36) as a means of deriving the following formula for radius of curvature of a plane trajectory given by $\mathbf{R} = x(t)\mathbf{I} + y(t)\mathbf{J}$:

$$\rho = \frac{(\dot{x}^2 + \dot{y}^2)^{\frac{3}{2}}}{|\dot{x}\ddot{y} - \dot{y}\ddot{x}|}$$

88. The position vector $\mathbf{R}$ of a fast-moving target in the xy plane climbing in the direction of a unit vector $\mathbf{T}$ at constant speed v is given at time t by (see Fig. 5.28)

$$\mathbf{R} = r\mathbf{L} = h\mathbf{J} + (vt)\mathbf{T}$$

where h and v are scalar constants, and $\mathbf{J}$ and $\mathbf{T}$ are constant unit vectors.   Express in terms of $\mathbf{T}$, $\mathbf{L}$, $\mathbf{M}$, r, v:
(a) The rate at which the target's distance from the origin $\mathbf{O}$ is increasing.
(b) The angular speed ω with which $\mathbf{L}$ rotates.

89. The position vector of a moving particle is given by

$$\mathbf{R} = (6 + 2 \sin t)\mathbf{I} + 5t\mathbf{J} \qquad \text{ft, sec}$$

For $t = 1.0$ sec, find:
(a) The radial component of $\mathbf{V}$.
(b) The transverse component of $\mathbf{V}$.
(c) The radial component of $\mathbf{A}$.
(d) The transverse component of $\mathbf{A}$.

90. A wheel of radius 24 in. rolls without slipping along a level road at 8 in./sec.   An insect walks outward along a spoke at the speed (relative to the wheel) of 5 in./sec. What is the actual speed of the insect at the instant when his spoke is vertical upward and his distance from the center is 1 ft?

91. A brick is dropped from the top of a high building.   Ten feet below the starting point is the top of a window 10 ft high.   How long does the brick spend in passing the window?

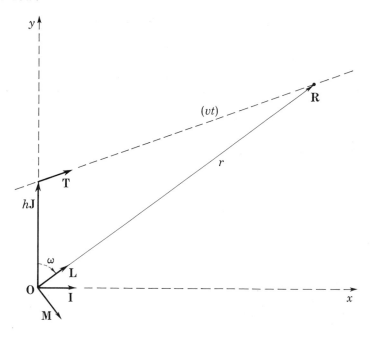

Figure
5.28

92. A man can throw a ball at 100 ft/sec. He stands on a platform 50 ft above the ground. How high above the ground can he throw the ball? With what maximum and what minimum speeds can he make the ball hit the ground?

93. A train starts from a station with a constant acceleration and reaches a speed of 60 mph in 2 min. It runs for 10 min at this speed and then reduces its speed uniformly during the next 3 min and stops at the next station. What in miles is the distance between the stations?

94. A point starts from the origin along the positive x axis with a velocity (meters per second) inversely proportional to $x + 5$ (m). It takes it 10 sec to go a distance of 20 m. What was the starting velocity?

95. A horse runs 10 mph on a circular mile track in the center of which is a lamppost which casts a shadow of the horse on a straight fence tangent to the track at the starting point. Find the acceleration of both horse and shadow (in miles per hour per hour) when he is $\frac{1}{8}$ mile from the starting point.

96. A particle moving on the x axis with an acceleration given by

$$a = 2.52 - 0.07t^2 \qquad \text{ft/sec}^2 \text{ for } t \text{ in sec}$$

starts from rest at the origin at $t = 0$.
(a) What is its speed at time $t = 3$ sec?
(b) When does the speed start to decrease?
(c) What is the maximum value of x?
(d) For what t does the particle return to the origin?

97. At time $t = 0$ sec, a particle which travels on the x axis is at the point $x = 10$ cm. If the speed of the motion is given by $v = 0.02x^2$ (cm, sec):
(a) What is the initial acceleration?
(b) Where is the particle at $t = 2.5$ sec?

98. A particle in motion on the x axis has an acceleration given by

$$u = 15 \quad 5x \qquad \text{ft/sec}^2, \text{ ft}$$

When $x = 0$ ft, the speed $v = 3$ ft/sec.
(a) Find v for $x = 3$ ft.
(b) How long does it take the particle to travel from $x = 0$ to $x = 3$?
(c) Characterize the motion.

99. The velocity of a point moving from rest at the origin along the positive x axis is given by

$$v = 20t^{\frac{1}{2}} \qquad \text{cm/sec, sec}$$

(a) Find the position of the particle for $t = 16$ sec.
(b) What is the acceleration when $x = 343$ cm?

100. The velocity of a point starting from rest at the origin and traveling on the x axis is given by

$$v = 20x^{\frac{1}{3}} \qquad \text{cm/sec, cm}$$

(a) What is the acceleration for $x = 3,600$?
(b) How long does it take the point to reach the position specified in (a)?

101. A particle in motion along the x axis in a damping medium may have a velocity-dependent acceleration of the form

$$a = a_0 - bv^n$$

where n depends on the speed and both a_0 and b are positive. Assume that the particle starts from rest at the origin.

(a) By inspection of the above equation determine the *terminal speed* v_t which the particle attains.

(b) For the cases $n = 1$ and $n = 2$, derive the formulas for the time t and position x at which the particle attains speed $\bar{v}$, where $0 < \bar{v} < v_t$. Use integral tables if necessary.

102. A particle moves on the x axis starting from rest at the origin subject to the equation

$$a = 12 - 0.5v \qquad \text{mks units}$$

(a) How many seconds will elapse before it has attained a speed of 12 m/sec?

(b) How far from the origin will the particle be after 1 sec?

103. A particle in simple harmonic motion with period τ and amplitude r obviously has an average speed $4r/\tau$.

(a) At what distance from the equilibrium position is the particle actually traveling at this average speed?

(b) What time intervals elapse between successive moments when the particle has this absolute speed?

(c) How does this average speed compare with the maximum speed?

104. A particle traveling in the xy plane is accelerated according to the equation

$$\mathbf{A} = -b\dot{\theta}\mathbf{L}$$

for some scalar constant b. Show that the hodograph (that is, the locus of points having as position vectors the velocity vector of the given motion) is a circle of radius b.

105. A gun emplacement is located on a coastal mountain 1,000 ft above sea level. It fires projectiles with a muzzle speed of 2,000 ft/sec at a naval surface target. It takes the projectiles 30 sec to reach the target. Find the range (horizontal) and angle of elevation of the gun. How high above sea level do the projectiles go?

106. A 5-ft uniform wire is bent to form an isosceles triangle with equal sides of length 2 ft. Find its centroid.

107. A particle moves on the x axis according to the equation

$$x = 10 \cos 2t$$

Plot the corresponding trajectory in the phase space having coordinates $(x,\dot{x})$.

108. Suppose that a particle moves on the x axis according to the law $x = e^t$, where x is in centimeters, t in seconds. Plot points on the trajectory in $x\dot{x}$ space for $t = -\infty$, -1, -0.5, 0, 0.5, 1, 2.

109. A tennis ball is dropped vertically from rest at a point at a distance $y = 4$ ft above the floor. Suppose that the rebound also is vertical to half the initial height. Plot a trajectory in $y\dot{y}$ space for several successive bounces.

110. The maximum range of a projectile is 2,000 yd. At what two angles of elevation will the range be 1,500 yd? (This assumes, of course, that the initial velocity always has the same magnitude.)

111. A projectile is shot uphill. Show that, for maximum range, the initial velocity vector should lie halfway between the vertical and the slope of the hill.

112. A particle moves in a plane orbit in such a way that the transverse component of its acceleration always vanishes (i.e., its acceleration is purely radial relative to some origin $\mathbf{O}$). Show that the angular speed of the radius vector $\mathbf{R}$ from $\mathbf{O}$ to the particle varies inversely as the square of the length of $\mathbf{R}$.

CHAPTER SIX

PARTICLE DYNAMICS

The laws of Newton state very clearly that, relative to inertial frames, accelerated motion is always the result of unbalanced forces. In Chap. 3 detailed attention has been given to sets of forces and to conditions for their equivalence. In Chap. 5 we have devised techniques and terminology for the study of motion. It is now time to bring these two lines of study together by showing in detail the relation between accelerated motion and the forces which cause it. The science of forces and their effects is called *dynamics*.

6.1. MASS OF A PARTICLE

The important notion of mass is often used as a primitive concept in treatises on mechanics. In this course, in order that we might have practice in visualizing and using vectors at an early stage, force was introduced first, and hence as a matter of convenience was taken as fundamental. This requires us to define mass in terms of force, length, and time, in order to keep the number of undefined concepts convenient. We approach this problem by first adopting as a postulate a special form of Newton's second law:

(6.1) *A particle subjected to a single force* $\mathbf{F}$ *experiences an acceleration* $\mathbf{A}$ *parallel to* $\mathbf{F}$. *The magnitude ratio* f/a *is a constant for a given particle.*

This fact is subject to experimental verification. For instance, one could use a calibrated spring to apply a variety of horizontal forces to a toy car with excellent wheel bearings or to a puck supported by escaping carbon dioxide. Such experiments would show within experimental error both aspects of Proposition (6.1). It is on this postulate that the theory of this chapter is based. The constant ratio of force magnitude to acceleration magnitude will be called the *mass* of the particle. Since this concept represents a quantitative measure of disinclination toward acceleration, it is often called *inertial mass*.

(6.2)
$$m = \frac{f}{a}$$

To illustrate the use of the postulate, suppose that two particles act on each other in such a way that the only unbalanced force on each particle is the force of interaction with the other. An example often used in physics demonstrations is that of two toy cars which "collide" and separate, with the force of interaction dependent on springs as in Fig. 6.1 or on repelling magnets. By Newton's reaction law (see Sec. 3.3), the forces on the two cars are equal and opposite, though varying in magnitude. Hence, by Eq. (6.2),

(6.3) $$m_1 a_1 = m_2 a_2$$

at every instant of the interaction. Suppose that t_0 is the time of closest approach of the colliding cars. At t_0 the two cars have equal velocity, of magnitude v_0. At any later time t, say, at the moment the force of interaction becomes zero, we have [cf. Eq. (5.50)]

$$v_1 = -v_0 + \int_{t_0}^{t} a_1 \, dt \qquad v_2 = v_0 + \int_{t_0}^{t} a_2 \, dt$$

Multiply the first of these equations by m_1, the second by m_2, and substitute (6.3), assuming m_1 and m_2 do not vary with time. We then get

(6.4) $$m_1(v_1 + v_0) = m_2(v_2 - v_0)$$

Since the three velocities can be observed and measured, we have here a way of determining a mass ratio without using calibrated springs. This is a standard approach in treatments where mass is taken as fundamental. For us it could serve as one means of verifying experimentally the following significant fact about particle masses:

(6.5) *The ratio of weights for two bodies at a given locality is equal to the ratio of masses.*

We anticipated this by defining the unit of force, the newton, in terms of the weight of a standard kilogram. Since the kilogram is the unit of mass in the mks system, we can always write, for a standard locality,

$$w \text{ (newtons)} = 9.81 \text{ (newtons/kg)} \, m \text{ (kg)}$$

For a freely falling body, (6.2) applies, giving us for a standard locality:

$$w \text{ (newtons)} = 9.81 \text{ (m/sec}^2) \, m \text{ (kg)}$$

We now have a test for a standard locality: it is one for which the acceleration of a falling body is 9.80665 m/sec². In the English gravitational system, we may write correspondingly

$$w \text{ (lb)} = 32.2 \text{ (lb/slug)} \, m \text{ (slugs)}$$

$$w \text{ (lb)} = 32.2 \text{ (ft/sec}^2) \, m \text{ (slugs)}$$

From the information in these equations it is apparent that the *slug* is a unit of mass given by

$$1 \text{ slug} = \frac{32.2 \times 4.45}{9.81} = 14.6 \text{ kg}$$

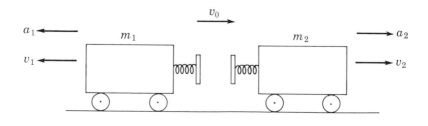

Figure
6.1

Name of System of Units	Unit of Force, f, w	Unit of Mass, m	Acceleration of Gravity, Standard Locality, g
mks................	newton	kilogram	9.81 m/sec²
English, gravitational..	pound	lb-sec²/ft, slug	32.2 ft/sec²
English, absolute	lb_m-ft/sec², poundal	lb_m	32.2 ft/sec²
cgs, absolute	dyne	gram	981 cm/sec²
cgs, gravitational	gram	g-sec²/cm	981 cm/sec²

Figure 6.2

Each of the four equations just listed can be expressed concisely in algebraic form:

$$(6.6) \qquad\qquad w = mg \quad \text{or} \quad m = \frac{w}{g}$$

These relations are in fact always valid, provided that the units of a single system of units are used. Selected sets of mechanical units are exhibited in Fig. 6.2. Other systems are quite possible, but these are the principal ones encountered in elementary physics. In this course we shall have little need to use "poundal," "slug," "lb_m," or the cgs units. They are included in this one section so that the student may have at least a passing acquaintance with them.

EXERCISES

1. How great a force will cause an object of mass 9.81 kg to accelerate at 1 m/sec²?
2. What is the mass of an object which experiences an acceleration of 10 ft/sec² when subjected to a force of 2 lb?
3. What acceleration will result if a force of 16.1 poundals is applied to an object of mass 2.0 lb_m?
4. Express as poundals a force of 1 newton.
5. An object of mass 1 lb_m is subjected to a force of 1 lb. What acceleration results?
6. At a standard locality two objects, respectively, of mass 1 lb_m and weight 1 lb are placed in the pans of an equal-arm balance. What occurs?
7. What in dynes is the weight of an object whose mass is 1 lb_m?
8. What in poundals is the weight of an object whose mass is 0.07 g-sec²/cm?
9. Express as dynes a force of 1 newton.

6.2. DYNAMICS OF A PARTICLE

From the results of the preceding section we can at once assert as the principal equation governing the motion of a particle

$$(6.7) \qquad\qquad \mathbf{F} = m\mathbf{A} \quad \text{or} \quad \mathbf{F} = \frac{w}{g}\mathbf{A}$$

The first form is more useful in working with absolute systems of units (for us the mks system primarily); the second, for gravitational systems (mainly the English fps system). If the particle in question happens to be subjected to several forces, the single $\mathbf{F}$ of (6.7) is replaced by the resultant $\bar{\mathbf{F}}$ of the concurrent forces. How then shall we solve problems involving the motion of a single particle? In outline, the procedure is quite simple. First we isolate the particle, selecting all the forces acting on the isolated matter from the outside. Second, since for a particle these forces are necessarily concurrent, we make use of relation (6.7):

$$\bar{\mathbf{F}} = \Sigma\,\mathbf{F} = m\mathbf{A} \qquad \text{or} \qquad \bar{\mathbf{F}} = \Sigma\,\mathbf{F} = \frac{w}{g}\,\mathbf{A}$$

or by judicious selection of axes we may use the scalar equations equivalent to the vector ones:

$$(6.8) \qquad \Sigma f_x = m\frac{d^2x}{dt^2} \qquad \Sigma f_y = m\frac{d^2y}{dt^2} \qquad \Sigma f_z = m\frac{d^2z}{dt^2}$$

As before, m may be replaced by w/g. These equations of motion are in the form of differential equations. To get information useful for the interpretation of varied physical situations, one will then expect to carry out integrations and to solve differential equations. Especially significant types of integrations are described in the sections on energy and momentum. In this first section the applications are mostly very direct and simple. Further possibilities are, however, suggested in Examples 5 and 6.

Example 1

A 10-lb box slides down a plane inclined at 40° even though restrained by a horizontal force of 1 lb. If the coefficient of sliding friction is 0.10, what acceleration results?

Solution

Isolating the box, we find the forces portrayed in Fig. 6.3. We may choose axes as shown. (Other choices are quite as suitable.) Since d^2y/dt^2 is clearly zero, we may write

$$\Sigma f_y = 0$$

or

$$-10\cos 40° + n - 1.0\sin 40° = 0$$

This yields, as a value for the normal force, $n = 8.31$ lb. Since the coefficient of friction is 0.1, $f = 0.83$ lb. Now using

$$\Sigma f_x = \frac{w}{g}\,a_x$$

we have

$$10\sin 40° - 1.0\cos 40° - 0.83 = (10/32.2)a_x$$

or

$$a_x = 15.6\ \text{ft/sec}^2$$

By using the kinematical techniques of Chap. 5, many detailed questions concerning the motion could now be answered.

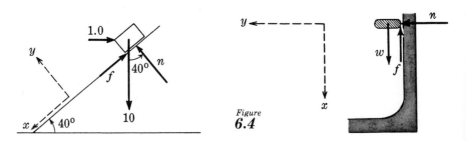

Figure
6.3

Figure
6.4

Example 2

A motorcyclist rides around on the inside of a vertical cylinder of radius 45 ft. The coefficient of friction is 0.5.   What is the minimum "safe" speed?

Solution

Isolate man and motorcycle as shown in Fig. 6.4, treating the combination as a particle.   The isolating forces are the weight, the friction preventing downward slip, and the normal reaction of the wall.   Choosing axes as shown in Fig. 6.4,

$$a_y = \frac{v^2}{r} \qquad a_x = 0$$

From Eqs. (6.8),

$$\Sigma f_x = w - f = 0$$

But $f = \mu n$ for the critical case where slipping is imminent; thus $n = w/\mu$. Also, we have

$$\Sigma f_y = \frac{w}{\mu} = \frac{w}{g}\frac{v^2}{r}$$

or

$$v^2 = \frac{gr}{\mu} = \frac{(32.2)(45)}{0.5}$$

or

$$v = 53.8 \text{ ft/sec (36.7 mph)}$$

Example 3

A particle of mass 100 g starts from rest and travels around a horizontal circular track of radius 50 cm with a speed proportional to the time.   If it would take 2 sec to make the first complete revolution, what horizontal force must act on it after a total time of 0.5 sec?

Solution

First we compute the acceleration.   We have given $v = kt$. Integrating, we get $s = 0.5kt^2$. k may be evaluated in terms of the given data:

$$k = \frac{2s}{t^2} = \frac{2(2\pi)(0.5)}{2^2} = 0.5\pi$$

Now

$$a_T = \frac{dv}{dt} = k = 0.5\,\pi$$

$$a_N = \frac{v^2}{r} = \frac{(0.5\pi)^2 t^2}{0.5}$$

and at $t = 0.5$, $a_N = 1.23$.   Consequently, the magnitude of the total acceleration is given by

$$a = \sqrt{(1.57)^2 + (1.23)^2} = 2.04 \text{ m/sec}^2$$

The force may now be computed:

$$f = ma = (0.1)(2.04) = 0.204 \text{ newton}$$

Example 4

A bob of mass m is supported by a vertical spring of negligible mass which provides a tension $-ks$ when it is stretched downward by an amount s. With what period will the bob oscillate if it is displaced vertically and then released?

Solution

When the bob is in equilibrium, the equation of equilibrium, $\Sigma f_y = 0$, is

$$+mg - ks_0 = 0$$

where s_0 denotes the amount that the spring is stretched in order to support the bob at rest. When the bob oscillates, the equation of motion is

$$+mg \quad k(y + s_0) = m \frac{d^2(y + s_0)}{dt^2}$$

where y is the vertical displacement from equilibrium position (positive downward), or, using the previous equation,

$$-ky = m \frac{d^2y}{dt^2}$$

By Proposition (5.60) this equation is recognizable as simple harmonic motion of period

$$\tau = 2\pi \sqrt{\frac{m}{k}}$$

Example 5.   F a Function of Time

Suppose that a projectile of mass m is launched vertically from rest by a force $f(t)$ varying with the time. What is the speed as a function of t if m and g are constant?

Solution

Isolating the projectile and taking components vertically upward,

$$f(t) - mg = m \frac{dv}{dt}$$

Integrating [cf. Eq. (5.50)],

$$v = \frac{1}{m} \int_0^t [f(t) - mg] \, dt = \frac{1}{m} \int_0^t f(t) \, dt - gt$$

Example 6.   F a Function of Displacement

Suppose that a particle of mass m is in motion on the x axis subject to a net force $f(x)$ parallel to the axis. If the speed is v_0 when $x = x_0$, express in terms of x the speed v for another position.

Solution

Isolating the particle and taking components along the x axis,

$$f(x) = ma_x = mv \frac{dv}{dx}$$

Integrating [cf. Eq. (5.51)],

$$\int_{v_0}^{v} v\,dv = \frac{1}{m}\int_{x_0}^{x} f(x)\,dx$$

or

$$v^2 - v_0^2 = \frac{2}{m}\int_{x_0}^{x} f(x)\,dx$$

so that

$$v = \left[\frac{2}{m}\int_{x_0}^{x} f(x)\,dx + v_0^2\right]^{\frac{1}{2}}$$

This sort of development can profitably be applied to Example 4.

Example 7

A particle of mass m' moves subject to three forces:

$$\mathbf{F}_1 = f \sin \omega t\,\mathbf{I} \qquad \mathbf{F}_2 = f \cos \omega t\,\mathbf{J} \qquad \mathbf{F}_3 = f_3\mathbf{K}$$

where f, f_3, ω are constants. If at $t = 0$ the velocity is $v_0\mathbf{E}$, where $\mathbf{E} = l\mathbf{I} + m\mathbf{J} + n\mathbf{K}$ with l, m, n, v_0 constants, what is the velocity at time t?

Solution

The equation of motion is

$$\mathbf{F}_1 + \mathbf{F}_2 + \mathbf{F}_3 = m'\frac{d\mathbf{V}}{dt}$$

which may be integrated

$$\mathbf{I}f\int_0^t \sin \omega t\,dt + \mathbf{J}f\int_0^t \cos \omega t\,dt + \mathbf{K}f_3\int_0^t dt = m'\int_{v_0\mathbf{E}}^{\mathbf{V}} d\mathbf{V}$$

Carrying out the integration,

$$\mathbf{I}\left(\frac{f}{\omega}\right)(1 - \cos \omega t) + \mathbf{J}\left(\frac{f}{\omega}\right)\sin \omega t + \mathbf{K}f_3 t = m'(\mathbf{V} - v_0\mathbf{E})$$

The final velocity $\mathbf{V}$ then has components

$$v_x = v_0 l + \left[\frac{f}{m'\omega}\right](1 - \cos \omega t)$$

$$v_y = v_0 m + \left[\frac{f}{m'\omega}\right]\sin \omega t$$

$$v_z = v_0 n + (f_3/m')t$$

EXERCISES

10. A body weighing 160 lb slides on level ground and is retarded by a constant frictional force. If the initial speed of the body is 16 ft/sec and the coefficient of friction is 0.25, how long will it take the body to come to rest?

11. A weight of 3 tons is raised from the ground to a height of 80 ft in 5 sec by a constant tension in the hoisting cable. How great is this tension?

12. A 200-lb man must slide down a rope guaranteed to withstand a tension of 150 lb. How great should his acceleration be?

13. A 16-lb particle is acted on by the following forces (pounds):

$$6\mathbf{I} - 7\mathbf{J} + 3\mathbf{K} \qquad -16\mathbf{K} \qquad -5\mathbf{I} + 7\mathbf{J} + 10\mathbf{K}$$

Find the acceleration.

14. An elevator weighing 2.5 tons starts from rest and descends with constant acceleration a distance of 100 ft in 10 sec. Neglecting friction, what is the tension in the cable?

15. A 150-lb man climbs a vertical rope with an acceleration of 0.4 ft/sec². Find the tension in the rope.

16. A cake of ice weighing 60 lb is pulled on level ground by a constant force of 20 lb applied at an angle of 30° above the horizontal. If the coefficient of friction between the ice and the ground is 0.1, how long will it take to move the cake of ice a distance of 300 ft starting from rest?

17. A 10-lb particle traveling at 15 ft/sec is being subjected to forces whose resultant is at a given moment a 40-lb force making an angle of 30° with the tangent vector $\mathbf{T}$. What is the radius of curvature of the path at that instant? What is the instantaneous rate of increase of speed?

18. An object of mass 2 kg is free to slide along a smooth horizontal rod. Starting from rest it is propelled by a force parallel to the rod whose magnitude is given by

$$f(t) = 5t - t^2$$

f in newtons, t in seconds. What is the speed after 5 sec?

19. An elevator is descending at 10 ft/sec when the cable breaks. On each of two sides of the car a brake is immediately applied against the shaft with a normal force of magnitude p. If the coefficient of friction is 0.6, how great must p be in order to stop the car in 20 ft? The elevator and load weigh 1,600 lb.

20. An automobile starts from rest and travels around a circular unbanked track 400 ft in radius with a constant tangential acceleration of 2 ft/sec². After how many seconds will it start to slip if the coefficient of friction is 0.5?

21. A particle of mass 0.49 kg moves on the x axis subject solely to a force

$$\mathbf{F} = -7(x - 5)\mathbf{I}$$

newtons for x in meters. If the velocity is equal to $2\mathbf{I}$ when $x = 1$, what will the speed be when $x = 6$?

6.3. THE SIMPLE PENDULUM

A simple pendulum consists of a small spherical bob of mass m attached to a light flexible inextensible string of length l whose other end is tied to a fixed point O. In equilibrium the string hangs vertically. If the bob is displaced slightly and released, an oscillation results. What is the nature of this oscillation and its period? To solve this problem, we isolate the bob in a typical position where the angular displacement is θ, as in Fig. 6.5. The forces acting on it are the pull of the cord $\mathbf{P}$ and the weight $\mathbf{W}$. The path is necessarily circular; therefore we may write

$$\mathbf{A} = (\alpha l)\mathbf{T} + (\omega^2 l)\mathbf{N}$$

Taking tangential components of $\bar{\mathbf{F}} = m\mathbf{A}$, we have

$$-w \sin \theta = m\alpha l$$

or

$$-g \sin \theta = \alpha l$$

To find the period, we write α as $d^2\theta/dt^2$ and consider the resulting equation

$$\frac{d^2\theta}{dt^2} = -\frac{g}{l} \sin \theta$$

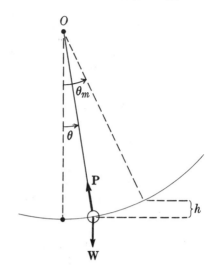

Figure
6.5

It turns out that the exact integration of this equation involves nonelementary mathematics. A full analysis would reveal that the period increases slightly with amplitude. We can manage an approximate solution, however, if we agree that θ is to be kept small so that $\sin \theta$ may be replaced by θ in the equation. In that case we can apply (5.60), which identifies the motion as simple harmonic in θ with period

(6.9a)
$$\tau = 2\pi \sqrt{\frac{l}{g}}$$

(6.9b)
$$\tau = 2\pi \sqrt{\frac{l}{g}} \left(1 + \frac{\theta_m^2}{16}\right)$$

Formula (6.9a) is noteworthy in that it is independent of the amplitude and of the mass of the bob. Formula (6.9b) is a better approximate formula, showing how the period actually does vary slightly with the amplitude θ_m.

If we go back to the original equation and this time replace α by $\omega(d\omega/d\theta)$, we get an equation which we can integrate exactly. Assuming that ω is zero when θ has its maximum value θ_m,

$$-g \int_{\theta_m}^{\theta} \sin \theta \, d\theta = l \int_0^{\omega} \omega \, d\omega$$

Integrating,

$$g \left(\cos \theta - \cos \theta_m\right) = \tfrac{1}{2} l \omega^2$$

Substituting v/l for ω and noting that $l \cos \theta - l \cos \theta_m$ is the vertical distance h between the two positions considered, we can easily conclude, whether θ_m is small or not:

(6.10) *The speed at any level in the path of a simple pendulum is the speed which the bob would have attained in a free fall to the same level; i.e.,*

$$v = (2gh)^{\frac{1}{2}}$$

The simple pendulum plays numerous roles in physics. Since its motion is periodic, it constitutes a primitive timing device, variations of which are used in pendulum clocks. When other timers are available it affords a simple means of measuring the acceleration due to gravity, and hence the local strength of the gravitational field. In frames which are not inertial frames, the simple pendulum becomes a device for measuring departures from inertial behavior (see, for instance, the discussion of the Foucault pendulum in Sec. 14.6). As the simplest sort of pendulum, it serves as a prototype for describing more sophisticated pendulums (see Sec. 16.4).

EXERCISES

22. Find the maximum speed of the bob of a 2-ft pendulum released from rest at an angle of 60° with the downward vertical.

23. A 40-lb object is suspended by a cord 10 ft long and is free to swing. What is the greatest speed with which it can swing through its lowest position if the cord will break at a tension of 80 lb?

24. Compute the period of a pendulum 1.5 m long, swinging with amplitude 60°, using both forms of (6.9).

6.4. FLUID FRICTION, TERMINAL SPEED, AND EXPONENTIAL BEHAVIOR

In Sec. 3.8 we encountered frictional forces which depend on materials and normal forces. There are many situations in physics and engineering in which frictional drags are speed-dependent. Bearings with fluid lubricants, aircraft subject to viscous drag, and charged droplets moving in air subject to an electric field, all are influenced by speed-dependent forces. Wherever a particle moves in a fluid, the frictional or viscous force of resistance varies with speed. Usually, such a force is approximately proportional to some power of the speed, at least for a certain range of speeds. Suppose, then, that we consider motion subject to a force of magnitude f_r given by

$$(6.11) \qquad f_r = rv^k$$

where r and k are constants. In the smooth flow often associated with moderate speeds, k may be taken as 1. For higher speeds and turbulent motion, k is usually greater than 1.

Suppose that a particle of mass m moves along the x axis driven by a constant force f and retarded by a force f_r as described above. The dynamical equation for the particle has the form

$$(6.12) \qquad f - rv^k = m\frac{dv}{dt}$$

Certain general characteristics of the motion can be discerned without formal mathematics. If the particle is released at rest, the acceleration instantaneously is f/m since v is zero. As v increases, the acceleration diminishes. As the acceleration approaches zero, the speed approaches a *terminal speed* $v_t = (f/r)^{1/k}$.

Specific quantitative predictions follow from the integration of the simple differential equation (6.12), possibly with dv/dt replaced by $v\,dv/dx$. As an important specific example, consider a particle falling under its weight subject to a force varying as the first power of v. First we have

$$(6.13) \qquad w - rv = m\frac{dv}{dt}$$

or

$$-\frac{r}{m}\,dt = \frac{-r\,dv}{w - rv}$$

This yields, upon integration,

$$-\frac{r}{m}t = \ln(w - rv) + \text{const}$$

Let v_0 be the initial speed; then the constant of integration is evaluated as

$$\text{const} = -\ln(w - rv_0)$$

The preceding equation may then be rewritten as

$$(6.14) \qquad\qquad v - v_0 = \left(\frac{w}{r} - v_0\right)(1 - e^{-(r/m)t})$$

This equation shows that the terminal speed is that given by $rv = w$,

$$(6.15) \qquad\qquad\qquad v_t = \frac{w}{r}$$

and that v approaches v_t *exponentially* (see Fig. 6.6). Thus the terminal speed theoretically is approached, but never attained.

The statement "v starts at v_0 and approaches v_t exponentially" describes a sort of situation occurring widely in physics and other sciences. The time required (see Exercise 25) for the variable to get from its current value to a value 63.2 per cent nearer the final value is called the *time constant* of the exponential (the reciprocal of e is 0.368). For the case under discussion, the time constant τ_e is given by

$$(6.16) \qquad\qquad\qquad \tau_e = \frac{m}{r} = \frac{v_t}{g}$$

Note in Fig. 6.6 that the slope of the curve at *any* point is equal to $\Delta v / \tau_e$; that is, the rate of change of v is proportional to the change in v still to be accomplished. This is typical of exponential decay.

It should be emphasized that the equations of this section were derived for a body falling in a resisting medium, for in Eq. (6.13) w represents the only force besides friction. The method, however, can be adapted very easily to other situations. The basic procedure is merely to set up an equation of motion analogous to (6.13) and then to integrate, evaluating constants of integration in terms of initial conditions or other specified conditions.

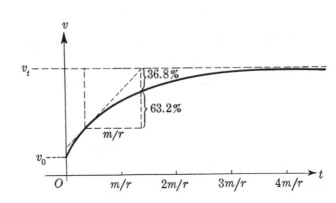

Figure
6.6

EXERCISES

25. Suppose that $y(t)$ approaches a limit $y(\infty) = a$ exponentially, i.e., that y can be expressed

$$y(t) = a + be^{-(t/\tau_e)}$$

where a and b are constants and τ_e is the time constant. At any time t, $y(t)$ is the *current value*. Prove that, in one time constant, y will get 63.2 per cent of the way toward its limit, i.e., that

$$y(t + \tau_e) - y(t) = 0.632[y(\infty) - y(t)]$$

26. At the point where $t = t'$, a tangent is drawn to the graph of

$$y(t) = a + be^{-(t/\tau_e)}$$

Show that this tangent cuts the line $y = a$ at the point where

$$t = t' + \tau_e$$

27. A raindrop has a terminal speed of 25 ft/sec. If the resistance is proportional to the speed: (a) How long would it take such a drop, starting from rest, to acquire a speed of 15 ft/sec? (b) How far from rest will such a drop fall in 2 sec?

28. A man and his parachute weigh 150 lb. Fifteen feet per second will be considered a safe landing speed. The material of the parachute, tested in a 15-mph wind blast, creates a force of $\frac{1}{2}$ lb/ft². The resistance is proportional to the speed. (a) What should be the minimum diameter of the parachute? (b) How much of a drop is necessary for acquiring a speed of 12 ft/sec?

6.5. INTERACTING PARTICLES

When two or more particles are in contact, their motions are interdependent. Insight into these motions can be gained by isolating the particles separately and then writing for each an equation of motion of the form $\bar{\mathbf{F}} = m\mathbf{A}$. The accelerations of different particles may be limited by definite constraints, which can be expressed mathematically. For instance, a cord joining them may be of constant length. As we shall see in the examples, such relationships, together with the separate equations of motion, often make possible a full solution.

Example I

Two blocks B and C rest on an inclined plane whose angle with the horizontal is 30° as in Fig. 6.7. The weights are, respectively, 5 and 10 lb. C is smooth, but

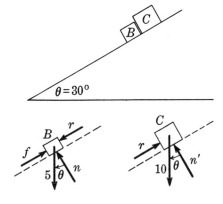

Figure
6.7

the coefficient of friction for B is 0.3.   With what acceleration do the blocks slide down the incline?   Find the force with which one pushes the other.

Solution

First isolate B.   The forces are the weight, normal and tangential reactions of the plane, and the force $\mathbf{R}$ exerted by C.   Taking normal components, we get

$$-5 \cos 30° + n = 0$$

or

$$n = 4.33 \text{ lb}$$

The coefficient of friction is known; thus we have at once $f = 1.3$ lb.   Now taking tangential components,

$$-1.3 + 5 \sin 30° + r = (5/32.2)a_T$$

Next isolate C.   The forces are the reaction to $\mathbf{R}$, the weight, and a normal reaction $\mathbf{N}'$ with the plane.   Utilizing horizontal components,

$$-r + 10 \sin 30° = (10/32.2)a_T$$

We have used the same acceleration symbol for both blocks since they apparently will remain in contact.   Eliminating r,

$$6.2 = (15/32.2)a_T$$

or

$$a_T = 13.3 \text{ ft/sec}^2$$

Going back to the previous equations, we can solve for r:

$$r = 5 - \frac{(10)(6.2)(32.2)}{(32.2)(15)} = 0.9 \text{ lb}$$

It is well worth noting that a general solution using letters instead of numbers is in many ways more satisfactory than a forthright numerical solution such as has been outlined above.   Literal equations have the advantage that they can be checked dimensionally (in terms of length, force, and time) at any stage.   For this example, literal equations might be written as follows:

$$-w \cos \theta + n = 0$$

so

$$f = \mu w \cos \theta$$

Then

$$-\mu w \cos \theta + w \sin \theta + r = \left(\frac{w}{g}\right)a_T \qquad \text{for } B$$

and

$$-r + w' \sin \theta = \left(\frac{w'}{g}\right)a_T \qquad \text{for } C$$

Adding member by member to eliminate r,

$$(w + w') \sin \theta - \mu w \cos \theta = \left(\frac{w + w'}{g}\right)a_T$$

(Observe that this equation is the isolation equation for B and C together.)   From

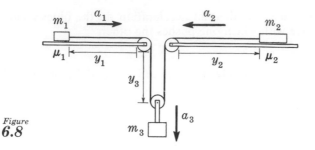

Figure
6.8

the preceding equation we get

$$a_T = g\left(\sin\theta - \frac{\mu w}{w + w'}\cos\theta\right)$$

and

$$r = w'\left(\sin\theta - \frac{a_T}{g}\right) = \frac{\mu w w'\cos\theta}{w + w'}$$

These two general answers can now be used as a source for numerical answers. Substituting the data of this example should yield the same results as before.

Example 2

Given the masses and coefficients of friction as shown in Fig. 6.8. Assume that $m_3 g$ is greater than $(\mu_1 m_1 g + \mu_2 m_2 g)$. Neglect pulley masses and frictions.

Solution

Isolate the three masses separately. Denote by t the magnitude of the tension in the cord:

$$t - \mu_1 m_1 g = m_1 a_1$$
$$m_3 g - 2t = m_3 a_3$$
$$t - \mu_2 m_2 g = m_2 a_2$$

There are four unknown quantities: t, a_1, a_2, a_3. A fourth equation relating them is obtained by using the fact that the cord does not stretch.

$$y_1 + y_2 + 2y_3 = \text{const}$$

Differentiating twice with respect to time,

$$-a_1 - a_2 + 2a_3 = 0$$

Now, with four equations, the four unknown quantities may be determined.

EXERCISES

29. How would the equations at the end of Example 1 need to be altered if the coefficient of friction for block C is taken as μ' instead of zero?

In each of the following ignore pulley friction and pulley inertia. Assume cords flexible and inextensible. In each case find the accelerations and tensions.

30. Figure 6.9.
31. Figure 6.10.
32. Figure 6.11.
33. Figure 6.12.
34. Figure 6.13.
35. Figure 6.14.

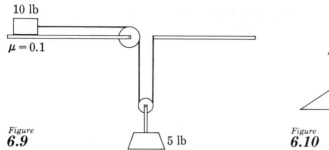

Figure
6.9

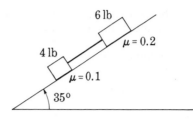

Figure
6.10

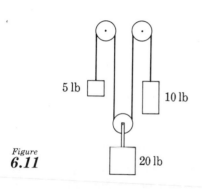

Figure
6.11

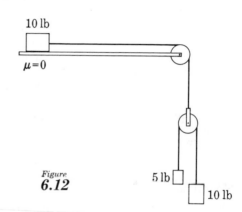

Figure
6.12

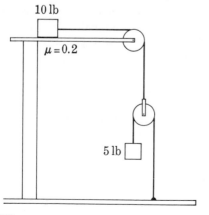

Figure
6.13

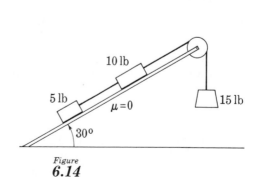

Figure
6.14

36. Suppose, as a generalization of Example 1, that n blocks of weights $w_1, \ldots, w_n$ are arranged on a plane inclined at angle θ so that $\mu_1 > \mu_2 > \cdots > \mu_n$. Show that the acceleration is given by $a = g\,(\sin\theta - \bar\mu\cos\theta)$, where $\bar\mu$ is an average coefficient of friction. Express $\bar\mu$ in terms of $\mu_1, \ldots, \mu_n$.

6.6. AGGREGATES OF PARTICLES

In our study of statics the objects allowed were things that could be regarded approximately as mass particles or as rigid bodies. Thus far our study of dynamics has been limited to particles either singly or in small groups. The easiest way for us to extend these results to rigid bodies is to develop a theory for large groups or aggregates of particles. Suppose that we have given a collection of particles whose masses are $m_1, m_2, \ldots, m_n$. These particles may interact. By the reaction law the forces between pairs of particles are equal and opposite. Such interaction forces will be signalized by primes and called *internal forces*. Forces acting from the outside on particles of the collection will be called *external forces*. For a typical particle, say, the one with subscript i on its mass in the list above, in other words for the ith *particle*, let $\bar{\mathbf{F}}_i$ denote the resultant of the external forces and let $\bar{\mathbf{F}}'_i$ be the resultant of the internal forces. Our basic dynamics equation allows us then to state, having isolated this particle,

$$\bar{\mathbf{F}}_i + \bar{\mathbf{F}}'_i = m_i \mathbf{A}_i$$

n such equations may be written down. If we add corresponding members of these n equations, we get

(6.17) $$\Sigma\,\bar{\mathbf{F}}_i = \Sigma\, m_i \mathbf{A}_i$$

No primed forces appear because they occur in equal and opposite pairs which cancel. We had a simple example of this in Example 1 of the preceding section. The interaction forces $\mathbf{R}$ and $-\mathbf{R}$ appear in tangential equations of motion for the particles B and C taken separately. But when these equations were added member by member, we were left with an equation with reference to $\mathbf{R}$ eliminated. The two particles B and C constituted a very small aggregate for which $\mathbf{R}$ and $-\mathbf{R}$ were internal forces. Equation (6.17) is more easily appreciated if the notion of *center of mass* is introduced. This concept was mentioned in Sec. 5.10, Example 3, and it will receive additional attention in Chap. 15. In general terms, the center of mass is a mean position relative to the distribution of mass in an aggregate. For a system of particles, the center of mass is defined to be the point whose position vector $\bar{\mathbf{R}}$ is given by

(6.18) $$\bar{\mathbf{R}} = \frac{\Sigma\, m_i \mathbf{R}_i}{\Sigma\, m_i}$$

where $\mathbf{R}_i$ is the position vector of the ith particle. If this equation is differentiated twice with respect to time, we get, assuming that the masses are constant,

(6.19) $$\bar{\mathbf{A}} = \frac{\Sigma\, m_i \mathbf{A}_i}{\Sigma\, m_i}$$

This enables one to rewrite (6.17) as

(6.20) $$\Sigma\,\bar{\mathbf{F}}_i = (\Sigma\, m_i)\bar{\mathbf{A}}$$

In words, we may phrase it as follows:

(6.21) *The center of mass of an aggregate of particles behaves like a single particle having the total mass of the aggregate and subjected to external forces equal to those acting on particles of the aggregate.*

A surprising application of the preceding result is that the effect of a force on the motion of the center of mass of an aggregate of particles is independent of the point of application of the force.

These conclusions are welcome because of their simplicity. They point out that, however chaotic the motion of an aggregate may be, there underlies a pattern as uncomplicated as the motion of a single particle.

For many practical problems it is helpful to replace (6.18) by the following scalar equations:

$$(6.22) \qquad \bar{x} = \frac{\Sigma\, m_i x_i}{\Sigma\, m_i} \qquad \bar{y} = \frac{\Sigma\, m_i y_i}{\Sigma\, m_i} \qquad \bar{z} = \frac{\Sigma\, m_i z_i}{\Sigma\, m_i}$$

Location of Center of Mass. For two particles of masses m_1 at $\mathbf{R}_1$ and m_2 at $\mathbf{R}_2$, the center of mass is given by

$$(6.23) \qquad \bar{\mathbf{R}} = \frac{m_1 \mathbf{R}_1 + m_2 \mathbf{R}_2}{m_1 + m_2}$$

It is worth noting that this may be rewritten as

$$(6.24) \qquad \bar{\mathbf{R}} = \mathbf{R}_1 + \frac{m_2}{m_1 + m_2}\,(\mathbf{R}_2 - \mathbf{R}_1) = \mathbf{R}_2 + \frac{m_1}{m_1 + m_2}\,(\mathbf{R}_1 - \mathbf{R}_2)$$

This makes it clear that

(6.25) *The center of mass of a system of two particles lies on the line between them, and it divides the segment inversely as the masses.*

(You may wish to review ratio formulas with the aid of Appendix 2, Sec. A2.1.)

This approach may be easily extended to systems of more than two particles, for the center of mass of a system of n particles may be considered as the center of mass of a system of two particles, one of these being a particle of mass $m_1 + m_2 + \cdots + m_{n-1}$ at the center of mass of the corresponding $n - 1$ particles, the other being the nth particle. Letting

$$\bar{\mathbf{R}}_{n-1} = \frac{m_1 \mathbf{R}_1 + \cdots + m_{n-1} \mathbf{R}_{n-1}}{m_1 + \cdots + m_{n-1}}$$

we can show by direct substitution that

$$(6.26) \qquad \bar{\mathbf{R}} = \bar{\mathbf{R}}_{n-1} + \frac{m_n}{\Sigma\, m_i}\,(\mathbf{R}_n - \bar{\mathbf{R}}_{n-1})$$

The details of the substitution are left for Exercise 37. This result means in practice that one may find a center of mass by using (6.25) again and again. For example, consider three equal masses at the vertices of a triangle, as in Fig. 6.15. The center of mass of No. 1 and No. 2 [by (6.25)] is the mid-point. Now think of the system No. 1 plus No. 2 as concentrated at this mid-point. The whole problem of three particles is thus reduced to two two-particle problems. The center of mass of the three original objects is immediately seen [by (6.25) again] to be at the point on the median of the triangle two-thirds of the way from the vertex (i.e., at the centroid of the triangle itself). One's intuitive understanding of a center of mass is often assisted by thinking

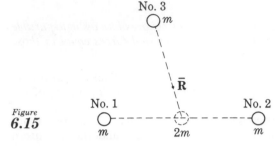

Figure
6.15

of it as a center of gravity.   For instance, to locate the center of mass of a baseball bat, you balance it horizontally on a finger and you feel confident that the center of mass is above the balance point.   With an aggregate of particles of a freer sort this experiment may not be feasible, but you can at least imagine that the particles of the aggregate are instantaneously held in fixed relative positions by weightless wires (or dotted lines as in Fig. 6.15) and that a balance point has been located.   It is not obvious that this balance point determined with the help of gravity is the same as the center of mass defined in Eq. (6.18).   You can quite easily, if you wish, prove this result for special cases.   We shall return to a more general treatment in Chap. 15.

EXERCISES

37. Verify Eq. (6.26).
38. Three particles of masses 1, 2, and 3 kg, respectively, are at the vertices of an equilateral triangle of side 1 m.   Find the center of mass.
39. Instantaneously, the particles of Fig. 6.16 are subjected to the forces as listed below.
 (*a*) Find the center of mass initially.
 (*b*) Find the instantaneous acceleration of the center of mass.

particle	Mass, kg	Coordinates, m	Forces, newtons
A	3	(0,1)	$-3\mathbf{J}$, $2\mathbf{I} - \mathbf{J}$, $\mathbf{I} + \mathbf{J}$
B	1.5	(0,0)	$-2\mathbf{I}$, $3\mathbf{J}$
C	0.5	(2,0)	$2\mathbf{I}$, $-2\mathbf{I} + \mathbf{J}$, $2\mathbf{J}$

40. Show that the aggregate consisting of the falling weights and pulley of Fig. 6.12 satisfies (6.20).

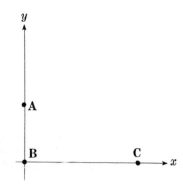

Figure
6.16

6.7. METHOD OF D'ALEMBERT

Whenever an equation of the form $\Sigma \mathbf{F} = m\mathbf{A}$ is valid, it is equally clear that one may assert

$$\Sigma \mathbf{F} + (-m\mathbf{A}) = \mathbf{O}$$

For any one particle, then, one can treat a dynamics problem as a problem in statics just by adding an *inertia force* equal to the product of the mass of the particle times the opposite of the acceleration vector. For a system of particles one may add to each particle a force $-m\mathbf{A}$, or for the whole system one may add the resultant of such inertia forces. There are several circumstances, as we shall see later, where this point of view is advantageous. For example, on a decelerating bus a standing passenger, struggling to keep his balance, feels naturally that he is (or is not) achieving an equilibrium by counterbalancing forces associated with the change of speed. This approach, here treated superficially, is associated with the work of d'Alembert. Strictly speaking, this change in point of view must be justified by considering motion in an accelerated reference frame. Later in the course we shall study moving reference frames.

Example

A wheel of radius r rotates at angular speed ω about a vertical axis. A string of length l ties a bob of mass m to a point on the rim of the wheel as shown in Fig. 6.17a. In steady state the bob and string remain in a plane containing the axis of rotation. Find a relation between ω and the angle θ between the string and the vertical.

Solution

The acceleration of the bob is purely centripetal:

$$a = \omega^2(r + l\sin\theta)$$

Isolating the bob, we include, along with the tension $\mathbf{P}$ and the weight $-mg\mathbf{J}$, the d'Alembert force

$$-m\mathbf{A} = m\omega^2(r + l\sin\theta)\mathbf{I}$$

From the force triangle in Fig. 6.17b, we get

$$ma = mg\tan\theta$$

Thus we find that

$$\omega^2 = \frac{g\tan\theta}{r + l\sin\theta}$$

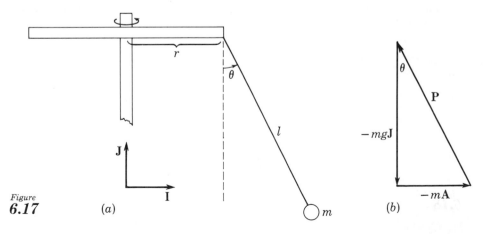

Figure
6.17   (a)   (b)

REVIEW EXERCISES

41. A 200-lb man stands on the floor of an elevator. What force does he exert on the elevator:

    (a) When it is falling at 10 ft/sec and at the same time slowing down at 10 ft/sec^2?

    (b) When it is rising with a uniform speed of 10 ft/sec?

42. The driver of an automobile traveling along a straight level road suddenly applies the brakes so that the car slides for 2 sec, covering a distance of 32 ft before coming to a stop. Assuming uniform deceleration, find the coefficient of friction between road and tires.

43. The upward speed v in feet per second of a runaway elevator is given by

$$v = 10 + 5t + t^2$$

    For what value of t will a 200-lb passenger push against the floor with a force of 300 lb?

44. A 10-lb particle traveling at 15 ft/sec is being subjected to forces whose resultant is at a given moment a 40-lb force making an angle of 30° with the path as shown in Fig. 6.18.

    (a) What is the radius of curvature of the trajectory at that instant?

    (b) What is the instantaneous rate of increase of the speed?

45. A 200-lb man can just lift a 240-lb weight when at rest on the ground. How heavy a weight can he just lift from the floor of an elevator with an upward acceleration of 8 ft/sec^2? With a downward acceleration of the same magnitude? Compute both, assuming (a) the crucial muscles are leg muscles and (b) the crucial muscles are arm muscles.

46. An elevator weighing 1,000 lb moves upward with uniform velocity of 12 ft/sec. If the frictional resistance is 20 lb, how far will it continue to rise if the cable is suddenly cut?

47. An automobile starting on an icy pavement takes 30 sec to attain a speed of 5 mph. What is the coefficient of friction?

48. A book rests on the level top of an automobile. The automobile starts from rest and, accelerating uniformly, attains a speed of 15 mph in 44 ft. If the book does not slip, what can be said about the coefficient of friction between book and car top?

49. A horizontal turntable starts from rest and accelerates according to the equation

$$\frac{d\theta}{dt} = 4t \qquad \text{rad/sec}$$

    A small eraser rests on the table at a point 18 in. from the center. It just starts to slip after 0.866 sec. What is the coefficient of friction between the eraser and the surface of the turntable?

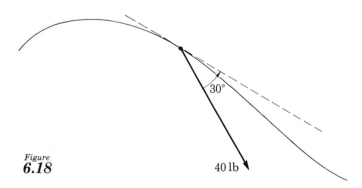

Figure
6.18
                                        40 lb

50. A block slides down a roof inclined at an angle of 30°. It slides from rest a distance of 50 ft before leaving the roof at a speed of 20 ft/sec. What is the coefficient of friction? After falling for 2 sec, what will be its horizontal distance from the edge of the roof?

51. A horizontal board performs simple harmonic oscillations horizontally. The total displacement is 2 ft. There are 20 oscillations per minute. A book on the board does not slip. Compute a least possible value for the coefficient of friction between book and board.

52. A 10-lb particle hangs at the end of a vertical rope. The tension in the rope (in pounds) varies with time t (in seconds) according to the equation

$$f = 10 + 0.5t^2$$

At $t = 0$, the particle is at rest. After 4 sec how far has it moved and how fast is it moving?

53. A gasoline-powered model airplane weighs 0.5 lb. It travels in a horizontal circle at the end of a light 100-ft cord which is elevated at 25° above the horizontal. It takes 2.5 sec for each trip around the circle. What is the tension in the cord?

54. A 10-lb particle subjected to a force $\mathbf{F} = -12x\mathbf{I} - 10\mathbf{J}$ (lb for x in ft) is launched from the origin with initial velocity $\mathbf{V_0} = 60\mathbf{I} + 80\mathbf{J}$ (ft/sec).
    (a) After how much time will the y component of velocity vanish?
    (b) What is the maximum x coordinate attained by the particle?
    (c) How long is required for this maximum x to be attained?

55. A pendulum bob suspended by a cord from the ceiling describes at uniform speed a horizontal circle. Show that the period is the same as that for a simple pendulum whose length is equal to the vertical distance from the circle to the ceiling.

56. (a) A 320-lb canoe maintains a speed of 7.5 mph when pulled by a steady force of 5.5 lb. If the force is removed, what will be the speed of the canoe after 10 sec? (Assume that the resistance is proportional to the speed.) (b) How far will the canoe glide during the time interval specified in part (a)?

57. Repeat Exercise 56, using the assumption that the resistance is proportional to the *square* of the speed.

58. An object falls from rest in a medium where the resistance is proportional to the speed. The terminal speed would be v_t, but in time t_1 the object attains a speed v_1 in falling a distance x_1. In a free unresisted fall it would take the object time t_2 to attain the speed v_1. Show that

$$x_1 = v_t(t_1 - t_2)$$

59. A small object travels in a circle on a smooth horizontal table at the end of an elastic cord. The object has mass 1 kg. The cord has an unstrained length of 1 m, and its stiffness factor is 200 newtons/m. If the other end of the cord is fixed at the center of the circle, for what angular speed is the length doubled?

60. Consider two oscillating systems depicted in Fig. 6.19. One is a bob of mass m_1 at the end of a light spring whose length, when the system is in equilibrium, is l_1. When this system is in vertical oscillation, the period is τ_1. The other is a simple pendulum of mass m_2, length l_2, period τ_2. Prove that these periods can be equal only if l_1 is greater than l_2.

61. Three blocks A, B, and C, each of mass 1.5 kg, are connected by light inelastic strings as shown in Fig. 6.20. The pulley is light and frictionless.
    (a) Find the acceleration of the system.
    (b) Find the tension in the cord from B to C.

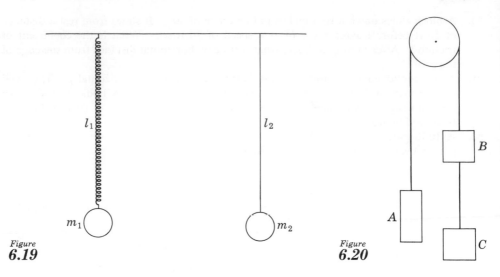

Figure
6.19

Figure
6.20

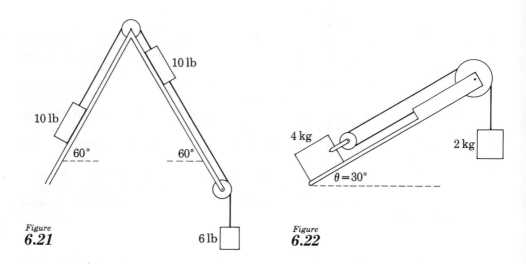

Figure
6.21

6 lb

Figure
6.22

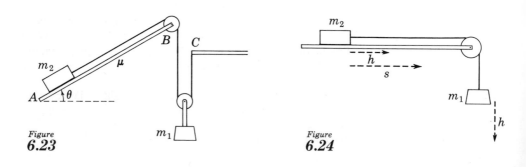

Figure
6.23

Figure
6.24

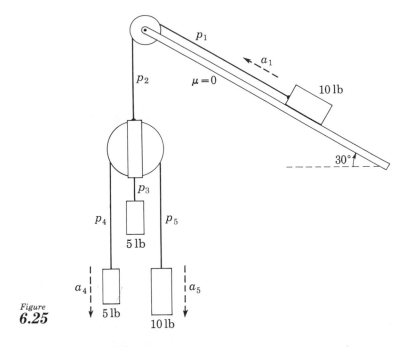

Figure
6.25

62. Ignore pulley friction and pulley inertia. The two 10-lb objects in Fig. 6.21 slide on inclined planes with coefficient of friction 0.30. The cords are light and inextensible. (*a*) Find the acceleration of the system. (*b*) Find the tension in the cord between the two 10-lb objects.

63. In the system shown in Fig. 6.22 find the acceleration of the hanging (2-kg) load. Neglect all friction. Neglect inertia of both pulleys. As usual, assume cord to be flexible, very light, and inextensible.

64. The plane *AB* and the point *C* shown in Fig. 6.23 may be regarded as rigidly fixed. The object of mass m_1 is sufficiently heavy to cause the object of mass m_2 to slide up the plane in spite of the friction (coefficient μ). Find the tension in the cord in terms of m_1, m_2, θ, μ, g. Neglect friction and inertia of pulleys.

65. Figure 6.24 shows two objects of masses m_1 and m_2 connected by a cord passing over a pulley at the edge of a table. The coefficient of friction is μ. When m_2 is held at rest so that m_1 is above the floor by a distance h and then released, m_2 slides a distance s before coming to rest. The cord is long enough so that the sliding object does not strike the pulley. Show that (for various choices of h) s always satisfies the equation

$$s = kh$$

where k is a constant. Determine k in terms of μ and the mass ratio $\rho = m_1/m_2$.

66. Ignoring friction and pulley inertia, find accelerations and tensions for the system shown in Fig. 6.25.

67. A conical funnel whose vertex angle is 90° spins at 5 rad/sec about its vertical axis. An insect walks slowly up the side of the rotating cone. If the coefficient of friction is 0.50, how far from the apex can it climb before slipping uphill?

68. A physics teacher wishes to demonstrate accelerated motion by applying a 4-lb force to a 10-lb object on a horizontal table. To produce the 4-lb force he attaches a cord to the object and lets the cord pass over a smooth pulley to a hanging weight. What is the proper weight to use if the coefficient of friction between object and table is 0.25?

CHAPTER SEVEN

ENERGY and MOMENTUM

In the preceding chapter Newton's celebrated second law was applied to the motion of a particle. The immediate result, a differential equation, usually needs to be integrated in order to provide information useful for applications. In Sec. 6.2, Examples 6 and 7, sample integrations were carried out. In the present chapter we study general physical interpretations of the integrated forms of the basic equations of motion. This process of integration is not merely a mathematical maneuver. It allows us to shift from consideration of just forces and accelerations to a consideration of such central mechanics concepts as momentum and energy, with their remarkable conservation laws.

7.1. IMPULSE

First we shall deliberate briefly concerning the time integral of a force. As in elementary physics, a constant force $\mathbf{F}$ acting for a time interval $t_1 - t_0$ is said to exert an impulse $\mathbf{P}$ equal to the product of the force by the length of the interval:

$$(7.1) \qquad\qquad \mathbf{P} = \mathbf{F}(t_1 - t_0)$$

Impulse is a vector concept. In this simple case it has the direction of the force $\mathbf{F}$. When $\mathbf{F}$ is variable, one needs a more careful definition of impulse. This can be approached by dividing the time interval under consideration into subintervals as is suggested by the diagram of the time axis in Fig. 7.1. Suppose that, at some instant during the interval Δt_i, the force function $\mathbf{F}$ has the value $\mathbf{F}_i$. Then a reasonable approximation to the net impulse exerted ought to be given by the sum of the impulses which would have been exerted had each $\mathbf{F}_i$ remained constant during Δt_i:

$$\mathbf{P} = \Sigma \, \mathbf{F}_i \, \Delta t_i$$

By taking smaller and smaller subdivisions of the time interval during which the variable force acts, we get approximations which are more and more significant since more details are utilized. It is thus fairly natural to define impulse for a variable

Figure
7.1

$O \qquad\qquad t_0 \qquad\qquad\qquad\qquad t_1 \quad t$

with labels $\Delta t_1 \ \Delta t_2$ and Δt_n

force as the limit, if it exists, of such summations.

$$(7.2) \qquad \mathbf{P} = \lim_{\Delta t \to 0} \Sigma \, \mathbf{F}_i \, \Delta t_i = \int_{t_0}^{t_1} \mathbf{F} \, dt$$

The $\mathbf{P}$ defined by this equation has a direction determined by the mean (using time as a basis for averaging) of the forces $\mathbf{F}$ during the time interval.

Let us observe that the component of the impulse vector in any direction is merely the impulse which is associated with the component in the same direction of the variable force. Thus, for any constant direction specified by the unit vector $\mathbf{E}$,

$$(7.3) \qquad \mathbf{P}_E = (\mathbf{P} \cdot \mathbf{E})\mathbf{E} = \mathbf{E} \int_{t_0}^{t_1} (\mathbf{F} \cdot \mathbf{E}) \, dt$$

In particular, taking $\mathbf{E}$ successively as $\mathbf{I}$, $\mathbf{J}$, and $\mathbf{K}$,

$$(7.4) \qquad \mathbf{P} = \mathbf{I} \int_{t_0}^{t_1} f_x \, dt + \mathbf{J} \int_{t_0}^{t_1} f_y \, dt + \mathbf{K} \int_{t_0}^{t_1} f_z \, dt = p_x \mathbf{I} + p_y \mathbf{J} + p_z \mathbf{K}$$

Note, too, that

(7.5) *The impulse exerted by the resultant of a number of concurrent forces is equal to the sum of the impulses exerted by the forces taken separately.*

This follows at once from additive properties of integrals:

$$\int_{t_0}^{t_1} (\Sigma \, \mathbf{F}_i) dt = \Sigma \int_{t_0}^{t_1} \mathbf{F}_i \, dt$$

Example

A force is given by

$$\mathbf{F} = 2t\mathbf{I} - 10\mathbf{J} + 3t^2\mathbf{K}$$

Express the net impulse exerted by $\mathbf{F}$, since $t = 0$, as a function of t.

Solution

$$\mathbf{P} = \int_0^t \mathbf{F} \, dt = \mathbf{I} \int_0^t 2t \, dt + \mathbf{J} \int_0^t (-10) \, dt + \mathbf{K} \int_0^t 3t^2 \, dt = t^2\mathbf{I} - 10t\mathbf{J} + t^3\mathbf{K}$$

The visualization of any concept expressible as an integral is likely to be aided by the use of graphs. The variation of impulse components with time can be thought of in terms of the area under the force-component curves as in Fig. 7.2.

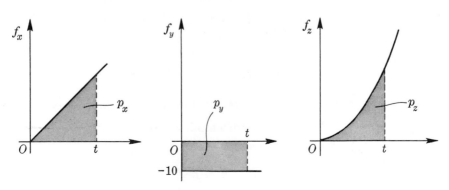

Figure
7.2

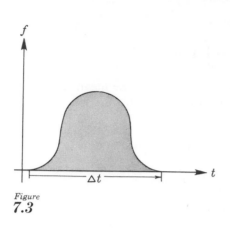

Figure
7.3

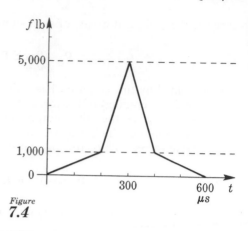

Figure
7.4

In practical problems impulses often occur for which the force pattern is un-known. For instance, when a bat hits a ball, the exact nature of the force is hard to determine. Its magnitude might vary according to a graph such as Fig. 7.3. In an impact the duration Δt of the pulse might be extremely short; therefore, presum-ably, the force is correspondingly large. The impulse-momentum approach often allows us to forget our ignorance of forces by concentrating on the observable effects of the impulses.

EXERCISES

1. A 15-lb force is applied for 2.4 sec in a direction parallel to the vector $9\mathbf{I} - 12\mathbf{J} + 20\mathbf{K}$. Compute the z component of the impulse.
2. An impulse of 500 newton-sec is due to a force whose graph is given in Fig. 7.3. If the total duration is 1,000 microseconds (μsec), what is the average magnitude of the force?
3. The magnitude of a force as a function of time is shown in Fig. 7.4. Compute the magnitude of the total impulse.
4. The profile of a force is the complete arch of a sine curve (sine x, $0 \leq x \leq \pi$). If the total duration of the pulse is 500 μsec and the magnitude of the impulse is 100 lb-sec, how large does the force get?

7.2. THE IMPULSE-MOMENTUM PRINCIPLE FOR A SINGLE PARTICLE

To evaluate the dynamical effect of an impulse on a particle of mass m, we need only integrate the equation $\Sigma \mathbf{F} = m\mathbf{A}$ with respect to time.

$$\int_{t_0}^{t_1} (\Sigma \mathbf{F})dt = \int_{t_0}^{t_1} m\frac{d\mathbf{V}}{dt}\,dt = m\int_{\mathbf{V}_0}^{\mathbf{V}_1} d\mathbf{V}$$

or

(7.6) $$\Sigma \mathbf{P} = \Sigma \int_{t_0}^{t_1} \mathbf{F}\,dt = m\mathbf{V}_1 - m\mathbf{V}_0$$

The right member of this equation is called the *change in momentum*.

(7.7)   Momentum $= m\mathbf{V}$

Equation (7.6) may be written succinctly as

(7.8) $$\Sigma \mathbf{P} = \Delta(m\mathbf{V})$$

This is the impulse-momentum principle.   In words,

(7.9) *The change of momentum of a particle during a time interval is equal to the net impulse exerted by the external forces during this interval.*

Example 1

A block slides for 5 sec down a plane inclined at 40°, the coefficient of friction being 0.4.   How much does the speed increase?

Solution

The procedure is rather simple—and distinctly similar to techniques used many times before.   First, we isolate the block as in Fig. 7.5.   The external forces are the weight w, the normal reaction n, and the friction f.   We now compute the net impulse exerted by these forces.   In the y direction the net impulse is zero, since $w \cos \theta = n$.   In the x direction the net impulse is given by

$$p_x = (w \sin \theta - f)t = w(\sin \theta - \mu \cos \theta)t$$

This may be set equal to the x component of the change in momentum:

$$w(\sin \theta - \mu \cos \theta)t = \Delta(mv) = \frac{w}{g}(\Delta v)$$

whence

$$\Delta v = g(\sin \theta - \mu \cos \theta)t = 32.2(0.337)(5.0) = 54 \text{ ft/sec}$$

Example 2

A baseball weighing 9 oz originally traveling at 120 ft/sec across home plate leaves the bat at 160 ft/sec at an angle of 45° with the horizontal directly over the first-base line.   Find the impulse in magnitude and direction.

Solution

Taking home plate as origin and the base lines as x and y axes, the initial velocity is

$$\mathbf{V_0} = 120(-0.7\mathbf{I} - 0.7\mathbf{J})$$

The final velocity is

$$\mathbf{V} = 160(0.7\mathbf{I} + 0.7\mathbf{K})$$

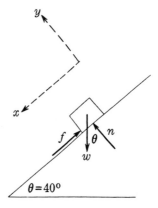

Figure
7.5

$\theta = 40°$

We have, then,

$$\mathbf{P} = \Delta(m\mathbf{V}) = m \times 0.7[160(\mathbf{I} + \mathbf{K}) - 120(-\mathbf{I} - \mathbf{J})]$$

$$= \left(\frac{9}{16 \times 32}\right)(0.7)(280\mathbf{I} + 120\mathbf{J} + 160\mathbf{K})$$

$$= 4.2(0.81\mathbf{I} + 0.35\mathbf{J} + 0.46\mathbf{K}) \qquad \text{lb-sec}$$

This shows that the impulse was 4.2 lb-sec in the direction of the unit vector appearing in parentheses.

The concept of momentum makes it possible for us to rephrase our basic dynamics equation in a form closer to Newton's second law (3.8):

(7.10) $$\Sigma\,\mathbf{F} - \frac{d}{dt}(m\mathbf{V})$$

Example 3

An object of mass m traveling at velocity $\mathbf{V}_0$ strikes a smooth plane surface whose normal makes an acute angle θ with $\mathbf{V}_0$. The object is deflected by the surface and travels along it as shown in Fig. 7.6. Find the impulse exerted and the final speed.

Solution

Since the surface is smooth, the impulse is normal to the plane:

$$\mathbf{P} = -p\mathbf{N}$$

The change in momentum may be written

$$m(\mathbf{V} - \mathbf{V}_0) = -p\mathbf{N}$$

To solve for p, take the scalar product with $\mathbf{N}$:

$$m(\mathbf{V} \cdot \mathbf{N} - \mathbf{V}_0 \cdot \mathbf{N}) = -p(\mathbf{N} \cdot \mathbf{N})$$

Clearly $\mathbf{V} \cdot \mathbf{N} = 0$; thus

$$p = m\mathbf{V}_0 \cdot \mathbf{N} = mv_0 \cos \theta$$

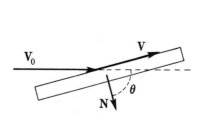

Figure
7.6

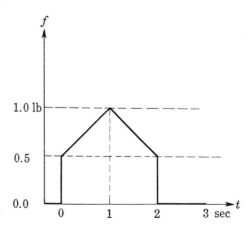

Figure
7.7

Taking components normal to $\mathbf{N}$ in the plane of $\mathbf{V}_0$ and $\mathbf{N}$, we get

$$v - v_0 \sin \theta = 0$$

We see here how impact with a smooth surface cannot change the tangential component of velocity.

EXERCISES

5. The resultant force acting on a 100-lb particle is given at time t by

$$\mathbf{F} = 3t^2\mathbf{I} - 7\mathbf{K} \quad \text{lb}$$

   When $t = 0$, the velocity is $5\mathbf{J}$ ft/sec. What is the velocity when $t = 2$ sec?

6. A sled reaches the bottom of a hill at 40 ft/sec and coasts across a level field for 3.5 sec before coming to rest. What was the coefficient of friction?

7. A ball weighing 9 oz travels at 75 mph. What net sudden impulse will change its direction by 30°, leaving its speed unchanged?

8. The initial velocity of a 9-oz ball is east and horizontal at 75 mph. A variable force whose magnitude is plotted in Fig. 7.7 and whose direction is always north and horizontal is applied. Find for $t = 3$ sec the speed and direction cosines of the ball's motion.

9. A spherical particle of mass m strikes a hard smooth surface at speed v with an angle of incidence (i.e., angle with normal) of θ. It rebounds according to the *law of regular reflection* (making equal angles with the normal). (a) Prove that the speed of the rebound is v. (b) Derive a formula for the magnitude of the impulse exerted by the surface.

7.3. THE IMPULSE-MOMENTUM PRINCIPLE FOR AN AGGREGATE OF PARTICLES

When dealing with an aggregate of particles, we distinguish between the effects of internal and of external forces. Suppose that a typical particle of mass m_i and initial velocity $\mathbf{V}_{0_i}$ is acted on during a given time interval by external forces whose resultant impulse is $\mathbf{P}_i$ and internal forces whose resultant impulse is $\mathbf{P}'_i$. Then the final velocity $\mathbf{V}_i$ is determined by Eq. (7.6):

(7.11) $$\mathbf{P}_i + \mathbf{P}'_i = m_i\mathbf{V}_i - m_i\mathbf{V}_{0_i}$$

Let such an equation be written down for each of the particles. Then, if corresponding members are added, one gets

$$\Sigma \mathbf{P}_i + \Sigma \mathbf{P}'_i = \Sigma m_i\mathbf{V}_i - \Sigma m_i\mathbf{V}_{0_i}$$

If the internal forces act during the given interval in opposite pairs as dictated by Newton's third law, their impulses add up to zero. Let us call the vector sum of the momenta of the individual particles by the name *momentum of the aggregate*:

(7.12) $$\text{Momentum} = \Sigma m_i\mathbf{V}_i$$

Our conclusion then may be stated as follows:

(7.13) *The change of momentum during a time interval of an aggregate of particles is equal to the sum of the impulses exerted by external forces.*

Example I

Initially, three pool balls of mass m have velocities, respectively, $2(\mathbf{I} + \mathbf{J})$ m/sec, $\mathbf{O}, \mathbf{O}$.   After the first has hit the second and the second has hit the third, the velocities are (not necessarily in the same order): $0.5(-\mathbf{I} - \mathbf{J})$, $0.4(\mathbf{I} - \mathbf{J})$, and $0.1(-2\mathbf{I} - \mathbf{J})$ m/sec.   What resultant impulse was exerted on the balls by the cushions during this time interval?   Neglect frictional forces.

Solution

The final momentum, since the masses are equal, is m times the sum of the stated velocities, or

$$m(-0.3\mathbf{I} - 1.0\mathbf{J})$$

The initial momentum was $m(2\mathbf{I} + 2\mathbf{J})$. The change in momentum is then $m(-2.3\mathbf{I} - 3.0\mathbf{J})$. If m is expressed in kilograms, then this is equal to the net external impulse in newton-seconds.

Example 2

A chain 9 ft long weighs 18 lb. It is held up vertically so that the bottom link touches the floor and is then allowed to drop. What is the total force on the floor when the last link hits? Neglect rebounds.

Solution

Isolating the whole chain of length l and mass m, the external forces are the total weight w downward and the upward force f of the floor.   Let y be the length already on the floor.   Then consider the momentum change for a time Δt during which an additional length Δy reaches the floor at speed v.   During this time interval the piece of length Δy ceases to move.   This means a momentum change of

$$-\frac{m}{l} \Delta y \, v$$

The momentum of the chain still in the air increases, however, because the speed has increased with an acceleration g.   This momentum change is approximately

$$+m\left(1 - \frac{y}{l}\right)g \, \Delta t$$

The corresponding impulse is $(w - f)\,\Delta t$ (where now f actually denotes the *average* force).   Equating, dividing by Δt, and taking limits as Δt approaches zero,

$$m\left(1 - \frac{y}{l}\right)g - \frac{mv^2}{l} = w - f$$

or

$$f = \frac{mv^2}{l} + \frac{y}{l}\,mg$$

The speed v, since every link falls with an acceleration g, is given by

$$v^2 = 2gy$$

The conclusion is then

$$f = 3\frac{y}{l}\,w$$

This result is based on the implicit assumption that the links are very tiny, for otherwise each link would produce its own separate impulse and the net impulse would not be so simple.   For the moment when $y = l$, we get

$$f = 3w = 54 \text{ lb}$$

Example 3

Water under an absolute pressure p flowing steadily and smoothly at speed v through a horizontal pipe of cross-sectional area a has its direction changed by an angle θ (see Fig. 7.8).   Neglecting friction and assuming homogeneity of flow, what net force must be provided by the walls of the pipe?

Solution

A sample of the water may be regarded as an aggregate of particles.   Let us isolate a section bounded by normal planes and including the corner.   Consider this section as it advances during an interval Δt.   During this interval in effect a segment of length $v \, \Delta t$ has been transferred from the pipe before the corner to the pipe after the corner.   This segment has mass

$$m = va \, \delta \, \Delta t$$

and the corresponding change in momentum is given by

$$\Delta(m\mathbf{V}) = v^2 a \, \delta \, \Delta t (\cos \theta \mathbf{I} + \sin \theta \mathbf{J} - \mathbf{I})$$
$$= v^2 a \, \delta \, \Delta t [(\cos \theta - 1)\mathbf{I} + \sin \theta \mathbf{J}]$$

The impulses due to pressure on the normal bounding planes are

$$pa\mathbf{I} \, \Delta t + pa(-\cos \theta \mathbf{I} - \sin \theta \mathbf{J}) \, \Delta t$$

Let $\mathbf{F}$ denote the unknown force; then the impulse-momentum equation is

$$\mathbf{F} \, \Delta t + pa[(1 \quad \cos \theta)\mathbf{I} - \sin \theta \mathbf{J}] \, \Delta t = v^2 a \, \delta \, \Delta t[(\cos \theta - 1)\mathbf{I} + \sin \theta \mathbf{J}]$$

The conclusion is then

$$\mathbf{F} = (v^2 \, \delta + p)a[(\cos \theta - 1)\mathbf{I} + \sin \theta \mathbf{J}]$$

The magnitude of the vector in brackets is $\sqrt{2(1 - \cos \theta)}$; thus

$$f = \sqrt{2}(v^2 \, \delta + p)a\sqrt{(1 - \cos \theta)}$$

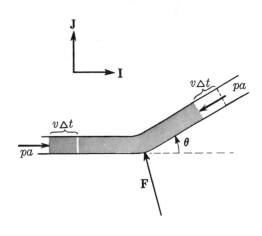

Figure
7.8

Observe that when the liquid is at rest, the force associated with p is the same; thus the additional force due solely to the change in momentum is

$$f' = \sqrt{2}\bar{v}^2 \, \delta a \sqrt{1 - \cos \theta}$$

It often happens that one has little interest in the individual motions of the members of an aggregate. In such a case information concerning the overall motion may be desirable. It is then most convenient to study the behavior of the center of mass. From the familiar equation

$$(\Sigma \, m)\bar{\mathbf{R}} = \Sigma \, m\mathbf{R}$$

one obtains, by differentiating with respect to t,

(7.14) $$(\Sigma \, m)\bar{\mathbf{V}} = \Sigma \, m\mathbf{V}$$

The statement in words follows:

(7.15) *The momentum of an aggregate is equal to the momentum of a single hypothetical particle having the whole mass of the aggregate and the velocity of the center of mass.*

The corresponding dynamical result might be phrased thus:
The change in momentum during a time interval of the center of mass of an aggregate of particles is equal to the sum of the impulses exerted on the aggregate by external forces.

It is to be understood that the "momentum of the center of mass" is a technical term having to do with the hypothetical particle of (7.15). In symbolic form our proposition is

(7.16) $$\Sigma \, \mathbf{P} = (\Sigma \, m)\bar{\mathbf{V}} - (\Sigma \, m)\bar{\mathbf{V}}_0$$

Example 4

Let us solve Example 2 using a differentiated form of Eq. (7.16). When the chain on the floor is of length y, the center of mass has coordinate $\bar{y}$ given by

$$l\bar{y} = y(0) + \frac{(l - y)^2}{2}$$

Taking the time derivative,

$$l\dot{\bar{y}} = -(l - y)\dot{y}$$

so the momentum is given by

$$m\dot{\bar{y}} = m\left(1 - \frac{y}{l}\right)(-\dot{y})$$

The differentiated form of (7.16), taking $\bar{\mathbf{V}}_0$ as a constant, is

(7.17) $$\Sigma \, \mathbf{F} = \frac{d}{dt}\{(\Sigma \, m)\bar{\mathbf{V}}\}$$

In our example the y components of this equation yield, differentiating the expression for $m\dot{\bar{y}}$,

$$f - w = m\frac{\dot{y}^2}{l} + m\left(1 - \frac{y}{l}\right)(-\ddot{y})$$

As before, $\dot{y}^2 = 2gy$, $\ddot{y} = g$, so we get, writing w for mg,

$$f - w = \frac{2wy}{l} - w + \frac{wy}{l}$$

Thus, as before, $f = 3wy/l$.

Since m is a constant, it is clear that (7.17) is in this case merely a restatement of the old formula $\Sigma \mathbf{F} = (\Sigma m)\bar{\mathbf{A}}$ in a slightly more general form—actually a form close to our first statement of Newton's second law in Sec. 3.6.

Example 5

A rocket of initial gross mass m_0 takes off vertically, exhaust gases having a constant relative speed v'. Derive an expression for the speed of the rocket as a function of time, neglecting frictional resistance.

Solution

At a typical instant t, denote the gross mass of the rocket by m and its speed by v. During an interval Δt the rocket discharges gas $-\Delta m$. The only external impulse, taking components vertically up, on the system of mass m is $-mg\,\Delta t$. The initial momentum is mv, and the final momentum at the end of the interval is

$$(m + \Delta m)(v + \Delta v) + (-\Delta m)(v - v')$$

The impulse-momentum equation then is

$$-mg\,\Delta t = [mv + (\Delta m)v + m\,\Delta v + \Delta m\,\Delta v - (\Delta m)v + (\Delta m)v'] - [mv]$$

Simplifying, dividing by Δt, and taking limits as Δt approaches zero,

$$-mg = m\dot{v} + \dot{m}v'$$

This equation gives the acceleration $\dot{v}$ for any stage of the firing. This differential equation may be rewritten as

$$-g\,dt = dv + \frac{dm}{m}v'$$

which integrates at once into

$$-gt = v + v'\ln m + \text{const}$$

At $t = 0$, suppose $v = 0$, $m = m_0$; then the constant of integration is equal to $-v'\ln m_0$, so that the equation for speed is

$$v = v'\ln\frac{m_0}{m} - gt$$

Some further simple rocket problems appear as exercises.

EXERCISES

10. A rocket ship of gross weight 5 tons is traveling at 500 ft/sec. Approximately how large a rocket charge should be fired at right angles to the ship's trajectory in order to change the course of the ship by 5°? (The firing speed is 2,500 ft/sec.)

11. A pile of 10 balls, each weighing 75 g, is scattered by a blow from a 2-kg block traveling at 12 m/sec. If the block is brought to rest by the blow, what is the resulting speed of the center of mass of the original aggregate of balls after the impact?

12. The upper end of a 10-m chain of linear density 0.5 kg/m is held at rest 20 m above a horizontal floor. If the chain is released, what total force will it exert on the floor at the moment when its middle link strikes?

13. Water from a fire hose with a nozzle 2 in. in diameter strikes a plate-glass window at an angle of 65° with the normal and is deflected parallel to the glass. What force does the window sustain if the water is delivered at 600 gal/min?

14. Show that the net effective propelling force (thrust) of a rocket, using the symbolism of Example 5, is equal to $-\dot{m}v'$.

7.4. CONSERVATION OF MOMENTUM

If an aggregate of particles is subject to no external forces during a given time interval, the change in momentum during that interval must be zero. This corollary of (7.13) is called the *law of conservation of momentum.*

(7.18) *The momentum of an aggregate is constant when there is no net external impulse.*

It immediately follows that

(7.19) *The center of mass of an aggregate which is subject to no external forces travels in a straight line at constant velocity.*

It appears that momentum is a persistent invariant for isolated mechanical systems. Since momentum changes only through the action of external impulse, situations involving small forces and short time intervals may often be treated as if no forces were present.

Example 1

A billiard ball moving at 10 ft/sec strikes squarely another ball initially at rest. The first ball comes to rest in the collision. The momentum of the first ball is transferred to the second. Actually, frictional forces between the balls and the surface of the billiard table exert impulses during collision. But the impulses are negligibly small if the duration of the skid is short. Thus the experiment is an excellent demonstration of momentum conservation even though external impulses are not quite absent.

Example 2

A 2-kg sphere with a velocity of $3\mathbf{I} - 4\mathbf{J}$ m/sec collides with a 3-kg sphere of velocity $-\mathbf{I} + \mathbf{J}$ m/sec. After the collision the 3-kg sphere has velocity $\mathbf{I} + \mathbf{J}$ m/sec. Find the new velocity of the 2-kg sphere.

Solution

By the conservation law the total momentum after impact is equal to that before.
$$2(3\mathbf{I} - 4\mathbf{J}) + 3(-\mathbf{I} + \mathbf{J}) = 2(v_x\mathbf{I} + v_y\mathbf{J}) + 3(\mathbf{I} + \mathbf{J})$$

Equating x and y components,
$$6 - 3 = 2v_x + 3 \quad \text{or} \quad v_x = 0 \text{ m/sec}$$
$$-8 + 3 = 2v_y + 3 \quad \text{or} \quad v_y = -4 \text{ m/sec}$$

Example 3

When an artillery shell explodes in mid-air, the velocity of the center of mass is unchanged since the only impulses are internal.

EXERCISES

15. A single freight car coasting at 4 ft/sec bumps into and is coupled to a car twice as heavy which initially is at rest. What is their common speed after the impact?

16. A 2-kg sphere of velocity $3\mathbf{I} - 4\mathbf{J}$ m/sec has its velocity exactly reversed by collision with a moving 4-kg sphere. What change in velocity does the latter undergo?

17. A 2-lb duck flying at 40 ft/sec is struck from the side by 2 oz of shot traveling at 800 ft/sec. How much is the path deflected if the shot lodges in the bird?

18. A rocket of gross mass m and initial velocity $\mathbf{V_0}$ emits a charge of mass m' at relative velocity $\mathbf{V}'$. In order that the rocket undergo a velocity change $\Delta\mathbf{V}$, show that $\mathbf{V}'$ must be given by

$$\mathbf{V}' = \left(1 - \frac{m}{m'}\right)\Delta\mathbf{V}$$

19. A rocket of instantaneous gross mass m emits a continuous blast of gases at relative velocity $\mathbf{V}'$ and at a rate $(-dm/dt)$. Show that the acceleration of the rocket is given by

$$\frac{d\mathbf{V}}{dt} = \frac{1}{m}\left(\frac{dm}{dt}\right)\mathbf{V}'$$

(HINT: Replace m' in Exercise 18 by $-\Delta m$, and use limiting process.)

20. A rocket of net mass $\bar{m}$ and propellant mass m'' is coasting in interstellar space at speed v_0. If the relative escape speed of the rocket's gases is v', show that the maximum increase in speed to be gotten from the remaining fuel is given by

$$\Delta v = v' \ln\left(1 + \frac{m''}{\bar{m}}\right)$$

(HINT: Use an integrated form of the result of Exercise 19.)

7.5. COEFFICIENT OF RESTITUTION

If a tennis ball is dropped onto a hard floor, the rebound is high if the ball is good, low if the ball is poor. These judgments describe qualitatively the ability of the ball to resume its shape when it is deformed. In this section we study a concept which is useful in dealing with collisions exhibiting varying degrees of recoil. When a uniform solid spherical ball strikes at right angles a fixed smooth plane surface such as a wall or floor, the process of collision may be studied in terms of the impulses generated. Isolating the ball, we may say that the wall exerts an impulse $\mathbf{P}$ while the ball is being brought to rest. High-speed photographs show that a golf ball undergoes flattening when subjected to such an impulse. Ordinarily, the ball does not remain at rest, although one made of putty might. Usually, there is a rebound, and the ball tends to regain its shape, although some permanent deformation may occur. This requires a brief period of acceleration while the ball is still in contact with the barrier. Let the impulse exerted by the barrier during this period be indicated by $\mathbf{P}'$. Now $\mathbf{P}'$ may be zero, as in the case of the putty, or it may be practically equal to $\mathbf{P}$, as in the case of a good rubber ball (or it might even be greater than $\mathbf{P}$ in case it is properly charged with an explosive). Ordinarily, $\mathbf{P}'$ is somewhere between zero and $\mathbf{P}$. Since the surface is smooth and the collision is normal, $\mathbf{P}'$ will have the same direction as $\mathbf{P}$; thus we may write

(7.20) $\mathbf{P}' = e\mathbf{P}$

For spheres, e is nearly a constant at moderate speeds although it does depend on shape and material. For very low speed of collision, so that there is no permanent deformation of the collision surface, e is normally about 1. We shall assume in the problems of this text that e is a constant for the speeds encountered, and we call e the *coefficient of restitution*. Note that (7.20), together with the assumption that e is a constant, constitutes a minor postulate based, as in earlier more significant cases, on empirical evidence. If U is the velocity of approach (see Fig. 7.9) and V the velocity of rebound, we have as impulse-momentum equations

$$\mathbf{O} - m\mathbf{U} = \mathbf{P}$$

$$m\mathbf{V} - \mathbf{O} = \mathbf{P}'$$

so

$$m\mathbf{V} = e(-m\mathbf{U})$$

or

(7.21) $$\mathbf{V} = -e\mathbf{U}$$

Except for the change in direction, then, the coefficient of restitution appears as the ratio of velocity after and before impact. If at the moment of collision the barrier happens to be moving in the direction of $\mathbf{U}$ or $\mathbf{P}$, the velocities in (7.21) are replaced by relative velocities. The details of this deduction are left for Exercise 22.

Let us now consider a less special example of impact from the point of view of restitution. Consider two smooth spheres in collision. Let their line of centers at the moment of collision have a direction designated by the unit vector $\mathbf{I}$ as in Fig. 7.10. Before impact the velocities are, respectively, $\mathbf{U}$ and $\mathbf{U}'$. The center of mass must have a constant velocity $\bar{\mathbf{U}}$ throughout. After impact the velocities are $\mathbf{V}$ and $\mathbf{V}'$. At one moment of closest approach the spheres have a common normal velocity component $\bar{\mathbf{U}} \cdot \mathbf{I} = \bar{u}_x$. The impulse before this moment is $\mathbf{P}$, and after this moment it is $\mathbf{P}'$. We assume that (7.20) still holds. Isolating the bodies separately and applying the impulse-momentum equation, we have

$$m\bar{\mathbf{U}} - m\mathbf{U} = \mathbf{P} \qquad m'\bar{\mathbf{U}} - m'\mathbf{U}' = -\mathbf{P}$$

$$m\mathbf{V} - m\bar{\mathbf{U}} = \mathbf{P}' \qquad m'\mathbf{V}' - m'\bar{\mathbf{U}} = -\mathbf{P}'$$

Figure
7.9

Figure
7.10

Taking the scalar products with $\mathbf{I}$, these equations become

$$m\bar{u}_x - mu_x = p \qquad m'\bar{u}_x - m'u'_x = -p$$
$$mv_x - m\bar{u}_x = p' \qquad m'v'_x - m'\bar{u}_x = -p'$$

Using the relationship $p' = ep$,

$$v_x - \bar{u}_x = e(\bar{u}_x - u_x) \qquad v'_x - \bar{u}_x = e(\bar{u}_x - u'_x)$$

Separating terms in $\bar{u}_x$,

$$\bar{u}_x(1 + e) = v_x + eu_x = v'_x + eu'_x$$

Rearranging terms in the last two members,

(7.22) $$v_x - v'_x = -e(u_x - u'_x)$$

or

$$(\mathbf{V} - \mathbf{V}') \cdot \mathbf{I} = -e(\mathbf{U} - \mathbf{U}') \cdot \mathbf{I}$$

The essence of this result may be summarized as follows:

(7.23) *When two smooth spheres collide, the impact being in the direction of the x axis, the x component of their relative velocity reverses signs and is diminished by a factor equal to the coefficient of restitution.*

It is interesting, although not surprising, to observe how symmetrical is the motion relative to the center of mass in the situation just described. Rearranging the equations before (7.22), we have

(7.24) $$v_x - \bar{u}_x = -e(u_x - \bar{u}_x) \qquad v'_x - \bar{u}_x = -e(u'_x - \bar{u}_x)$$

This should be compared with both (7.22) and (7.21). The latter comparison shows that both spheres behave as if they were bouncing off a wall of normal $\mathbf{I}$ which moves with the center of mass.

The theory of restitution has been developed here for spheres only. In simple problems involving symmetrical bodies other than spheres, we shall assume that Eqs. (7.20) and (7.22) are valid. Detailed analysis of these extensions will not be given here. A collision is called *perfectly elastic* when $e = 1$, *inelastic* when $e = 0$.

Example I

When two smooth spheres collide, their line of centers is parallel to the x axis. Just before collision their velocities were

$$\mathbf{U} = 10\mathbf{I} - 5\mathbf{J} \text{ cm/sec} \qquad \text{and} \qquad \mathbf{U}' = 5\mathbf{J} \text{ cm/sec}$$

If the coefficient of restitution is 0.5 and if the mass of the first is twice that of the second, what is the velocity of the second right after the collision?

Solution

The restitution equation (7.22) is here

$$v_x - v'_x = -\tfrac{1}{2}(10 - 0) = -5$$

The x components in the conservation-of-momentum equation gives

$$10(2m) = 2mv_x + mv'_x$$

Solving simultaneously,

$$v'_x = 10 \text{ cm/sec} \qquad v'_y = u'_y = 5 \text{ cm/sec}$$

Thus

$$\mathbf{V}' = 10\mathbf{I} + 5\mathbf{J} \qquad \text{cm/sec}$$

Example 2

A sphere of radius r and mass m_1 is at rest on a billiard table. A second sphere of radius r and mass m_2 strikes the first sphere squarely at speed u. The coefficient of restitution is e. What are the possible outcomes?

Solution

Proceeding first in a general way, the momentum equation is

$$m_2 u = m_1 v_1 + m_2 v_2$$

The restitution equation is

$$v_2 - v_1 = -eu$$

Solving this pair of equations, we get

$$v_2 = \frac{(m_2 - m_1 e)u}{m_1 + m_2} = \frac{[(m_2/m_1) - e]u}{1 + (m_2/m_1)} - \frac{(1 - m_1 e/m_2)u}{1 + m_1/m_2}$$

$$v_1 = \frac{(1 + e)m_2 u}{m_1 + m_2} = \frac{(1 + e)(m_2/m_1)u}{1 + (m_2/m_1)} = \frac{(1 + e)u}{1 + (m_1/m_2)}$$

If $e = 0$, we have $v_1 = v_2$; that is, the spheres cohere. Now suppose that $e > 0$. If $m_2 > m_1 e$, both v_1 and v_2 are positive, but if $m_2 = m_1 e$, the balls interchange momentum. If $m_2 \gg m_1$, $v_2 = u$ while $v_1 = (1 + e)u$; that is, the ball initially in motion is undeterred by the collision while the target ball outspeeds the other, having a speed relative to the other of eu. If $m_2 < m_1 e$, the two spheres travel in opposite directions after collision. If $m_2 \ll m_1$, v_2 is equal to $-eu$, just as if the target sphere were a stationary wall, while $v_1 = 0$.

Arguments of this sort are sometimes useful in dealing with collisions of the particles of atomic physics. (See, for instance, Exercise 86.)

EXERCISES

21. A particle strikes a fixed plane wall with an angle of incidence (i.e., with normal) of θ_1. Using only (7.20) and the laws of impulse and momentum, derive an expression for $\tan \theta_2$ (where θ_2 is the angle between normal and velocity after impact) in terms of θ_1 and e [and μ in (b)], (a) assuming that the wall is smooth; (b) assuming that the wall is rough (coefficient of friction $= \mu$) and that slipping is imminent during the whole contact.

22. A spherical particle strikes perpendicularly at a speed u a massive smooth wall which is receding at a constant speed u'. The coefficient of restitution is e. Using only (7.20) and the laws of impulse and momentum, derive an expression for the speed of the particle after impact.

23. A number of identical perfectly elastic spheres are lined up almost touching. Another such sphere traveling at speed v along the same line strikes the end of the column. Show that, after the full impact, the sphere on the opposite end has acquired the speed v while all the others are at rest.

24. Two spheres of identical radius but different mass roll on a horizontal plane surface. The first, of mass 200 g, is traveling with a velocity of 80 cm/sec in the x direction. It is struck by the other whose mass is 150 g and which has a velocity of 60**J** cm/sec. The line of centers is parallel to **J** at the impact. Find both velocities right after impact if the coefficient of restitution is 0.6.

25. A 2-lb particle and a 3-lb particle collide head on in such a way that the 2-lb particle is "stopped dead" while the 3-lb particle has its velocity just reversed in direction. Find the coefficient of restitution.

7.6. WORK AND POWER

Next we turn to the space integral of a force, but the approach to this idea will be gradual. A force is completely specified if its magnitude, direction, and point of application are known. If the point of application moves while the force is applied, the force is said to do work. For a constant force and a straight-line displacement (see Fig. 7.11), the work is equal to the scalar product of the force times the displacement:

$$(7.25) \qquad \text{Work} = \mathbf{F} \cdot \Delta\mathbf{R}$$

In other terms, we may say that only the component of force parallel to the displacement contributes to the work done: this component times the length of the displacement is equal to the work. If the particle makes a succession of displacements $\Delta\mathbf{R}_1, \ldots, \Delta\mathbf{R}_n$, the work done by $\mathbf{F}$ is the sum of the works for individual displacements:

$$\text{Work} = \mathbf{F} \cdot \Delta\mathbf{R}_1 + \mathbf{F} \cdot \Delta\mathbf{R}_2 + \cdots + \mathbf{F} \cdot \Delta\mathbf{R}_n$$

Of course, if $\mathbf{F}$ is constant throughout, by the distributive law we have

$$(7.26) \qquad \text{Work} = \mathbf{F} \cdot (\Delta\mathbf{R}_1 + \Delta\mathbf{R}_2 + \cdots + \Delta\mathbf{R}_n) = \mathbf{F} \cdot \overline{\Delta\mathbf{R}}$$

where $\overline{\Delta\mathbf{R}}$ is the vector sum of the given displacements. On the other hand, if more than one force $\mathbf{F}_1, \ldots, \mathbf{F}_n$ acts at a single point, say, on a single particle, then, for a displacement $\Delta\mathbf{R}$, one has

$$\text{Work} = \mathbf{F}_1 \cdot \Delta\mathbf{R} + \mathbf{F}_2 \cdot \Delta\mathbf{R} + \cdots + \mathbf{F}_n \cdot \Delta\mathbf{R}$$

and again by the distributive law,

$$(7.27) \qquad \text{Work} = (\mathbf{F}_1 + \cdots + \mathbf{F}_n) \cdot \Delta\mathbf{R} = \bar{\mathbf{F}} \cdot \Delta\mathbf{R}$$

So the work done by an aggregate of concurrent forces is equal to the work done by the resultant for the same displacement.

Example I

In Fig. 7.12 a car free to move along fixed rails is acted on by four constant forces while the car moves 10 ft to the right. The work done by the forces is tabulated below:

Pounds	Foot-pounds
50	500
25	0
100	500
70.7	500

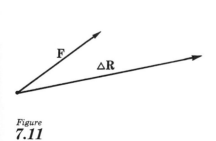

Figure
7.11

Figure
7.12

The net work done by the system of four forces is $+500$ ft-lb.   The resultant force on the car can be written $50\mathbf{I} + 12\mathbf{J}$, and the displacement is $10\mathbf{I}$, so, more formally, the work is computed as $(50\mathbf{I} + 12\mathbf{J}) \cdot 10\mathbf{I} = 500$.

Let us now confront the more general situation of a variable force and a curvilinear displacement of the point of application.   In Fig. 7.13 a curved path is shown, along with pictures of the force at selected points.   While the simple equations (7.25) to (7.27) do not at once apply to this more complex context, they at least do suggest our approach.   Assuming that the force varies smoothly in both direction and magnitude, it is clear that, for a small displacement $\Delta\mathbf{R}$ and a value of $\mathbf{F}$ associated with some point in this displacement, the scalar product given by (7.25) is approximately what we should wish to call the work done during that displacement.

By approximating the whole path by a zigzag polygon consisting of successive displacements $\Delta\mathbf{R}_1, \Delta\mathbf{R}_2, \ldots$, as in Fig. 7.14, we can consider the sum of such elements of work:

$$\text{Work} \cong \mathbf{F}_1 \cdot \Delta\mathbf{R}_1 + \mathbf{F}_2 \cdot \Delta\mathbf{R}_2 + \cdots$$

or

$$\text{Work} \cong \Sigma\, \mathbf{F}_i \cdot \Delta\mathbf{R}_i$$

We should expect to get a more significant value for zigzag paths more closely fitting the curve.   Consequently, it is natural to define work in this general case as the limit of such approximations as the lengths of the $\Delta\mathbf{R}$'s are made smaller and smaller.

$$(7.28) \qquad \text{Work} = \lim_{|\Delta\mathbf{R}_i|\to 0} \Sigma\, \mathbf{F}_i \cdot \Delta\mathbf{R}_i$$

In ordinary practical cases the limit exists.   The form of the definition already suggests the ideas of integral calculus reviewed in Sec. 5.10.   This limit of a sum, involving as it does a summation along a path, is called a *line integral*.   It is written

$$\lim_{|\Delta\mathbf{R}_i|\to 0} \Sigma\, \mathbf{F}_i \cdot \Delta\mathbf{R}_i = \int_{\mathbf{R}_0}^{\mathbf{R}_1} \mathbf{F} \cdot d\mathbf{R}$$

Thus

$$(7.29) \qquad \text{Work} = \int_{\mathbf{R}_0}^{\mathbf{R}_1} \mathbf{F} \cdot d\mathbf{R}$$

The $\mathbf{R}_0$ and $\mathbf{R}_1$ designate the starting and stopping points and hence set the limits for the summation. $\mathbf{F}$ may vary from point to point; therefore $\mathbf{F}$ must be regarded as

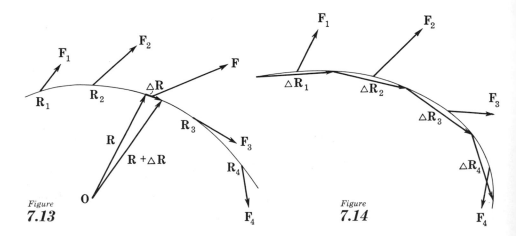

Figure
7.13

Figure
7.14

a function of $\mathbf{R}$. The significance of the line integral in terms of components is seen by expanding the scalar products:

$$(7.30) \qquad \int_{\mathbf{R}_0}^{\mathbf{R}_1} \mathbf{F} \cdot d\mathbf{R} = \lim_{\Delta x_i \to 0} \Sigma f_{i_x} \Delta x_i + \lim_{\Delta y_i \to 0} \Sigma f_{i_y} \Delta y_i$$

$$+ \lim_{\Delta z_i \to 0} \Sigma f_{i_z} \Delta z_i = \int_{x_0}^{x_1} f_x \, dx + \int_{y_0}^{y_1} f_y \, dy + \int_{z_0}^{z_1} f_z \, dz$$

The same extended scalar form of (7.29) may be obtained by expanding the symbolic scalar product of the integrand. Taking

$$\mathbf{F} = f_x \mathbf{I} + f_y \mathbf{J} + f_z \mathbf{K} \qquad \mathbf{R}_1 = x_1 \mathbf{I} + y_1 \mathbf{J} + z_1 \mathbf{K}$$
$$\mathbf{R}_0 = x_0 \mathbf{I} + y_0 \mathbf{J} + z_0 \mathbf{K} \qquad d\mathbf{R} = dx\mathbf{I} + dy\mathbf{J} + dz \, \mathbf{K}$$

we have again

$$(7.31) \qquad \text{Work} = \int_{\mathbf{R}_0}^{\mathbf{R}_1} \mathbf{F} \cdot d\mathbf{R} = \int_{x_0}^{x_1} f_x \, dx + \int_{y_0}^{y_1} f_y \, dy + \int_{z_0}^{z_1} f_z \, dz$$

For these scalar integrations to be carried out, each integrand must be represented as a function of the corresponding independent variable. This usually requires a knowledge of equations of the path. In most of the applications considered in this chapter, the full scope of this definition of work will not be employed.

Example 2

A variable force $\mathbf{F}$ is given by

$$\mathbf{F} = 2y\mathbf{I} + xy\mathbf{J}$$

For a straight-line displacement from the origin to the point $\mathbf{R}_1 = 2\mathbf{I} + \mathbf{J}$, what work is done?

Solution

An equation of this line is $2y = x$. For points on the line, then, the force may be written

$$\mathbf{F} = x\mathbf{I} + 2y^2\mathbf{J}$$

The work may now be computed

$$\text{Work} = \int_{\mathbf{O}}^{\mathbf{R}_1} \mathbf{F} \cdot d\mathbf{R} = \int_0^2 x \, dx + 2\int_0^1 y^2 \, dy = 2.67$$

If several forces have the same point of application, then, as in (7.27), the net work done, i.e., the algebraic sum of the work done by the individual forces, is equal to the work done by the resultant. This follows at once from the distributive law for scalar products and from the additive property of definite integrals. Thus, if $\bar{\mathbf{F}} = \Sigma \, \mathbf{F}$, we have

$$(7.32) \qquad \Sigma \int \mathbf{F} \cdot d\mathbf{R} = \int (\Sigma \, \mathbf{F}) \cdot d\mathbf{R} = \int \bar{\mathbf{F}} \cdot d\mathbf{R}$$

Equation (7.31) may be thought of as a special case of this since $\mathbf{F}$ is the resultant of the three forces $f_x\mathbf{I}, f_y\mathbf{J}, f_z\mathbf{K}$.

Example 3

A block is pushed up an inclined plane by a force **F** parallel to the plane through a distance l as in Fig. 7.15.   The work done by **F** is

$$\text{Work} = fl$$

Regarding **F** as the resultant of $f_x\mathbf{I}$ and $f_y\mathbf{J}$ and the displacement as

$$\Delta\mathbf{R} = l\cos\theta\mathbf{I} + l\sin\theta\mathbf{J}$$

$$\text{Work} = (f_x\mathbf{I})\cdot(l\cos\theta\mathbf{I} + l\sin\theta\mathbf{J}) + (f_y\mathbf{J})\cdot(l\cos\theta\mathbf{I} + l\sin\theta\mathbf{J})$$

$$= (f_x\cos\theta + f_y\sin\theta)l$$

Now $f_x = f\cos\theta$ and $f_y = f\sin\theta$; thus this last expression becomes

$$\text{Work} = (f\cos^2\theta + f\sin^2\theta)l = fl$$

as before.

Example 4.   Work Done by a Constant Force

If **F** is constant as indicated in Fig. 7.16, we have

$$\text{Work} = \int_{\mathbf{R_0}}^{\mathbf{R_1}}\mathbf{F}\cdot d\mathbf{R} = \mathbf{F}\cdot\int_{\mathbf{R_0}}^{\mathbf{R_1}}d\mathbf{R} = \mathbf{F}\cdot(\mathbf{R_1} - \mathbf{R_0})$$

This means that the work done is independent of the path; one needs merely to compute the work that would be done by the force during a straight-line displacement from the initial to the final point.   This result is very important.   It is also so beguilingly simple that one wishes to use it.   Please remember, however, that we have justified it only for forces constant in both magnitude and direction.

Example 5.   Work Done by Gravity in a Restricted Locality on a Particle
             or an Aggregate of Particles

By the last result, when a particle moves from one position to another by any path,

$$\text{Work} = \mathbf{W}\cdot(\mathbf{R_1} - \mathbf{R_0}) = m\mathbf{G}\cdot(\mathbf{R_1} - \mathbf{R_0})$$

For an aggregate of particles,

$$\text{Work} = \Sigma\, m\mathbf{G}\cdot(\mathbf{R_1} - \mathbf{R_0}) = \mathbf{G}\cdot(\Sigma\, m\mathbf{R_1} - \Sigma\, m\mathbf{R_0}) = (\Sigma\, m)\mathbf{G}\cdot(\bar{\mathbf{R}}_1 - \bar{\mathbf{R}}_0)$$

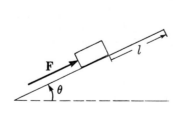

Figure
7.15

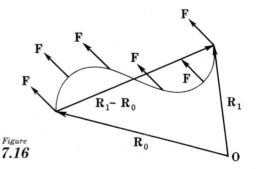

Figure
7.16

It is easy to calculate $\mathbf{G} \cdot (\bar{\mathbf{R}}_1 - \bar{\mathbf{R}}_0)$ as $-g\, \Delta h$, where the latter symbol denotes the vertical displacement or increase of height of the center of mass (see Fig. 7.17). For a particle, aggregate of particles, or rigid body, then, the work done by gravity is, in a restricted locality, always equal to the magnitude of the weight times the vertical displacement downward.

$$(7.33) \qquad\qquad \text{Work (due to gravity)} = -w\, \Delta h$$

Power. The time rate of performance of work is called *power*. It is measured in foot-pounds per second (ft-lb/sec), horsepower (550 ft-lb/sec $= 1$ hp), or joules per second (watts).

$$(7.34) \qquad\qquad \text{Power} = \frac{d}{dt}(\text{work}) = \lim_{\Delta t \to 0} \frac{\mathbf{F} \cdot \Delta \mathbf{R}}{\Delta t} = \mathbf{F} \cdot \mathbf{V}$$

This suggests a number of convenient alternative formulas for work:

$$(7.35) \qquad\qquad \text{Work} = \int_{t_0}^{t_1} \mathbf{F} \cdot \mathbf{V}\, dt = \int_{t_0}^{t_1} \mathbf{F} \cdot \frac{ds}{dt}\, \mathbf{T}\, dt = \int_{s_0}^{s_1} f_T\, ds$$

Thus work is either the time integral of the power or the arc-length integral of the tangential component of the force.

Example 6

A 2-ton automobile drives at 30 mph up a 30° incline for a distance of 1,000 ft. At what rate is work done by gravity?

Solution

$\mathbf{F} \cdot \mathbf{V}$ in this case is (see Fig. 7.18)

$$(4,000 \text{ lb})(44 \text{ ft/sec}) \cos 120° = -88,000 \text{ ft-lb/sec} = -160 \text{ hp}$$

EXERCISES

26. A 100-lb log is dragged at uniform speed up a 30° ramp 10 ft long by a rope making an angle of 10° above the ramp.   If the coefficient of friction is 0.4, find the work done (*a*) by the friction; (*b*) by the normal reaction with the ramp; (*c*) by the force exerted by the rope; (*d*) by gravity.
27. A force with *x*, *y*, and *z* components of 3, 4, and 12 lb is displaced from the point $(1,2,3)$ to the point $(2,-3,1)$.   How much work does it do?

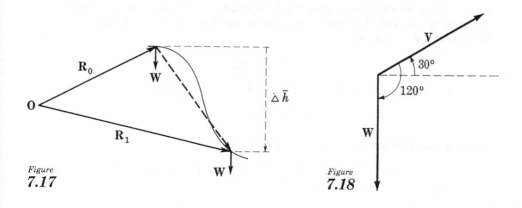

Figure
7.17

Figure
7.18

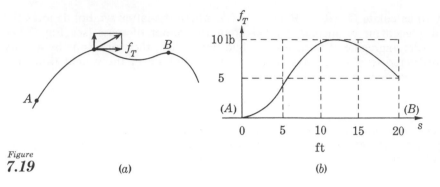

f_T

Figure
7.19   (a)   (b)

28. If the force acting on a body at the position (x,y) m is

$$\mathbf{F} = y\mathbf{I} + 5\mathbf{J} \qquad \text{newtons}$$

how much work is done on the body in going from $(-5,0)$ to $(5,0)$ m (a) by a straight-line path?   (b) by a straight-line path from $(-5,0)$ m to $(0,5)$ m followed by a straight-line path from $(0,5)$ m to $(5,0)$ m?

29. A particle moves in the xy plane from $(0,2)$ m to $(2,0)$ m along a straight-line path while subject to a force $\mathbf{F} = 10(\mathbf{I} + \mathbf{J})$ newtons.   How much work is done by the force?

30. Find the work done in excavating a circular 10-ft well 6 ft in diameter at the top and 4 ft in diameter at the bottom.   The dirt forms a conical pile 6 ft deep.   Assume that a cubic foot of the soil weighs 100 lb.

31. A 10-ft chain weighing 5 lb hangs over a small pulley, with 6 ft hanging down on one side.   If it is released, how much work will have been done by gravity by the time the chain leaves the pulley?

32. An elevator weighing 1,700 lb is hauled up a vertical mine shaft 1,000 ft deep.   The total weight of the cable used is 1,500 lb.   What work is done if the cable is wound on a drum of negligible bearing friction?

33. A 3-ft 1-lb simple pendulum oscillates with an amplitude of 5°.   How much work is done by gravity when it swings from its highest to its lowest point?

34. A particle is displaced a total distance of 20 ft from A to B along a curve drawn to scale above (Fig. 7.19).   It is subject to a variable force whose tangential component is represented in Fig. 7.19b.   Estimate the work done by the force.

7.7. THE WORK-ENERGY PRINCIPLE FOR A PARTICLE

In this section we shall investigate the dynamical significance of work.   Suppose that a particle is subjected to forces whose resultant is $\mathbf{F}$.   Then, of course, we may use the equation $\mathbf{F} = m\mathbf{A}$, or

$$\mathbf{F} = m\frac{d\mathbf{V}}{dt}$$

To bring work into the discussion, we take the scalar product with

$$d\mathbf{R} = \frac{d\mathbf{R}}{dt}\,dt = \mathbf{V}\,dt$$

and then integrate between corresponding limits

$$\int_{\mathbf{R}_0}^{\mathbf{R}_1}\mathbf{F}\cdot d\mathbf{R} = \int_{t_0}^{t_1} m\frac{d\mathbf{V}}{dt}\cdot\mathbf{V}\,dt = \int_{\mathbf{V}_0}^{\mathbf{V}_1} m\mathbf{V}\cdot d\mathbf{V}$$

The right member is easily integrated since

$$\frac{d}{dt}(\mathbf{V} \cdot \mathbf{V}) = \frac{d\mathbf{V}}{dt} \cdot \mathbf{V} + \mathbf{V} \cdot \frac{d\mathbf{V}}{dt} = 2\mathbf{V} \cdot \frac{d\mathbf{V}}{dt}$$

so that

$$\int_{\mathbf{V}_0}^{\mathbf{V}_1} m\mathbf{V} \cdot d\mathbf{V} = \frac{1}{2} m\mathbf{V} \cdot \mathbf{V} \Big|_{\mathbf{V}_0}^{\mathbf{V}_1}$$

Our conclusion is

(7.36) $$\int_{\mathbf{R}_0}^{\mathbf{R}_1} \mathbf{F} \cdot d\mathbf{R} = \tfrac{1}{2} m\mathbf{V}_1 \cdot \mathbf{V}_1 - \tfrac{1}{2} m\mathbf{V}_0 \cdot \mathbf{V}_0$$

The left member is total work done [in view of (7.32)] on the particle during its displacement from $\mathbf{R}_0$ to $\mathbf{R}_1$. The quantity appearing twice in the right member is called the *kinetic energy*, i.e., the energy of motion, of the particle:

(7.37)   Kinetic energy $= \text{k.e.} = \tfrac{1}{2} m\mathbf{V} \cdot \mathbf{V} = \tfrac{1}{2} mv^2$

Note that

(7.38) $\text{k.e.} = \tfrac{1}{2} mv_x^2 + \tfrac{1}{2} mv_y^2 + \tfrac{1}{2} mv_z^2$

In terms of this concept the right member of (7.36) is equal to the kinetic energy of the particle at the end of the displacement minus its kinetic energy at the beginning of the displacement, i.e., to the change in kinetic energy. This conclusion is called the *work-energy principle* for a particle.

(7.39) *The change in kinetic energy of a particle during a displacement is equal to the net work done by all the forces acting on it during this displacement.*

In short,

(7.40)   Work $= \Delta(\text{k.e.})$

In applying this principle, a plan of attack such as the following may be used. First, isolate the body. Second, compute the work done by each of the isolating forces during the displacement in question. Third, equate the sum of these works to the final kinetic energy minus the initial kinetic energy and solve for whatever unknown there may be. In some cases the net work can best be computed by first finding the resultant force and then evaluating the work done by the resultant.

Example I

An electrically charged particle of mass m (kg) and charge q (coulombs) is accelerated from rest through a potential difference of V (volts). What speed is attained?

Solution

If other forces are negligible, the work done by electric forces on the particle is equal to Vq. Assuming that the speed attained is small compared with the speed of light, so that relativity corrections may be ignored, the kinetic energy attained is expressed by the usual formula $\tfrac{1}{2} mv^2$. By the work-energy principle,

$$Vq = \tfrac{1}{2} mv^2$$

Hence

$$v = \left(\frac{2Vq}{m}\right)^{\frac{1}{2}}$$

Example 2

A baseball is thrown with a speed of 100 ft/sec at an angle θ. When it reaches its maximum height of 64 ft, how fast is it traveling? Neglect air friction.

Solution

The only force is the weight. The work done by this force is $-w\,\Delta h$, or

$$\text{Work} = -64w$$

The change in kinetic energy is equal to this work:

$$\frac{1}{2}\left(\frac{w}{g}\right)v^2 - \frac{1}{2}\left(\frac{w}{g}\right)(100)^2 = -64w$$

Hence

$$v^2 = 100^2 - 128g = 5{,}880 \qquad v = 76.7\ \text{ft/sec}$$

Example 3

A hockey puck is projected along level ice at 60 ft/sec. If the coefficient of friction is 0.06, how far will it slide?

Solution

Let the distance be s. Then

$$\Delta(\text{k.e.}) = 0 - \frac{1}{2}\left(\frac{w}{g}\right)60^2$$

The weight and normal reaction do zero work since the displacement is horizontal and hence perpendicular to them. The work done by friction is negative:

$$\text{Work} = -0.06ws$$

Equating these, we get

$$s = \frac{3{,}600}{0.12g} = 931\ \text{ft}$$

Example 4

A grocer's scale descends 1 in. when a 1-lb potato is placed on it. If the potato is dropped from a height of 3 ft onto the scale, how far is the scale depressed (assuming that the energy losses of impact can be ignored)?

Solution

The kinetic energy initially is zero. When the scale reaches its lowest point, the kinetic energy is again zero. Hence the net work done is zero. Let y be the amount the scale is depressed. Then the work done by gravity on the potato is $wh = 1(3 + y)$. The work done by the spring in the scale must now be computed. It presumably deflects an inch per pound, or the force is

$$f = -12y$$

and the work is

$$\text{Work} = \int_0^y f\,dy = -12\int_0^y y\,dy = -6y^2$$

We have then

$$6y^2 - y - 3 = 0$$

whence

$$y = 9.5\ \text{in.}$$

Example 5

A simple pendulum of mass m and length l is displaced by 90° and then released from rest.   At what angle with the vertical is the tension equal to the weight?

Solution

Since this problem involves the tension which does zero work, the work-energy approach can hardly be expected to provide the full solution.   It is an aid, however. First isolate the bob, and use the equation $\Sigma\, F = mA$, taking components along the string for an intermediate position θ.   Letting f denote the magnitude of the tension,

$$f - mg \cos\theta = m\,\frac{v^2}{l}$$

The work-energy equation is

$$\tfrac{1}{2}mv^2 = mgl \cos\theta$$

Eliminating v^2,

$$f - mg \cos\theta = 2mg \cos\theta$$

Now let $f = mg$, and we get

$$\cos\theta = \tfrac{1}{3} \qquad \theta = 70.5°$$

EXERCISES

35. What is the maximum kinetic energy of a simple pendulum 4 m long weighing 2.6 newtons and with an amplitude of 8°?

36. A block slides down a plane surface inclined at an angle of 30° with the horizontal. If the initial speed is 20 m/sec and the coefficient of friction 0.6, how far will it slide before coming to rest?

37. A 200-lb load on the end of a rope is hauled up vertically with an initial force of 250 lb which diminishes uniformly at the rate of a pound per foot.   Find the speed after it has ascended 30 ft.

38. A block weighing 100 lb slides from rest a distance of 32 ft down a plane inclined at 60° before attaining a speed of 32 ft/sec.   Find the coefficient of friction.

39. A 1,000-lb elevator breaks loose and falls from rest a distance of 16 ft, gaining a speed of 20 ft/sec.   How much work was done by the friction which was the only impeding force?

40. A $\tfrac{1}{2}$-oz bullet traveling at 1,000 ft/sec strikes squarely a 1-in. board and emerges at 700 ft/sec.   If the force of resistance is constant, how far would such a bullet penetrate into a thick block of the same material?

41. An automobile (rear-wheel drive, uniform weight distribution) starting on an icy but level pavement was able to pick up a speed of 12 mph only after it had gone 300 ft. What was the coefficient of friction between tires and ice?

42. A boy runs and then slides a distance of 100 ft on an ice-covered lake.   If he tries again with twice the initial velocity, how far will he be able to slide?

43. A 10-lb steel ball B attached by an 8-ft wire to a fixed pin A is held at rest so that the wire AB is taut and horizontal.   It is then released.   What angle does AB make with the horizontal when the tension in the wire is equal to twice the weight of the ball?

44. Show that, for a particle subject to forces of resultant $\mathbf{F}$, the following equation holds:

$$\int_{x_0}^{x_1} f_x\, dx = \tfrac{1}{2}mv_{1x}^2 - \tfrac{1}{2}mv_{0x}^2$$

45. Starting with the definition of kinetic energy and the equation $\Sigma\, F = mA$, prove in detail the following: The rate of increase of kinetic energy of a particle is equal to the net power exerted by external forces.

7.8. WORK AND ENERGY FOR AN AGGREGATE
OF PARTICLES

When we attempt to apply the ideas of the last section to an aggregate of particles, we find definite limitations. First, consider the matter of work. In our previous studies of aggregates, only temporary account was taken of internal forces. Their net contribution to force equations and to impulse equations was zero. Suppose that two equal and opposite forces $\mathbf{F}'$ and $-\mathbf{F}'$ act, respectively, at $\mathbf{R}_1$ and $\mathbf{R}_2$, where $\mathbf{R}_1 = \mathbf{R}_2 + \mathbf{Q}$ as in Fig. 7.20. Then the total work due to these internal forces is computed thus:

$$\text{Work}' = \int \mathbf{F}' \cdot d\mathbf{R}_1 + \int (-\mathbf{F}') \cdot d\mathbf{R}_2 = \int \mathbf{F}' \cdot (d\mathbf{R}_2 + d\mathbf{Q}) + \int (-\mathbf{F}') \cdot d\mathbf{R}_2$$

or

(7.41)
$$\text{Work}' = \int_{\mathbf{Q}_0}^{\mathbf{Q}_1} \mathbf{F}' \cdot d\mathbf{Q}$$

For a typical situation where the force is one of attraction between two particles, the scalar product is easily expressed in terms of the distance q between the particles:

(7.42)
$$\text{Work}' = -\int_{q_0}^{q_1} f' \, dq$$

This work is zero when the relative position of the two points is constant. Thus if two particles are joined by an inextensible cord, the internal forces might be neglected, but if they are connected by an elastic cord, the work done by it affects the energy equation. *When the particles are rigidly connected (as in a rigid body), the internal work is zero.*

Now suppose we have given a set of particles of which a typical one has mass m and is acted on by external forces and internal forces. During a given time interval the velocity of such a particle changes from $\mathbf{V}_0$ to $\mathbf{V}_1$. Denoting the work done during this interval by both external and internal forces by "work," we have, by (7.40),

$$\text{Work} = \tfrac{1}{2}m\mathbf{V}_1 \cdot \mathbf{V}_1 - \tfrac{1}{2}m\mathbf{V}_0 \cdot \mathbf{V}_0$$

Such an expression can be written down for each particle of the aggregate. Summing these expressions, we get

(7.43)
$$\text{Total work} = \Sigma \tfrac{1}{2}m\mathbf{V}_1 \cdot \mathbf{V}_1 - \Sigma \tfrac{1}{2}m\mathbf{V}_0 \cdot \mathbf{V}_0 = \Delta(\text{k.e.})$$

The kinetic energy of a system of particles may be related to the behavior of the center of mass. Let us consider velocities $\mathbf{V}'$ of the particles relative to the center of mass. Then

$$\mathbf{V} = \bar{\mathbf{V}} + \mathbf{V}'$$

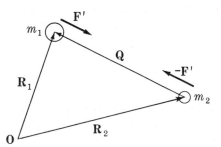

Figure
7.20

Consequently, for the whole system,

$$\text{k.e.} = \Sigma \tfrac{1}{2}m(\bar{\mathbf{V}} + \mathbf{V}') \cdot (\bar{\mathbf{V}} + \mathbf{V}')$$
$$= \Sigma \tfrac{1}{2}m\bar{\mathbf{V}} \cdot \bar{\mathbf{V}} + \Sigma\, m\mathbf{V}' \cdot \bar{\mathbf{V}} + \Sigma \tfrac{1}{2}m\mathbf{V}' \cdot \mathbf{V}'$$

Since $\bar{\mathbf{V}}$ is the same for each term in the summations, this may be factored out:

$$\text{k.e.} = \tfrac{1}{2}(\Sigma\, m)\bar{\mathbf{V}} \cdot \bar{\mathbf{V}} + (\Sigma\, m\mathbf{V}') \cdot \bar{\mathbf{V}} + \Sigma \tfrac{1}{2}m\mathbf{V}' \cdot \mathbf{V}'$$

In the right member of this equation the first term may be called the *kinetic energy of the center of mass*: it is the energy of a single particle at the center of mass and having the whole mass of the system.   The second term is equal to zero, for

$$\Sigma\, m\mathbf{V}' = \Sigma\, m(\mathbf{V} - \bar{\mathbf{V}}) = \Sigma\, m\mathbf{V} - (\Sigma\, m)\bar{\mathbf{V}}$$

which, by Eq. (7.14), is null.   The third term may be called the *kinetic energy relative to the center of mass*.   The conclusion may be written, for an aggregate,

(7.44) $$\text{k.e.} = \tfrac{1}{2}(\Sigma\, m)\bar{v}^2 + \Sigma\, (\tfrac{1}{2}mv'^2)$$

Example I

Two objects of mass 1 and 3 kg are connected by a light inextensible cord passing over a frictionless light pulley.   If these are released at the same level, how fast will the system be going after a displacement of 50 cm?

Solution

Only gravity does work.   We could measure this in terms of the displacement of the center of mass.   It is probably quicker to do it for the objects separately.

$$\text{Work} = 1(-0.5)9.8 + 3(0.5)9.8 = 9.8 \text{ joules}$$

Since the cord does not stretch, the speeds of the two particles are equal:

$$\text{k.e.} = \tfrac{1}{2}(1 + 3)v^2$$

Using (7.43),

$$2v^2 = 9.8 \qquad v = 2.2 \text{ m/sec}$$

Example 2

Two blocks of mass 3 and 5 kg are tied together with a spring compressed between.   If the blocks are released, the spring expands, obeying Hooke's law.   Its force initially is 8 newtons, and after expanding 4 cm the force is 4 newtons.   What is the velocity of the 3-kg block at that moment?

Solution

The spring obeys Hooke's law; thus $f = -ky$.   The work done as it expands is

$$\int_{y_0}^{y} f\, dy = -\frac{1}{k} \int_{f_0}^{f} f\, df = \frac{1}{2k} (f_0^2 - f^2)$$
$$= \frac{1}{2k} (f_0 + f)(f_0 - f)$$
$$= \tfrac{1}{2}(f_0 + f)(y - y_0)$$
$$= \tfrac{1}{2}(8 + 4)(0.04) = 0.24 \text{ joule}$$

The kinetic energy attained may be written, using the conservation of momentum law, $mv + m'v' = 0$,

$$\frac{1}{2}mv^2 + \frac{1}{2}m'v'^2 = \frac{1}{2}mv^2 + \frac{1}{2}m'\left(\frac{-mv}{m'}\right)^2$$

$$= \frac{1}{2}mv^2\left(1 + \frac{m}{m'}\right) = \tfrac{1}{2}(1 + \tfrac{3}{5})v^2 = 2.4v^2$$

Finally, by the work-energy principle, these may be equated:

$$2.4v^2 = 0.24 \qquad \text{or} \qquad v = 0.32 \text{ m/sec}$$

Example 3

A 12-lb 6-ft chain rests with 4 ft held on a horizontal table top, the two remaining feet hanging over the smooth edge. If the coefficient of friction is 0.3, with what speed will the last link leave the table if the chain is released?

Solution

Initially, the center of mass is given by (see Fig. 7.21)

$$\bar{y} = \frac{2(0) + 1(1)}{3}$$

that is,

$$\bar{y} = 0.33 \text{ ft} \qquad \text{or} \qquad 4 \text{ in.}$$

When the last link is leaving the table,

$$\bar{y} = 3 \text{ ft}$$

The work done by gravity is then

$$12(3 - \tfrac{1}{3}) = 32 \text{ ft-lb}$$

The work done by friction during a displacement dy is, when y represents the length of the hanging portion,

$$-0.3\left(\frac{6 - y}{6}\right)12 \, dy$$

During the whole displacement it is

$$-0.6\int_{2}^{6}(6 - y)\,dy = -0.6\left[6y - \frac{y^2}{2}\right]_{2}^{6} = -4.8 \text{ ft-lb}$$

The work-energy equation then gives

$$32 - 4.8 = \tfrac{1}{2}(12/32.2)\,v^2$$

from which

$$v = 12.1 \text{ ft/sec}$$

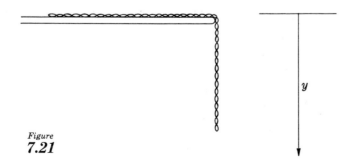

Figure
7.21

As in nearly all cases, there are advantages for a purely literal solution, substituting numerical values in the last step. Here we have used a numerical approach in order to keep energy magnitudes and units in sight. A literal approach will be used in an alternative solution.

Alternative Solution

Just as a check let us compute the preceding result from the methods of Chap. 6. Isolating the overhanging portion of the chain, the forces are weight and tension. Isolating the portion on the table, the forces having components in the direction of the acceleration are tension and friction. Combining the two equations of motion (the tensions canceling), we have

$$w' - \mu w'' = \frac{w' + w''}{g} a$$

The weights of the overhanging and remaining portions for a given position y may be substituted as follows:

$$\frac{y}{l} w - \mu \frac{l - y}{l} w = \frac{w}{g} v \frac{dv}{dy}$$

Integrating this equation,

$$\frac{g}{l} \int_{l/3}^{l} [(1 + \mu)y - \mu l] \, dy = \int_{0}^{v} v \, dv$$

Solving for v^2,

$$v^2 = \frac{4gl}{9} (2 - \mu)$$

Note that v does not depend on the density of the chain. Now we may put in numerical values.

$$v = \tfrac{2}{3}[gl(2 - \mu)]^{\frac{1}{2}} = \tfrac{2}{3}[32.2(6)(2 - 0.3)]^{\frac{1}{2}} = 12.1 \text{ ft/sec}$$

Energy Losses in Collisions. Let us finally seek a formula for the energy loss when a pair of spheres collides, as in Sec. 7.5. By (7.44) we know that the kinetic energy of the system is equal to the kinetic energy associated with the center of mass plus the kinetic energy of relative motion. Since the center of mass maintains the same velocity throughout in the case of two colliding spheres, only the relative velocity need be considered. Since all the y and z components are unchanged by the collision, we have only x terms:

$$-\Delta(\text{k.e.}) = \tfrac{1}{2}m(u_x - \bar{u}_x)^2 + \tfrac{1}{2}m'(u'_x - \bar{u}_x)^2 - \tfrac{1}{2}m(v_x - \bar{u}_x)^2 - \tfrac{1}{2}m'(v'_x - \bar{u}_x)^2$$

Using (7.24), this becomes

$$-\Delta(\text{k.e.}) = [\tfrac{1}{2}m(u_x - \bar{u}_x)^2 + \tfrac{1}{2}m'(u'_x - \bar{u}_x)^2](1 - e^2)$$

Now

$$u_x - \bar{u}_x = u_x - \frac{mu_x + m'u'_x}{m + m'} = \frac{m'}{m + m'} (u_x - u'_x)$$

and

$$u'_x - \bar{u}_x = u'_x - \frac{mu_x + m'u'_x}{m + m'} = \frac{m}{m + m'} (u'_x - u_x)$$

Using these expressions, we get

(7.45)
$$-\Delta(\text{k.e.}) = \frac{1}{2}\left(\frac{mm'}{m + m'}\right)(u_x - u'_x)^2(1 - e^2)$$

Note that this result depends on the *reduced mass* μ of the system, where μ is defined by $1/\mu = (1/m) + (1/m')$ and on the x component of the relative velocity. When the collision is perfectly elastic ($e = 1$), no energy loss occurs; when the energy is inelastic ($e = 0$), the energy loss is maximum.

Example 4

For the collisions described in Sec. 7.5, Example 2, what are the possibilities for energy dissipation?

Solution

For the case where $u'_x = 0$, we have energy loss equal to

$$\frac{1}{2} \frac{m_1 m_2}{m_1 + m_2} u^2 (1 - e^2)$$

The energy available was $\frac{1}{2} m_2 u^2$. Hence the fractional energy lost was

$$\frac{m_1}{m_1 + m_2} (1 - e^2) = \frac{1 - e^2}{1 + (m_2/m_1)}$$

For maximum energy dissipation, then, e should be as small as possible and the target sphere as massive as possible. Both of these conclusions agree with an intuitive analysis of the problem. When all the momentum is transferred from one sphere to the other so that, by the previous example, $m_2/m_1 = e$, the fractional energy lost is

$$\frac{1 - e^2}{1 + e} = 1 - e$$

In particular, when the sphere masses are equal and the collision perfectly elastic, no energy is lost.

EXERCISES

46. Two particles of mass 0.5 kg each are initially at rest on a smooth horizontal table. Initially they are separated by a distance of 1 m. The magnitude of the force of attraction between them is given by

$$f = \frac{0.1}{q^2} \qquad \text{newtons}$$

(q is the separation in meters). What speed does each have by the time the separation is reduced to 10 cm?

47. Neglecting friction and inertia of the pulley, find (in Fig. 7.22) (a) the velocity after w_2 has moved from rest a distance of 50 cm; (b) the tension in the cord if w_1 is an object of mass 1 kg and w_2 of mass 0.5 kg.

48. Find the speed after a displacement of 25 cm for the system shown in Fig. 7.23. The inertia and friction of the pulleys may be neglected. The system starts from rest.

49. A 28-ft chain weighing 11 lb is held on a 30° smooth roof with 14 ft hanging over the edge as in Fig. 7.24. If it is released, with what speed will the last link leave the edge?

50. Two 1-lb blocks of wood rest on a smooth table joined by a spring whose unstretched length is 12 in. They are held 24 in. apart by 5-lb forces, then released. What is their speed when they are 18 in. apart?

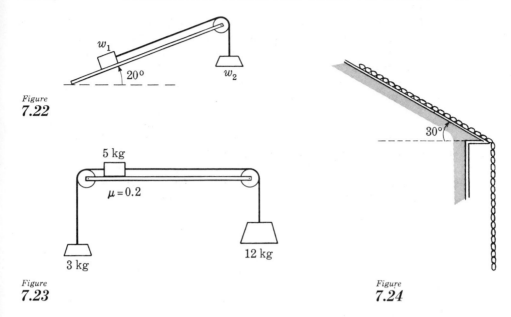

Figure
7.22

Figure
7.23

Figure
7.24

51. Show that the kinetic energy relative to the center of mass of an aggregate consisting of two particles can be written

$$\tfrac{1}{2}\mu(\mathbf{V}_2 - \mathbf{V}_1)\cdot(\mathbf{V}_2 - \mathbf{V}_1)$$

where μ stands for the reduced mass given by

$$\mu = \frac{m_1 m_2}{m_1 + m_2}$$

7.9. CONSERVATIVE FORCES AND POTENTIAL ENERGY

Energy is sometimes described as a measure of capacity for doing work. Associated with a particle in motion is an energy $\tfrac{1}{2}mv^2$. In what sense can the particle cause work to be done? This question can be answered by considering the converse problem of how to deprive the particle of its energy. This can be accomplished by applying a suitable force to the particle and letting it do work. When the particle is brought to rest, the net work done by this force is, by the work-energy principle, equal to $-\tfrac{1}{2}mv^2$. But by the reaction postulate (3.1) we know that the force gave rise to an equal and opposite companion force. This force, exerted by the particle on whatever was stopping it, did work equal to $+\tfrac{1}{2}mv^2$. In this sense the kinetic energy is a precise appraisal of the work which the particle can stimulate.

A particle may also have a capacity for causing work to be done because of its position or state. An example is the driving weight of a "grandfather's clock." When the clock is wound, the weight is in such a position that the work of running the clock can be done. Such stored energy is usually called *potential energy*. In this case it is associated with the gravitational pull on the weight. In a spring clock a potential energy is stored in the spring. Energy may also be stored in electrical and magnetic, as well as mechanical, devices.

Not all forces can reasonably be thought of as generators of potential energy.

Only forces that can do positive as well as negative work are suitable. This rules out dissipative forces which cannot do positive work. Another necessary characteristic is uniqueness. If potential energy is to be a useful index of capacity to do work, each position or state of the body having the energy must correspond to a unique value of the potential energy, independent of the method of computation. Consider a particle of weight 2 lb moving in a vertical plane as follows: east 1 ft, up 1 ft, west 1 ft, down 1 ft. We shall evaluate the work done by the gravitational force in each of these displacements. During the easterly displacement the weight does zero work, but during the displacement up the weight does -2 ft-lb of work and 2 ft-lb of potential energy is stored in the system. The westerly displacement again involves no work. Now when the particle descends, the stored energy is used and the gravitational force does work of $+2$ ft-lb. The particle has been carried around a particular closed path, and the potential energy has balanced perfectly. Such a balance is always achieved for closed paths with forces which are called *conservative*.

Now consider a 2-lb object resting on a table where the coefficient of sliding friction is 0.3. Suppose that the object is caused by a varying horizontal force to slide along the surface of the table describing a circle of circumference 4 ft. We compute the work done by the frictional force, which is easily seen to be a 0.6-lb force. Since this force always opposes the motion, the work for each part of the journey is negative. For the total closed path the work done by the frictional force is -2.4 ft-lb. This is quite in contrast with the other example, where positive and negative work offset each other. This frictional force is an example of a nonconservative force. Note that when the path is retraced in the reverse direction, a different force pattern is encountered. Magnitudes are the same, but directions are reversed, so again the work is negative. The concept of *conservative force* will now be defined precisely. It will then be shown that such a force is suitable for use in discussions of potential energy.

Given a force $\mathbf{F}$, defined for all positions which may be occupied by the particle or body under consideration, then $\mathbf{F}$ is said to be a *conservative force* if the net work done by it for a displacement around every closed path is zero. Two symbolic statements follow:

$$(7.46) \qquad \int_{\mathbf{R}_0}^{\mathbf{R}_0} \mathbf{F} \cdot d\mathbf{R} = 0 \qquad \text{or} \qquad \oint \mathbf{F} \cdot d\mathbf{R} = 0$$

A conservative force must satisfy our first criterion of being able to do positive as well as negative work. Since the net work is zero, there are only two alternatives: either it always does zero work or it does work of both signs. If it does zero work, it is of only trivial interest from the energy standpoint. An example of such a force is the normal reaction between a rolling object and an inclined plane. This kind of force is called a constraint. It clearly could not contribute to potential energy. If, on the other hand, a conservative force does negative work during part of a displacement, it must do positive work during another part in order that the net work be zero.

Example I

Any constant force is conservative. For, as was shown in Sec. 7.6, Example 4, the work done by such a force is a multiple of the net displacement. (The net displacement for a closed path is obviously zero.) In particular, *weight* is a conservative force for any locality.

Example 2

Consider a force $\mathbf{F} = f(x)\mathbf{E}$, where $\mathbf{E}$ is a constant unit vector. Then $\mathbf{F}$ is conservative because

$$\oint \mathbf{F} \cdot d\mathbf{R} = \int_{\mathbf{R}_0}^{\mathbf{R}_0} f(x)(l\mathbf{I} + m\mathbf{J} + n\mathbf{K}) \cdot (dx\,\mathbf{I} + dy\,\mathbf{J} + dz\,\mathbf{K})$$

$$= l \int_{x_0}^{x_0} f(x)\,dx + m f(x) \int_{y_0}^{y_0} dy + n f(x) \int_{z_0}^{z_0} dz = 0$$

Example 3

An elastic force obeying a form of Hooke's law, $\mathbf{F} = -k\mathbf{R}$, is conservative. ($k$ is a constant.) For

$$\oint (-k\mathbf{R}) \cdot d\mathbf{R} = \oint (-kr\mathbf{L}) \cdot (dr\,\mathbf{L} + r\,d\theta\,\mathbf{M})$$

$$= \oint -kr\,dr = -k\frac{r^2}{2}\Big|_{r_0}^{r_0} = 0$$

Further examples will be investigated in Chap. 17.

We can now define potential energy for any conservative force. Let there be given a body or particle subjected to a conservative force $\mathbf{F}$. Let $\mathbf{B}$ be designated as a base point or reference point. This choice is arbitrary; therefore in practice it is selected on the grounds of expediency. Then at position $\mathbf{R}$ the particle or body is said to possess by virtue of $\mathbf{F}$ *potential energy relative to* $\mathbf{B}$ equal to minus the work done by $\mathbf{F}$ in a displacement from $\mathbf{B}$ to $\mathbf{R}$.

(7.47) $$\text{p.e.} = -\int_{\mathbf{B}}^{\mathbf{R}} \mathbf{F} \cdot d\mathbf{R}$$

We can now check on the second criterion for a suitable force: is the potential energy relative to $\mathbf{B}$ unique, or does it depend on the path taken from $\mathbf{B}$ to $\mathbf{R}$? In Fig. 7.25 two routes for the displacement are shown. We need merely use (7.46), together with underlying properties of any integration, to show that

$$\int_{\mathbf{B}}^{\mathbf{R}} \mathbf{F} \cdot d\mathbf{R}_1 = \int_{\mathbf{B}}^{\mathbf{R}} \mathbf{F} \cdot d\mathbf{R}_2$$

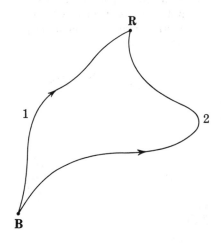

Figure
7.25

This follows from the identity

$$\int_{B}^{R} \mathbf{F} \cdot d\mathbf{R} = -\int_{R}^{B} \mathbf{F} \cdot d\mathbf{R}$$

and the following form of (7.46):

(7.48) $$\int_{B}^{R} \mathbf{F} \cdot d\mathbf{R}_1 + \int_{R}^{B} \mathbf{F} \cdot d\mathbf{R}_2 = 0$$

(The excursion B-1-R-2-B is a closed path.)   This result may be stated in more general terms:

(7.49) *The work done by a conservative force during a displacement from one point to another is independent of the path taken between these two points.*

Example 4

When the force in question is the weight of a body (or aggregate of particles), the potential energy is expressible in terms of the height of the center of mass above the level of the base point B (see Fig. 7.26).

(7.50) $$\text{p.e.} = w\bar{h}$$

This follows from (7.33).

Example 5

When the force is that of a spring obeying Hooke's law, with the base point at the unstretched position, the potential energy is given by

(7.51) $$\text{p.e.} = -\int_{R}^{B} \mathbf{F} \cdot d\mathbf{R} = -\int_{B}^{R} (-k\mathbf{R}) \cdot d\mathbf{R} = \int_{0}^{r} kr\, dr = \tfrac{1}{2}kr^2$$

EXERCISES

52. Compute $\oint \mathbf{F} \cdot d\mathbf{R}$ for the force of friction when a 10-lb object is constrained to slide around a circle of radius 10 in. on a horizontal table when the coefficient of friction is 0.4.   The circuit is accomplished at uniform speed in 3 sec.

53. Show that $\Delta(\text{p.e.})$ is independent of the base point B.

54. An object hangs at the end of a vertical spring which obeys Hooke's law. Taking the equilibrium position as base point, find a formula for potential energy taking account of both gravity and spring.

55. A system of particles consists of n objects of masses $m_1, m_2, \ldots, m_n$. Show that the potential energy relative to gravity of the subsystem $m_1, m_2, \ldots, m_k$, plus the potential energy of the subsystem $m_{k+1}, m_{k+2}, \ldots, m_n$, is equal to the potential energy of the whole system.

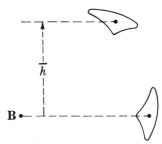

Figure
7.26

7.10. LAW OF CONSERVATION OF MECHANICAL ENERGY

The concept of potential energy is primarily useful as a means of dodging explicit computation of work. Since the force is to be conservative, by (7.49) the work for a displacement as in Fig. 7.27 from $\mathbf{R_0}$ to $\mathbf{R_1}$ can be evaluated by changing the route to include $\mathbf{B}$.

$$\int_{\mathbf{R_0}}^{\mathbf{R_1}} \mathbf{F} \cdot d\mathbf{R} = \int_{\mathbf{R_0}}^{\mathbf{B}} \mathbf{F} \cdot d\mathbf{R} + \int_{\mathbf{B}}^{\mathbf{R_1}} \mathbf{F} \cdot d\mathbf{R}$$

or

(7.52)
$$\int_{\mathbf{R_0}}^{\mathbf{R_1}} \mathbf{F} \cdot d\mathbf{R} = (\text{p.e.})_0 - (\text{p.e.})_1$$

that is,

$$\text{Work} = -\Delta(\text{p.e.})$$

In words, we have shown that

(7.53) *The work done by a conservative force is equal to the loss in potential energy of the object on which the force acts.*

Example 1

A spring initially a foot long stretches an inch when a 2-lb force is applied. The constant k appearing in (7.51) is then $k = 24$ lb/ft. The potential energy formula then is

$$\text{p.e.} = 12r^2$$

Let us now compute the work done by the spring as it contracts from 16 to 14 in.:

$$\text{Work} = 12(r_0^2 - r_1^2) = 12[(\tfrac{1}{3})^2 - (\tfrac{1}{6})^2] = 1 \text{ ft-lb}$$

Let us now combine (7.52) with the work-energy principle:

(7.54)
$$\Delta(\text{k.e.}) = \text{work} = -\Delta(\text{p.e.})$$

or

(7.55)
$$\Delta(\text{k.e.} + \text{p.e.}) = 0$$

This is a symbolic statement of one of the best-known propositions of mechanics:

(7.56) *If a particle, system of particles, or rigid body is subject to a conservative force only, then the sum of kinetic plus potential energies is a constant.*

This is immediately extended to the case where several conservative forces act in concert; then the potential energy is the sum of the separate potential energies.

Example 2

A bead slides from rest down a smooth curved wire (see Fig. 7.28) in the vertical xy plane from (x,y) ft to the origin. What speed does it have at the origin? Since the shape of the curve is not specified, this is a problem of considerable generality.

Solution

Initially,
$$\text{k.e.} = 0 \qquad \text{p.e.} = wy$$

Finally,
$$\text{k.e.} = \frac{1}{2}\left(\frac{w}{g}\right)v^2 \qquad \text{p.e.} = 0$$

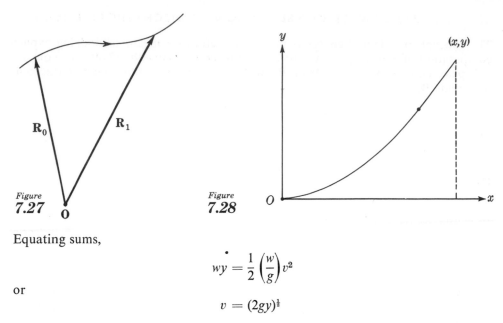

Figure
7.27

Figure
7.28

Equating sums,

$$wy = \frac{1}{2}\left(\frac{w}{g}\right)v^2$$

or

$$v = (2gy)^{\frac{1}{2}}$$

The idea that energy is essentially indestructible although subject to changes in form is central in physics. Consider, for instance, the behavior of a simple pendulum *in vacuo*. As it oscillates back and forth the form of its mechanical energy periodically changes. At its maximum displacement from equilibrium the kinetic energy is zero while its potential energy is maximum (positive, negative, or zero, depending on the choice of reference point). As the pendulum bob moves toward equilibrium position, the potential energy decreases and the kinetic energy increases correspondingly. This idealized process of periodic energy interchange is a typical example of energy conservation. From the analysis given so far, one would expect the oscillation to continue forever. Actually, the vacuum is imperfect, the cord probably flexes a little, the support tends to warm up slightly, etc. But the experiment is not declared a failure, and the conservation law a falsehood. Rather, we explain or even compute how energy is dissipated, mostly into thermal forms of energy. Such considerations take us outside the scope of simple mechanics. They show, however, how firmly entrenched is the idea of energy conservation. It is convenient to insist that only the form of energy changes even if it is necessary to invent new vehicles for energy.

7.11. ENERGY AND OSCILLATIONS

If the position of a particle in oscillation is given in terms of a single coordinate (e.g., angle for a pendulum), the potential energy may have a graph like that in Fig. 7.29. As was discussed in the preceding section, the kinetic energy is maximum when the potential energy is minimum, say, at $\theta = \theta_0$ in the figure. Likewise, the kinetic energy is zero when the potential energy is maximum, say, at $\theta = \theta_m$ and $\theta = \theta_{m'}$. As the particle oscillates, its representative point on the potential-energy graph also oscillates about the minimum point. Thus a potential-energy graph often is suggestive of physical performance. More will be said about this in Sec. 17.3.

Quantitative, as well as qualitative, information about small oscillations may be obtained from energy considerations.   One approach is to differentiate an energy equation to get an equation of motion which can be recognized as simple harmonic. This is a natural step, since our original energy equations were reached by integrating $\mathbf{F} = m\mathbf{A}$.   This method often involves approximations for small angles:

(7.57) $$\sin \theta \to \theta$$

Also,

$$1 - \cos \theta = 2 \sin^2 \frac{\theta}{2} \to 2 \left(\frac{\theta}{2}\right)^2 = \frac{\theta^2}{2}$$

Thus

(7.58) $$\cos \theta \to 1 - \frac{\theta^2}{2} \to 1$$

Another approach is to assume that the motion is simple harmonic and then to determine the period τ by the property

(7.59) $$\tau = \frac{2\pi(\text{amplitude})}{\text{maximum speed}}$$

This property is easily verified from the elementary theory of simple harmonic motion such as is given in Sec. 5.9.

Example I

Let a light spring with a stiffness constant k support a bob of mass m.   With what period will the system oscillate about its equilibrium position?   Neglect dissipatory factors.

First Solution

Let s_0 denote the extension of the spring for equilibrium position when the bob is attached (so that $ks_0 = mg$) and let x be the coordinate of the bob relative to this equilibrium position (see Fig. 7.30).   To use the methods of this section we need formulas for kinetic and potential energy.   For a reference level select arbitrarily the equilibrium position of the unloaded spring.   Then the two potential energies

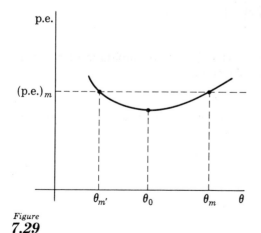

Figure
7.29

Figure
7.30

(one for spring and one for gravity) give us

$$\text{p.e.} = \tfrac{1}{2}k(s_0 + x)^2 - mg(s_0 + x)$$

Also,

$$\text{k.e.} = \tfrac{1}{2}m\dot{x}^2$$

By conservation of energy,

$$\tfrac{1}{2}k(s_0 + x)^2 - mg(s_0 + x) + \tfrac{1}{2}m\dot{x}^2 = \text{const}$$

Now take the time derivative

$$k(s_0 + x)\dot{x} - mg\dot{x} + m\dot{x}\ddot{x} = 0$$

Since, in general, $\dot{x} \neq 0$ and since $ks_0 - mg = 0$, we have

$$\ddot{x} + \frac{k}{m}x = 0$$

By Proposition (5.60), this is recognized as simple harmonic motion of period $2\pi(m/k)^{\frac{1}{2}}$.

Second Solution

This time we consider maximum kinetic and potential energies.   When $x = 0$, k.e. $= \tfrac{1}{2}mv_m^2$ (where v_m is the maximum speed) and p.e. $= \tfrac{1}{2}ks_0^2 - mgs_0$.   When x is equal to the amplitude x_m, k.e. $= 0$, while p.e. $= \tfrac{1}{2}k(s_0 + x_m)^2 - mg(s_0 + x_m)$. By conservation of energy, then,

$$\tfrac{1}{2}mv_m^2 + \tfrac{1}{2}ks_0^2 - mgs_0 = 0 + \tfrac{1}{2}ks_0^2 + ks_0x_m + \tfrac{1}{2}kx_m^2 - mgs_0 - mgx_m$$

Simplifying and using again the relation $ks_0 = mg$, we have the striking equality

$$\tfrac{1}{2}mv_m^2 = \tfrac{1}{2}kx_m^2$$

from which we deduce

$$\frac{x_m}{v_m} = \sqrt{\frac{m}{k}}$$

Using Eq. (7.59), we get again for period τ

$$\tau = 2\pi\left(\frac{m}{k}\right)^{\frac{1}{2}}$$

Example 2

Use energy methods to determine the period for small amplitude of a simple pendulum of length l and mass m.   Neglect damping.

First Solution

Letting the angle between cord and vertical be θ (as in Fig. 6.5), we have for potential energy relative to equilibrium position

$$\text{p.e.} = mgl(1 - \cos\theta)$$

while

$$\text{k.e.} = \tfrac{1}{2}m(l\dot{\theta})^2$$

By conservation of energy,

$$mgl(1 - \cos\theta) + \tfrac{1}{2}m(l\dot{\theta})^2 = \text{const}$$

Take the time derivative and simplify:

$$g \sin \theta + l\ddot{\theta} = 0$$

For small θ, $\sin \theta \to \theta$, so we use

$$\ddot{\theta} + \left(\frac{g}{l}\right)\theta = 0$$

and by Proposition (5.60), obtain

$$\tau = 2\pi \left(\frac{l}{g}\right)^{\frac{1}{2}}$$

Second Solution

When $\theta = 0$, p.e. $= 0$, k.e. $= \frac{1}{2}mv_m^2$, where v_m is the maximum speed. When $\theta = \theta_m$, θ_m being the maximum angular displacement, we have k.e. $= 0$, p.e. $= mgl(1 - \cos \theta_m)$. By conservation of energy,

$$\tfrac{1}{2}mv_m^2 = mgl(1 - \cos \theta_m)$$

But for small θ_m, $1 - \cos \theta_m \to \theta_m^2/2$, so we get, letting $x_m = l\theta_m$,

$$v_m^2 = gl\left(\frac{x_m}{l}\right)^2$$

so that

$$\frac{x_m}{v_m} = \sqrt{\frac{l}{g}}$$

yielding, by Eq. (7.59), the same equation as before.

EXERCISES

56. Draw and label appropriately a potential-energy curve analogous to that of Fig. 7.29 for the simple oscillator of Example 1.
57. With what period will a bead oscillate at the bottom of a smooth vertical semicircular wire of radius r?

7.12. THE PRINCIPLE OF VIRTUAL WORK

The concepts of work and energy can be very useful in statics problems. Suppose that we have given a system of interacting particles and rigid bodies. Each member of the system may be subject to three kinds of forces.

Internal Forces. These are, as before, forces of interaction between members. They occur in equal but opposite pairs. When the system is displaced, each pair may do work if the distance between the points of application can vary. For interconnections such as hinges, inextensible taut strings, and smooth sliding contacts, the net work done by each such pair of forces is zero.

Constraints. A constraint is a force of interaction between a member of the system and an external object directly limiting the motion of the member. Constraints restrict the geometrical character of the motion of the system. Examples are the *normal* reaction of a wire on a bead which is constrained to slide on the wire, the force exerted by a hinge which binds a member of the system to an external object, forces exerted by bearings which constrain a rigid body to have one fixed axis. For a displacement of the system, a constraint does zero work, for it is always normal to the path of its point of application. Now the force of reaction between a member of the system and an external object may involve friction. Such a tangential component will be considered as a force in the next category.

Applied Forces. Applied forces are external forces other than constraints. They include pushes and pulls, weight, and frictional forces. An applied force may do and usually does do positive work when the system experiences a suitable displacement.

If our system of interacting particles and rigid bodies is in static equilibrium, we naturally do not expect any work to be done. If there are no constraints, the system could, of course, be in a state of unaccelerated translation even when the forces are in equilibrium. In such a case, it would be possible to compute a rate of doing work, i.e., the power, for each force. But we shall not be concerned with *actual* motion or actual work in this section. What is proposed is this: We shall *imagine* various possible sets of infinitesimal displacements of the parts of the system, taking care that we consider only displacements that do not violate the limitations imposed by the constraints. Such hypothetical displacements are usually called *virtual displacements*. The work which would be done by the forces, treated as constant, during such a virtual displacement is called *virtual work*.

Example I

Consider the system in equilibrium shown in Fig. 7.31. A 100-lb load is hung at one end of a light bar. At a distance s from this end is a horizontal pivot. At the other end, a distance s' from the pivot, is applied a force **F** normal to the bar. In this case certain constraints at the pivot ensure that the only possible motion of the bar is about one fixed axis. One virtual displacement consistent with the constraints for this system would be a small rotation in either direction. This could involve a displacement of the point of application of **F** equal to $s'\,\Delta\theta$ and in a direction opposite to **F**. The 100-lb object would have a displacement $s\,\Delta\theta$ in a direction making an angle θ with the vertical. The virtual work associated for this displacement with **F** is $-fs'\,\Delta\theta$; with **W**, it is $100s\cos\theta\,\Delta\theta$.

Let the system now be thought of as divided into small elements. When the system undergoes its displacement consistent with the constraints, a typical element has its displacement $\Delta\mathbf{R}_i$. We shall compute for each element the virtual work. Since for a single element the forces are concurrent, it is clear that, denoting internal forces by primes,

$$\Sigma\,\mathbf{F}_i\cdot\Delta\mathbf{R}_i + \Sigma\,\mathbf{F}'_i\cdot\Delta\mathbf{R}_i = \bar{\mathbf{F}}_i\cdot\Delta\mathbf{R}_i$$

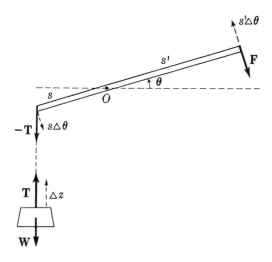

Figure
7.31

where $\bar{\mathbf{F}}_i$ is the resultant of all forces acting on the element. If the element is in equilibrium, then $\bar{\mathbf{F}}_i$ is equal to a null vector. Such an equation can be written for each element, and these equations may be added member by member. Internal forces involved in no expansion or contraction of the system do no *net* work. Similarly, the constraints do no work. Our conclusion is this:

(7.60) *If a system of particles and rigid bodies is in equilibrium, the virtual work associated with the applied forces for any virtual displacement consistent with the constraints is zero.*

Internal forces involved in expansions or contractions must be treated here as applied forces.

Example 2

Referring again to Fig. 7.31, since the system is given in equilibrium, we conclude immediately that the sum of the virtual works is zero:

$$-fs'\,\Delta\theta + 100s \cos\theta\,\Delta\theta = 0$$

Thus

$$f = 100\frac{s}{s'}\cos\theta$$

It should perhaps be noted that another type of virtual displacement is consistent with the constraints. The bar could be left fixed with the 100-lb load raised by an amount Δz. In this case, work would be done by the internal tension (treated as constant) in the cord supporting the load. Call this $\mathbf{T}$. Then the virtual work equation is

$$-100\,\Delta z + t\,\Delta z = 0$$

or

$$t = 100 \text{ lb}$$

Let us now consider the converse proposition. Suppose that, for every set of virtual displacements consistent with the constraints, it turns out that the virtual work of the applied forces is zero. Is the system then in equilibrium? Suppose the contrary. Then acceleration takes place, and the system acquires kinetic energy. But the initial actual infinitesimal displacements are a perfectly good set of virtual displacements; thus, by our hypothesis, the net work is zero. By the work-energy principle, then, no kinetic energy may be acquired; thus the system is in equilibrium, contrary to our assumption. We conclude:

(7.61) *If the virtual work associated with all possible virtual displacements (consistent with the constraints) of a system of particles and rigid bodies is zero, then the system must be in equilibrium.*

One of the advantages of this criterion for equilibrium is that only the applied forces have to be studied. The constraints or "hidden forces" as they used to be called can be ignored.

Example 3

A freely jointed symmetrical framework such as is shown in Fig. 7.32 is supported at A and withstands a force $\mathbf{W}$ at the other end. The frame is maintained in rigid form because of a crossbar BD. The problem is to find the force exerted by the strut BD.

Solution

As the problem stands, there are no useful displacements consistent with the constraints. We remedy this by imagining that the strut BD is removed, the frame

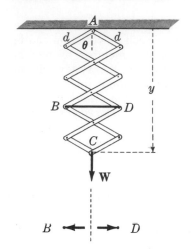

Figure
7.32

being kept in place by forces of magnitude f at B and D.   From the geometry of the situation, the point of application of **W** is given by

$$y = 8d \cos \theta$$

and the point D is given by

$$x = d \sin \theta$$

B is symmetrically located.   For our virtual displacement, let x be increased by Δx. The corresponding change in y is Δy.   The total virtual work is expressible as

$$w\,\Delta y + 2f\,\Delta x = 0$$

A relationship between Δy and Δx can be obtained by finding dy and dx in terms of $d\theta$:

$$\Delta y = dy = -8d \sin \theta\, d\theta$$

$$\Delta x = dx = d \cos \theta\, d\theta$$

which gives

$$w(-8d \sin \theta\, d\theta) + 2f(d \cos \theta\, d\theta) = 0$$

Hence

$$f = 4w \tan \theta$$

The principle of virtual work is most impressive when dealing with hidden or complex mechanisms where frictional effects are negligible.

Example 4

Consider, for instance, a set of scales for weighing express packages.   The inner mechanism is concealed, but it presumably consists of levers and pivots.   The forces, then, are constraints.   If when the platform is depressed a millimeter the beam is raised 50 mm, what force on the beam will provide equilibrium when a 160-lb man steps on the platform?   Here, aside from the constraints, only two forces are involved.   The weights of various parts of the mechanism are already balanced; therefore the sum of their virtual works will be zero for any suitable virtual displacement.   The two remaining forces have virtual displacements which are in a ratio depending on the geometry of the mechanism.   Writing the work equation as

$$f_1\,\Delta y_1 + 160\,\Delta y_2 = 0$$

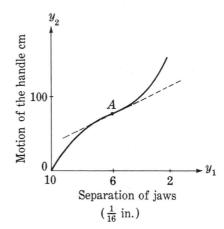

Figure
7.33

we can express the original evidence as

$$\Delta y_1 = -50 \, \Delta y_2$$

From the two equations we compute f_1 as 3.2 lb.
    The ratio of displacements might be available as the slope, at a particular point, of a curve which is a summary of the characteristic geometry of the mechanism.

$$\frac{\Delta y_1}{\Delta y_2} = \frac{dy_1}{dy_2}$$

Example 5

    The displacement geometry of a wire cutter is recorded graphically in the Fig. 7.33. What is the minimum force which will be exerted at the knife when a force of 60 lb is used on the handle?

Solution

    The knife force is smallest for a fixed applied force when the slope is minimum. This occurs at A, and is numerically about $\frac{4}{9}$. Allowing for the difference in scales,

$$-\frac{dy_2}{dy_1} = \frac{4}{9} \times \frac{20 \text{ cm}}{(2.54 \text{ cm/in.})(\frac{1}{16} \text{ in.})} = 56$$

From this ratio the virtual work equation yields

$$f_2 = 56 \times 60 = 3{,}360 \text{ lb}$$

EXERCISES

58. Referring to Fig. 7.34, find the force exerted by BD if A is a fixed point and the force at D is normal to AD. (The figure represents a vertical plane.)

59. Referring to Fig. 7.35, find the force exerted by AC if A is a fixed point and the force at D is normal to AD. (The figure represents a vertical plane.)

60. Find the tension exerted by the support AB of the stepladder shown in Fig. 7.36. The floor is smooth.

61. Four 6-ft rods are hinged smoothly to form a rhombus $ABCD$ as in Fig. 7.37. Rod AD is fixed in a horizontal position. Angle BAD is 60°. A 500-lb load is attached at C. A strut DB keeps the frame rigid. Neglecting the weights of the frame, find the force exerted by the strut DB.

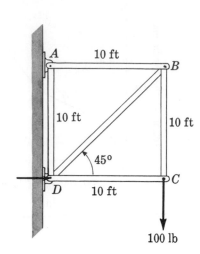

Figure
7.34

100 lb

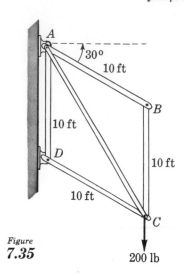

Figure
7.35

200 lb

62. Frictionless pulleys are attached to the tops of two smooth tracks, one of which is plane and inclined at an angle of 60° while the other is cylindrical (see Fig. 7.38). A cord passes over the pulleys and between two objects which slide on the tracks. The object on the plane weighs 0.5 lb; that on the cylinder weighs 1 lb. The radius of the cylinder drawn to the second object makes an angle θ with the vertical. Find the value of θ for which the system is in equilibrium.

63. The jaws of a lever wrench have a separation x varying with the separation x' of the handles as recorded in the following table. The units are centimeters.

x	3.20	2.71	2.22	1.93	1.49	1.23	0.97	0.71	0.51	0.29	0.13	0.00
x'	22.8	21.8	20.6	19.7	18.4	17.4	16.4	15.3	14.0	12.7	11.8	10.1

If the handles are closed with a force of 20 lb, what force can be exerted on a sphere of diameter 2 mm? Of diameter 25 mm?

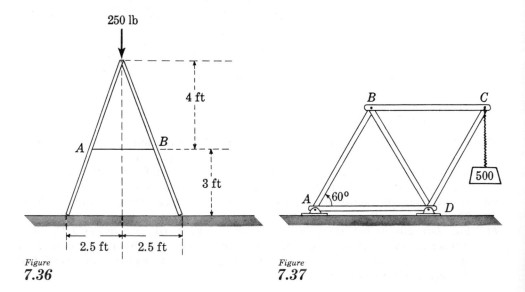

Figure
7.36

Figure
7.37

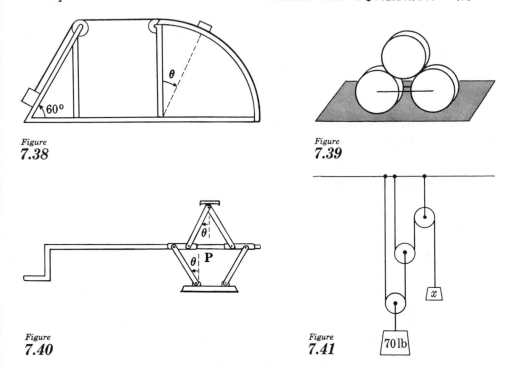

Figure
7.38

Figure
7.39

Figure
7.40

Figure
7.41

$\boxed{70\,\text{lb}}$

$\boxed{x}$

64. Two smooth cylinders each of weight 100 lb and radius 6 in. are connected at their centers by two cords of length 16 in., as in Fig. 7.39. They rest on a smooth horizontal plane and support a third cylinder of weight 200 lb and radius 6 in. What is the tension in each of the cords?

65. Find the tension **P** in the tie rod of the cantilever jack shown in Fig. 7.40 when the angle θ is 60° and the load is 3,000 lb.

66. The pulleys shown in Fig. 7.41 are frictionless, and the cords are perfectly flexible and without weight. Each pulley weighs 10 lb, and the load is 70 lb. How large a weight x will hold the system in equilibrium?

7.13. ENERGY AND EQUILIBRIUM

The concept of potential energy can be applied usefully to problems in equilibrium. Suppose that a system is in equilibrium subject to (a) conservative forces and (b) constraints. If the system is allowed any virtual displacement, we know that the virtual work done is zero. Let us see what sort of potential-energy change is associated with this virtual work. If $\mathbf{F}_i$ is a typical conservative force and $\Delta\mathbf{R}_i$ the corresponding virtual displacement, then we may write, from (7.52),

$$(7.62) \qquad\qquad \Delta(\text{p.e.})_i = -\mathbf{F}_i \cdot \Delta\mathbf{R}_i$$

Such an equation may be written for each conservative force. Adding, member by member,

$$(7.63) \qquad\qquad \Delta(\text{p.e.}) = \Sigma\,\Delta(\text{p.e.})_i = -\Sigma\,\mathbf{F}_i \cdot \Delta\mathbf{R}_i = 0$$

The criterion for equilibrium then may be described as follows:

(7.64) *A system acted on by conservative forces and constraints is in equilibrium if and only if the potential-energy change associated with every virtual displacement consistent with the constraints is zero.*

In many practical problems, the virtual displacement of the system can be described in terms of a single coordinate, say, θ. Then this criterion for equilibrium can be stated succinctly thus:

(7.65)
$$\frac{d(\text{p.e.})}{d\theta} = 0$$

Example I

Consider the simple oscillator of Example 1 in Sec. 7.11. The potential energy in terms of the single coordinate x was found to be

$$\text{p.e.} = \tfrac{1}{2}k(s_0 + x)^2 - mg(s_0 + x)$$

Applying the new criterion for equilibrium, we have

$$\frac{d(\text{p.e.})}{dx} = k(s_0 + x) - mg = 0$$

Hence the equilibrium position is given by $x = mg/k - s_0 = 0$, which is the expected result.

Example 2

Consider the modification of a simple pendulum consisting of a bob of mass m and a light rigid stem (instead of a string) connecting the bob to the point of suspension. As in Sec. 7.11, Example 2, the potential energy is given in terms of an angle θ by

$$\text{p.e.} = mgl(1 - \cos \theta)$$

The condition for equilibrium,

$$\frac{d(\text{p.e.})}{d\theta} = mgl \sin \theta = 0$$

is satisfied by both $\theta = 0°$ and $\theta = 180°$.

Equation (7.65) points out that a point of equilibrium might be a point of maximum potential energy, minimum potential energy, or neither. These possibilities are illustrated by points c, a, and b, respectively, in Fig. 7.42. In the neighborhood of a maximum, the potential energy is smaller than at the equilibrium point. This must correspond to an increase in kinetic energy if the forces are conservative and if the system was in equilibrium at the maximum point. Such a point is called a point of *unstable equilibrium*.

(7.66) *Unstable equilibrium* $\dfrac{d(\text{p.e.})}{d\theta} = 0$, p.e. *a maximum.*

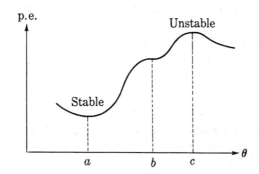

Figure
7.42

Similarly, in the neighborhood of a minimum, the potential energy is larger than at the minimum. Hence the kinetic energy should tend to be smaller rather than larger. Hence we have a point of *stable equilibrium.*

(7.67) *Stable equilibrium* $\dfrac{d(\text{p.e.})}{d\theta} = 0$, p.e. *a minimum.*

Example I'

Applying the preceding test to Example 1,

$$\frac{d^2(\text{p.e.})}{dx^2} = k > 0$$

Thus the equilibrium is stable.

Example 2'

In Example 2 we have

$$\frac{d^2(\text{p.e.})}{d\theta^2} = mgl \cos \theta$$

Here $\cos \theta > 0$ for $\theta = 0°$, < 0 for $\theta = 180°$; hence the two equilibrium positions are, respectively, stable and unstable.

The mechanism of stability or instability can be visualized in terms of the forces involved when the equilibrium position is deserted. For a displacement $\Delta \mathbf{R} = \Delta s \mathbf{T}$ of a particle in the direction of the unit vector $\mathbf{T}$, Eq. (7.62) becomes

$$\Delta(\text{p.e.}) = -(\mathbf{F} \cdot \mathbf{T}) \, \Delta s$$

Dividing by Δs and taking the limit as Δs approaches zero, we get

$$\mathbf{F} \cdot \mathbf{T} = f_s = -\frac{d(\text{p.e.})}{ds}$$

Thus, when the potential energy is increasing, the force is a restoring force, tending to cause a return to the equilibrium position. This is a sign of stability. When the potential energy is decreasing, f_s is positive; therefore the equilibrium is unstable.

EXERCISES

67. Solve Exercise 62 of Sec. 7.12 by the method of this section. Test for stability.
68. Two beads of masses $3m$ and $2m$ are on a smooth circular wire of radius r which is standing in a vertical plane. The beads are joined by a cord of length r. Find an equilibrium position for the beads, assuming the cord to be taut. Test for stability.

7.14. SUMMARY OF METHODS FOR MECHANICS OF PARTICLES

Thus far we have considered a number of different though interrelated methods for handling simple mechanics situations for particles. For situations involving equilibrium, the methods have been:

   I. Use of criterion $\Sigma \mathbf{F} = \mathbf{O}$ and hence of vector diagrams
  II. Use of components $\Sigma f_s = 0$ for any s axis
 III. Virtual work
 IV. Potential-energy criteria

For situations involving acceleration the methods have been:
   V. Use of the vector equation $\Sigma\,\mathbf{F} = m\mathbf{A}$
   VI. Use of corresponding component equations $\Sigma f_s = ma_s$
   VII. Use of impulse and momentum, or conservation of momentum
VIII. Use of work and energy, or conservation of energy
   IX. Use of d'Alembert's principle along with the methods for equilibrium
These methods will be supplemented in later chapters, particularly by techniques using the concepts of moment of a force and moment of momentum.

It is useful to consider the general strategy of selecting weapons from this arsenal. We have seen how method I gives understanding as well as results in plane problems. Method II, however, is a work-horse method which can always be resorted to. Furthermore, if axes for components are chosen sagaciously, parallel or perpendicular to crucial directions, the work may be very slight. We have seen how method III is particularly advantageous when nondissipative hidden forces are to be ignored. Here again, it is often a matter of adroitness to select virtual displacements which are natural for the setup at hand. Method IV is limited to situations where a potential energy can be defined, that is, where the forces aside from constraints are conservative. Some use of this method is suggested whenever stability is in question. It is often a more amiable substitute for method III.

In dynamics problems the integrated equations provided by methods VII and VIII are likely choices when the forces are given as functions, respectively, of time and displacement. Methods V and VI, like methods I and II, are indispensable but often pedestrian. It is helpful to keep in mind a physical synopsis of the problem at hand: think of a force as exerting an impulse which can change momentum or performing work which can change the energy of a particle or system. The equations and phenomena go hand in hand. Often a mixture of methods is desirable.

Consider the simple experiment of shooting a bullet into a heavy pendulum bob which initially is at rest. Start with the bullet unfired. The trigger is pulled, setting off chemical reactions which generate a very hot gas which exerts a huge force on the bullet. The chemistry is mostly over, but thermodynamics remains in the picture as the gas expands! Limiting the discussion to mechanics, a large and undoubtedly varying force shoves the bullet down the barrel, overcoming retarding forces exerted by the barrel and the air. This force of propulsion exerts on the bullet an impulse over the short time interval during which the bullet remains in the barrel. This impulse and the momentum imparted are both vectors along the line of fire. The same force of propulsion does work on the bullet, more than offsetting the negative work done by retarding forces, so the bullet acquires a high kinetic energy. From a broad point of view we could apply conservation of energy to what has happened, but since chemical, thermal, and acoustical, as well as mechanical, energies have been involved, this is not useful for the mechanics problem. We also can apply conservation of momentum. Before the trigger is pulled, the cartridge, the rifle, and a man's shoulder can be regarded approximately as three particles in a row. After the firing the ingredients of the cartridge, except for the shell, have considerable momentum in one direction. By conservation of momentum, which is always valid in the absence of external impulses, it must follow that the shell, rifle, and shoulder together have a net equal momentum in the opposite direction.

Now turn to the remainder of the experiment. The bullet, carrying a large kinetic energy and an impressive momentum vector, imbeds itself abruptly in the pendulum bob. Almost immediately most of the kinetic energy is spent: heat is generated, fibers are crushed, and only a modest part of the energy remains in kinetic form as the pendulum, harboring the bullet, moves slowly. Here again, conservation of energy in the broad sense gives us a reassuring feeling that Nature is orderly, but it does not help solve the mechanics problem because nonconservative forces play a role in the collision. Is momentum conserved? If the collision happens quickly, it is fair to assert so, for the only possible external impulses are vertical, because of weight and tension in the cord. Finally, consider the swing of the pendulum. It finds itself with a kinetic energy and moves until this energy has been spent at the end of the swing. Where did the energy go? By the work-energy principle, external forces must have done negative work. The principal such force is gravitational, for as the pendulum swings, it becomes elevated. Forces of fluid friction also do negative work, but these forces are small for such low speeds. Ignoring friction, since weight is a conservative force, we can describe the swing of the pendulum as an example of energy conservation as was done in Sec. 7.11.

Example 1

A bullet of mass m' is fired horizontally with muzzle speed v' from a gun of mass m'' into a simple pendulum of mass m and length l. Find the speed of recoil for the gun, the angle of displacement for the pendulum, and the tension in the cord after impact.

Solution

Assuming that the gun is free to move, use the law of conservation of momentum, taking horizontal components

$$m''v'' + m'v' = 0 \qquad \text{so} \qquad v'' = - \left(\frac{m'}{m''}\right) v'$$

Again taking horizontal components, $m'v' = (m + m')v$, so the initial speed of the pendulum is $v = [m'/(m + m')]v'$. To find the angle of deflection, using conservation of energy,

$$\tfrac{1}{2}(m + m')v^2 = (m + m')gl(1 - \cos \theta)$$

which may be solved for θ. To get the tension f, use method VI, taking vertical components:

$$f - (m + m')g = \frac{(m + m')v^2}{l}$$

Example 2. Compton Effect

An interesting application of both energy and momentum methods appears in elementary analyses of the Compton effect. An X-ray photon collides with an electron, yielding an altered photon having a different direction. We treat a photon as a particle of momentum h/λ and energy hc/λ. The problem will be to find how much the wavelength λ is changed by the collision. In Fig. 7.43 the incident photon has momentum of magnitude h/λ; the scattered photon has momentum $[h/(\lambda + \Delta\lambda)]$ at angle θ with the original path. The electron, initially at rest, acquires a momentum mv at an angle ϕ. Using conservation of momentum, we treat the vector triangle (Fig. 7.44) as isosceles to get

$$mv = \frac{2h}{\lambda} \sin \frac{\theta}{2}$$

Conservation of energy yields

$$\frac{hc}{\lambda} = \frac{hc}{\lambda + \Delta\lambda} + \tfrac{1}{2}mv^2$$

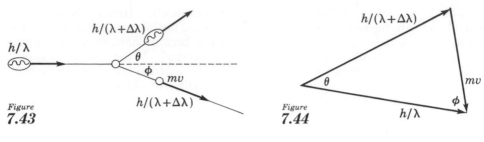

Figure
7.43

Figure
7.44

or

$$\frac{hc}{\lambda}\left(1 - \frac{1}{1 + \Delta\lambda/\lambda}\right) = \frac{hc}{\lambda}\frac{\Delta\lambda/\lambda}{1 + \Delta\lambda/\lambda} = \tfrac{1}{2}mv^2$$

Solving for $\Delta\lambda$, we have, approximately, $\Delta\lambda = mv^2\lambda^2/2hc$. Eliminating v between this equation and the previous one for momentum of the electron, we now have $\Delta\lambda = (2h/mc)\sin^2(\theta/2)$.

Example 3

A smooth cone rotates at ω rad/sec about its vertical axis as shown in Fig. 7.45. If the vertex angle of the cone is 2θ, how far from the apex will a small button rest in equilibrium relative to the cone? Test for stability. It is assumed, of course, that for each position x, the button is given the same angular speed ω about the axis of the cone, so that slipping may take place only in the x direction.

First Solution

First let us use methods V and VI. The button travels a circle of radius $\rho = x \sin\theta$. The acceleration is horizontal and equal to $v^2/\rho = \omega^2\rho = \omega^2 x \sin\theta$. Let n be the magnitude of the normal reaction force. Taking vertical components, $n \sin\theta - mg = 0$, since the vertical acceleration is zero. Taking horizontal components, $n \cos\theta = m\omega^2 x \sin\theta$.
Eliminating n,

$$x = \frac{g \cos\theta}{\omega^2 \sin^2\theta}$$

Second Solution

This problem might well be solved by d'Alembert's method. Introducing the "inertia force" $f = m\omega^2\rho$, one has a force triangle as shown in Fig. 7.46. From the figure $\tan\theta = g/\omega^2\rho$, or $\tan\theta = g/\omega^2 x \sin\theta$, so that

$$x = \frac{g}{\omega^2 \sin\theta \tan\theta}$$

This solution blends methods I and IX.

Third Solution

Finally, let us combine methods IV and IX. The potential energy associated with the force mg is given by

$$(\text{p.e.})_1 = mgx \cos\theta$$

Let us now compute a potential energy for the force $m\omega^2 x \sin\theta$ (which is conservative according to Sec. 7.9, Example 3). For a displacement dx, the work done by

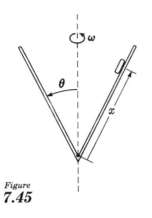

Figure
7.45

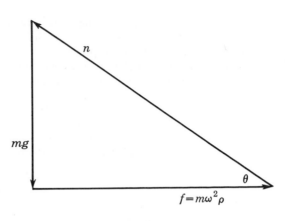

Figure
7.46

$f = m\omega^2 \rho$

this force f is $f \cos (90° - \theta)\, dx$, so

$$(\text{p.e.})_2 = -m\omega^2 \sin^2 \theta \int_0^x x\, dx = -\frac{(m\omega^2 \sin^2 \theta)x^2}{2}$$

We have, then,

$$\text{p.e.} = mgx \cos \theta - \frac{m\omega^2 x^2 \sin^2 \theta}{2}$$

Hence

$$\frac{d(\text{p.e.})}{dx} = mg \cos \theta - m\omega^2 x \sin^2 \theta = 0$$

So, as before, the position of equilibrium is given by

$$x = \frac{g \cos \theta}{\omega^2 \sin^2 \theta}$$

To test for stability,

$$\frac{d^2(\text{p.e.})}{dx^2} = -m\omega^2 \sin^2 \theta < 0$$

Hence equilibrium is unstable.

REVIEW EXERCISES

69. An object of weight 32 lb is subjected to a force

$$\mathbf{F} = 3t^2\mathbf{I} - 10\mathbf{J} \quad \text{lb}$$

Initially, the velocity is $-8\mathbf{I} + 5\mathbf{K}$ ft/sec. What is the velocity after 3 sec?

70. A force field is given by

$$\mathbf{F} = 5\mathbf{I} - 10\mathbf{J} - 6z\mathbf{K}$$

Compute the potential energy (with respect to the origin) at the point with coordinates (4,6,2). Assume that mks units are used.

71. A particle of weight 2 lb initially has velocity $33\mathbf{I} - 56\mathbf{J}$ ft/sec. A force given by $32t\mathbf{I} + 42t^2\mathbf{J}$ poundals acts on the particle for 2 sec.
(a) What impulse is exerted by the force during this time interval?
(b) What work is done by the force during this interval?

72. A 9-oz baseball is to be suspended by a piece of twine whose breaking tension is 6 lb. How long must the twine be in order that it shall not break when the ball is given a sudden horizontal impulse of 1.7 lb-sec?

73. A 10-lb body moving in a straight line received an impulse during a certain interval of 5 lb-sec in the line of its motion. If the work done by the force in this interval was 60 ft-lb, what was the final speed?

74. When a simple pendulum is deflected "statically" by a horizontal force on the bob, the deflection (if small) is proportional to the force:

$$\theta = kf$$

When it is deflected "ballistically" by a quick horizontal impulse on the bob, the deflection (if small) is proportional to the impulse:

$$\theta = k'p$$

Demonstrate both of these statements, and evaluate the ratio $k'\tau/k$, where τ is the period of the pendulum.

75. If the same powder charge (and hence the same energy) is always used in a certain gun while projectiles of different mass may be used, how does the recoil (reaction to impulse) vary with the projectile mass? (The force acting on the projectile during its trip along the gun barrel may be taken as constant.)

76. A simple pendulum of weight w and length l hangs at rest. It receives a horizontal impulse of such magnitude that it whirls through a complete vertical circle of radius l.

(*a*) Find a minimum value for the impulse.

(*b*) Find the instantaneous tension in the cord.

(*c*) Find the speed at the top of the circle if the impulse was minimum.

77. A hockey puck of mass m slides on perfectly smooth ice at speed v_0. It strikes a spring damper (see Fig. 7.47) which applies to the puck a deterring force of magnitude kx, where k is a constant.

(*a*) Determine the shape of the force profile (analogous to Fig. 7.3 or Fig. 7.4).

(*b*) Compute the duration of the pulse.

(*c*) What is the peak value of the force?

(*d*) Compute the impulse.

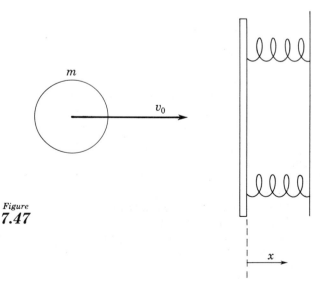

Figure
7.47

78. A 0.5-oz bullet traveling horizontally at 810 ft/sec strikes and lodges in a block suspended by a 5-ft cord. The block is initially at rest.
(*a*) How big an impulse was given to the block? (State units.)
(*b*) What, in pounds, instantaneously after impact is the tension in the cord?

79. Two objects *A* and *B* are initially at rest a meter apart. They attract each other with a force inversely proportional to the square of the distance between them. The initial value of this force is 0.4 newton. The masses of *A* and *B* are, respectively, 300 and 600 g. When the distance between the objects has decreased to 50 cm, how fast will *A* be moving?

80. Two particles having momenta $m_1 V_1$ and $m_2 V_2$ collide and stick together. The resulting velocity of the coalesced pair is **V**. Show that the energy lost in the collision is expressible as

$$\tfrac{1}{2}\mu(V_2 - V_1) \cdot (V_2 - V_1)$$

where μ is the *reduced mass* of the aggregate, given by

$$\mu = \frac{m_1 m_2}{m_1 + m_2}$$

81. Two smooth uniform solid spheres of unequal mass collide in such a way that their line of centers at the moment of contact is parallel to the *x* axis. After the rebound the total kinetic energy is the same as it was before the collision. Show that the *x* component of the relative velocity merely reversed in sign during the collision.

82. Two spheres are to collide head on with a relative speed *v*. The sum of the masses of the two spheres is *m*. The coefficient of restitution is *e*. Show that the maximum energy is lost in the collision if the spheres have equal masses.

83. A ball is dropped from a height *h* onto a hard pavement. On the second rebound the ball reaches a height *h'*. Express the coefficient of restitution in terms of *h* and *h'*.

84. An object weighing 100 lb and traveling 100 ft/sec collides head on with a 20-lb object traveling at 300 ft/sec. The lighter object rebounds at 200 ft/sec. Find the final speed of the first object, the energy lost in collision, and the coefficient of restitution.

85. A long skinny toy balloon is inflated and then released. It propels itself horizontally rocketwise by discharging the gas confined within it. Will the horizontal velocity attained be greater or less if the balloon is inflated with helium rather than air? Substantiate your answer. Feel free to make reasonable idealizing assumptions such as equal effect of friction in the two cases.

86. A neutron (mass 1) traveling at speed *u* strikes squarely a free nucleus (mass *a*) initially at rest and rebounds (i.e., is scattered through 180°). The neutron's new speed is *v*, while that of the nucleus is *v'*. Assume that the collision is perfectly elastic. Let the energy ratio $\rho = 0.5mv^2/0.5mu^2$ be regarded as a measure of the failure of this kind of collision for moderating neutron velocities. For what value of *a* is this ratio least? Evaluate the ratio for this case and also for the cases where the nucleus is carbon 12 and uranium 238.

87. A fine flexible chain is 12 ft long and weighs 1.2 lb. It is held at rest from one end vertically, with the other end touching the floor. It is then released. After how many seconds is the momentum maximum? At that instant what is the total force exerted on the chain by the floor?

88. Two objects, *A* and *B*, initially are at rest 10 ft apart. They attract each other with a force inversely proportional to the distance between them. The initial value of this force is 0.0028 lb. The masses of *A* and *B* are, respectively, 7.5 and 15 lb. When the distance between the objects has decreased to 5 ft, how fast will *B* be moving?

89. A ball weighing 1 lb falls vertically from rest 100 ft to a pavement and bounces 10 ft into the air.
(a) What is the coefficient of restitution?
(b) What is the impulse?

90. A 5-lb plastic sphere is thrown onto the floor with such a speed that it strikes at 30 ft/sec. It rebounds to a height of 6 ft.
(a) What impulse is provided by the floor?
(b) What is the coefficient of restitution?

91. A 200-g sphere with velocity 50**I** cm/sec is struck by a 100-g sphere with velocity 50**J** cm/sec. The line of centers during the collision is parallel to **J**, the spheres are smooth, and the coefficient of restitution is 0.2. What in **IJK** form are the velocities after collision?

92. A small 4-lb sphere is suspended from a fixed hook by a 10-ft cord. The sphere is struck squarely by a second 2-lb sphere traveling horizontally at 30 ft/sec. If the coefficient of restitution is 0.5, find the velocities of both spheres right after the collision.

93. A track athlete sets up a 20-lb shot on the pavement, pretending it is a golf ball. He then takes a 16-lb hammer, sets it whirling at 50 ft/sec, and lets it strike the shot horizontally. The line of centers at impact is horizontal and makes an angle of 30° with the velocity of the hammer. The coefficient of restitution may be taken as 0.25, and the spheres are to be considered as smooth. Find:
(a) The momentum (before impact) of the hammer.
(b) The initial speed of the shot right after impact.
(c) The total energy (in foot-pounds) lost in impact.

94. Prove or disprove the proposition: If two particles have momenta which are equal in magnitude before collision, then they must also be equal after they collide.

95. Bullets from a machine gun strike a heavy steel target at the rate of three per second. The rebound is negligible. Each bullet weighs 40 g. The speed is 600 m/sec. Find the average force exerted by the target.

96. Wooden spools weighing 15 g are carried at 4 m/sec by a horizontal conveyor belt. The coefficient of friction is 0.2. There are about 80 spools per meter of belt. The spools are taken off the belt by a smooth vertical vane which makes an angle of 30° with the direction of motion of the conveyor. If most of the spools leave the belt in a line parallel to the vane: (a) What is the speed of departure? (b) What force does the vane sustain? (HINT: The motion of spools relative to the belt must, in general, be normal to the smooth vane; hence the friction force also may be considered as normal to the vane.)

97. A rectangular box of depth d, weight w, and specific gravity s floats at equilibrium in water. What work must be exerted to submerge the box?

98. An object of mass m slides from the top of a sphere of radius a. Assuming that the sphere offers no resistance to the sliding of the object over its surface and that the normal force exerted by the sphere is p when the line from the center of the sphere to it makes an angle θ with the radius to the top of the sphere, for what value of θ does the following equation hold:

$$p = 0.5mg$$

99. A spiral spring 2.5 ft long compresses an inch for each 2 lb of load. It is standing vertical and carrying a very light platform on its top when a 2-lb weight falling freely from a height of 5 ft lands on the platform. What will be the maximum compression of the spring?

100. A block is caused to slide up a plane, making an angle θ with the horizontal at an initial speed v_0. If the coefficient of friction is μ, with what speed will the block return to the starting point? (Assume that $\tan \theta$ is greater than μ.)

101. A particle of mass m is attracted toward a fixed point O by a force inversely proportional to the cube of its distance from O. From an initial distance r_1 it is launched with an initial velocity V_0 directly away from O. (After launching, it is subject solely to the inverse cube force.) Derive a formula for the maximum distance r_2 away from O attained by the particle.

102. A chain 5 ft long is held on a rough horizontal table, half of it hanging over the smooth edge. If it is released, with what speed will the last link leave the table? (The coefficient of friction is 0.5.)

103. A chain of length l on a smooth horizontal table has an initial overhang y_0 when the chain is at rest. It is released, and the last link leaves the table with speed v_0. Show that y_0 is given by

$$y_0 = l\left(1 - \frac{2v_0^2}{v_1^2}\right)^{\frac{1}{2}}$$

where v_1 is the speed which the whole chain would acquire in a free fall from rest through a distance equal to its length.

104. Show that the kinetic energy of a system of two particles can be expressed as

$$\tfrac{1}{2}\frac{m_1 m_2}{\mu}\,\bar{\mathbf{V}} \cdot \bar{\mathbf{V}} + \tfrac{1}{2}\mu(\mathbf{V}_2 - \mathbf{V}_1) \cdot (\mathbf{V}_2 - \mathbf{V}_1)$$

where μ is the reduced mass $m_1 m_2/(m_1 + m_2)$ and $\bar{\mathbf{V}}$ is the velocity of the center of mass.

105. A 1-lb block (see Fig. 7.48) is placed on the smooth sloping face of a right triangular $45°$ prism which weighs 4 lb. The prism rests on a smooth horizontal plane. If the initial position of the block is 12 in. above the plane, how fast will the prism be moving by the time the block reaches the end of the slope?

106. A sphere of radius r is placed on the top of a rough stationary horizontal cylinder of radius r'. The sphere is released. It rolls without slipping, leaving the cylinder at a point whose angular distance from the top is ϕ. Find ϕ.

107. A *parabolic spring* has a characteristic given by

$$f = kx^2$$

From what height h above the spring should an object of mass m be dropped onto the spring in order that the dynamic deflection so obtained will be twice the static deflection (obtained when the object is supported in equilibrium by the spring)?

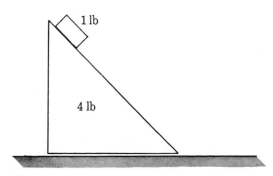

Figure
7.48

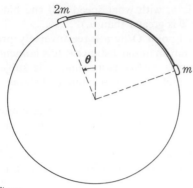

Figure
7.49

108. A smooth cylinder is fixed with its axis horizontal.   Two particles of masses m and $2m$ are joined by a cord whose length is equal to one-quarter of the circumference of the cylinder.   If the cord is laid across the cylinder as shown in Fig. 7.49, what is the equilibrium position?   Is it stable?

109. Equations (7.11), (7.12), and (7.24) are written from the point of view of a "fixed" laboratory reference frame.   Rewrite these equations from the point of view of a translating center-of-mass reference frame (origin at center of mass, uniform speed, axes not rotating relative to laboratory frame).   Use these new equations to derive (7.45).   Compare Exercises 51, 80, and 104.

110. A particle of mass 200 g is free to move parallel to the x axis subject to a conservative force.   The corresponding net potential energy is graphed in Fig. 7.50.
(*a*) Plot roughly the x component of the net force acting on the particle.
(*b*) For what approximate value (or values) of x could the particle be in equilibrium? For what approximate value (or values) of x could the particle be in stable equilibrium?
(*c*) If the particle is released from rest at $x = 0.63$ cm, with what speed will it pass the point $x = 0.33$ cm?
(*d*) If the particle is displaced slightly from the stable equilibrium position and then released, with what period, approximately, will it oscillate?

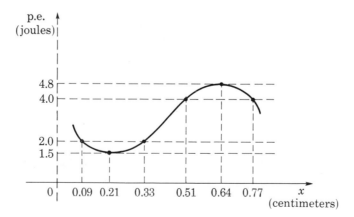

Figure
7.50

CHAPTER EIGHT

APPLICATIONS: VIBRATIONS in ONE DIMENSION

A full study of oscillations would include a large part of the subjects of acoustics, electrical and radio engineering, and even of atomic theory. Uncontrolled oscillations may result in bridge failures, in howling amplifiers, or in noisy motors. We already have investigated important cases of small oscillations: the simple pendulum and the bob on a spring. Thus far no account has been taken of the effect of friction, yet we realize that all mechanical motion is, to some extent, dissipative. The oscillations thus far considered have not been driven; thus problems of resonance have not arisen. These topics will be touched on in this chapter, using the point of view of electrical analogies. Several of the methods from the two preceding chapters will be used.

8.1. EFFECTIVE MASS OF A SIMPLE OSCILLATOR

An exhaustive study even of mechanical vibrations would demand too much time and too much mathematics for this course. As an introduction to the subject, we shall analyze the one-dimensional behavior of an oscillator consisting of a uniform spring, a bob, and a damper. We shall assume that the three functions of these elements can be separated one from another. Thus the system will be described by three numbers, assumed constant. These three numbers are called the compliance, the mass, and the mechanical resistance of the system. They are denoted by c, m, and r, and they are associated primarily with the spring, the bob, and the damper, respectively, as is indicated in Fig. 8.1. We proceed to review the significance of each of these quantities. First we evaluate the effective mass m.

When this system is oscillating, the bob and the damper always have identical velocities; therefore we should expect that the effective oscillatory mass m would include the masses of these parts. For the spring, the situation is less clear. The upper end of the spring has zero velocity; the lower end moves with the bob; and all intermediate values are found at intermediate points. To find the effective mass contribution of the spring, let us analyze its kinetic energy. Assuming that the spring is quite uniform, the ratio (see Fig. 8.2) y'/y is constant for any state of stretch that the spring is in,

$$y' = ky$$

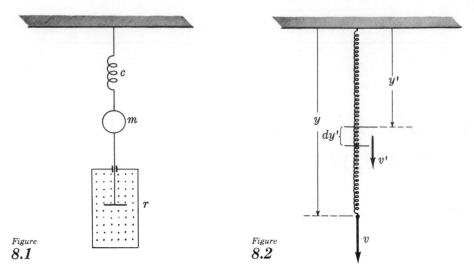

Figure
8.1

Figure
8.2

Consequently, differentiating,

$$v' = kv$$

For an element of length dy, the kinetic energy is

$$d(\text{k.e.}) = \frac{1}{2}\left(\frac{m'}{y}\,dy'\right)v'^2$$

where m' is the mass of the spring. Substituting the two preceding equations and integrating,

$$\text{k.e.} = \frac{m'v^2}{2y^3}\int_0^y y'^2\,dy' = \frac{1}{2}\left(\frac{m'}{3}\right)v^2$$

Thus the effective mass m of the whole system is given by

(8.1) $$m = m_{\text{bob}} + m_{\text{damper}} + \tfrac{1}{3}(m_{\text{spring}})$$

8.2. MECHANICAL RESISTANCE AND COMPLIANCE

In Sec. 6.4 we considered the motion of a particle subject to frictional force of the type associated with the damper in Fig. 8.1:

$$f_r = rv$$

The constant of proportionality r is called *mechanical resistance*, and the equation just written is a mechanical analogue of Ohm's law. The relation between r and terminal speed was discussed in Sec. 6.4.

We have several times discussed springs that obey Hooke's law, so that force is proportional to displacement. Now it is convenient to reverse the proportionality and speak of displacement as proportional to tension,

$$s = cf_c$$

where the factor of proportionality is called *compliance*. Let us apply the definition to combinations of ideal springs. In Fig. 8.3a, the total f for a displacement s is equal to the sum of the tensions for the two springs:

$$f = f' + f''$$

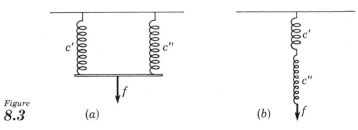

Figure
8.3   (a)   (b)

But $s = c'f' = c''f''$; hence $f = s/c' + s/c''$. If we define effective compliance c of the combination of springs by $s = cf$, we get

(8.2) $$\frac{1}{c} = \frac{1}{c'} + \frac{1}{c''} \quad \text{or} \quad c = \frac{c'\,c''}{c' + c''}$$

In Fig. 8.3b, let s' and s'' be the extension of the two springs separately under the applied force f. Then the total extension s is given by

$$s = s' + s''$$

so that

$$cf = c'f + c''f$$

or

(8.3) $$c = c' + c''$$

EXERCISES

1. What are the dimensions of mechanical resistance and compliance?
2. What in terms of c' and c'' is the compliance of the system of springs shown in Fig. 8.4?
3. What in terms of c' and c'' is the compliance of the system of springs shown in Fig. 8.5?
4. What in terms of c' and c'' is the compliance of the system of springs shown in Fig. 8.6?
5. What in terms of c' and c'' is the compliance of the system of springs shown in Fig. 8.7?

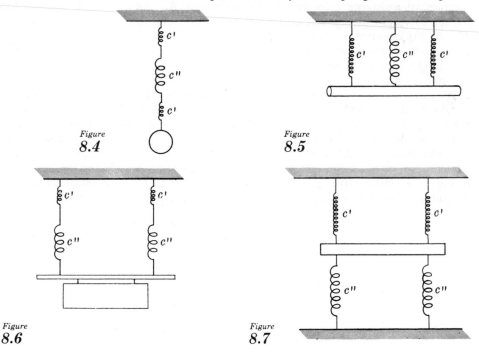

Figure
8.4

Figure
8.5

Figure
8.6

Figure
8.7

6. A spring balance has a 6-in. scale reading from 0 to 60 lb.   What is the compliance of the spring?   What work must be done in applying a 60-lb force to the balance?

7. Plot a graph of the potential energy stored in the spring of Exercise 6 as a function of the displacement x ranging from 0 to 6 in.

8.3. DYNAMICAL ANALOGUES OF ELECTRIC CIRCUITS

Since this is a course in mechanics, we shall not study electric oscillations.   It is nevertheless a fact that the study of electric oscillations is very highly developed and rather well known.   In an elementary physics course one usually studies alternating-current theory to some extent.   Topics in electrical transients may be included, too. For instance, the voltage pattern for a charging or discharging capacitor may be familiar to readers of this text.   Much use is often made of the language and methods of electrical theory in dealing with other kinds of oscillations.   This approach has been particularly fruitful in the field of acoustics.   The topics in this chapter will be developed as analogies with electrical situations.   An electrical analogue of Fig. 8.1 is shown in Fig. 8.8.   The equation of motion (vertical components) for the mechanical system is

(8.4)
$$mg - rv - \frac{x}{c} = m\frac{dv}{dt}$$

This is merely the x-component form of $\Sigma\,\mathbf{F} = m\mathbf{A}$, taking the x axis as positive downward.   Correspondingly, Kirchhoff's law for the electric circuit yields

(8.5)
$$V - RI - \frac{Q}{C} - L\frac{dI}{dt} = 0$$

It is easy to see the mathematical similarity between the two equations.   The compliance c corresponds to the capacitance C, the mass m to the inductance L, and the mechanical resistance r to the electric resistance R.   Any constant applied force f (such as weight in Fig. 8.1) corresponds to a constant applied electromotive force V.   A displacement s of the mechanical system, measuring the amount that the spring is contracted or stretched from its equilibrium position, corresponds to the charge Q on the capacitor.

We assume that, for a given system, c, m, and r are constants.   In the first two cases this involves nothing new, for we have dealt only with linear springs and constant masses.   In the case of r, it implies that frictional force is proportional to the first power of the speed.   Actual physical behavior is usually more complicated, but for moderate speed in liquids or gases this assumption gives fairly good results.

The details of the analogy between mechanical and electrical situations are sometimes startling.   For instance, in the preceding section we found that the springs in Fig. 8.3a combine like capacitors in series although they are geometrically parallel. To judge series and parallel combinations, we need a physical rather than geometric

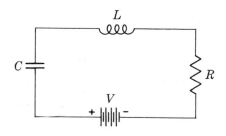

Figure
8.8

test.   Two electric elements are in parallel only if the potential is always the same. This corresponds to the equality in tension for the springs in Fig. 8.3*b*.   (In the method of lumped parameters which we are using, we treat the springs as weightless, assigning the proper mass to the whole system according to Sec. 8.1.)   Similarly, two electric elements are in series only if the current is always the same.   This corresponds to equality of velocity, and hence of displacement for the springs in Fig. 8.3*a*.

8.4. MECHANICAL ANALOGUES OF THE *LC*, *RL*, AND *RC* CIRCUITS

Example 1 of Sec. 7.11 may now be reinterpreted as a study of the system depicted in Fig. 8.1 for the special case when $r = 0$.   In Fig. 8.9, s_0 refers to extension of spring to equilibrium position.   In terms of compliance, the key energy equations can be written

$$(8.6) \qquad \tfrac{1}{2}mv^2_{max} = \frac{1}{2}\left(\frac{1}{c}\right)x^2_{max} = \frac{1}{2}\,cf^2_{max}$$

where f_{max} is the maximum amount by which the tension of the spring exceeds mg. The following are immediate consequences:

$$(8.7) \qquad x_{max} = \sqrt{mc}\;v_{max}$$

$$(8.8) \qquad f_{max} = \sqrt{\frac{m}{c}}\;v_{max}$$

$$(8.9) \qquad f_{max}x_{max} = mv^2_{max}$$

The electrical analogues of these last three equations are useful in connection with "tank circuits."

Using (7.59), the period of the oscillation can be identified as

$$\tau = 2\pi\,\frac{x_{max}}{v_{max}}$$

or

$$(8.10) \qquad \tau = 2\pi\,\sqrt{mc}$$

As another special case, consider the part of Sec. 6.4 for the case where the equation $f_r = rv$ is satisfied.   The preceding item dealt with a special case of Fig. 8.1: the damper was omitted, and we had $r = 0$.   This time the spring is omitted as

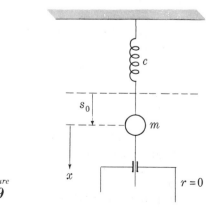

Figure
8.9

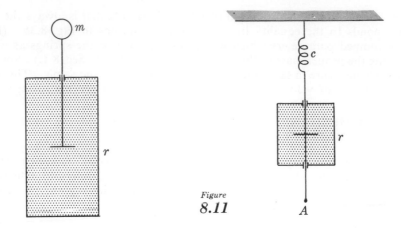

Figure
8.10

Figure
8.11

A

in Fig. 8.10, or we might say, the spring has infinite compliance. In this special case, as we have seen, no oscillation takes place.

The analogue of an RC circuit is given by letting $m = 0$. This situation, clearly, is difficult to realize exactly. When a system is light, its behavior may sometimes be predicted by neglecting the mass. This is particularly feasible when the motion is slow. Figure 8.11 represents a light spring with heavy damping. The restoring force of the spring just offsets the drag of the damper when no other force is applied. The force equation is

(8.11)
$$-r\frac{dx}{dt} - \frac{x}{c} = 0$$

or

$$\frac{dx}{x} = -\frac{dt}{rc}$$

If the initial displacement is x_0, the return toward equilibrium position is given by

(8.12)
$$x = x_0 e^{-(t/rc)}$$

This is diagramed in Fig. 8.12. The time constant for this exponential is rc.

(8.13)
$$\tau_e = rc$$

The electrical analogy of a discharging condenser should be obvious. The equation for charging is left as Exercise 15.

EXERCISES

8. Referring to Fig. 8.13, the bob weighs 10 lb, and the weight of the spring is negligible. A force of 10 additional pounds will draw the mass downward 2 in. It is then released. Friction may be ignored.
   (a) How much energy was stored in the spring just before release?
   (b) With what period will it oscillate?
   (c) What will be the maximum speed?

9. Refer to Fig. 8.13. The maximum speed of the bob is 26 cm/sec. When the displacement is 5 cm, the speed is only 24 cm/sec. What is the period of the oscillation? What is the amplitude of the oscillation?

10. Refer to Fig. 8.13. The maximum total tension in the spring is to be 25.0 lb, and the corresponding maximum displacement from equilibrium position is to be 7.0 in. If the period is to be 0.935 sec, find the required mass and compliance.

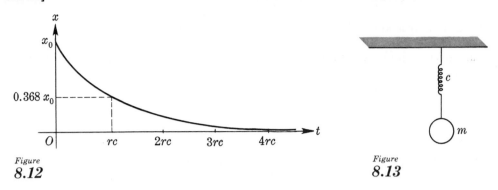

Figure
8.12

Figure
8.13

11. Referring to Fig. 8.3*b*, the data are as follows:
   c': 1-in. stretch for 5 lb additional tension
   c'': 1-in. stretch for 10 lb additional tension
   m: weight of bob is 16 lb, weight of springs may be neglected
   (*a*) What is the period of oscillation?
   (*b*) If the bob is displaced by 6 in. from the equilibrium position and then released, what is the maximum speed the bob will attain?
12. In the highly damped system discussed in the preceding section, the damper is held at rest at a displacement of 15 in. by a tension of 1 lb and then released. In 3 sec it moves 3 in. Find the resistance constant r.
13. In a system similar to the one just described, the damper is held at rest, is released, and in 10 sec is halfway back toward the equilibrium position. What is the time constant of the exponential?
14. Refer to Fig. 8.11. If r has the value 300 kg/sec, if c has the value 0.05 sec²/kg, and if the initial displacement from the equilibrium position is 0.25 m:
   (*a*) What is the maximum speed of return (assuming that the damper is held at rest and then released)?
   (*b*) In how many seconds will the speed be half of its maximum?
   (*c*) In how many seconds will the displacement be 0.125 m?
15. A system like the one in Fig. 8.11 is initially in equilibrium. A downward force f is suddenly applied at A.
   (*a*) Plot the velocity as a function of time.
   (*b*) Plot the tension in the spring as a function of time.

8.5. FREE DAMPED VIBRATION

We now consider the general case where r, m, and c have arbitrary values. To simplify the equation of motion we measure the displacement x of the bob as in Fig. 8.9 from the equilibrium position. The equation of motion

$$mg - \frac{1}{c}(s_0 + x) - r\frac{dx}{dt} = m\frac{d^2x}{dt^2}$$

becomes, since $mg = s_0/c$,

(8.14) $$\frac{d^2x}{dt^2} + \frac{r}{m}\frac{dx}{dt} + \frac{1}{mc}x = 0$$

Note that we have now written dx/dt in place of v, d^2x/dt^2 in place of dv/dt. Since the time derivatives of $s_0 + x$ are equal to those of x, s_0 being a constant, this equation is substantially the same as the one in Sec. 8.3. This is a standard second-order linear homogeneous differential equation, and it is easy to find functions $x(t)$ which satisfy it. A student who has had a course covering such solutions may wish to pass over some of the following. We observe that the second derivative of the function

$$xe^{rt/2m}$$

is related to Eq. (8.14) for

(8.15) $$\frac{d^2}{dt^2}(xe^{rt/2m}) = \left(\frac{d^2x}{dt^2} + \frac{r}{m}\frac{dx}{dt} + \frac{r^2}{4m^2}x\right)e^{rt/2m}$$

With this in mind we get a simpler equation by multiplying (8.14) by $e^{rt/2m}$ and subtracting from (8.15). We get

(8.16) $$\frac{d^2}{dt^2}(xe^{rt/2m}) + \left(\frac{1}{mc} - \frac{r^2}{4m^2}\right)xe^{rt/2m} = 0$$

The nature of the solutions of this equation depends on the relative importance of the resistance r; we therefore consider three cases separately. These cases depend on the quantity in parentheses,

$$\frac{1}{mc} - \frac{r^2}{4m^2}$$

Note that, for a critical value of r (called the *critical damping resistance r_c*), this quantity is equal to zero. It is easy to solve for r_c:

(8.17) $$r_c = 2\sqrt{\frac{m}{c}}$$

In this section we shall limit our discussion to what is called *underdamping*, determined by

(8.18) $$r < r_c$$

This hypothesis allows us to write (8.16) in the familiar form.

(8.19) $$\frac{d^2y}{dt^2} + \omega^2 y = 0$$

where

$$y = xe^{rt/2m}$$

(8.20) $$\omega = \sqrt{\frac{1}{mc} - \frac{r^2}{4m^2}}$$

This equation we know to represent a simple harmonic motion of period $2\pi/\omega$. Hence the general solution of (8.16) may be written

(8.21) $$xe^{rt/2m} = a\sin(\omega t + \epsilon)$$

where a and ϵ are constants. The displacement x is then given in full by

(8.22) $$x = ae^{-(rt/2m)}\sin\left(\sqrt{\frac{1}{mc} - \frac{r^2}{4m^2}}\,t + \epsilon\right)$$

This is the product of a sine of period

(8.23) $$\tau = \frac{2\pi}{\sqrt{(1/mc) - (r^2/4m^2)}}$$

by a damping exponential of time constant

(8.24)
$$\tau_e = \frac{2m}{r}$$

Note that (8.23) may now be written

(8.25)
$$\frac{1}{\tau_0^2} - \frac{1}{\tau^2} = \frac{1}{(2\pi\tau_e)^2}$$

where τ_0 is the undamped period.

A function of t such as x in (8.22) is known as a *damped oscillation*. In the solution of problems *where the damping is slight*, it is often expedient to neglect r in computing ω. The displacement is then regarded as the product of an *undamped* sinusoid by a damping exponential.

The graph of Eq. (8.22) is a sine curve oscillating between two damping exponentials as shown in Fig. 8.14.

EXERCISES

16. Show that the zeros of a damped oscillation occur every half period.
17. Show that the peaks of a damped oscillation occur every half period, but that the separations of peaks and zeros are not quarter periods.
18. Let x_n and x_{n+1} denote two successive peak values of a damped oscillation. Treat them both as positive quantities. The quantity

$$\lambda = \ln \frac{x_n}{x_{n+1}}$$

is called the *logarithmic decrement per half period*. Prove that (a) $\lambda = \tau/2\tau_e$ (hence λ is independent of n); (b) for small λ, $x_{n+1} = x_n e^{-\lambda} = x_n(1 - \lambda)$.

19. The turning points of a particle in damped oscillation are recorded by taking readings on a single scale. Three successive scale readings are s_1, s_2, s_3. Show that the equilibrium position is given by the scale reading

$$s_0 = \frac{s_1 s_3 - s_2^2}{s_1 - 2s_2 + s_3}$$

20. Three successive excursions on a ballistic galvanometer were read as $+20.4$, -18.9, $+19.0$. The equilibrium position would not be exactly zero, since the scale was slightly off center. Give corrected values for the three excursions.
21. Three successive deflections of a ballistic galvanometer are $+25.4$, -25.0, $+24.6$. (a) What approximately is the logarithmic decrement per half period? (b) After how many complete oscillations will the deflection be less than 50 per cent of the initial deflection?

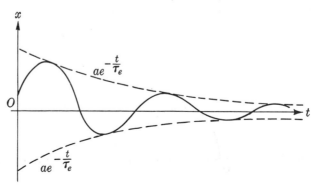

Figure
8.14

22. A damped harmonic oscillation has period 0.5 sec and logarithmic decrement (per half period) of 0.025. The effective mass is 1 kg. (*a*) What is the compliance of the spring? (*b*) What is the resistance?

8.6. CRITICAL DAMPING AND OVERDAMPING

When a speedy return to equilibrium is desired, the system may be adjusted for critical damping. In this case the resistance satisfies $r = r_c$, and $\omega = 0$. No oscillation takes place. A typical displacement curve is shown in Fig. 8.15. The case of critical damping will here be considered as the limit, as ω becomes small, of underdamping cases. This can be handled easily if we use a different form of our underdamped equation. Equation (8.22) may be written

$$(8.26) \qquad x = e^{-(t/\tau_e)}(b \sin \omega t + d \cos \omega t)$$

The constants of integration b and d, or *arbitrary constants* as they are often called, can be evaluated in terms of initial conditions. If the initial displacement was x_0 and the initial velocity v_0, we find at once that

$$(8.27) \qquad d = x_0$$

Now differentiate (8.26) with respect to t:

$$\frac{dx}{dt} = e^{-(t/\tau_e)}(\omega b \cos \omega t - \omega d \sin \omega t) - \frac{1}{\tau_e} x$$

Substituting the initial values,

$$v_0 = \omega b - \frac{x_0}{\tau_e}$$

or

$$(8.28) \qquad b = \frac{v_0 + (x_0/\tau_e)}{\omega}$$

We may then write (8.26) as

$$(8.29) \qquad x = e^{-(t/\tau_e)}\left[\frac{v_0 + (x_0/\tau_e)}{\omega} \sin \omega t + x_0 \cos \omega t\right]$$

This equation is useful in dealing with underdamped problems where initial conditions are known.

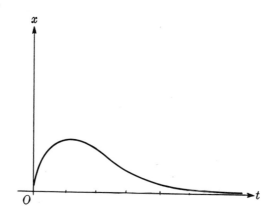

Figure
8.15

To get an equation for critical damping, we now take limits as ω approaches zero. We use the facts that

$$\lim_{\omega \to 0} \cos \omega t = 1$$

and

$$\lim_{\omega \to 0} \frac{\sin \omega t}{\omega} = \lim_{\omega \to 0} \left(\frac{\sin \omega t}{\omega t} \right) t = t$$

We get, then, as a *critical damping equation*

$$(8.30) \qquad x = e^{-(t/\tau_e)} \left[\left(v_0 + \frac{x_0}{\tau_e} \right) t + x_0 \right]$$

Note that x is now the product of a linear function of t by an exponential whose time constant is

$$(8.31) \qquad \tau_e = \frac{2m}{r_c} = \sqrt{mc}$$

Further properties of Eq. (8.30) are investigated in Exercises 23 and 24.

Overdamping. When the resistance in a system such as we have discussed is excessive, the behavior becomes sluggish and, for most purposes, less interesting. The forces of spring and friction may be so large that inertia forces are negligible. In that case an approximate picture of what happens may be obtained by neglecting the mass and proceeding as in Sec. 8.4. If a more exact analysis is desired, Eq. (8.16) may again be integrated. Now that

$$(8.32) \qquad r > r_c$$

we have

$$\frac{r^2}{4m^2} - \frac{1}{mc} > 0$$

so the equation has the form

$$\frac{d^2y}{dt^2} = w^2 y$$

the general solution of which is

$$y = ae^{wt} + be^{-wt}$$

Substituting

$$w = \sqrt{\frac{r^2}{4m^2} - \frac{1}{mc}} \qquad y = xe^{rt/2m}$$

and then solving for x yields

$$(8.33) \qquad x = ae^{-\left(\frac{r}{2m} - \sqrt{\frac{r^2}{4m^2} - \frac{1}{mc}} \right)t} + be^{-\left(\frac{r}{2m} + \sqrt{\frac{r^2}{4m^2} - \frac{1}{mc}} \right)t}$$

As before, the constants a and b depend on initial conditions. If the initial speed and displacement are v_0 and x_0, they may be evaluated as

$$(8.34) \qquad a = \frac{x_0}{2} + \frac{v_0 + (r/2m)x_0}{2\sqrt{(r^2/4m^2) - (1/mc)}} \qquad b = \frac{x_0}{2} - \frac{v_0 + (r/2m)x_0}{2\sqrt{(r^2/4m^2) - (1/mc)}}$$

The exponents in Eq. (8.33) are always negative; therefore the function x is always the sum of two decreasing exponentials of different time constants. The second term has the smaller time constant; thus the first term is the last to die out. It is important that the first term dies out most quickly when $w = 0$, that is, when the damping is critical.

EXERCISES

23. We have seen that for critical damping the displacement from equilibrium is given as

$$x = l(t)e^{-(t/\sqrt{mc})}$$

where $l(t)$ is a linear function of t. Let t_0 be the value of t for which $l(t) = 0$. Show that x has a maximum (or minimum) for

$$t = t_0 + \sqrt{mc}$$

24. Assuming that x_0 is positive in Exercise 23: (a) What positive values of v_0 would give rise to a *maximum* value of x for a positive t? (b) What negative values of v_0 would give rise to a *minimum* value of x for a positive t?

25. A damped harmonic oscillation has period 1.3 sec and logarithmic decrement 1.95 (per half period). The effective mass of the system is 1 kg. (a) What is the compliance of the spring? (b) What is the resistance constant? (c) With the same mass and spring, what resistance constant would provide critical damping?

26. A mass suspended by a spring and equipped with a damping device is free to oscillate vertically as in Fig. 8.1. The data are:

Mass: 32.2 lb

Spring: 3 lb tension produces 1 in. extension

Resistance force: Proportional to speed

Assume that the displacement is zero and the speed 12 ft/sec at time $t = 0$. Plot displacement against time for the first 2 sec of motion for each of the following values of the resistance constant:

(a) $r = 0$.   (b) $r = 1.5$ lb-sec/ft.
(c) $r = 12$ lb-sec/ft.   (d) $r = 20$ lb-sec/ft.

8.7. DAMPED VIBRATIONS WITH A DRIVING FORCE

A simple system made up of mass, spring, and damper shows remarkable and important properties when driven by a periodic force. We shall continue to illustrate phenomena by single examples. Here we imagine the spring of the preceding section to be attached to a gadget (see Fig. 8.16) which impresses a displacement

$$(8.35) \qquad\qquad y = y_0 \cos \omega' t$$

on the upper end of the spring. A sinusoidal drive is used because it is typical of periodic disturbances prevalent in machinery, and also because other periodic functions can be studied in terms of sines and cosines by means of Fourier analysis.

In Eq. (8.35) the coordinate y is considered as positive downward. The coordinate x is measured from the equilibrium position corresponding to $y = 0$. In writing the equations of motion, we use the same terminology as before:

$$m\frac{d^2x}{dt^2} = mg - \frac{1}{c}(s_0 + x - y) - r\frac{dx}{dt}$$

or

$$(8.36) \qquad\qquad \frac{d^2x}{dt^2} + \frac{r}{m}\frac{dx}{dt} + \frac{x}{mc} = \frac{y_0}{mc}\cos\omega' t$$

Since y/c is the effective force applied to the mass, we write

$$(8.37) \qquad\qquad \frac{y_0}{c} = f_0$$

This shows that the same performance would follow if a force

(8.38)
$$f = f_0 \cos \omega' t$$

were applied to the bob.

The general solution to (8.36) has two parts:

(8.39)
$$x = x_{\text{transient}} + x_{\text{steady state}}$$

The transient part of the solution is the so-called complementary function, the general solution of the related homogeneous equation

$$\frac{d^2x}{dt^2} + \frac{r}{m}\frac{dx}{dt} + \frac{x}{mc} = 0$$

Using the result (8.22) of the preceding section, we get

(8.40)
$$x_{\text{transient}} = ae^{-(rt/2m)} \sin\left(\sqrt{\frac{1}{mc} - \frac{r^2}{4m^2}}\, t + \epsilon\right)$$

(It is, of course, assumed here that the resistance is less than critical.)   The arbitrary constants a and ϵ cannot be determined until the whole solution x has been formulated.

The steady-state part of the solution is the oscillation generated by the driving force.   It is a particular integral of the main equation (8.36).   We shall try to fit the following form to that equation:

(8.41)
$$x_{\text{steady state}} = b \sin \omega' t + d \cos \omega' t$$

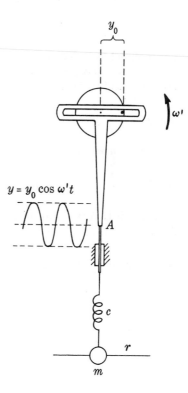

$y = y_0 \cos \omega' t$

Figure
8.16

Substituting (8.41) in (8.36), we get

$$-b\omega'^2 \sin \omega't - d\omega'^2 \cos \omega't + \frac{rb\omega'}{m} \cos \omega't$$

$$-\frac{rd\omega'}{m} \sin \omega't + \frac{b}{mc} \sin \omega't + \frac{d}{mc} \cos \omega't = \frac{f_0}{m} \cos \omega't$$

In order that this equation hold for all t, the coefficients of sine and cosine separately must agree:

$$-b\omega'^2 - \frac{rd\omega'}{m} + \frac{b}{mc} = 0$$

and

$$-d\omega'^2 + \frac{rb\omega'}{m} + \frac{d}{mc} = \frac{f_0}{m}$$

These two equations may be solved for b and d as follows:

(8.42)
$$b = \frac{f_0 r}{\omega'\left[r^2 + \left(\omega'm - \frac{1}{\omega'c}\right)^2\right]}$$

$$d = \frac{f_0\left(\frac{1}{\omega'^2 c} - m\right)}{\left[r^2 + \left(\omega'm - \frac{1}{\omega'c}\right)^2\right]}$$

Equation (8.41) with constants as in (8.42) is a particular integral of (8.36)

8.8. MECHANICAL IMPEDANCE AND RESONANCE

The ungainly expressions (8.42) derived in the preceding section are conveniently abbreviated according to the pattern used in electrical theory. For each ω', the system is said to have a *mechanical reactance r'* given as

(8.43)
$$r' = \omega'm - \frac{1}{\omega'c}$$

and a *mechanical impedance* whose magnitude z is given by

(8.44)
$$z^2 = r^2 + \left(\omega'm - \frac{1}{\omega'c}\right)^2 = r^2 + r'^2$$

Actually, it is very useful to deal with z as a complex number, as is usually done in electrical work. In this limited treatment, only the magnitude will be introduced. Note that the frequency for which the reactance is zero is the natural undamped frequency determined by Eq. (8.10).

In terms of reactance and impedance, the coefficients of the steady-state equation are

(8.45)
$$b = \frac{f_0 r}{\omega' z^2}$$

$$d = \frac{-f_0 r'}{\omega' z^2}$$

so the equation becomes

$$(8.46) \qquad x_{\text{steady state}} = \frac{f_0}{\omega' z^2} \left(r \sin \omega' t - r' \cos \omega' t \right)$$

or, using a little trigonometry,

$$(8.47) \qquad x_{\text{steady state}} = \frac{f_0}{\omega' z} \sin \left(\omega' t - \tan^{-1} \frac{r'}{r} \right)$$

It may be interesting, if you know some circuit theory, to think about the electrical analogue of this equation. Letting V_c be the rms or peak potential across the capacitor in an LCR series circuit, having a generator of potential V and angular frequency ω,

$$\frac{Q}{C} = V_c = \frac{I}{\omega C} = \frac{V}{\omega C Z}$$

Hence $Q = V/\omega Z$, which is clearly analogous to the rms or peak versions of Eq. (8.47),

Resonance. It appears then from Eqs. (8.39), (8.40), and (8.47) that when a sinusoidal force is applied to a spring-mass system having resistance, the displacement consists of two separate patterns of behavior superimposed. The transient pattern has the characteristics of a free damped oscillation, but the steady-state behavior reflects the frequency of the driving force. The amplitude of this steady-state displacement depends on the impedance of the system at the driving frequency. In many problems of engineering design, it is essential to know under what conditions this amplitude will become large. From Eq. (8.47) it should be clear that this amplitude will be maximum when $\omega'^2 z^2$ is a minimum. Using Eq. (8.44), we find the derivative with respect to ω', set it equal to zero, and solve for the critical value. This is a standard calculus problem, and the conclusion is this: The steady-state amplitude is maximum when

$$(8.48) \qquad \omega' = \sqrt{\frac{1}{mc} - \frac{r^2}{2m^2}}$$

This condition of maximum amplitude is called *resonance*. Note that for small r this is essentially equal to the value for a free vibration [compare Eq. (8.23)]. In fact, for really small r, both values are approximately the same as the undamped value: $1/\sqrt{mc}$.

For resonance with *low resistance*, then,

$$(8.49) \qquad \omega' = \frac{1}{\sqrt{mc}}$$

or

$$\omega' m = \frac{1}{\omega' c}$$

or

$$r' = 0$$

or

$$z = r$$

For small r it is interesting to compute the *magnification factor* at resonance:

$$\text{Magnification factor} = \frac{\text{output amplitude}}{\text{input amplitude}} = \frac{f_0/\omega' z}{y_0} = \frac{f_0/\omega' r}{f_0 c}$$

or

(8.50)   Magnification factor $= \dfrac{1}{r\omega'c} = \dfrac{\omega'm}{r}$

In electrical analogues this factor is called the Q of the circuit.   For a high-Q circuit the resonant response is sharp and often violent.

Phase Relationships.   In the preceding discussions the input displacement was

$$y = y_0 \cos \omega' t$$

The corresponding output displacement (8.47) may be written

(8.51) $x_{\text{steady state}} = \dfrac{f_0}{\omega' z} \cos\left(\omega't - \tan^{-1}\dfrac{r'}{r} - 90°\right)$

The speed of displacement is obtained by differentiating (8.47):

(8.52) $v_{\text{steady state}} = \dfrac{f_0}{z} \cos\left(\omega't - \tan^{-1}\dfrac{r'}{r}\right)$

At *resonance*, we may observe that the output speed is *in phase* with the input displacement, while the output displacement lags by 90° (i.e., the peak values of $x_{\text{steady state}}$ occur one quarter period later than those of y).   The reactance r' [see Eq. (8.43)] is positive for frequencies greater than the resonance value and negative for frequencies smaller than the resonance value.   For small r, then, if the frequency is reduced, the angle whose tangent is r'/r approaches $-90°$; thus y and $x_{\text{steady state}}$ are nearly in phase for low frequencies.   Similarly, we can deduce that for high frequencies $x_{\text{steady state}}$ lags y by 180°.   These phase relationships are verified by experiment. A student familar with complex impedances in electrical work will readily translate these results.

Mechanical Isolation.   In practical engineering it is frequently desirable to keep forced oscillations well away from resonance.   In mounting electric motors, for instance, spring or rubber supports are used to prevent the transmission of vibration.   If a vibrating mass is subjected to a periodic force (see Fig. 8.17)

$$f_0 \cos \omega' t$$

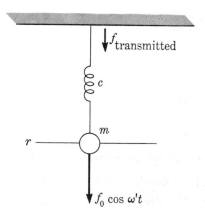

Figure
8.17

the equation of motion is as given by Eqs. (8.36) and (8.37), and the steady-state displacement is given by (8.47): a sine of amplitude

$$\frac{f_0}{\omega' z}$$

The maximum periodic force transmitted to the rigid support is merely the maximum displacement from equilibrium divided by the compliance of the spring; therefore the ratio of maximum transmitted force to maximum applied force is easily computed:

(8.53)
$$\frac{f_{\text{transmitted}}}{f_{\text{applied}}} = \frac{x_{\text{max}}}{cf_0} = \frac{f_0}{\omega' z c f_0} = \frac{1}{\omega' cz}$$

If the resistance is small and the mass and frequency fixed, it is possible to control the ratio (8.53) by adjusting c. Numerical examples are given as exercises. Note that this last equation has a form easily suggested by the electrical analogue

$$\frac{V_c}{V} = \frac{Z_c}{Z}$$

EXERCISES

27. (See Fig. 8.16.) Data: A force of 1 lb produces an elongation of 1 in. in the spring. When A is held fixed, the free period of oscillation is 3.142 sec. It takes 20 complete oscillations for the amplitude in the free oscillation to reach 37 per cent of the initial displacement. The wheel rotates with angular speed ω' and imparts to A a simple harmonic motion of amplitude $y_0 = 1$ ft. Find the steady-state amplitude of the displacement of the mass when (a) $\omega' = 0.2$ rad/sec; (b) $\omega' = 2.0$ rad/sec.

28. A periodic force

$$f = f_0 \cos \omega' t$$

is applied to an object of mass 0.72 kg suspended by a simple spring. The spring will stretch 1 cm under a force of 60 newtons. When $\omega' = 100$ rad/sec and $f_0 = 6.5$ newtons, the steady-state amplitude is 0.5 cm. (a) What value of ω' will produce resonance? (b) What is the resistance r? (c) What would be the amplitude of the oscillation at resonance?

29. Express the magnification factor to be expected from a low-r system operated at resonance entirely in terms of the logarithmic decrement per half period of the undriven system.

30. An electric motor and the platform on which it is mounted weigh together 500 lb. At 600 rpm, a force

$$f_0 \cos 20\pi t$$

is effectively applied to the system. To isolate the vibration, the platform is supported on four like coil springs (see Fig. 8.18). The maximum force transmitted to the floor for steady state is not to be more than 10 per cent of the maximum impressed force f_0. What is the minimum permissible compliance for each of the four springs? (Neglect damping.)

31. An electric motor weighing 200 lb is suspended by vertical springs which stretch 6 in. when the motor is attached. (a) If the flywheel had its center of gravity off center, for how many rpm would resonance be expected? (b) For steady state, what fraction of the vibrational force is transmitted to the ceiling when the motor is operated at 600 rpm?

32. What phase relationships will exist between the input displacement y and the output speed for very low and for very high frequencies?

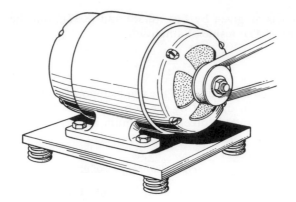

Figure
8.18

REVIEW EXERCISES

33. A uniform spring has mass m, unloaded length l (i.e., the length when lying slack on a smooth horizontal surface), and compliance c. When suspended from one end and allowed to extend under its own weight, how long is it?

34. One end of a rubber cord is attached to the ceiling. When a 1-lb ball is attached to the other end, the cord is stretched 6 in. to a new equilibrium position. Now when the ball is displaced (by further stretching of the cord) 4 in. more and released, the ball oscillates vertically.
(a) What is the period of the oscillation?
(b) What will be the maximum speed of the ball's motion?

35. A 20-kg object, suspended by two identical springs as shown in Fig. 8.19, oscillates with a period of 4 sec.
(a) Neglecting the damping, find the compliance of each spring.
(b) Neglecting damping, find the maximum speed if the maximum displacement is 10 cm.
(c) If successive displacements are 10.0, −9.5, 9.0, −8.6, 8.1, −7.7, . . . , what is the damping constant r?
(d) What r would produce critical damping?

36. A spring with bob attached is displaced vertically and allowed to oscillate. Peak displacements from equilibrium position are recorded in the accompanying table. The stiffness of the spring is evaluated by noting that the addition of 1 kg weight stretches the spring 8.0 cm.

t, sec	x, cms
0.11	22.0
0.52	−18.0
0.93	14.8
1.34	−12.1
1.75	9.9
2.16	−8.1

What are:
(a) The logarithmic decrement per half period?
(b) The period?
(c) The time constant of damping?
(d) The effective mass of the oscillating system?
(e) The resistance constant? (Friction is proportional to speed.)

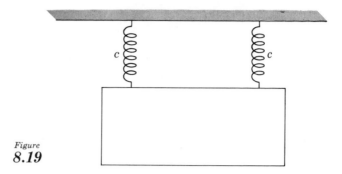

Figure
8.19

37. A light damper of resistance r is attached to a spring of compliance c. A constant force f is suddenly applied to the damper. If $r = 30$ newton-sec/m, $c = 0.06$ m/newton, and $f = 15$ newtons, find x and dx/dt for $t = 1.8$ sec.

38. Initially, a light damper on a light spring has a speed v_0 toward the equilibrium position. Show that the speed of the damper is proportional to the displacement from the equilibrium position.

39. A motor weighing 644 lb is mounted on springs so that the natural period of oscillation is 1.571 sec. The resistance r is small. In fact, it takes 25.0 sec for the amplitude of a free oscillation to decay to 37 per cent of its original value.
  (*a*) Compute the compliance of the system of springs.
  (*b*) Compute the resistance constant of the system.
  (*c*) If the motor operates at its resonance frequency, what is the theoretical magnification factor?
  (*d*) If the motor operates at a frequency 20 times that of resonance, what is the mechanical impedance? (Watch units.)

40. A spring supports a load with damping. The mechanical resistance is small, but not negligible. The effective weight of the system is given by

$$w = mg = 1.64 \text{ lb}$$

A force of 0.25 lb produces a static stretch of 1.0 in. in the spring. It takes 25 complete free oscillations for the amplitude to reduce by 37 per cent.
  (*a*) What is the compliance of the spring?
  (*b*) What would be the undamped period of oscillation?
  (*c*) What is the mechanical resistance?
  (*d*) What is the mechanical impedance for forced oscillations at 10 rad/sec?
  (*e*) At the frequency given in (*d*), what steady-state amplitude will result from a sinusoidal force of peak value 0.55 lb?
  (*f*) What fraction of this applied force is transmitted to the support?
  (*g*) A new damper is inserted for which the resistance is 0.500 lb-sec/ft. The spring breaks at the top, allowing the system to fall, subject only to gravity. What terminal speed results?
  (*h*) In (*g*), how long will it take to attain the terminal speed (say, 5 time constants)?

41. The 10-lb weight in Fig. 8.20 is suspended between two stretched springs. The top spring has a constant of 5 lb/in.; the bottom spring has a constant of 10 lb/in.
  (*a*) What work must be done to displace the mass upward by 1 in? (*b*) Downward by 1 in? (*c*) With what period will it oscillate?

42. A 200-g sphere is supported by two vertical springs (as in Fig. 8.20). The compliances are

$$c_1 = 0.010 \text{ m/newton} \qquad c_2 = 0.015 \text{ m/newton}$$

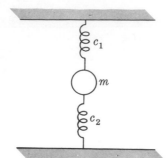

Figure
8.20

When the sphere is at equilibrium, the tension in the lower spring is f. (*a*) What force will displace the sphere vertically 3 cm from equilibrium position? (*b*) With what period will it oscillate if released?

43. A spring of compliance 0.05 ft/lb has a damper of resistance 40 lb-sec/ft. The system is initially at rest in equilibrium, as shown in Fig. 8.11. A sudden downward force of 40 lb is applied. How long will it take to get halfway to its new equilibrium position?

44. In Exercise 43 how long before the rate of energy storage in the spring is a maximum?

45. If the mass m in the underdamped system of Sec. 8.5 is started at rest with an initial displacement x_0, show that the constants in Eq. (8.22) have the values

$$a = \frac{x_0}{(1 - \rho^2)^{\frac{1}{2}}} \qquad \epsilon = \tan^{-1}\frac{-\rho}{(1 - \rho^2)^{\frac{1}{2}}}$$

where ρ is the ratio of the resistance r to the critical resistance r_c.

46. Equation (8.23) shows that the period τ of a damped oscillation is longer than the corresponding undamped period τ_0. Show that (using λ as in Exercise 18)

$$\frac{\tau}{\tau_0} = \left(1 + \frac{\lambda^2}{\pi^2}\right)^{\frac{1}{2}}$$

47. Show that the constants of Exercise 45 may be written as

$$a = x_0\left(1 + \frac{\lambda^2}{\pi^2}\right)^{\frac{1}{2}} \qquad \epsilon = \tan^{-1}\frac{-\lambda}{\pi}$$

48. Each successive excursion of the system in Exercise 42 is nine-tenths as long as the previous one. What is the resistance?

49. Referring to Fig. 8.1, at time $t = 0$ the 1-lb bob goes through equilibrium position with a speed of 3 ft/sec. The spring is such that a force of 8.75 lb produces an extension of 8.5 in. Find the time and magnitude of the first excursion of the bob if (*a*) $r = 0.1r_{\text{critical}}$; (*b*) $r = r_{\text{critical}}$.

50. Show that the magnification factor to be expected from a low-r system operated at resonance is equal to

$$\frac{r_{\text{critical}}}{2r}$$

51. For the case where r is negligible, show that the ratio of the transmitted to applied force will be less than k when the springs are so chosen that the natural period τ will satisfy (see Fig. 8.17)

$$\tau > \tau'\left(\frac{1 + k}{k}\right)^{\frac{1}{2}}$$

where τ' is the period of the applied force.

CHAPTER NINE

VECTOR PRODUCTS

The vector operations of Chap. 2 have already found an abundance of physical applications. Vector addition has been used to show how forces, velocities, and accelerations are combined. The difference of two vectors has occurred in the description of displacement, in expressing change of momentum, and in defining the derivative of a vector function. Products of vectors by scalars occur as often as we write the familiar $m\mathbf{A}$ or integrals such as impulse. The inner product of two vectors has appeared as a tool for computing components of any vector quantity and in expressions for work and energy. We now turn to an additional operation peculiarly suited to life in three dimensions.

9.1. VECTOR PRODUCTS OF TWO VECTORS

The remaining operation to be introduced at this stage is in many ways the most interesting of all. When applied to two vectors, the operation yields a new vector. The procedure resembles multiplication enough to deserve the name *vector product*, yet many of the usual properties of a product are missing. Since the result of this operation is a vector, both a direction and a magnitude must be specified. For two nonparallel vectors $\mathbf{A}$ and $\mathbf{B}$, the direction is that of a unit vector $\mathbf{N}$ perpendicular to the plane determined by the two vectors $\mathbf{A}$ and $\mathbf{B}$. Two such unit vectors are possible ($\mathbf{N}$ and $-\mathbf{N}$ in Fig. 9.1), but we choose $\mathbf{N}$ so that the rotation of $\mathbf{A}$ into $\mathbf{B}$ as seen from the tip of $\mathbf{N}$, looking back at the plane, is counterclockwise. The same kind of choice was made in Sec. 2.2 in selecting a positive z axis. In Fig. 9.2 $\mathbf{N}$ is directed out of the page toward the reader. The magnitude of this vector product is defined to be the product of the magnitudes of the two vectors times the sine of the angle between. A defining equation for the vector product of $\mathbf{A}$ times $\mathbf{B}$ (denoted by $\mathbf{A} \times \mathbf{B}$, and hence often called the *cross product* or *outer product*) is

$$(9.1) \qquad \mathbf{A} \times \mathbf{B} = ab \sin \theta \, \mathbf{N}$$

It is interesting to note that the magnitude of $\mathbf{A} \times \mathbf{B}$ is equal to the area of the parallelogram determined (as in Fig. 9.2) by the vectors $\mathbf{A}$ and $\mathbf{B}$. Thus

$$(9.2) \qquad \mathbf{A} \times \mathbf{B} = (\text{area})\mathbf{N}$$

Hence the magnitude of $\mathbf{A} \times \mathbf{B}$ can be expressed as the magnitude of $\mathbf{A}$ times the component of $\mathbf{B}$ normal to $\mathbf{A}$, or as the magnitude of $\mathbf{B}$ times the component of $\mathbf{A}$

normal to **B**.   From the definition of **N** it should be at once obvious that this kind of multiplication is not commutative:

(9.3) $$\mathbf{A} \times \mathbf{B} = -\mathbf{B} \times \mathbf{A}$$

In describing the direction of **N**, we considered **A** and **B** as being nonparallel.   For parallel vectors, however, sin θ is zero; thus our defining equation may be used for all cases.

This suggests the following criterion for parallelism or antiparallelism: two non-null vectors **A** and **B** are parallel or antiparallel if and only if **A** × **B** = **O**.

Example

Consider **A** × **B**, where $\mathbf{A} = 5/\underline{40°}$ and $\mathbf{B} = 2/\underline{-110°}$.   Then

$$\mathbf{A} \times \mathbf{B} = (5)(2)(\sin 150°)(-\mathbf{K}) = -5\mathbf{K}$$

Similarly,

$$\mathbf{B} \times \mathbf{A} = (5)(2)(\sin 150°)(\mathbf{K}) = 5\mathbf{K}$$

Special Conclusions

1. **A** × **A** = **O**.   This is, of course, a special case of the criterion just stated.
2. Note that

(9.4)
$$\mathbf{I} \times \mathbf{J} = \mathbf{K} \qquad \mathbf{J} \times \mathbf{K} = \mathbf{I} \qquad \mathbf{K} \times \mathbf{I} = \mathbf{J}$$
$$\mathbf{J} \times \mathbf{I} = -\mathbf{K} \qquad \mathbf{K} \times \mathbf{J} = -\mathbf{I} \qquad \mathbf{I} \times \mathbf{K} = -\mathbf{J}$$

3. For two unit vectors **E** and **F** having between them an angle θ,

$$\mathbf{E} \times \mathbf{F} = \sin \theta \ \mathbf{N}$$

Hence the sine of the angle is given by the magnitude of the vector product:

(9.5) $$\sin \theta = |\mathbf{E} \times \mathbf{F}|$$

More generally, for any two vectors **A** and **B**

(9.6) $$\sin \theta = \left| \frac{\mathbf{A} \times \mathbf{B}}{ab} \right|$$

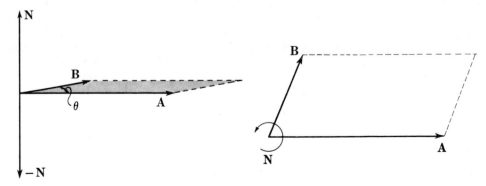

Figure
9.1

Figure
9.2

4. Suppose that **N** is a *unit vector perpendicular to* **A**. Then **N** × **A** is a vector equal to **A** but at right angles to **A** (as in Fig. 9.3).

(9.7) *The operation* **N** × *may be thought of as merely rotating* **A** *through* 90°. (*Similarly, the operation* × **N** *may be thought of as merely rotating* **A** *through* −90°.)

Note that **N** × (**N** × **A**) = −**A**. This suggests an analogy between the operation **N** × and multiplication by $i = \sqrt{-1}$ in the algebra of complex numbers.

5. If **B**′ is the projection of **B** normal to **A**, then

(9.8) $$\mathbf{A} \times \mathbf{B} = \mathbf{A} \times \mathbf{B}'$$

Hence, if **B** and **B**″ have equal projections normal to **A**, it follows that **A** × **B** = **A** × **B**″ as shown in Fig. 9.4. We must then resist the temptation to cancel **A** from both sides of Eq. (9.8). The student should use the definition of vector product to verify these relations and also the following similar ones:

(9.9) $$\mathbf{A}' \times \mathbf{B} = \mathbf{A} \times \mathbf{B} = \mathbf{A}'' \times \mathbf{B}$$

Algebraic Properties. It is easy to show that scalar factors may be factored out of a vector product:

(9.10) $$(c\mathbf{A}) \times (d\mathbf{B}) = cd(\mathbf{A} \times \mathbf{B})$$

The proof is listed for Exercise 6.

We have seen already that vector multiplication is not commutative:

$$\mathbf{A} \times \mathbf{B} \neq \mathbf{B} \times \mathbf{A}$$

Later it will be shown that this kind of multiplication is not associative:

$$\mathbf{A} \times (\mathbf{B} \times \mathbf{C}) \neq (\mathbf{A} \times \mathbf{B}) \times \mathbf{C}$$

We shall next seek to prove that vector multiplication is distributive with respect to vector addition, i.e., that the following equation is in general valid.

$$\mathbf{A} \times (\mathbf{B} + \mathbf{C}) = \mathbf{A} \times \mathbf{B} + \mathbf{A} \times \mathbf{C}$$

The proof is given in Sec. 9.2

EXERCISES

1. Use the defining equations for vector products to compute in **IJK** form the vector product of each of the following pairs of vectors:

(a) $\mathbf{A} = 4/\underline{20°}$, $\mathbf{B} = 7/\underline{-25°}$.

(b) $\mathbf{A} = 5/\underline{-55°}$, $\mathbf{B} = 10/\underline{125°}$.

(c) $\mathbf{A} = 5/\underline{55°}$, $\mathbf{B} = 10/\underline{35°}$.

(d) $\mathbf{A} = 5/\underline{40°}$, $\mathbf{B} = 5/\underline{40°}$.

(e) $\mathbf{A} = \mathbf{I} + \mathbf{J}$, $\mathbf{B} = \mathbf{J} + \mathbf{K}$.

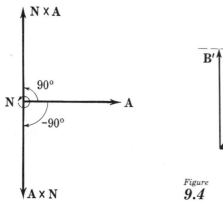

Figure
9.3

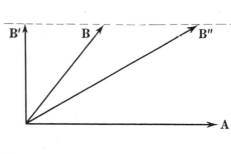

Figure
9.4

2. Compute in polar form the following vector products:

(a) $\mathbf{K} \times \mathbf{I}$.

(b) $\mathbf{K} \times 10\underline{/30°}$.

(c) $\mathbf{K} \times \mathbf{J}$.

(d) $\mathbf{K} \times (2\mathbf{I} + 2\mathbf{J})$.

(e) $10\underline{/30°} \times \mathbf{K}$.

(f) $\mathbf{K} \times \{\mathbf{K} \times [\mathbf{K} \times (\mathbf{K} \times 2\underline{/36°})]\}$.

3. $\mathbf{R}$ is a vector in the xy plane. $\mathbf{I}$ as usual is a unit vector parallel to the x axis. It is given that

$$\mathbf{I} \times \mathbf{R} = \mathbf{K}$$

where $\mathbf{K}$ is the unit vector parallel to the z axis. How much can be concluded about $\mathbf{R}$? Describe the locus of points in the xy plane for which $\mathbf{R}$ may be position vector.

4. Use the definition of scalar and vector products to prove the following: If

$$\mathbf{A} \times \mathbf{B} = \mathbf{C} \quad \text{and} \quad \mathbf{B} \times \mathbf{C} = \mathbf{A}$$

then

$$\mathbf{B} \cdot \mathbf{A} = 0 \quad \mathbf{C} \cdot \mathbf{A} = 0 \quad \mathbf{B} \cdot \mathbf{C} = 0 \quad \mathbf{A} \cdot \mathbf{A} = \mathbf{C} \cdot \mathbf{C} \quad \mathbf{B} \cdot \mathbf{B} = 1$$

5. Use the definitions of scalar and vector products to prove the identity

$$(\mathbf{A} \times \mathbf{B}) \cdot (\mathbf{A} \times \mathbf{B}) = (\mathbf{A} \cdot \mathbf{A})(\mathbf{B} \cdot \mathbf{B}) - (\mathbf{A} \cdot \mathbf{B})(\mathbf{A} \cdot \mathbf{B})$$

6. Prove that for vectors $\mathbf{A}$, $\mathbf{B}$ and scalars c, d the following identity is valid:

$$(c\mathbf{A}) \times (d\mathbf{B}) = cd(\mathbf{A} \times \mathbf{B})$$

9.2. THE DISTRIBUTIVE LAW FOR VECTOR PRODUCTS

It is so natural to accept equations like

$$2 \times 3 = 3 \times 2 \qquad 3 \times (1 + 2) = 3 \times 1 + 3 \times 2$$

as inevitable truisms that proofs of corresponding vector relationships might first impress the student as unnecessary. Any such complacency should be dispelled by the discovery in the preceding section that the operation called *vector product* is not commutative. The distributive law to which this section is devoted is of unusual interest because of its very close connection with certain problems in mechanics. Fairly detailed attention to the law and its applications will help greatly in getting accustomed to this rather strange new operation.

Let us now proceed with a proof of

(9.11) $$\mathbf{A} \times (\mathbf{B} + \mathbf{C}) = \mathbf{A} \times \mathbf{B} + \mathbf{A} \times \mathbf{C}$$

Let $(\mathbf{B} + \mathbf{C})'$ denote the projection of $(\mathbf{B} + \mathbf{C})$ perpendicular to $\mathbf{A}$. As was pointed out in Sec. 9.1, special conclusion 5,

$$\mathbf{A} \times (\mathbf{B} + \mathbf{C}) = \mathbf{A} \times (\mathbf{B} + \mathbf{C})'$$

But $(\mathbf{B} + \mathbf{C})'$ is merely the projection of the sum $\mathbf{B} + \mathbf{C}$ onto a plane normal to $\mathbf{A}$. The parallelogram representing the vector addition $\mathbf{B} + \mathbf{C}$ projects onto a parallelogram representing the addition $\mathbf{B}' + \mathbf{C}'$, where $\mathbf{B}'$ and $\mathbf{C}'$ are the projections of $\mathbf{B}$ and $\mathbf{C}$ onto a plane normal to $\mathbf{A}$. Diagonals project into diagonals, so

$$(\mathbf{B} + \mathbf{C})' = \mathbf{B}' + \mathbf{C}'$$

(A formal proof for this equation is given in Appendix 2, Sec. A2.4.)   Substituting this expression for $(\mathbf{B} + \mathbf{C})'$ and writing $a\mathbf{E}$ for $\mathbf{A}$ (that is, we denote the unit vector $\mathbf{A}/a$ by $\mathbf{E}$), we have

$$\mathbf{A} \times (\mathbf{B} + \mathbf{C}) = a\mathbf{E} \times (\mathbf{B}' + \mathbf{C}')$$

where $\mathbf{E}$ is a unit vector perpendicular to both $\mathbf{B}'$ and $\mathbf{C}'$.   In Sec. 9.1, special conclusion 4, it was observed that the operation $\mathbf{E} \times$ merely rotates vectors normal to $\mathbf{E}$ through 90°, as in Fig. 9.5.   If the parallelogram representing the addition of $\mathbf{B}'$ and $\mathbf{C}'$ is rotated in its own plane by 90°, each of the three vectors $\mathbf{B}'$, $\mathbf{C}'$, and $\mathbf{B}' + \mathbf{C}'$ is also rotated through 90°.   In symbols, then,

$$\mathbf{E} \times (\mathbf{B}' + \mathbf{C}') = \mathbf{E} \times \mathbf{B}' + \mathbf{E} \times \mathbf{C}'$$

(This equation is, of course, a statement of the distributive law for a very special case.)   Substituting this in the previous equation, we get

$$\mathbf{A} \times (\mathbf{B} + \mathbf{C}) = a(\mathbf{E} \times \mathbf{B}' + \mathbf{E} \times \mathbf{C}')$$

Using the distributive property of the operation of multiplication of vectors by scalars (see exercises of Sec. 2.8), using again the result on projections, etc., we have

$$\mathbf{A} \times (\mathbf{B} + \mathbf{C}) = a(\mathbf{E} \times \mathbf{B}') + a(\mathbf{E} \times \mathbf{C}')$$
$$= a\mathbf{E} \times \mathbf{B}' + a\mathbf{E} \times \mathbf{C}'$$
$$= \mathbf{A} \times \mathbf{B}' + \mathbf{A} \times \mathbf{C}'$$
$$= \mathbf{A} \times \mathbf{B} + \mathbf{A} \times \mathbf{C}$$

It is left for Exercise 10 to show that the reverse form of the distributive law also holds, i.e., that

(9.12) $$(\mathbf{A} + \mathbf{B}) \times \mathbf{C} = \mathbf{A} \times \mathbf{C} + \mathbf{B} \times \mathbf{C}$$

and that the laws hold in more extensive form,

(9.13) $$\mathbf{A} \times (\mathbf{B} + \mathbf{C} + \mathbf{D}) = \mathbf{A} \times \mathbf{B} + \mathbf{A} \times \mathbf{C} + \mathbf{A} \times \mathbf{D}$$

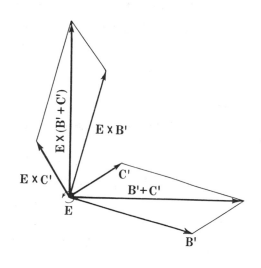

Figure
9.5

Working Formulas for Vector Products. Having established the distributive law for vector multiplication, we are now able to derive a formula for such a product in terms of x, y, and z components. By a direct substitution we have

$$(\mathbf{A} \times \mathbf{B}) = (a_x\mathbf{I} + a_y\mathbf{J} + a_z\mathbf{K}) \times (b_x\mathbf{I} + b_y\mathbf{J} + b_z\mathbf{K})$$

Now using the distributive laws, the law for factoring out scalars, the commutative and associative laws for vector addition, etc., we get

(9.14) $$\mathbf{A} \times \mathbf{B} = (a_y b_z - a_z b_y)\mathbf{I} + (a_z b_x - a_x b_z)\mathbf{J} + (a_x b_y - a_y b_x)\mathbf{K}$$

Note that one can get one component from the preceding by a cyclic substitution of subscripts: y for x, z for y, x for z. A compact way of writing this result is in terms of a determinant:

(9.15) $$\mathbf{A} \times \mathbf{B} = \begin{vmatrix} a_x & a_y & a_z \\ b_x & b_y & b_z \\ \mathbf{I} & \mathbf{J} & \mathbf{K} \end{vmatrix} = \begin{vmatrix} a_y & a_z \\ b_y & b_z \end{vmatrix}\mathbf{I} + \begin{vmatrix} a_z & a_x \\ b_z & b_x \end{vmatrix}\mathbf{J} + \begin{vmatrix} a_x & a_y \\ b_x & b_y \end{vmatrix}\mathbf{K}$$

The student who has had no previous work with determinants should not be dismayed by the introduction of this notation. All that is desired is a systematic way of computing components of the vector product. The x component of the product is obtained from the y and z components of the factors by subtracting the *diagonal products* of the square array shown before the $\mathbf{I}$ above, and similarly for other components, cyclic order being observed in each case: x from y and z, y from z and x, z from x and y. It just happens that the determinant machinery handles the same kind of problem.

If we denote the vector $\mathbf{A} \times \mathbf{B}$ by the letter $\mathbf{C}$, so that

$$\mathbf{C} = \mathbf{A} \times \mathbf{B}$$

then it should be clear that the components c_x, c_y, and c_z are contained in the columns indicated in the diagram below.

$$\begin{array}{cccc} & \overbrace{}^{c_x} & & \\ a_x & a_y & a_z & a_x \\ b_x & b_y & b_z & b_x \\ & \underbrace{}_{c_z} & \underbrace{}_{c_y} & \end{array}$$

Taking the difference of diagonal products in each case, one obtains

$$c_x = a_y b_z - a_z b_y \qquad c_y = a_z b_x - a_x b_z \qquad c_z = a_x b_y - a_y b_x$$

Example

Compute the components of the vector product $\mathbf{A} \times \mathbf{B}$, where $\mathbf{A} = 3\mathbf{I} - 7\mathbf{J}$ and $\mathbf{B} = \mathbf{I} + \mathbf{J} - 2\mathbf{K}$.

Solution

Writing down the array of components of $\mathbf{A}$ and $\mathbf{B}$ in cyclic order,

$$\begin{array}{cccc} 3 & -7 & 0 & 3 \\ 1 & 1 & -2 & 1 \end{array}$$

the components of the product may be read off as

$$c_x = (-7)(-2) - (0)(1) = 14$$
$$c_y = (0)(1) - (3)(-2) = 6$$
$$c_z = (3)(1) - (-7)(1) = 10$$

Collecting these results, we have

$$\mathbf{A} \times \mathbf{B} = 14\mathbf{I} + 6\mathbf{J} + 10\mathbf{K}$$

Relations between the new operation and other procedures should be pointed out.   Using the ordinary Δ method, one can demonstrate the differentiation formula

(9.16)
$$\frac{d}{dt}(\mathbf{R} \times \mathbf{S}) = \frac{d\mathbf{R}}{dt} \times \mathbf{S} + \mathbf{R} \times \frac{d\mathbf{S}}{dt}$$

Also, by checking on derivatives, one can shown that for a constant vector $\mathbf{C}$

(9.17)
$$\int \mathbf{C} \times \mathbf{V} \, dt = \mathbf{C} \times \int \mathbf{V} \, dt$$

In both of these the important thing is to preserve the original order of factors since the new operation is not commutative.

EXERCISES

7. Compute in IJK form the vector product of each of the following pairs of vectors:
    (a) $\mathbf{A} = 2\mathbf{J}$, $\mathbf{B} = \mathbf{I} + \mathbf{J} + \mathbf{K}$.
    (b) $\mathbf{A} = \mathbf{I} + 2\mathbf{J} + 3\mathbf{K}$, $\mathbf{B} = 3\mathbf{I} + 2\mathbf{J} + \mathbf{K}$.
    (c) $\mathbf{A} = 2\mathbf{I} - 4\mathbf{K}$, $\mathbf{B} = -0.5\mathbf{I} + \mathbf{K}$.
8. The vectors $2\mathbf{I} - 3\mathbf{J} + 4\mathbf{K}$ and $\mathbf{I} + b\mathbf{J} + c\mathbf{K}$ are parallel. Use a vector product to find b and c.
9. If the vectors $\mathbf{R}$, $\mathbf{R}'$, and $\mathbf{F}$ and $\mathbf{N}$ have, respectively, the components (x,y,z), (x',y',z'), (f_x,f_y,f_z), and (n_x,n_y,n_z), write three scalar equations equivalent to the vector equation

$$\mathbf{N} = (\mathbf{R} - \mathbf{R}') \times \mathbf{F}$$

10. Using the distributive law as originally established in this section, devise careful proofs for each of the following:
    (a) $(\mathbf{A} + \mathbf{B}) \times \mathbf{C} = \mathbf{A} \times \mathbf{C} + \mathbf{B} \times \mathbf{C}$.
    (b) $\mathbf{A} \times (\mathbf{B} + \mathbf{C} + \mathbf{D}) = \mathbf{A} \times \mathbf{B} + \mathbf{A} \times \mathbf{C} + \mathbf{A} \times \mathbf{D}$.
11. Given the vectors $\mathbf{A} = \mathbf{I} - 2\mathbf{J} + \mathbf{K}$, $\mathbf{B} = 2\mathbf{J} + 2\mathbf{K}$, $\mathbf{C} = -\mathbf{I} + \mathbf{K}$.
    (a) Find in IJK form the vector $(\mathbf{A} \times \mathbf{B}) \times \mathbf{C}$.
    (b) Find in IJK form the vector $\mathbf{A} \times (\mathbf{B} \times \mathbf{C})$.
    (c) Compare the values of $(\mathbf{A} \times \mathbf{B}) \cdot \mathbf{C}$ and $\mathbf{A} \cdot (\mathbf{B} \times \mathbf{C})$.
12. Find a unit vector perpendicular to both of the following vectors: $\mathbf{I} - \mathbf{J} + 3\mathbf{K}$ and $-\mathbf{I} - \mathbf{K}$.
13. $\mathbf{L}$ and $\mathbf{M}$ are unit vectors in the xy plane such that $\mathbf{L} \times \mathbf{M} = \mathbf{K}$. $\mathbf{A}$ is any vector parallel to the xy plane. Show that

$$\mathbf{L} \times \mathbf{A} = (\mathbf{L} \times \mathbf{M})(\mathbf{M} \cdot \mathbf{A})$$

9.3. SOME KINEMATICAL APPLICATIONS OF THE VECTOR PRODUCT

The next few chapters will have numerous uses for the vector product in different mechanical contexts.   In this section we pause to point out applications particularly to kinematics of a particle.

The vector product provides efficient machinery for determining directions normal to any two different given directions and hence, for example, normal to a plane. In discussing the trajectory of a particle we saw that the osculating plane appeared as the plane determined by the unit tangent vector $\mathbf{T}$ and the unit principal normal vector $\mathbf{N}$. We now can specify at once a unit vector $\mathbf{B}$, normal to the osculating plane by

$$\mathbf{B} = \mathbf{T} \times \mathbf{N}$$

This equation is quite analogous to $\mathbf{K} = \mathbf{I} \times \mathbf{J}$. $\mathbf{B}$ is called the *unit binormal vector*, as was pointed out in Chap. 5. We have already seen that $d\mathbf{T}/ds = \kappa\mathbf{N}$. It is easy to show (Exercise 14) that when $d\mathbf{B}/ds$ does not vanish, it also is a vector parallel to $\mathbf{N}$. As the particle moves along its trajectory, the osculating plane for a twisted curve will rotate and so will the binormal vector. The rate of rotation in radians per arc length is the *torsion* τ. With a natural sign convention, we have then

$$\frac{d\mathbf{B}}{ds} = -\tau\mathbf{N}$$

The formula for $d\mathbf{N}/ds$ is left for Exercise 15. The three formulas for arc-length derivatives of $\mathbf{T}$, $\mathbf{N}$, and $\mathbf{B}$ are prominent in elementary differential geometry, where they are known as the Serret-Frenet formulas.

The vector product, along with the scalar product, may be used systematically in solving vector equations. For instance, from the expressions $\mathbf{V} = v\mathbf{T}$ and $\mathbf{A} = \dot{v}\mathbf{T} + \kappa v^2\mathbf{N}$, it is clear that

$$\mathbf{V} \cdot \mathbf{A} = v\dot{v} \qquad \mathbf{V} \times \mathbf{A} = \kappa v^3\mathbf{B}$$

Example

Apply the preceding equations to Sec. 5.6, Example 4. Previously, we had $\mathbf{V} = 2\mathbf{I} - 1.5\mathbf{J}$, $\mathbf{A} = -6\mathbf{J}$, $v = 2.5$.

$$\mathbf{V} \cdot \mathbf{A} = 9 = 2.5\dot{v} \qquad \text{hence} \qquad a_T = \dot{v} = 9/2.5 = 3.6$$
$$\mathbf{V} \times \mathbf{A} = -12\mathbf{K} = \kappa(2.5)^3\mathbf{B} \qquad \text{so} \qquad \rho = (2.5)^3/12 = 1.3$$

Thus we have a kinematic method of finding the radius of curvature of a trajectory.

Another situation appropriate for this technique occurs in the use of polar reference vectors: $\mathbf{K}$, $\mathbf{L}$, $\mathbf{M}$, where $\mathbf{K} = \mathbf{L} \times \mathbf{M}$. Starting with the equation

$$\mathbf{V} = \dot{r}\mathbf{L} + r\dot{\theta}\mathbf{M}$$

we see that

$$\mathbf{L} \cdot \mathbf{V} = \dot{r}$$

while

$$\mathbf{L} \times \mathbf{V} = r\dot{\theta}\mathbf{K}$$

You may wish, for practice, to apply the second of these equations to Examples 2 and 3 of Sec. 5.7.

EXERCISES

14. Show that $d\mathbf{B}/ds$ is parallel to $\mathbf{N}$.   [HINT: Evaluate $\mathbf{N} \times (d/ds)(\mathbf{T} \times \mathbf{N})$.]
15. Assuming that $d\mathbf{B}/ds = -\tau\mathbf{N}$, where τ is a scalar, verify the formula

$$d\mathbf{N}/ds = -\kappa\mathbf{T} + \tau\mathbf{B}$$

16. Use the methods of the preceding section to find for points on the axes of symmetry the radius of curvature of an ellipse of major and minor axes $2a$ and $2b$, respectively. [HINT: A particle with position vector $\mathbf{R} = (a \cos t)\mathbf{I} + (b \sin t)\mathbf{J}$ traces out such an ellipse.]

17. The position vector of a moving particle is given by

$$\mathbf{R} = 3t^2\mathbf{I} - 4t\mathbf{J} \qquad \text{ft for time in sec}$$

For $t = 0.5$ sec, find:
(*a*) The unit radial vector $\mathbf{L}$ (in **IJK** form).
(*b*) The speed v.
(*c*) The unit tangential vector $\mathbf{T}$ (in **IJK** form).
(*d*) The tangential acceleration a_T.
(*e*) The normal acceleration a_N.
(*f*) The radius of curvature of the trajectory at that point ρ.
(*g*) The angular speed ω with which the position vector is rotating.

9.4. THE SCALAR TRIPLE PRODUCT

We have seen how for any two vectors **A** and **B** two products $\mathbf{A} \cdot \mathbf{B}$ and $\mathbf{A} \times \mathbf{B}$ are defined. If either **A** or **B** happens to have entered the discussion as the result of vector multiplication, we are confronted by triple products such as

$$\mathbf{A} \cdot (\mathbf{C} \times \mathbf{D}) \qquad (\mathbf{C} \times \mathbf{D}) \cdot \mathbf{B} \qquad \mathbf{A} \times (\mathbf{C} \times \mathbf{D}) \qquad (\mathbf{C} \times \mathbf{D}) \times \mathbf{B}$$

Such combined products have a number of interesting and useful properties.

Consider for three vectors **A**, **B**, and **C** the product $\mathbf{A} \cdot (\mathbf{B} \times \mathbf{C})$. This is called a *scalar triple product*. Note first that the parentheses may be omitted since $(\mathbf{A} \cdot \mathbf{B}) \times \mathbf{C}$ is meaningless, or, giving it an obvious meaning, we should use the notation $(\mathbf{A} \cdot \mathbf{B})\mathbf{C}$. The product $\mathbf{B} \times \mathbf{C}$ has magnitude equal to the area of the parallelogram determined by **B** and **C**; therefore let us write

$$\mathbf{B} \times \mathbf{C} = (\text{area})\mathbf{N}$$

and

$$\mathbf{A} \cdot \mathbf{B} \times \mathbf{C} = (\text{area})(\mathbf{A} \cdot \mathbf{N})$$

Since $\mathbf{A} \cdot \mathbf{N}$ is the component of **A** normal to the plane of the parallelogram, it is evident that this expression is equal to a volume if the angle θ between **A** and **N** is acute or to minus a volume if θ is obtuse. The volume clearly is that of the parallelepiped having edges **A**, **B**, and **C** (see Fig. 9.6).

$$(9.18) \qquad\qquad \mathbf{A} \cdot \mathbf{B} \times \mathbf{C} = \pm\text{volume}$$

The volume of the solid does not depend on the point of view of the observer. The three vectors have similar roles in determining the parallelepiped. This fact leads, as an examination of a number of figures would show, to the following identities:

$$(9.19) \qquad\qquad \mathbf{A} \cdot \mathbf{B} \times \mathbf{C} = \mathbf{B} \cdot \mathbf{C} \times \mathbf{A} = \mathbf{C} \cdot \mathbf{A} \times \mathbf{B}$$

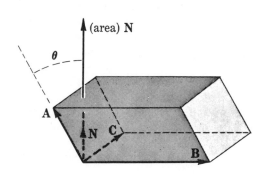

Figure
9.6

Further verification will be found later when expressions for these products in terms of components are examined.   Since scalar products commute, we may write

$$\mathbf{A} \cdot \mathbf{B} \times \mathbf{C} = \mathbf{B} \times \mathbf{C} \cdot \mathbf{A}$$

and similarly for the other products.   In the light of the other identities we conclude that the $\times$ and the $\cdot$ may be interchanged; thus

(9.20) $$\mathbf{A} \cdot \mathbf{B} \times \mathbf{C} = \mathbf{A} \times \mathbf{B} \cdot \mathbf{C}$$

and similarly for the other products.   If $\mathbf{B} \times \mathbf{C}$ is replaced by $\mathbf{C} \times \mathbf{B}$, the sign is reversed, since θ is replaced by its supplement.   Thus

$$\mathbf{A} \cdot \mathbf{C} \times \mathbf{B} = \mp \text{volume}$$

In summary, it is apparent that scalar triple products of three vectors $\mathbf{A}$, $\mathbf{B}$, and $\mathbf{C}$ fall into two groups: those with cyclic order of $\mathbf{ABC}$ and those having the opposite cyclic order $\mathbf{ACB}$.   One order yields equal positive results; the other yields the same magnitude but the opposite sign.

(9.21)
$$\begin{aligned} \pm \text{Volume} &= \mathbf{A} \cdot \mathbf{B} \times \mathbf{C} = \mathbf{B} \cdot \mathbf{C} \times \mathbf{A} = \mathbf{C} \cdot \mathbf{A} \times \mathbf{B} \\ &= \mathbf{A} \times \mathbf{B} \cdot \mathbf{C} = \mathbf{B} \times \mathbf{C} \cdot \mathbf{A} = \mathbf{C} \times \mathbf{A} \cdot \mathbf{B} \\ \mp \text{Volume} &= \mathbf{A} \cdot \mathbf{C} \times \mathbf{B} = \mathbf{C} \cdot \mathbf{B} \times \mathbf{A} = \mathbf{B} \cdot \mathbf{A} \times \mathbf{C} \\ &= \mathbf{A} \times \mathbf{C} \cdot \mathbf{B} = \mathbf{C} \times \mathbf{B} \cdot \mathbf{A} = \mathbf{B} \times \mathbf{A} \cdot \mathbf{C} \end{aligned}$$

The relationships just derived may be regarded also as immediate algebraic consequences of the following expression for the scalar triple product in terms of the usual components of the vectors.

(9.22)
$$\mathbf{A} \cdot \mathbf{B} \times \mathbf{C} = \begin{vmatrix} a_x & a_y & a_z \\ b_x & b_y & b_z \\ c_x & c_y & c_z \end{vmatrix} = \mathbf{A} \times \mathbf{B} \cdot \mathbf{C}$$

Students with previous acquaintance with determinants will remember that each interchange of a pair of rows results in a change of sign, while a cyclic rearrangement of rows requires an even number of interchanges and hence no change of sign.   Such considerations provide an alternative verification for such identities as

$$\mathbf{A} \cdot \mathbf{B} \times \mathbf{C} = -\mathbf{A} \cdot \mathbf{C} \times \mathbf{B} = \mathbf{C} \cdot \mathbf{A} \times \mathbf{B}$$

Example 1

Consider the product $\mathbf{A} \times \mathbf{B} \cdot \mathbf{A}$.   By the identities already given, this is equal to $\mathbf{A} \times \mathbf{A} \cdot \mathbf{B}$.   But $\mathbf{A} \times \mathbf{A} = \mathbf{O}$.   Therefore the product vanishes.   Conversely, it is interesting to point out that whenever the triple scalar product of nonzero vectors is equal to zero, it must follow that the vectors are parallel to a single plane (for their parallelepiped has zero volume).

Example 2

Evaluate $\mathbf{A} \times \mathbf{B} \cdot \mathbf{C}$, where $\mathbf{A} = \mathbf{I} + \mathbf{J} - \mathbf{K}$, $\mathbf{B} = \mathbf{I} - \mathbf{J} + \mathbf{K}$ and $\mathbf{C} = -\mathbf{I} + \mathbf{J} + \mathbf{K}$. One way of proceeding is to compute first the vector product $\mathbf{A} \times \mathbf{B} = -2\mathbf{J} - 2\mathbf{K}$ and then to compute the scalar product with $\mathbf{C}$:

$$\mathbf{A} \times \mathbf{B} \cdot \mathbf{C} = (0)(-1) + (-2)(1) + (-2)(1) = -4$$

Alternatively, one may set up the determinant and evaluate it using any of the methods which one has at his command.

$$\begin{vmatrix} 1 & 1 & -1 \\ 1 & -1 & 1 \\ -1 & 1 & 1 \end{vmatrix} = -4$$

Example 3

Geometric situations related to some of those investigated in other sections occasionally involve this type of combined product. For instance, find an equation for the plane through the three fixed points P', Q', R' (see Fig. 9.7). The vector $(P - P')$ for any variable point P in the plane must lie in the plane and hence be perpendicular to the normal

$$(Q' - P') \times (R' - P')$$

We have, then,

$$(P - P') \cdot (Q' - P') \times (R' - P') = 0$$

which is a suitable equation for the plane.

Example 4

It has been pointed out that $A \cdot E$ is the scalar component of A parallel to the unit vector E. It is obvious, then, that the scalar component of the vector product $B \times C$ parallel to E is given by the scalar triple product $B \times C \cdot E$. This use of a combined product will occur frequently.

EXERCISES

18. Given the four points $A(3,0,1)$, $B(1,-5,1)$, $C(6,0,2)$, and $D(4,-3,2)$. Evaluate

$$(B - A) \times (C - A) \cdot (D - A).$$

19. $A(-5,0,1)$ is a vertex of a parallelepiped. Edges run from A to $B(2,-2,5)$, to $C(-1,5,7)$, and to $D(-2,4,6)$. What is the volume of the parallelepiped?

20. The vector $x\mathbf{I} - 3\mathbf{J} + 4\mathbf{K}$ is parallel to the plane determined by $\mathbf{I} - \mathbf{J} + 2\mathbf{K}$ and $2\mathbf{I} - \mathbf{K}$. Find x.

21. Find an expression in terms of x, y, and z components for $(R - R') \times F \cdot E$, where the vectors listed have components, respectively, as follows:

$$x, y, z; \ x', y', z'; f_x, f_y, f_6; \ l, m, n$$

22. Show that three of the following vectors are parallel to a single plane:

$$-\mathbf{I} + \mathbf{J} - \mathbf{K}, \quad \mathbf{I} + \mathbf{J} - \mathbf{K}, \quad 3\mathbf{I} - \mathbf{J} - \mathbf{K}, \quad 3\mathbf{I} - 2\mathbf{J} + \mathbf{K}$$

23. What is the volume of the tetrahedron whose base is the triangle with vertices $(-2,6,0)$, $(3,2,1)$, and $(0,0,5)$ and whose apex is the origin? (HINT: Volume $= \frac{1}{3}$ base $\times$ altitude.)

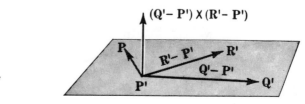

Figure
9.7

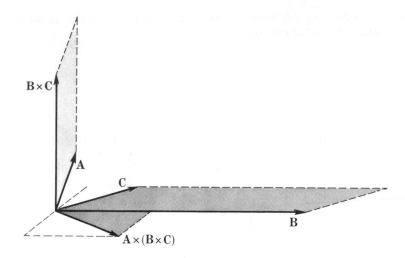

Figure
9.8

9.5. THE VECTOR TRIPLE PRODUCT

Next we shall devote some attention to a combined product of the form $\mathbf{A} \times (\mathbf{B} \times \mathbf{C})$. This is often called the *vector triple product*. Since $\mathbf{B} \times \mathbf{C}$ is normal to the plane of $\mathbf{B}$ and $\mathbf{C}$ (see Fig. 9.8) and $\mathbf{A} \times (\mathbf{B} \times \mathbf{C})$ is perpendicular to this normal, it follows that $\mathbf{A} \times (\mathbf{B} \times \mathbf{C})$ is parallel to the plane of $\mathbf{B}$ and $\mathbf{C}$. Similarly, one may conclude that $(\mathbf{A} \times \mathbf{B}) \times \mathbf{C}$ is parallel to the plane of $\mathbf{A}$ and $\mathbf{B}$. In general, then, the two expressions are not equal. This is a denial of the associative law for this type of multiplication:

(9.23) $$\mathbf{A} \times (\mathbf{B} \times \mathbf{C}) \neq (\mathbf{A} \times \mathbf{B}) \times \mathbf{C}$$

Example 1

In Sec. 2.12 it was demonstrated that the projection of $\mathbf{A}$ parallel to a unit vector $\mathbf{E}$ is given by $(\mathbf{A} \cdot \mathbf{E})\mathbf{E}$. It is easy to show that the projection of $\mathbf{A}$ perpendicular to $\mathbf{E}$ may be written as $\mathbf{E} \times (\mathbf{A} \times \mathbf{E})$. The proof is left as Exercise 27.

Example 2

Find an equation for a line through a fixed point $\mathbf{P}'$ and parallel to each of two planes whose normals are parallel, respectively, to $\mathbf{N}$ and $\mathbf{N}'$. For a variable point $\mathbf{P}$ on the line, the vector $(\mathbf{P} - \mathbf{P}')$ (see Fig. 9.9) is perpendicular to both $\mathbf{N}$ and $\mathbf{N}'$, and hence it is parallel to their vector product. Thus we may write

$$(\mathbf{P} - \mathbf{P}') \times (\mathbf{N} \times \mathbf{N}') = \mathbf{O}$$

which is a suitable equation for the line.

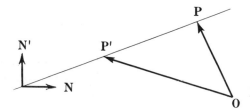

Figure
9.9

9.6. A CRUCIAL VECTOR IDENTITY

If $\mathbf{A} \times (\mathbf{B} \times \mathbf{C})$ is parallel to the plane of $\mathbf{B}$ and $\mathbf{C}$, it must be possible to express it as the sum of a vector in the $\mathbf{B}$ direction plus a vector in the $\mathbf{C}$ direction (compare Chap. 2, Exercise 27). A precise statement of this very important relationship is given in the following remarkable identity:

(9.24) $\mathbf{A} \times (\mathbf{B} \times \mathbf{C}) = (\mathbf{A} \cdot \mathbf{C})\mathbf{B} - (\mathbf{A} \cdot \mathbf{B})\mathbf{C}$

An alternative equivalent form which may be easier to remember is

$$\mathbf{A} \times (\mathbf{B} \times \mathbf{C}) = \mathbf{B}(\mathbf{A} \cdot \mathbf{C}) - \mathbf{C}(\mathbf{A} \cdot \mathbf{B})$$

It is possible to prove this in various ways. One very direct approach, using x, y, and z components, is left as Exercise 24. In this section we shall approach the problem through a sequence of special cases which will perhaps clarify the significance of the identity while establishing it and will at the same time afford some practice in using techniques developed in earlier sections.

First Special Case. We first consider a triple product in which the first factor is repeated. If $\mathbf{N}$ denotes the unit vector in the direction of $\mathbf{A} \times \mathbf{B}$, we may write, using the definition of vector product,

$$\mathbf{A} \times (\mathbf{A} \times \mathbf{B}) = \mathbf{A} \times (ab \sin \theta)\mathbf{N} = (ab \sin \theta)\mathbf{A}'$$

where the vector $\mathbf{A} \times \mathbf{N}$ is denoted by $\mathbf{A}'$. Since $\mathbf{N}$ is perpendicular to $\mathbf{A}$, we know from Sec. 9.1, special conclusion 4, that $\mathbf{A}'$ is $\mathbf{A}$ rotated through $-90°$. Since $\mathbf{A}$ and $\mathbf{A}'$ are perpendicular, one can easily resolve $\mathbf{B}$ into components in their directions (see Fig. 9.10):

$$\mathbf{B} = (b \cos \theta)\frac{\mathbf{A}}{a} - (b \sin \theta)\frac{\mathbf{A}'}{a}$$

Solving for $\mathbf{A}'$,

$$\mathbf{A}' = \left(\frac{\cos \theta}{\sin \theta}\right)\mathbf{A} - \left(\frac{a}{b \sin \theta}\right)\mathbf{B}$$

We may conclude, then:

$$\mathbf{A} \times (\mathbf{A} \times \mathbf{B}) = (ab \sin \theta)\mathbf{A}' = (ab \cos \theta)\mathbf{A} - (a^2)\mathbf{B} = (\mathbf{A} \cdot \mathbf{B})\mathbf{A} - (\mathbf{A} \cdot \mathbf{A})\mathbf{B}$$

Thus our identity is verified for the first special case.

A variant of this special case, readily proved from it, is next recorded: the reasons for the steps in the proof are omitted, since only basic and obvious properties are employed.

$$\mathbf{A} \times (\mathbf{B} \times \mathbf{A}) = -\mathbf{A} \times (\mathbf{A} \times \mathbf{B}) = -(\mathbf{A} \cdot \mathbf{B})\mathbf{A} + (\mathbf{A} \cdot \mathbf{A})\mathbf{B} = (\mathbf{A} \cdot \mathbf{A})\mathbf{B} - (\mathbf{A} \cdot \mathbf{B})\mathbf{A}$$

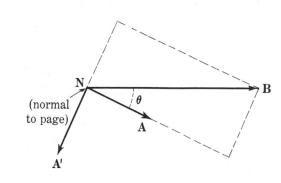

Figure
9.10

Second Special Case. We now prove the identity for the special case where A is parallel to the plane of B and C. In such a case we can write A as a *linear. combination* of B and C

$$A = mB + nC$$

for suitable scalars m and n. We have, then, substituting this expression and using the distributive property of vector products,

$$A \times (B \times C) = (mB + nC) \times (B \times C) = m[B \times (B \times C)] + n[C \times (B \times C)]$$

If we now use the identity for the first special case, this becomes

$$A \times (B \times C) = m(B \cdot C)B - m(B \cdot B)C + n(C \cdot C)B - n(C \cdot B)C$$

Using the distributive properties of the scalar product, the associative law for vector addition, and various properties of multiplication by scalars, we regroup the terms to get

$$A \times (B \times C) = [(mB + nC) \cdot C]B - [(mB + nC) \cdot B]C$$

Resubstituting A for $mB + nC$, we have, as desired,

$$A \times (B \times C) = (A \cdot C)B - (A \cdot B)C$$

The General Case. Now let N be the unit vector in the direction of B × C, and let A′ be the component of A perpendicular to N:

$$A' = A - (A \cdot N)N$$

(as in Fig. 2.32). Then, using Sec 9.1 special conclusion 5,

$$A \times (B \times C) = A' \times (B \times C)$$

where A′ lies in the plane of B and C. Applying the result of the second special case,

$$A \times (B \times C) = (A' \cdot C)B - (A' \cdot B)C$$

We now evaluate the coefficients of B and C, using the expressions for A′ above.

$$(A' \cdot C) = (A \cdot C) - (A \cdot N)(N \cdot C)$$

But

$$N \cdot C = 0$$

Hence

$$(A' \cdot C) = (A \cdot C)$$

Likewise

$$(A' \cdot B) = (A \cdot B)$$

For the general case, then, we can conclude as before

(9.25) $$A \times (B \times C) = (A \cdot C)B - (A \cdot B)C$$

EXERCISES

24. Verify the identity $A \times (B \times C) = (A \cdot C)B - (A \cdot B)C$ by computing the x component of each member in terms of the components a_x, a_y, a_z, b_x, b_y, b_z, c_x, c_y, c_z.

25. The scalar product of a vector by itself $A \cdot A$ is often written as the vector squared A^2. Use the results of this chapter to verify the identity

$$(A \times B)^2 + (A \cdot B)^2 = A^2 B^2$$

What familiar trigonometric identity is closely related to this?

26. If $E \times B = C$ and $B \times C = E$, where E is a unit vector, use direct substitutions and the methods of this chapter to prove that $C \times E = B$.
27. Prove that the component of A perpendicular to the unit vector E is $E \times (A \times E)$.
28. If $A \cdot B \times C = 1$ and one defines $A' = B \times C$, $B' = C \times A$, $C' = A \times B$, show that $A' \cdot B' \times C' = 1$.
29. If $A \cdot B \times C = 1$ and one defines A', B', C' as in the preceding problem and if, furthermore, one defines $A'' = B' \times C'$, $B'' = C' \times A'$, $C'' = A' \times B'$, then show that

$$A'' = A, \quad B'' = B, \quad C'' = C$$

9.7. INDEPENDENT VECTORS

In concluding this part of the course, we introduce some concepts which have been implicit in previous work and which will be used later. There are involved some manipulations which will provide practice in the use of vector identities.

We shall say that three vectors A, B, C are *independent* if $A \cdot B \times C \neq 0$. Clearly, this means geometrically that the vectors are non-null and not parallel to a given plane. One set of independent vectors consists of I, J, and K. It is interesting to note that if A, B, C are independent, then so are the three vectors $B \times C$, $C \times A$, and $A \times B$ (compare Exercise 30).

An elementary property of independent vectors is given in the following proposition:

(9.26) *If A, B, C are independent, then no non-null vector can be normal to all three at once.*

This is fairly clear geometrically, for if a vector D is not null, it may serve as a normal to a plane. Then the equations

$$D \cdot A = 0 \quad\quad D \cdot B = 0 \quad\quad D \cdot C = 0$$

indicate that A, B, and C are all parallel to any plane having D as normal, contrary to the assumptions of independence (see Sec. 2.12, Example 6). An algebraic proof may easily be constructed also (compare Exercises 31 and 32).

A corollary of the preceding result is the following fact:

(9.27) *For three independent vectors A, B, C the equations*

$$D \cdot A = D' \cdot A$$
$$D \cdot B = D' \cdot B$$
$$D \cdot C = D' \cdot C$$

imply that D and D' are equal. This could be interpreted as

(9.28) *Two vectors having equal components in the directions of three independent vectors are equal to each other.*

The ideas of this section are related to the concept of *dimension* in mathematics. A straight line is said to be one-dimensional; a plane is two-dimensional; ordinary euclidean space is three-dimensional; the space-time continuum of relativity theory is four-dimensional. The *three*-dimensional space in which we are working is said to be *spanned* by the *three* unit vectors I, J, K because any vector D in this space can be expressed as a linear combination of I, J, K:

$$D = d_x I + d_y J + d_z K$$

It is also true that

(9.29) *Any vector may be expressed as a linear combination of any independent set of vectors.* That is to say:

(9.30) *Three-dimensional space is spanned by any three independent vectors.*

Let us consider how these statements can be demonstrated.

Suppose that $\mathbf{A}$, $\mathbf{B}$, $\mathbf{C}$ are the three given independent vectors. We wish to show that for *any* vector $\mathbf{D}$ we can find scalar coefficients u, v, w such that

$$(9.31) \qquad \mathbf{D} = u\mathbf{A} + v\mathbf{B} + w\mathbf{C}$$

To determine u, we form $\mathbf{D} \cdot \mathbf{B} \times \mathbf{C}$ and substitute (9.31). Similarly, we find v and w. The results are, since $\mathbf{A} \cdot \mathbf{B} \times \mathbf{C} \neq 0$,

$$(9.32) \qquad u = \frac{\mathbf{D} \cdot \mathbf{B} \times \mathbf{C}}{\mathbf{A} \cdot \mathbf{B} \times \mathbf{C}} \qquad v = \frac{\mathbf{A} \cdot \mathbf{D} \times \mathbf{C}}{\mathbf{A} \cdot \mathbf{B} \times \mathbf{C}} \qquad w = \frac{\mathbf{A} \cdot \mathbf{B} \times \mathbf{D}}{\mathbf{A} \cdot \mathbf{B} \times \mathbf{C}}$$

You may recognize this as equivalent to Cramer's rule for solving a set of linear equations. We have shown that *if* $\mathbf{D}$ can be expressed as a linear combination of $\mathbf{A}$, $\mathbf{B}$, $\mathbf{C}$, the coefficients would be as in (9.32) and hence our assumption $\mathbf{A} \cdot \mathbf{B} \times \mathbf{C} \neq 0$ was necessary. It remains to prove that $\mathbf{D}$ is in fact equal to the right member of the following:

$$(9.33) \qquad \mathbf{D} = \frac{\mathbf{D} \cdot \mathbf{B} \times \mathbf{C}}{\mathbf{A} \cdot \mathbf{B} \times \mathbf{C}}\mathbf{A} + \frac{\mathbf{A} \cdot \mathbf{D} \times \mathbf{C}}{\mathbf{A} \cdot \mathbf{B} \times \mathbf{C}}\mathbf{B} + \frac{\mathbf{A} \cdot \mathbf{B} \times \mathbf{D}}{\mathbf{A} \cdot \mathbf{B} \times \mathbf{C}}\mathbf{C}$$

This can be done readily by applying (9.27), using as the three independent vectors $\mathbf{B} \times \mathbf{C}$, $\mathbf{C} \times \mathbf{A}$, $\mathbf{A} \times \mathbf{B}$ (cf. Exercise 30). The details are left for Exercise 34.

A converse result also holds. If *every* $\mathbf{D}$ can be expressed as a linear combination of the set of vectors $\mathbf{A}$, $\mathbf{B}$, $\mathbf{C}$, then $\mathbf{A}$, $\mathbf{B}$, $\mathbf{C}$ is an independent set. This may be shown to follow from Exercise 35.

To clarify vocabulary it should be pointed out that the idea of independent vectors developed here is consistent with the mathematical concept of *linear independence*. A set of n vectors $\mathbf{A}_1$, $\mathbf{A}_2$, $\ldots$, $\mathbf{A}_n$ are said to be linearly independent if an equality such as

$$s_1\mathbf{A}_1 + s_2\mathbf{A}_2 + \cdots + s_n\mathbf{A}_n = \mathbf{O}$$

can be valid only if each of the scalar coefficients s_1, s_2, $\ldots$, s_n is equal to zero. You may wish to convince yourself that for the case $n = 3$ linear independence is equivalent to independence as we have been using it.

EXERCISES

30. It is given that $\mathbf{A} \cdot \mathbf{B} \times \mathbf{C} \neq 0$. Show that $(\mathbf{B} \times \mathbf{C}) \cdot (\mathbf{C} \times \mathbf{A}) \times (\mathbf{A} \times \mathbf{B}) \neq 0$.

31. Show that the equations $\mathbf{D} \cdot \mathbf{A} = 0$ and $\mathbf{D} \cdot \mathbf{B} = 0$ imply that $\mathbf{W} = \mathbf{D} \times (\mathbf{A} \times \mathbf{B}) = \mathbf{O}$.

32. Show that the equations $\mathbf{D} \cdot \mathbf{A} = 0, \mathbf{D} \cdot \mathbf{B} = 0, \mathbf{D} \cdot \mathbf{C} = 0$ imply that $(\mathbf{A} \cdot \mathbf{B} \times \mathbf{C})\mathbf{D} = \mathbf{O}$. (HINT: Form $\mathbf{C} \times \mathbf{W}$, expand in terms of $\mathbf{A} \times \mathbf{B}$ and $\mathbf{D}$, and use Exercise 31, where $\mathbf{W}$ is as in Exercise 31.)

33. Verify (9.27).

34. Carry out the detailed verification on (9.33).

35. We have seen that any *three* independent vectors span three-dimensional space. Show that no *two* vectors can do so. (HINT: Show that if $\mathbf{D} = u\mathbf{A} + v\mathbf{B}$, then $\mathbf{D} \cdot \mathbf{A} \times \mathbf{B} = 0$, so that only a plane can be spanned.)

36. As an analogy to (9.33) verify the identity

$$\mathbf{D} = \frac{\mathbf{D} \cdot \mathbf{A}}{\mathbf{A} \cdot \mathbf{B} \times \mathbf{C}}(\mathbf{B} \times \mathbf{C}) + \frac{\mathbf{D} \cdot \mathbf{B}}{\mathbf{A} \cdot \mathbf{B} \times \mathbf{C}}(\mathbf{C} \times \mathbf{A}) + \frac{\mathbf{D} \cdot \mathbf{C}}{\mathbf{A} \cdot \mathbf{B} \times \mathbf{C}}(\mathbf{A} \times \mathbf{B})$$

37. (*a*) If $\mathbf{A}$, $\mathbf{B}$, $\mathbf{C}$ are independent and if $\mathbf{D} \times \mathbf{A} = \mathbf{D}' \times \mathbf{A}$, $\mathbf{D} \times \mathbf{B} = \mathbf{D}' \times \mathbf{B}$, $\mathbf{D} \times \mathbf{C} = \mathbf{D}' \times \mathbf{C}$, show that $\mathbf{D} = \mathbf{D}'$.

(*b*) Show that only two of the three conditions are needed.

9.8. DIMENSIONAL METHODS IN MECHANICS

Now that the last operation of vector algebra has been introduced, we may well pause to meditate upon the theoretical structure which we are putting together. We have discussed briefly how magnitudes of length, force, and time (l, f, and t) are assigned. From experimentally verifiable properties and from intuitive relationships accepted as postulates, various new conclusions have been deduced. Many of these have involved the idea of direction (epitomized by a unit vector $\mathbf{E}$) and also certain derived concepts. These derived or secondary concepts were defined in terms of the basic quantities. One way of making the interrelationships of such a science clear, and even of keeping units well in line, is the method of dimensions.

Our treatment of dimensions will elect as *ingredients* the five symbols

$$1, \mathbf{E}, l, f, t$$

Dimensional statements are denoted symbolically by brackets:

(9.34) [Pure number] $= [1]$ (omitted except in the absence of everything else)
[Any unit vector] $= [\mathbf{E}]$
[Length magnitude] $= [l]$
[Force magnitude] $= [f]$
[Time] $= [t]$

In terms of these five ingredients, our three *primary concepts* are analyzed as

$$\begin{aligned} [\mathbf{R}] &= [\text{length}] = [l\mathbf{E}] \\ [\mathbf{F}] &= [\text{force}] = [f\mathbf{E}] \\ [t] &= [\text{time}] = [t] \end{aligned}$$

(9.35)

The *secondary concepts* can be analyzed by seeking out their definitions and then analyzing the items making up the definition. Certain algebraic identities will occur. Samples are

$$[\mathbf{E} \cdot \mathbf{E}] = [1] \qquad [\mathbf{E} \times \mathbf{E}] = [\mathbf{E}]$$

The dimensional method will be illustrated by concepts already met in the course, as well as by some concepts to appear later. As each new mechanical entity is introduced in the remainder of the work, you should make a dimensional analysis.

Example I

Velocity is defined by $\mathbf{V} = d\mathbf{R}/dt$. Dimensionally,

$$[\mathbf{V}] = [\mathbf{R}t^{-1}] = [lt^{-1}\mathbf{E}]$$

Angle will be assigned dimension $[\mathbf{E}]$, the vector representing the axis about which the rotation takes place. This choice justifies itself when derived angular concepts are considered. A list of dimensional analyses for a selection of important derived concepts follows:

$$\begin{aligned} [\text{Angle}] &= [\mathbf{E}] \\ [\text{Area}] &= [\mathbf{R} \times \mathbf{R}] = [l^2\mathbf{E}] \\ [\text{Volume}] &= [\mathbf{R} \cdot \mathbf{R} \times \mathbf{R}] = [l^3] \\ [\text{Moment of force}] &= [\mathbf{R} \times \mathbf{F}] = [lf\,\mathbf{E} \times \mathbf{E}] = [lf\,\mathbf{E}] \\ [\text{Moment of inertia}] &= [i] = [lft^2] \\ [\text{Acceleration}] &= [lt^{-2}\mathbf{E}] \\ [\text{Angular velocity}] &= [t^{-1}\mathbf{E}] \\ [\text{Angular acceleration}] &= [t^{-2}\mathbf{E}] \\ [\text{Mass}] &= [l^{-1}ft^2] \\ [\text{Momentum}] &= [ft\mathbf{E}] \end{aligned}$$

(9.36)

Any correct formula or equation should check dimensionally; i.e., the dimensions of the two sides of the equation should agree.

Example 2

Let us ascertain whether $\Omega \times (\Omega \times R)$ is dimensionally an acceleration (where Ω is angular velocity as analyzed in Example 1).

$$[\Omega \times (\Omega \times R)] = [Et^{-1} \times (Et^{-1} \times lE)] = [Et^{-1} \times t^{-1}lE] = [lt^{-2}E]$$

Dimensional analysis affords a sound way of checking complicated units.

Example 3

The analysis for momentum given above should make it clear that the usual unit in the mks system, the kilogram-meter per second, is equivalent to the newton-second. Similarly, dimensions provide a pattern for changing units from one system to another.

Example 4

Suppose that it is desired to express a velocity of 30 mph in feet per second. The dimensions of velocity are $[lt^{-1}E]$ although of course only the $[lt^{-1}]$ are involved in a change of units. In the expression

$$30 \text{ mph} = 30 \times \frac{1 \text{ mile}}{1 \text{ hr}}$$

where the (1 mile)/(1 hr) follows the dimensional pattern, we can substitute

$$1 \text{ mile} = 5{,}280 \text{ ft}$$
$$1 \text{ hr} = 3{,}600 \text{ sec}$$

Thus

$$30 \text{ mph} = \frac{30 \times 5{,}280}{3{,}600} \text{ ft/sec} = 44 \text{ ft/sec}$$

Constructive Use of Dimensions. We have seen how the method of dimensions is an aid in checking equations qualitatively and in changing units systematically. Another important role which will be only hinted at here is its use as a means of discovering the forms of physical equations and interrelationships. This interesting tool is not one of the major objectives of this course, but it is too important to pass by entirely. We shall use only the ordinary scalar dimensions, omitting E. Easy examples are picked deliberately, so that attention may be called to the procedure without an undue expenditure of time at this stage.

Example 5

Let us try to see what form the equation for the period of a simple pendulum should have. The likely variables are m, l, g; therefore we shall assume a solution of the form

$$\tau = \text{const } m^a l^b g^c$$

Substituting dimensions,

$$[t] = [l^{-1}ft^2]^a [l]^b [lt^{-2}]^c$$
$$[t] = [l^{-a+b+c} f^a t^{2a-2c}]$$

In order that this expression may be dimensionally consistent, the following equations are satisfied:

$$0 = -a + b + c$$
$$0 = a$$
$$1 = 2a - 2c$$

Solving simultaneously, $a = 0$, $c = -\frac{1}{2}$, $b = \frac{1}{2}$; thus the desired expression is

$$\tau = \text{const} \sqrt{\frac{l}{g}}$$

Example 6

The velocity of a transverse wave along a string might be expected to depend on the mass m, the tension f, the length l. Let us seek a dimensional solution, proceeding as before:

$$v = \text{const } m^a f^b l^c$$
$$[lt^{-1}] = [l^{-1}ft^2]^a [f]^b [l]^c$$
$$[lt^{-1}] = [l^{-a+c}f^{a+b}t^{2a}]$$
$$1 = -a + c$$
$$0 = a + b$$
$$-1 = 2a$$

Thus $a = -\frac{1}{2}$, $b = +\frac{1}{2}$, $c = \frac{1}{2}$, giving

$$v = \text{const} \sqrt{\frac{fl}{m}}$$

EXERCISES

38. Analyze the following dimensionally:

(a) $\int_m \mathbf{V} \, dm$.

(b) $\frac{1}{2}m\mathbf{V} \cdot \mathbf{V}$.

(c) $m\mathbf{\Omega} \times \mathbf{\Omega}'$.

(d) $\mathbf{R} \times m\mathbf{V}$.

39. State units equivalent to (a) kg-m²/sec²; (b) kg-m/sec; (c) slug-ft²; (d) poundal-sec.

40. Check the following equations dimensionally, given that $[\mathbf{\Gamma}] = [lf\,\mathbf{E}]$ and $[\mathfrak{A}] = [t^{-2}\mathbf{E}]$.

(a) $\mathbf{\Gamma} = i\mathfrak{A}$.

(b) $\mathbf{A}_c = 2\mathbf{\Omega} \times \mathbf{V}$.

(c) $\int \mathbf{\Gamma} \cdot \mathbf{\Omega} \, dt = \frac{1}{2}i\mathbf{\Omega} \cdot \mathbf{\Omega}$.

(d) $\int \mathbf{\Gamma} \, dt = \int \mathbf{R} \times \mathbf{V} \, dm$.

41. To how many ft-lb-sec² is a moment of inertia of 10 kg-m² equivalent?

42. A pressure of 15 lb/in.² is equivalent to how many newtons/m²?

43. An important equation in mechanics is the inverse-square law of gravitational attraction

$$f = \frac{\gamma mm'}{r^2}$$

Find the dimensions of γ if r is a distance.

44. The velocity of a deep-water wave might be expected to depend on density, acceleration of gravity, and wavelength. Find a dimensional formula.

45. The velocity of a sound wave might be expected to depend on density; bulk modulus β, $[fl^{-2}]$; and wavelength. Find a dimensional formula.

46. The escape speed for a projectile depends on the gravitational constant γ of Exercise 43, the mass of the earth, and the distance from the center of the earth. Find a dimensional formula for v.

47. The time for a planet to go around the sun depends on the gravitational constant γ (see Exercise 43), on the combined mass of sun and planet, and on the semimajor axis of the orbit. Find a dimensional formula for this time.

REVIEW EXERCISES

48. Show that any position vector **R** must satisfy $(\mathbf{I} \times \mathbf{R}) \cdot (\mathbf{R} \times \mathbf{J}) = (\mathbf{I} \cdot \mathbf{R})(\mathbf{R} \cdot \mathbf{J})$.

49. Under what conditions is cancellation possible in an equation such as

$$\mathbf{A} \times \mathbf{C} = \mathbf{B} \times \mathbf{C}$$

Prove your answer.

50. Find in **IJK** form a vector which is perpendicular to both of the following vectors:

$$2\mathbf{I} - 3\mathbf{J} + 4\mathbf{K} \qquad \text{and} \qquad \mathbf{I} - 4\mathbf{K}$$

51. Use the scalar triple product to prove that a non-null vector **C** which can be written $\mathbf{C} = l\mathbf{A} + m\mathbf{B}$ for scalars l and m is parallel to the plane determined by vectors **A** and **B**.

52. Write a vector equation for the plane through the origin and parallel to both the vectors **U** and **V**.

53. Given the vectors $\mathbf{A} = \mathbf{I} - 3\mathbf{J} + 2\mathbf{K}$ and $\mathbf{B} = 2\mathbf{I} + \mathbf{J} - \mathbf{K}$. Find the projection of $\mathbf{A} \times \mathbf{B}$ parallel to $5\mathbf{I} - \mathbf{K}$.

54. The vertices of a cube are labeled **A** to **H** as shown in Fig. 9.11. Find the volume of the tetrahedron **ACHF** if the segment **AB** has length 1.

55. Prove that the following identity is valid:

$$\mathbf{A} \times (\mathbf{B} \times \mathbf{C}) + \mathbf{B} \times (\mathbf{C} \times \mathbf{A}) + \mathbf{C} \times (\mathbf{A} \times \mathbf{B}) = \mathbf{O}$$

56. Prove that the following identity is valid:

$$(\mathbf{A} \times \mathbf{B}) \times \mathbf{C} + (\mathbf{A} \cdot \mathbf{B})\mathbf{C} = (\mathbf{A} \times \mathbf{C}) \times \mathbf{B} + (\mathbf{A} \cdot \mathbf{C})\mathbf{B}$$

57. Prove that the following identity is valid:

$$(\mathbf{A} \times \mathbf{B}) \times (\mathbf{B} \times \mathbf{C}) = (\mathbf{A} \cdot \mathbf{B} \times \mathbf{C})\mathbf{B}$$

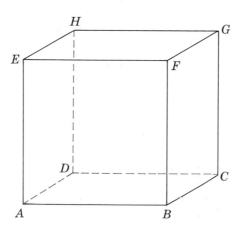

Figure
9.11

58. The terminal speed v of a spherical particle moving in a viscous medium subject to a constant force of magnitude f might be expected to depend on f, the cross section a of the sphere, and the coefficient of viscosity η, $[ftl^{-2}]$. Find dimensionally a formula for v.

59. The *cross-product commutator* of **A** and **B**, denoted by [**A**,**B**], is defined by

$$[\mathbf{A},\mathbf{B}] = \mathbf{A} \times \mathbf{B} - \mathbf{B} \times \mathbf{A}$$

(*a*) Simplify [**A**,[**B**,**C**]].

(*b*) Evaluate [**A**,[**B**,**C**]] + [**B**,[**C**,**A**]] + [**C**,[**A**,**B**]].

CHAPTER TEN

COUPLES and MOMENTS

In Chaps. 3 and 4 we considered forces and equilibrium. Our study of sets of forces had as main tools the principles of transmissibility and vector addition of forces. The statics problems were limited to special cases such as concurrent or coplanar forces. No generally workable criterion appeared for equilibrium of nonconcurrent forces, although the method of virtual work introduced in Chap. 7 has wide applicability. We now exploit the operation of vector product to bring into our treatment of mechanics the important concept of moment of a force.

10.1. THE MOMENT OF A COUPLE

In Sec. 3.5 we found that a pair of parallel or antiparallel forces are equivalent to a single force except in the special case where the pair of forces constitute a couple, i.e., where the forces are equal in magnitude but opposite in direction. Intuitively, it is clear that a couple is associated with a tendency to rotate about an axis normal to the plane of the lines of action of the couple and that forces of a given size acting as a couple are more effective in producing rotation if their lines of action are widely separated. For example, consider the problem of driving a screw into a board. A couple, the *output couple*, is applied by the bit of the screwdriver. The forces of this couple are large, but their separation is small. The couple applied by the hand to the screwdriver handle, the *input couple*, is substantially equivalent to the output couple. But its forces are smaller, while the separation is larger. In this sense a screwdriver is a *couple transformer*. The importance of a couple in causing rotation depends on both the magnitude and the separation of the forces. The corresponding physical concept is a vector called the *moment* **Γ** *of the couple*, directed normal to

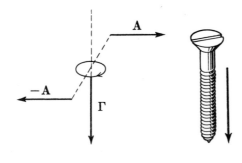

Figure
10.1

228

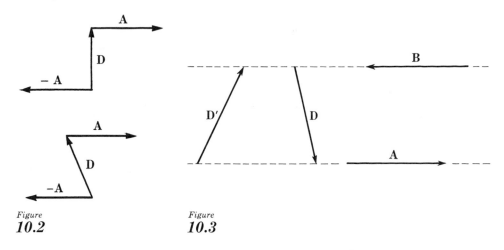

Figure
10.2

Figure
10.3

the plane of the couple in the sense dictated by the right-hand rule as indicated in Fig. 10.1. The defining equation of Γ involves a vector D between the lines of action of the forces. It is often convenient to let D join the points of application of the forces as in Fig. 10.2. Then

$$(10.1) \qquad\qquad \Gamma = D \times A$$

This expression for Γ is not unique, but various alternative expressions are easily seen to be equal (using the definition of vector product and special conclusion 5 of Sec. 9.1). For instance, in Fig. 10.3, where $B = -A$, we have the alternative expressions

$$(10.2) \qquad\qquad \Gamma = D \times A = D' \times B$$

In each such expression one has the product of a relative position vector by the corresponding force. Thus the magnitude of Γ is equal to separation times force magnitude. The first couple of Fig. 10.2, where D and A are at right angles, is said to be in *standard form*. Its moment has magnitude $\gamma = da$. By the transmissibility principle, any couple is equivalent to a couple in standard form.

10.2. EQUIVALENCE OF COUPLES

Associated with each couple is, we have just seen, a unique moment vector Γ summarizing the importance of the couple as a cause of rotation and indicating the axis orientation most closely associated with the couple. We now wish to show that any two couples having the same moment are equivalent. Suppose that two couples have the same moment Γ. Then we can start with the first couple and transform it into the second, using only three types of elementary transformations, each of which leaves Γ unchanged. These elementary transformations are:

1. Increase force magnitude and correspondingly decrease separation, or vice versa.

2. Rotate whole couple about an axis parallel to Γ.

3. Translate the whole couple without changing magnitudes or directions of the forces.

We must show that each of these elementary transformations will produce an equivalent couple.

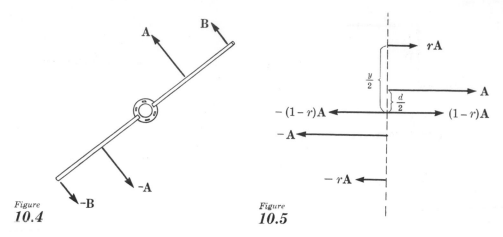

Figure
10.4

Figure
10.5

First we consider the question, is it possible to replace a couple having large forces and small separation by a couple having small forces and large separation? Practical experience with levers suggests this. In Fig. 10.4, for instance, one would expect that two strong men exerting forces **A**, −**A** would produce the same effect on the capstan as two weaker men with forces **B** and −**B**.

Let us start with a couple {**A**,−**A**} in standard form as in Fig. 10.5. Suppose that it is desired to find an equivalent couple of forces {r**A**,−r**A**}, where r is a scalar multiplier, say, between 0 and 1. Halfway between **A** and −**A** introduce equal and opposite forces (1 − r)**A**, −(1 − r)**A**. Now construct the resultant of **A** and −(1 − r)**A**. It is a force r**A** located [by Eq. (3.6)] above the center by an amount y/2 such that

$$\frac{1-r}{1} = \frac{(y/2) - (d/2)}{y/2} \qquad \text{or} \qquad y = \frac{1}{r} d$$

Similarly, the resultant of −**A** and (1 − r)**A** is a force −r**A** at a distance y/2 below the center. Thus the couple {**A**, −**A**} is equivalent to {r**A**,−r**A**}, the latter forces having a separation of d/r. The moment of both couples has magnitude da.

Next we show that if a couple is rotated about an axis parallel to its moment vector, the resulting couple is equivalent to the initial one. This result, which is intuitively credible, is easily demonstrated. Start with a couple {**A**,−**A**} in standard form, with **D** as the relative position vector as in Fig. 10.6. Let **D**′ be a copy of **D** rotated about its center in the plane of the couple through an arbitrary acute angle θ. At the ends of **D**′ construct vectors **A**′, −**A**′, **A**″, −**A**″ as shown, each of length a. Since the set of added vectors is equivalent to a null vector, we have the equivalence

$$\{\mathbf{A}, -\mathbf{A}\} \equiv \{\mathbf{A}, -\mathbf{A}, \mathbf{A}', -\mathbf{A}', \mathbf{A}'', -\mathbf{A}''\}$$

But the resultant of the two forces **A** and −**A**′ is, by symmetry, the opposite of the resultant of **A**″ and −**A**. Hence the subset of forces {−**A**′, **A**, −**A**, **A**″} is equivalent to a null force leaving, as desired,

$$\{\mathbf{A}, -\mathbf{A}\} \equiv \{\mathbf{A}', -\mathbf{A}''\}$$

Finally, consider in standard form two couples {**A**,−**A**} and {**A**′,−**A**′} distinguishable only by their location. Let the points of application of **A** and −**A** be, respectively, **P**, **Q** for the first couple and **P**′, **Q**′ for the second.

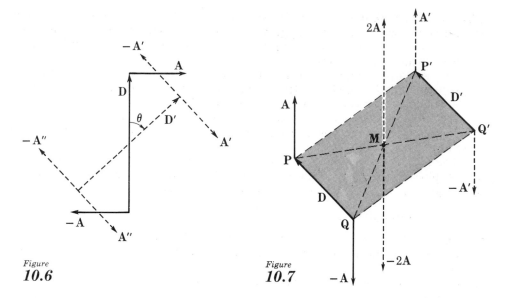

Figure
10.6

Figure
10.7

Since $\mathbf{D} = \mathbf{P}' - \mathbf{Q}' = \mathbf{P} - \mathbf{Q}$, it is seen immediately that $\mathbf{PQQ'P'}$ is a parallelogram. The diagonals intersect at $\mathbf{M}$. At $\mathbf{M}$ introduce opposite forces $2\mathbf{A}$ and $-2\mathbf{A}$ as in Fig. 10.7. But, using the methods of Sec. 3.5,

$$\{\mathbf{A}, -2\mathbf{A}\} \equiv \{-\mathbf{A}'\}$$

and

$$\{-\mathbf{A}, 2\mathbf{A}\} \equiv \{\mathbf{A}'\}$$

Hence we have

$$\{\mathbf{A}, -\mathbf{A}\} \equiv \{\mathbf{A}, -\mathbf{A}, 2\mathbf{A}, -2\mathbf{A}\} \equiv \{\mathbf{A}', -\mathbf{A}'\}$$

as desired.

This conclusion of the complete mobility of a couple (sometimes expressed by stating that a couple is a free vector) may seem hard to believe. Imagine, for instance, a circular board floating in water. Suppose that the board has two light identical handles (as in Fig. 10.8) to which one may apply a twist. One of these handles is at the center O, the other at O' near the edge. Now if a twist of, say, 1 ft-lb, is applied at O and then, under identical initial conditions, at O', will the results be the same? You might expect that in each case the board would tend to rotate about the handle being twisted. In practice, that is partly true, but this is due merely to the difficulty of applying a perfect couple, two equal forces, to a moving

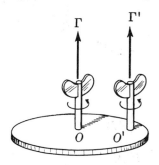

Figure
10.8

axis.   If this practical difficulty is overcome, then the board rotates about its center, regardless of where the couple is applied.   If the handle is not at the center, however, it will travel in a circle; therefore we must either provide a moving couple or judge the experiment instantaneously.

By successive applications of the three elementary maneuvers of expansion (or contraction), rotation, and translation, we can show that any two couples having the same moment are equivalent.   We state this as a formal conclusion:

(10.3) *If any two couples have the same moment, they are equivalent.*

Later on, as a consequence of Newton's second law, we shall arrive at the converse of this proposition.

The fact that any two couples having the same moment are indistinguishable in their physical effects on a rigid body makes it reasonable to specify a couple only by its moment.   This point is elaborated in the next section.

EXERCISES

1.   Figure 10.9 represents two forces lying in a plane.   How far from the center *O* should two 1-lb forces be drawn to give a couple in standard position equivalent to the couple shown?

2.   Show how the construction of Sec. 3.5, applied to a couple, yields a couple of equal moment.

3.   Draw a diagram analogous to Fig. 10.6 for the case where the axis of rotation is at a considerable distance from the given couple.   Verify that the proof is still correct.

10.3. ADDITION OF COUPLES

Let us see whether our decision to treat couples as vectors works satisfactorily when it comes to combining two or more couples: do they add as vectors?   Note first that any given non-null couple $\{A, -A\}$ is equivalent to a couple $\{A', -A'\}$ in the same plane having standard form and having a preassigned relative position vector **D**, where **D** also is a vector in the plane.   For if the moment of $\{A, -A\}$ is Γ, we need merely use forces at right angles to **D** of magnitude γ/d.   It is easy to see that

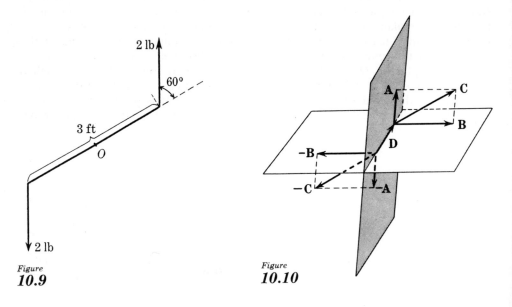

Figure
10.9

Figure
10.10

suitable forces are $\pm(\boldsymbol{\Gamma} \times \mathbf{D})/(\mathbf{D} \cdot \mathbf{D})$. The verification of this detail is left for Exercise 7.

Suppose now that we have two couples with nonparallel moment vectors. The planes of these forces meet in a straight line. Let $\mathbf{D}$ be any vector lying on this line. Represent each couple in standard form, using $\mathbf{D}$ as outlined in the first paragraph of this section. Two such couples $\{\mathbf{A}, -\mathbf{A}\}$ and $\{\mathbf{B}, -\mathbf{B}\}$ are illustrated in Fig. 10.10. Since $\mathbf{A}$ and $\mathbf{B}$ are concurrent forces, they are equivalent to a single vector $\mathbf{C}$. Thus the two given couples are equivalent to a new couple $\{\mathbf{C}, -\mathbf{C}\}$, where $\mathbf{C}$ also has $\mathbf{D}$ as relative position vector:

$$\{\mathbf{A}, -\mathbf{A}, \mathbf{B}, -\mathbf{B}\} \equiv \{\mathbf{C}, -\mathbf{C}\}$$

The moments of these couples are

$$\boldsymbol{\Gamma}_A = \mathbf{D} \times \mathbf{A} \qquad \boldsymbol{\Gamma}_B = \mathbf{D} \times \mathbf{B} \qquad \boldsymbol{\Gamma}_C = \mathbf{D} \times \mathbf{C}$$

But $\mathbf{A} + \mathbf{B} = \mathbf{C}$, so that

$$\boldsymbol{\Gamma}_C = \mathbf{D} \times \mathbf{C} = \mathbf{D} \times (\mathbf{A} + \mathbf{B}) = \mathbf{D} \times \mathbf{A} + \mathbf{D} \times \mathbf{B} = \boldsymbol{\Gamma}_A + \boldsymbol{\Gamma}_B$$

In the special case, where $\boldsymbol{\Gamma}_A$ and $\boldsymbol{\Gamma}_B$ are parallel, a single plane may be used and any vector $\mathbf{D}$ in the plane may serve as relative position vector. Our final conclusion, then, is this:

(10.4) *If couples are represented by their moments, they can be added as vectors; i.e., a family of couples* $\boldsymbol{\Gamma}_1, \boldsymbol{\Gamma}_2, \ldots, \boldsymbol{\Gamma}_n$, *however located, is equivalent to a single couple* $\bar{\boldsymbol{\Gamma}}$ *given by*

$$\bar{\boldsymbol{\Gamma}} = \boldsymbol{\Gamma}_1 + \boldsymbol{\Gamma}_2 + \cdots + \boldsymbol{\Gamma}_n$$

EXERCISES

4. In Fig. 10.11 forces and position vectors are labeled. Express carefully in terms of the symbols used in each diagram the moments of the couples shown.

5. Given two couples, as indicated schematically in Fig. 10.12, with

$$\mathbf{A} = 3\mathbf{I} + 4\mathbf{J} \quad \text{lb} \qquad \mathbf{D} = \mathbf{I} - 2\mathbf{J} + \mathbf{K} \quad \text{ft}$$
$$\mathbf{A}' = 4\mathbf{I} + 3\mathbf{K} \qquad \mathbf{D}' = 2\mathbf{J}$$

Find the magnitude and direction cosines of the moment of a single couple equivalent to the two given couples.

6. A rectangular box has its edges parallel to the coordinate axes. The lengths of these edges are, respectively, 6, 3, and 2 ft as shown in Fig. 10.13. Along the 12 edges act 12 forces comprising 6 couples. The magnitudes, in pounds, of these forces are indicated beside the force arrows in the figure. These 6 couples are equivalent to one single couple of moment $\bar{\boldsymbol{\Gamma}}$. Find $\bar{\boldsymbol{\Gamma}}$ in IJK form.

7. Verify the formula

$$\mathbf{F} = \frac{(\boldsymbol{\Gamma} \times \mathbf{D})}{(\mathbf{D} \cdot \mathbf{D})}$$

mentioned in the preceding section.

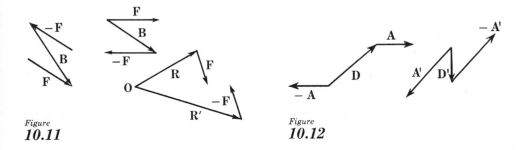

Figure
10.11

Figure
10.12

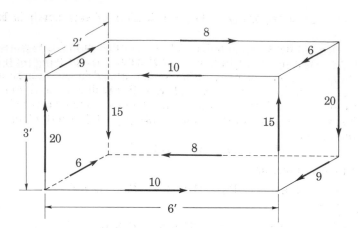

Figure
10.13

10.4. MOMENT OF A FORCE ABOUT A POINT

The moment of a couple was introduced as a measure of its importance in causing rotation. A single force **F** also may cause rotation, but since a force does not have the remarkable mobility of a couple, no unique moment can be expected. We must specify about what point or axis the tendency for rotation is to be computed. Choosing a desired reference point as origin **O**, suppose that **F** acts at a point with position vector **R**. In order to have our definition of moment for a single force harmonious with what has been done for a couple, let us introduce at **O** forces **F′** and −**F′**, where **F′** = **F**. The given single force is thus equivalent to the couple {**F**, −**F′**} of moment **R** × **F** and a single force **F′** at **O**. The force **F′** has no tendency to promote rotation about **O**, so we define the *moment* Γ_O *of* **F** *about* **O** to be equal to the moment of the couple {**F**, −**F′**}:

$$(10.5) \qquad\qquad \Gamma_O = \mathbf{R} \times \mathbf{F}$$

The magnitude of this vector Γ_O (see Fig. 10.14), by the definition of vector product, is equal to the magnitude of the force times its perpendicular distance from the point in question. The direction of the vector Γ_O is perpendicular to the plane of the point **O** and the force **F** and hence in the direction of the axis about which a force so placed would tend to cause rotation. The moment about a reference point of a set of forces (often called the *moment sum*) will be defined as the vector sum of the moments of the forces considered separately. Thus, if we have a set of n forces $\mathbf{F}_1, \mathbf{F}_2, \ldots, \mathbf{F}_n$ acting, respectively, at $\mathbf{R}_1, \mathbf{R}_2, \ldots, \mathbf{R}_n$, the moment $\bar{\Gamma}_O$ of the set is defined to be

$$(10.6) \qquad\qquad \bar{\Gamma}_O = \sum_{i=1}^{n} \mathbf{R}_i \times \mathbf{F}_i$$

As an application of this concept, let us consider a couple as a set of two forces. Given as in Fig. 10.15 a force −**A** acting at **R** and a force **A** acting at the point **R** + **D**, we have

$$\bar{\Gamma}_O = \mathbf{R} \times (-\mathbf{A}) + (\mathbf{R} + \mathbf{D}) \times \mathbf{A} = \mathbf{D} \times \mathbf{A}$$

Note that this result agrees with our definition for moment of a couple and is independent of **O**. We conclude, then, with relief: The moment about a given point of a couple is equal to the moment of the couple.

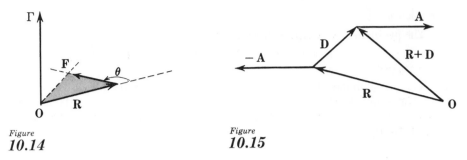

Figure
10.14

Figure
10.15

An important property of moments is crystallized in the *theorem of Varignon:*
(10.7) *The moment (about a point) of a family of concurrent forces is equal to the moment of their resultant.*
In symbols the assertion is

$$\bar{\Gamma}_O = \Sigma\, \Gamma$$

where Γ is the moment of a typical force in the family. It is easy to see that this theorem was essentially proved in the preceding chapter. If $F_1, F_2, \ldots, F_n$ are forces acting at P as in Fig. 10.16, then the moment of the family is given by

$$\bar{\Gamma}_O = P \times F_1 + P \times F_2 + \cdots + P \times F_n$$

By the distributive property of vector multiplication, this expression is equal to

$$P \times (F_1 + F_2 + \cdots + F_n)$$

But by successive application of Postulate (3.4), the sum

$$\bar{F} = F_1 + F_2 + \cdots + F_n$$

is the resultant of the set of concurrent forces.

It is not always convenient to use the origin for coordinates for the reference point in moment calculations. The needed modifications are simple: corresponding to (10.6), we have for moments about a fixed point Q

(10.8) $$\bar{\Gamma}_Q = \sum_{i=1}^{n} (R_i - Q) \times F_i$$

Example I

Find the magnitude of the moment about the origin of a force $5I + 5J$ lb if it acts at the point with coordinates $(2,1)$ ft as in Fig. 10.17.

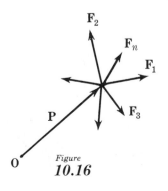

Figure
10.16

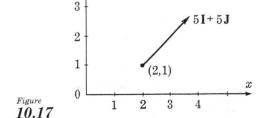

Figure
10.17

First Solution

The problem can be solved formally by vector manipulation.

$$\mathbf{R} \times \mathbf{F} = (2\mathbf{I} + \mathbf{J}) \times (5\mathbf{I} + 5\mathbf{J}) = 5\mathbf{K} \qquad \text{ft-lb}$$

Second Solution

The problem can be solved in terms of the elementary idea of moment as distance times magnitude. The distance may be computed variously as a problem in analytic geometry or trigonometry. For instance, an equation of the line of action of the force is

$$y - 1 = 1(x - 2)$$

or

$$x - y - 1 = 0$$

The distance of this line from 0 is 0.707. The force has magnitude 7.07. The product is then 5, which was the magnitude of the vector obtained in the first solution. (The student wishing to use his vector tools to the utmost will probably find the distance from 0 to the line by considering the component of **R** perpendicular to **F**.)

Third Solution

Using Varignon's theorem, the force may be replaced by two concurrent forces 5**I** and 5**J** whose moments may be read off at once from Fig. 10.18 by the method used in the preceding solution.

$$\gamma = (-)1 \times 5 + (+)2 \times 5 = 5$$

(Note the sign convention: $+$ for counterclockwise rotation, $-$ for clockwise. This is in agreement with our original choice of **K** as equal to **I** × **J**.) A graphical check could be achieved by plotting to scale on graph paper and counting squares in the parallelogram determined by **R** and **F** as shown in Fig. 10.19. The assignment of scales must, of course, be kept in mind.

Example 2

Compute the moment about the point (0,2,0) of the set of two forces 5**I** − 2**K** at (0,1,1) and 16**J** at (2,2,0). Units are meters and newtons.

Solution

The relative position vectors have components $(0,-1,1)$ and $(2,0,0)$. The moment sum is then

$$\bar{\Gamma} = \begin{vmatrix} 0 & -1 & 1 \\ 5 & 0 & -2 \\ \mathbf{I} & \mathbf{J} & \mathbf{K} \end{vmatrix} + \begin{vmatrix} 2 & 0 & 0 \\ 0 & 16 & 0 \\ \mathbf{I} & \mathbf{J} & \mathbf{K} \end{vmatrix} = (2\mathbf{I} + 5\mathbf{J} + 5\mathbf{K}) + (32\mathbf{K})$$

$$= 2\mathbf{I} + 5\mathbf{J} + 37\mathbf{K} \qquad \text{m-newtons}$$

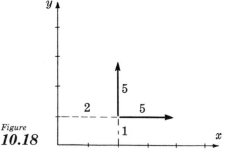

Figure
10.18

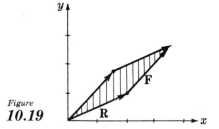

Figure
10.19

EXERCISES

8. Prove that the moment of a force about a point is not altered if the force is allowed to slide along its own line of action.

9. Given three forces in the xy plane: $10\underline{/30°}$ at $(1,0)$; $10\underline{/-60°}$ at $(0,-2)$; $10\underline{/120°}$ at $(0,-4)$. (Units are pounds and feet.) (a) Find the moment about the origin. (b) Find the moment about the point $(3,0)$ ft.

10. Given three forces in the xy plane: $10\underline{/60°}$ at $(3,2)$; $4\mathbf{I} - 4\mathbf{J}$ at $(-7,7)$; and $8\underline{/135°}$ at $(2,-4)$. (Units are newtons and meters.) Compute the moment about the origin.

11. A 60-lb force acts at the point with coordinates $(8,8,-5)$ ft. A second point on its line of action is $(10,9,-3)$ ft. Compute the magnitude of the moment of the force about the point $(1,2,3)$ ft.

10.5. MOMENT OF A FORCE ABOUT AN AXIS

In Sec. 10.4 it was remarked that the moment $\mathbf{\Gamma}_O$ of a force $\mathbf{F}$ about a point $\mathbf{O}$ is a vector directed along an axis about which rotation tends to take place. In mechanical work it often happens that only one particular axis is eligible to be an axis of rotation. The best possible example, perhaps, is a wheel with its axle set in fixed bearings. All forces applied to such a wheel may be resolved into components parallel and perpendicular to the axle. Only those components which are perpendicular will have any tendency to produce rotation. The parallel components merely conjure up equal and opposite bearing reactions. We shall then take into account only the perpendicular component when we define moment about an axis. In Fig. 10.20 force $\mathbf{F}$ acts at $\mathbf{R}$. The axle has the direction of the unit vector $\mathbf{E}$. $\mathbf{F}$ is resolved into components $\mathbf{F}''$ parallel to $\mathbf{E}$ and $\mathbf{F}'$ perpendicular to $\mathbf{E}$. Let $\mathbf{R}''$ be the point on the axle nearest to $\mathbf{R}$. Suppose that the origin is taken as any point on the axle. The vector $\mathbf{R}$ may then be thought of as resolved into components $\mathbf{R}''$ and $\mathbf{R}'$ (from $\mathbf{R}''$ to $\mathbf{R}$), respectively, parallel and perpendicular to $\mathbf{E}$. Since the moment of $\mathbf{F}'$ about $\mathbf{R}''$ is parallel to the axis of rotation, we shall define *moment of $\mathbf{F}$ about the axis* $\mathbf{E}$ by the equation

$$(10.9) \qquad\qquad \mathbf{\Gamma}_E = \mathbf{R}' \times \mathbf{F}' = \gamma_E \mathbf{E}$$

(We know that the vector is parallel to $\mathbf{E}$ because we made it that way.) The scalar γ_E is positive if the rotation associated with the couple leads by the right-hand rule to the direction of $\mathbf{E}$. In the figure, clearly, γ_E is negative.

Equation (10.9) is identical with (10.5), except that components of $\mathbf{R}$ and $\mathbf{F}$ perpendicular to $\mathbf{E}$ are used. In the important case of plane forces the moment

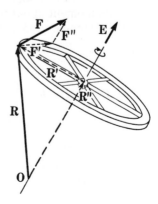

Figure
10.20

about an axis perpendicular to the plane is thus precisely the same as the moment about the point where the axis meets the plane.

It is interesting to find the magnitude γ_E of the vector $\mathbf{\Gamma}_E$ in terms of $\mathbf{R}$ and $\mathbf{F}$. Recall that in Chap. 9 we arrived at formulas for components perpendicular to a unit vector:

(10.10) $\mathbf{R}' = \mathbf{E} \times (\mathbf{R} \times \mathbf{E})$ $\mathbf{F}' = \mathbf{E} \times (\mathbf{F} \times \mathbf{E})$

If these equations are substituted in (10.9), we have rather formidable expressions which the student may wish to expand and simplify as a review exercise in vector algebra. If he does this correctly, he will arrive at

(10.11) $\mathbf{\Gamma}_E = (\mathbf{E} \cdot \mathbf{R} \times \mathbf{F})\mathbf{E}$

or

(10.12) $\gamma_E = \mathbf{R} \times \mathbf{F} \cdot \mathbf{E} = \mathbf{\Gamma} \cdot \mathbf{E}$

Since the direction of the vector was originally confined, the scalar form (10.12) is adequate. In words, the result may be stated as follows:

(10.13) *The moment of a force about an axis is equal to the component in the direction of the axis of the moment of the force about any point on the axis.*

The sum of the moments about an axis of a set of forces will be called simply the *moment of the set of forces about that axis*. The moment of a force or couple (especially about an axis) is often called the *torque* exerted by that force or couple.

Special properties of this new concept are easily provable from results already derived:

(10.14) *The moment about any axis of the forces of a couple is equal to the component parallel to that axis of the moment of the couple.*

(10.15) *The moment about an axis of a family of concurrent forces is equal to the moment of their resultant (Varignon).*

(10.16) *If a force $f_x\mathbf{I} + f_y\mathbf{J} + f_z\mathbf{K}$ acts at the point (x,y,z), then the moments of the force about the coordinate axes are, respectively,*

$$\gamma_x = yf_z - zf_y \qquad \gamma_y = zf_x - xf_z \qquad \gamma_z = xf_y - yf_x$$

Example

Given a force $2\mathbf{I} + 3\mathbf{J} + 4\mathbf{K}$ lb acting at the point with coordinates $(3,2,0)$ ft. Find:

a. Its moment about the origin.
b. Its moment about the coordinate axes.
c. Its moment about the line through the origin and $(1,1,1)$.
d. Its moment about the line through $(0,0,1)$ and $(1,0,0)$.

Solution

a. $\mathbf{\Gamma}_O = \mathbf{R} \times \mathbf{F} = \begin{vmatrix} 3 & 2 & 0 \\ 2 & 3 & 4 \\ \mathbf{I} & \mathbf{J} & \mathbf{K} \end{vmatrix} = 8\mathbf{I} - 12\mathbf{J} + 5\mathbf{K} \qquad$ ft-lb

b. $\gamma_x = \mathbf{\Gamma}_O \cdot \mathbf{I} = 8 \qquad \gamma_y = \mathbf{\Gamma}_O \cdot \mathbf{J} = -12 \qquad \gamma_z = \mathbf{\Gamma}_O \cdot \mathbf{K} = 5$

c. For the line given, $\pm\mathbf{E} = (\mathbf{I} + \mathbf{J} + \mathbf{K})/\sqrt{3}$. Let us arbitrarily select the plus sign. This means that we are choosing $\mathbf{E}$ as a vector heading into the first octant. This choice is equivalent to choosing which sense of rotation about the line is to be regarded as positive.

$$\gamma = \mathbf{\Gamma}_O \cdot \mathbf{E} = \frac{8}{\sqrt{3}} - \frac{12}{\sqrt{3}} + \frac{5}{\sqrt{3}} = 0.6 \text{ ft-lb}$$

d. Any point on the stated line may serve as reference point. Let us pick $\mathbf{Q}$ as the point $(0,0,1)$. Then

$$\mathbf{R} - \mathbf{Q} = 3\mathbf{I} + 2\mathbf{J} - \mathbf{K} \qquad \mathbf{E} = \frac{\mathbf{I} - \mathbf{K}}{\sqrt{2}}$$

Thus

$$\gamma_E = (\mathbf{R} - \mathbf{Q}) \times \mathbf{F} \cdot \mathbf{E} = \begin{vmatrix} 3 & 2 & -1 \\ 2 & 3 & 4 \\ \dfrac{1}{\sqrt{2}} & 0 & \dfrac{-1}{\sqrt{2}} \end{vmatrix} = \frac{6}{\sqrt{2}} = 4.23 \text{ ft-lb}$$

EXERCISES

12. Prove that the moment of a force about a line is not altered if the force is allowed to slide along its own line of action.

13. A 100-lb force acts along the line from $(0,1,0)$ to $(1,1,0)$ ft. Find its moment about the origin and about each of the coordinate axes.

14. A 100-lb force acts at the point $(9, -6, 3)$ ft. Its direction cosines are 0.667, -0.333, -0.667. Find its moment about an axis through the origin and the point $(0, -8, 6)$ ft.

15. A 5-lb force has direction cosines $(0.6, 0.8, 0.0)$. A point on its line of action is $(3, -2, 4)$ ft. Find its moment about each of the following points: $(0,0,0)$, $(3,0,0)$, $(0, -2, 0)$, $(0,0,4)$, $(1,1,1)$. Find its moments about the coordinate axes.

16. A 10-lb force parallel to the positive x axis acts at the point $(0,1,0)$ ft. Find its moment about an axis through the origin and parallel to the vector $6\mathbf{I} - 6\mathbf{J} - 3\mathbf{K}$.

17. A 100-lb force acts at the origin. Its angles with the x and y axes are, respectively, $60°$ and $75°$. Find the magnitude of its moment about the line through $(0,2,0)$ parallel to the x axis.

18. A force $\mathbf{F} = 7.5\mathbf{I} - 10\mathbf{J}$ acting at $(-4,2)$ ft in the xy plane has a moment of minus $60\mathbf{K}$ ft-lb about the point with coordinates $(2,y)$ ft. Find y.

19. A rigid body is free to rotate about an axis having direction cosines 0.5, -0.5, 0.707 and passing through the point $(2,1, -3)$. A force whose components are 10, 0, -15 in the x, y, and z directions, respectively, acts at the point $(5,1,2)$. Find the moment of the force about the stated axis.

20. Prove Proposition (10.14).

21. Prove Proposition (10.15).

22. Prove Proposition (10.16).

10.6. A REDUCTION THEOREM

At the beginning of Sec. 10.4 we found it convenient to replace a single force at one given point by an equal force at another point, together with a compensating couple. The vector sum of the three forces is still $\mathbf{F}$, and the moment about any point or axis is still equal to that of the original force $\mathbf{F}$, for the effects of the forces introduced at the new point cancel each other. This sort of reasoning is often helpful. Imagine a force $\mathbf{F}$ acting on a spoke of a wheel as in Fig. 10.21. This force is equivalent to an equal force at the center $\mathbf{O}$ of the wheel, together with a couple whose moment is equal to the moment of the original force about the center. In this section this simple procedure is used to demonstrate that any set of forces is equivalent to one force at a preassigned point, together with a compensating couple.

Suppose we have a set of n forces acting at different points on a rigid body as in Fig. 10.22. Let $\mathbf{P}$ be a designated reference point. Each one of the n forces, say, $\mathbf{F}_i$, by the procedure just discussed, is equivalent to an equal force $\mathbf{F}'_i$ at $\mathbf{P}$, together with a couple $\mathbf{\Gamma}_i$. The given set of n forces is then equivalent to a set of n forces at $\mathbf{P}$, together with n couples. The forces at $\mathbf{P}$, being concurrent, are by (3.5) equivalent to a single force $\mathbf{\bar{F}}$ through $\mathbf{P}$, where

$$(10.17) \qquad\qquad \mathbf{\bar{F}} = \sum_{i=1}^{n} \mathbf{F}_i$$

and the n couples may by (10.4) be added to give a single couple $\mathbf{\bar{\Gamma}}$, where

$$(10.18) \qquad\qquad \mathbf{\bar{\Gamma}} = \sum_{i=1}^{n} \mathbf{\Gamma}_i$$

The vector $\mathbf{\Gamma}_i$ is equal to the moment of the original force $\mathbf{F}_i$ about $\mathbf{P}$. Let us state our conclusions carefully:

(10.19) *Any set of forces* $\mathbf{F}_1, \mathbf{F}_2, \ldots, \mathbf{F}_n$ *is equivalent to a force* $\mathbf{\bar{F}}$ *at any pre-assigned point* $\mathbf{P}$ *together with a couple* $\mathbf{\bar{\Gamma}}$. $\mathbf{\bar{F}}$ *is equal to the vector sum of the given forces;* $\mathbf{\bar{\Gamma}}$ *is equal to the moment about* $\mathbf{P}$ *of the given set of forces (i.e., to the moment sum of the set).*

(10.20) *The moment of the new system about any point or axis is the same as that of the old system.*

This latter proposition follows from the observation made at the beginning of this section that the addition of canceling forces at $\mathbf{P}$ changes neither the vector sum of forces nor the total moment about any point. A direct formal verification is also possible. The original set may be expressed $\{\mathbf{F}_i \text{ at } \mathbf{R}_i\}$, where it is understood that i will stand successively for the integers $1, 2, \ldots, n$. The new set is represented by $\{\mathbf{\bar{F}} \text{ at } \mathbf{P}, \mathbf{\bar{\Gamma}}\}$, where $\mathbf{\bar{F}} = \sum_{i=1}^{n} \mathbf{F}_i$ and the couple $\mathbf{\bar{\Gamma}}$ has moment

$$\mathbf{\bar{\Gamma}} = \sum_{i=1}^{n} (\mathbf{R}_i - \mathbf{P}) \times \mathbf{F}_i = \Sigma \, \mathbf{R}_i \times \mathbf{F}_i - \mathbf{P} \times \mathbf{\bar{F}}$$

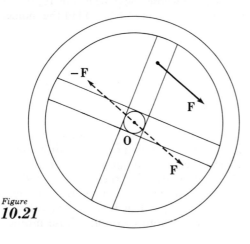

Figure
10.21

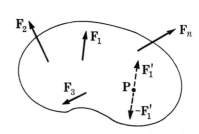

Figure
10.22

We now may compute moments about an arbitrary point **Q**. For the first set of forces the moment is
$$\mathbf{\Gamma}_Q = \Sigma\,(\mathbf{R}_i - \mathbf{Q}) \times \mathbf{F}_i = \Sigma\,\mathbf{R}_i \times \mathbf{F}_i - \mathbf{Q} \times \Sigma\,\mathbf{F}_i = \Sigma\,\mathbf{R}_i \times \mathbf{F}_i - \mathbf{Q} \times \bar{\mathbf{F}}$$
For the second set of forces the corresponding moment is
$$\mathbf{\Gamma}'_Q = (\mathbf{P} - \mathbf{Q}) \times \bar{\mathbf{F}} + \bar{\mathbf{\Gamma}} = (\mathbf{P} \times \bar{\mathbf{F}} - \mathbf{Q} \times \bar{\mathbf{F}}) + (\Sigma\,\mathbf{R}_i \times \mathbf{F}_i - \mathbf{P} \times \bar{\mathbf{F}})$$
Clearly, the two moments are equal. From $\mathbf{\Gamma}_Q = \mathbf{\Gamma}'_Q$ it follows at once that $\mathbf{\Gamma}_Q \cdot \mathbf{E} = \mathbf{\Gamma}'_Q \cdot \mathbf{E}$, so if result (10.20) is true for moments about any point, it is a fortiori true for moments about any axis.

Example

Three forces act as follows: $8\mathbf{I} + 6\mathbf{J}$ at $(0,6,0)$; $4\mathbf{I} + 5\mathbf{J} + 6\mathbf{K}$ at $(6,6,6)$; $10\mathbf{K}$ at $(6,0,0)$, as in Fig. 10.23. Find an equivalent force (at the origin) and couple.

Solution

The force at the origin $\bar{\mathbf{F}}$ will be equal to the sum of the forces listed: $\bar{\mathbf{F}} = 12\mathbf{I} + 11\mathbf{J} + 16\mathbf{K}$. The moment of the couple will be the sum of the moments about **O** of the forces listed.
$$\mathbf{\Gamma}_1 = 6\mathbf{J} \times (8\mathbf{I} + 6\mathbf{J}) = -48\mathbf{K}$$
$$\mathbf{\Gamma}_2 = \begin{vmatrix} 6 & 6 & 6 \\ 4 & 5 & 6 \\ \mathbf{I} & \mathbf{J} & \mathbf{K} \end{vmatrix} = 6\mathbf{I} - 12\mathbf{J} + 6\mathbf{K}$$
$$\mathbf{\Gamma}_3 = 6\mathbf{I} \times 10\mathbf{K} = -60\mathbf{J}$$
Hence
$$\bar{\mathbf{\Gamma}} = 6\mathbf{I} - 72\mathbf{J} - 42\mathbf{K}$$

Each of the separate terms in the expressions for $\mathbf{\Gamma}_i$ can be checked by looking at the figure, where each force is resolved into components whose moments involve just simple multiplications.

Equivalent Sets of Forces. It is interesting to apply the reduction theorem (10.19) to general problems concerning systems of forces. Suppose that two sets of forces $\{\mathbf{F}_1, \mathbf{F}_2, \dots, \mathbf{F}_n\}$ and $\{\mathbf{F}'_1, \mathbf{F}'_2, \dots, \mathbf{F}'_m\}$ are being compared. Relative to a

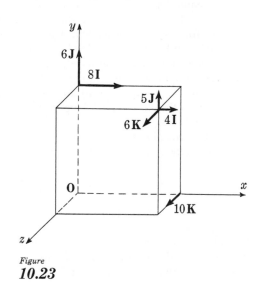

Figure
10.23

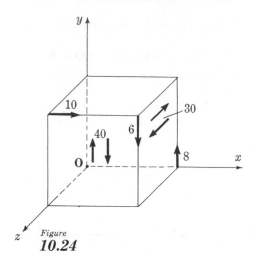

Figure
10.24

point **P**, the first is equivalent, by (10.19), to $\{\bar{\mathbf{F}}, \bar{\boldsymbol{\Gamma}}\}$ and the second to $\{\bar{\mathbf{F}}', \bar{\boldsymbol{\Gamma}}'\}$. If $\bar{\mathbf{F}} = \bar{\mathbf{F}}'$ and $\bar{\boldsymbol{\Gamma}} = \bar{\boldsymbol{\Gamma}}'$, then the reduced sets $\{\bar{\mathbf{F}}, \bar{\boldsymbol{\Gamma}}\}$ and $\{\bar{\mathbf{F}}', \bar{\boldsymbol{\Gamma}}'\}$ are equivalent. This is a consequence of Proposition (10.3). It follows at once that the two original systems are equivalent.

(10.21) *If two systems of forces have the same vector sum and the same moment sum about a point, then they are equivalent.*

Now, conversely, suppose that the two original systems were given as equivalent. It then follows that the reduced systems are equivalent and, by Proposition (3.9), $\bar{\mathbf{F}} = \bar{\mathbf{F}}'$. Can we conclude too that $\bar{\boldsymbol{\Gamma}} = \bar{\boldsymbol{\Gamma}}'$? This result, quite valid, is not entirely accessible to us at this stage. It depends on the converse of Proposition (10.3), which, as stated earlier, will be deduced later from Newton's second law.

EXERCISES

23. Three forces **2I**, **3J**, and **4K** act at one corner of a cube along its edges. These forces are equivalent to a couple $\bar{\boldsymbol{\Gamma}}$ and a force $\bar{\mathbf{F}}$ at the diagonally opposite corner of the cube. Find the magnitude and the direction cosines for both $\bar{\boldsymbol{\Gamma}}$ and $\bar{\mathbf{F}}$.

24. The following forces act on a rigid body: $(10\mathbf{K} - 10\mathbf{I})$ at (1,0,0); $(10\mathbf{I} - 10\mathbf{J})$ at (0,1,0); $(10\mathbf{J} - 10\mathbf{K})$ at (0,0,1). Find their resultant.

25. A cube oriented so that its edges are parallel with the coordinate axes has one corner at the origin, as shown in Fig. 10.24. Separate forces of 10, 6, and 8 lb act at vertices as shown. Couples of 40 and 30 ft-lb act in the faces toward the reader. If the edges of the cube are 4 ft long, find a couple and force at the origin equivalent to the given forces.

26. In the reduction theorem (10.19), show that for a given set of forces the scalar product $\bar{\mathbf{F}} \cdot \bar{\boldsymbol{\Gamma}}$ is the same for all choices of reference point **P**.

10.7. CONDITIONS FOR EQUILIBRIUM

We have seen that a set of forces acting on a rigid body is, at worst, equivalent to a force and a couple. Hence, by (3.10), if a body is known to be in equilibrium, the force $\bar{\mathbf{F}} = \Sigma \, \mathbf{F}_i$ is a null force. This implies that the force vectors determine a closed polygon and also that the sum of components in the direction of *any* axis is zero. It also follows that for any point **P**, $\bar{\boldsymbol{\Gamma}}_P = \Sigma \, (\mathbf{R}_i - \mathbf{P}) \times \mathbf{F}_i$ is a null vector. Hence the sum of moments about any point or axis also must vanish. If we are dealing with concurrent forces as in the statics of a particle, the moment conditions are potentially useful but not inescapable. In a really general case, we must be sure that both vectors $\bar{\mathbf{F}}$ and $\bar{\boldsymbol{\Gamma}}$ vanish. By the material on independent vectors in Sec. 9.7, we know that such a vector will vanish if its components vanish in three independent directions. So we should expect six scalar equations as necessary conditions for equilibrium in a general case. Note, for instance, that a non-null couple $\boldsymbol{\Gamma} = \gamma\mathbf{K}$ would satisfy five of these six equations ($\Sigma f_x = 0$, $\Sigma f_y = 0$, $\Sigma f_z = 0$, $\Sigma \gamma_x = 0$, $\Sigma \gamma_y = 0$), but a single couple is not a set of forces in equilibrium. In practice, however, it is often true that we know in advance that some of these six conditions are satisfied trivially, so the solution of statics problems is often less burdensome than might at first appear. The investigation of techniques for solving problems in statics will be left for the most part to the next chapter on applications.

As a general application of the conditions of equilibrium, suppose that a rigid body is in equilibrium under three forces $\mathbf{F}$, $\mathbf{F}'$, $\mathbf{F}''$ at points $\mathbf{P}$, $\mathbf{P}'$, $\mathbf{P}''$. The points $\mathbf{P}$, $\mathbf{P}'$, and $\mathbf{P}''$ form a triangle which determines a plane of normal, say, $\mathbf{N}$. If the points happened to lie on a line, one of the forces could be slid to a new point off the line except for the uninteresting case where the forces all lie along the line. In order that equilibrium obtain, the moment of $\mathbf{F}''$ about $\mathbf{PP}'$ is zero. Hence $\mathbf{F}''$ is either parallel to $\mathbf{PP}'$ or intersects it. In either case it lies in the plane of the triangle. Similarly for $\mathbf{F}'$ and $\mathbf{F}''$; therefore we infer that $\mathbf{F}$, $\mathbf{F}'$, and $\mathbf{F}''$ are *coplanar*. If they are not all parallel, two of them have lines of action intersecting at a point in the plane and are therefore equivalent [by Postulate (3.3)] to a single force through that point. The system is then reduced to two forces which must be equal, opposite, and with a common line of action. Consequently the third force passes through the point of intersection of the other two. The conclusion is:

(10.22) *If three nonparallel forces are in equilibrium, they are coplanar and concurrent.*

Example

Three points of support of a light shelf are arranged as in Fig. 10.25 so that they form an isosceles triangle ABC with a base AC of length 32 in. and an altitude BD of 14 in. A and C are smooth hinges, while at B is attached a cord inclined at 60° with the horizontal in the vertical plane through B normal to the line AC. A 100-lb load is placed halfway between B and D. Find the tension in the cord and the forces (normal to AC) sustained by each hinge.

Solution

Suppose that each hinge force is resolved into projections as indicated in Fig. 10.26, where $\mathbf{H}$ and $\mathbf{H}'$ are horizontal and normal to AC, $\mathbf{T}$ and $\mathbf{T}'$ are horizontal and along AC, and $\mathbf{V}$ and $\mathbf{V}'$ are vertical. Similarly, the cord tension is resolved into vertical and horizontal projections $\mathbf{V}''$ and $\mathbf{H}''$. In a complicated problem one might not know the sense of these arrows: for instance, should the vertical force at A be up or vertically down? The arrows in the diagram represent merely a tentative agreement as to which sense is treated as positive. If $\mathbf{V}$ is wrongly directed, we shall get from our scalar equations of equilibrium a negative value for v.

Taking x components of forces, $h'' - h' - h = 0$.
Taking y components of forces, $t' - t = 0$.
Taking z components of forces, $v'' + v' + v - 100 = 0$.

Since we have used three independent directions, no new information can be expected from equations of this kind; so we turn to moments.

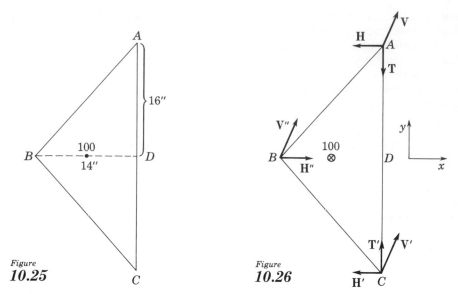

Figure
10.25

Figure
10.26

Taking moments about the line BD, $16v - 16v' = 0$, or $v = v'$. Taking moments about the normal line through D, $16h - 16h' = 0$, or $h = h'$. These two previous results we should usually write down at once without calculation because of the *symmetry* of the problem. The really interesting equation involves moments about AC: $14v'' - (7)(100) = 0$, $v'' = 50$ lb. From the previous equations we conclude that $v = v' = 25$ lb. Since the direction of the force at B is given, we know that $v''/h'' = \tan 60°$, so $h'' = 28.8$ lb and $h' = h = 14.4$ lb. No further information about t and t' can be expected because we do not know whether the shelf is compressed or stretched (or neither) by the hinges. Anyhow, $t = t'$, and if the hinges are properly installed, $t = t' = 0$. This uncertainty is an example of *static indeterminacy*, which will be mentioned again later.

It remains to put the parts together again. The normal hinge force at A is (see Fig. 10.27) $28.8\underline{/60°}$ lb. The cord tension is 57.7 lb.

Alternative Solution

If one wishes to use the symmetry of the problem from the beginning, a quicker solution to this particular problem is possible. Figure 10.28 shows the shelf in cross section, with **F** the resultant of the two hinge forces and **P** the cord tension. Since the problem is now reduced to a three-force-equilibrium problem, these three forces are concurrent (see dotted lines in the figure). Thus the direction of **F** is determined. Since the load is at the mid-point of BD, the geometry is very simple: the angle at D also is 60°. The force triangle is then isosceles as shown in Fig. 10.29, and the previous two answers are immediate. Note that a moment equation for a normal axis through D yields the tension immediately without any investigation of **F** (whose moment is zero in any case):

$$(14 \sin 60°)p = 700 \text{ in.-lb}$$

EXERCISES

27. Solve for the forces, tensions, or compressions, in the light truss shown in Fig. 10.30. The forces at B and C may be taken as vertical.

28. Two light rigid struts of lengths 6 and 10 ft are hinged together and pinned to a rigid

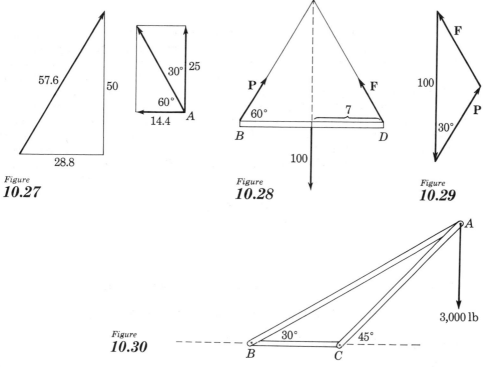

Figure
10.27

Figure
10.28

Figure
10.29

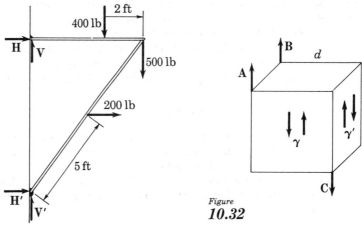

Figure
10.30

wall in order to form a wall bracket as shown in Fig. 10.31. The bracket is subjected to loads of 200, 400, and 500 lb as indicated. The pin reactions exerted on the bracket at the wall are resolved into horizontal and vertical components **H**, **V**, **H′**, **V′**. Find these four forces, taking the directions shown as positive.

29. A shelf 1 by 8 ft weighs 10 lb. It is held in horizontal position by two hinges at the ends of one long edge and by a vertical cord at one of the other corners. If a 20-lb load is hung on the fourth corner, find the tension in the cord.

30. A cubical block of edge d is subjected to forces **A**, **B**, and **C** as shown in Fig. 10.32. The block is also subject to two couples whose moments are normal to the faces on which they are indicated in the figure. If γ and γ' are known, find a, b, and c for equilibrium.

Figure
10.31

Figure
10.32

10.8. CENTER OF GRAVITY

We have been working with separate forces, each with a specific point of application. The most commonly encountered force, weight, has by courtesy been regarded as a single force acting at the center of any symmetric uniform object. Actually, we realize that the situation is considerably complicated, for each portion of a body is subject to forces due to gravity. Let us assume that the weight of an extended body is the resultant of the weights of pieces into which we might imagine the body to be divided, using the limiting processes involved in integral calculus. (This matter will be further clarified in Chap. 15.) Each element into which the body is divided we regard as a particle; so, if its mass is Δm, then its weight is $\Delta \mathbf{F} = (\Delta m)\mathbf{G}$, where $\mathbf{G}$ is the local acceleration of gravity. For any point $\mathbf{P}$ we conclude, as in Sec. 10.6, that the set of forces due to gravity is equivalent to a single force at $\mathbf{P}$:

$$\bar{\mathbf{F}} = \int d\mathbf{F} = \int \mathbf{G}\, dm = m\mathbf{G}$$

together with a couple of moment

$$\bar{\mathbf{\Gamma}} = \int (\mathbf{R} - \mathbf{P}) \times d\mathbf{F}$$

where $\mathbf{R}$ is the position vector of the element dm having weight $d\mathbf{F}$:

$$\bar{\mathbf{\Gamma}} = \int (\mathbf{R} - \mathbf{P}) \times \mathbf{G}\, dm = \left(\int \mathbf{R}\, dm \right) \times \mathbf{G} - \left(\int \mathbf{P}\, dm \right) \times \mathbf{G}$$

Now by Eq. (5.75) we can substitute

$$\int \mathbf{R}\, dm = m\bar{\mathbf{R}}$$

where $\bar{\mathbf{R}}$ is the position vector of the center of mass of the body, and since $\mathbf{P}$ is a constant, we may write

$$\int \mathbf{P}\, dm \times \mathbf{G} = m\mathbf{P} \times \mathbf{G}$$

We conclude then that

$$\bar{\mathbf{\Gamma}} = m(\bar{\mathbf{R}} - \mathbf{P}) \times \mathbf{G}$$

Usually, we wish to regard the gravitational forces as equivalent to a single force. Note that this is possible if we chose $\mathbf{P}$ on the vertical line through $\bar{\mathbf{R}}$, for then the vector $\bar{\mathbf{R}} - \mathbf{P}$ is parallel to the vector $\mathbf{G}$, so that $\bar{\mathbf{\Gamma}}$ is null. Since this would be the case also if the relative orientation of $\mathbf{G}$ could be changed, we conclude that the resultant always passes through $\bar{\mathbf{R}}$. Such a point is called the *center of gravity*. We have then shown the following statement:

(10.23) *Whenever the gravitational field may be considered as uniform, the center of gravity of an aggregate coincides with the center of mass.*

The concept of center of mass will be developed more fully in Chap. 15.

REVIEW EXERCISES

31. In the accompanying diagram the plane of the paper passes through the y axis and the point with coordinates (3,4,2) ft. In this plane the line of action of the 50-lb force $\mathbf{F}$ is directed as shown in Fig. 10.33.

(*a*) Find in **IJK** form the moment of $\mathbf{F}$ about the point (6,5,0) ft.

(*b*) Compute (with due regard for sign) the moment of $\mathbf{F}$ about each of the coordinate axes.

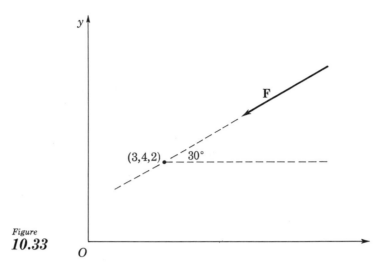

Figure
10.33

32. A wheel of diameter 6 ft is supported by fixed bearings.   A 200-lb force is applied at
the rim of the wheel, making an angle of 30° with the direction of the axle of the wheel.
The projection of this force onto the plane of the wheel makes an angle of 45° with the
spoke (radial) to the point of application of the force.   What is the moment of force
about the axle?

33. The moment of a couple is the same about any point.   For a given force **F** and moment
Γ, describe the locus of origins **O** for which the moment of **F** about **O** is **Γ**.

34. A spool of radius r and axle radius r' rests on a horizontal plane surface.   The thread
unwinding from the top of the spool is pulled at an angle θ above the horizontal with
a force **F**.   Find the moment of **F** about the line of contact with the plane (i.e., about
the point where the vertical plane through the thread cuts this line).

35. A 90-lb force acts along the line from $(-1,4,-3)$ to $(5,1,3)$.   Through the point
$(-1,0,0)$ is an axis whose direction cosines are 0.0, 0.6, 0.8, respectively.   Compute
the moment of the force about this axis.   (Units are feet for coordinates.)

36. A rigid body is subject to a couple of moment $70\mathbf{I} - 40\mathbf{K}$ ft-lb and, in addition, to the
following two forces: $20\mathbf{I}$ lb at the point with coordinates $(0,5,6)$ ft and $-50\mathbf{I} + 60\mathbf{J} -
20\mathbf{K}$ lb at the point with coordinates $(3,-2,1)$ ft.
(a) What is the moment of the first force about the origin?
(b) What is the moment of the second force about the y axis?
(c) Compute the component of the second given force parallel to the moment vector
of the given couple.   (Answer in scalar form, decimal, with units.)
(d) The given forces and couple are equivalent to a single force $\bar{\mathbf{F}}$ at the point
$(2,0,0)$ ft together with a couple $\bar{\mathbf{Γ}}$.   Express these two vectors in **IJK** form.

37. The three forces shown in Fig. 10.34 are equivalent to a single force at **P** $(10,0,0)$ ft,
together with a couple.
(a) Express the force in **IJK** form.
(b) Express the moment of the couple in **IJK** form.

38. The two forces shown in Fig. 10.35 (both parallel to coordinate axes) are equivalent
to a force $\bar{\mathbf{F}}$ at the origin, together with a couple $\bar{\mathbf{Γ}}$.   Express both $\bar{\mathbf{F}}$ and $\bar{\mathbf{Γ}}$ in **IJK** form.

39. A rigid body is subject to the following three forces:

$$80\mathbf{I} - 40\mathbf{J} \text{ newtons at } (2,1) \text{ m}$$
$$50\mathbf{J} \qquad\quad \text{ newtons at } (0,1.5) \text{ m}$$
$$-60\mathbf{I} - 40\mathbf{J} \text{ newtons at } (0,-2) \text{ m}$$

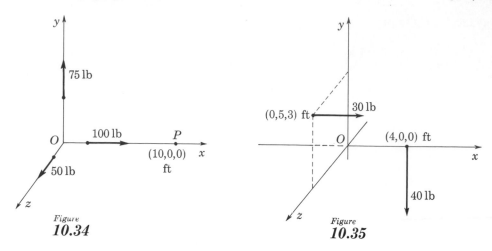

Figure
10.34

Figure
10.35

This family of forces is equivalent to a force **F** (acting through the origin), together with a couple made up of two 100-newton forces.

(*a*) Find **F** in **IJK** form.

(*b*) How far apart are the lines of action of the forces constituting the couple?

40. $\mathbf{F}_1$, $\mathbf{F}_2$, ..., $\mathbf{F}_n$ are forces acting on a rigid body. These forces all act in a single plane. **P** and **Q** are two distinct points of the plane. Show that the given system is equivalent to a system consisting of a force acting along a line through **P** and a force acting along a line through **Q**.

   Is this pair of forces uniquely determined by the given forces and the points **P** and **Q**? Prove it.

41. In the *xy* plane a system of forces consists (in pounds) of 9**I** at (0,2) ft, $-6\mathbf{I} + 4\mathbf{J}$ lb at origin, 10**J** at (0,−5), together with a pair of forces constituting a couple of moment 40**K** ft-lb. This system is equivalent to a new system consisting of a force **F** at (2,3) and a force **G** at (2,0). Find in **IJK** form such a pair of forces **F** and **G**.

42. The square plate 2 by 2 ft is subjected to five 10-lb forces as shown in Fig. 10.36.
   (*a*) Find in **IJK** form a force at the origin and a couple which together are equivalent to the original system of forces.
   (*b*) Carry out a further reduction (i.e., to a single force or single couple) if possible.

43. A given set of forces is equivalent to a force $\bar{\mathbf{F}}$ at **P** together with a couple $\bar{\boldsymbol{\Gamma}}$. The given system must also be equivalent to a force $\bar{\mathbf{F}}$ at $\mathbf{P} + \Delta\mathbf{P}$, together with a couple $\bar{\boldsymbol{\Gamma}} + \Delta\bar{\boldsymbol{\Gamma}}$. Derive an expression for $\Delta\bar{\boldsymbol{\Gamma}}$ in terms of $\bar{\mathbf{F}}$ and $\Delta\mathbf{P}$.

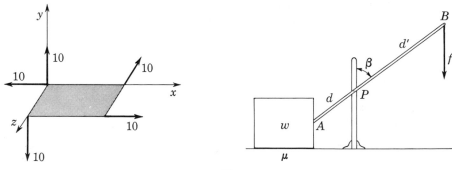

Figure
10.36

Figure
10.37

44. The end A of the beam AB makes a *smooth* contact with the box of weight w as shown in Fig. 10.37.   The beam is pivoted smoothly at P.   The vertical force of magnitude f is applied at B.   The distances AP and PB are, respectively, equal to d and d'.   The coefficient of friction between box and floor is μ.   How large a force F will be required to cause the box to start to slip?   Express the answer in terms of w, μ, d, d', and β (angle between beam and vertical), etc.

45. Prove that two nonparallel pairs of parallel forces in equilibrium are two couples, if not all concurrent.

CHAPTER ELEVEN

APPLICATIONS: RIGID-BODY STATICS

In Chap. 4 practice was given in handling sets of forces without serious reliance on the concept of moments. For concurrent forces and even for nonconcurrent coplanar forces, it was possible to solve with ease a variety of problems concerning equilibrium. In dealing with rigid bodies, the concepts of couple and moment are so natural and useful as to be indispensable. In the present chapter practice will be afforded in determining resultants of force sets and in solving statics problems.

11.1. RESULTANTS OF COPLANAR OR OF PARALLEL FORCES

We have seen that any set of forces $\{\mathbf{F}_i\}$ is equivalent, for an arbitrary point $\mathbf{P}$, to a force $\bar{\mathbf{F}}$ acting at $\mathbf{P}$ *and* a couple $\bar{\mathbf{\Gamma}}$:

$$\{\mathbf{F}_i \text{ at } \mathbf{R}_i, i = 1, \ldots, n\} \equiv \{\bar{\mathbf{F}} \text{ at } \mathbf{P}, \bar{\mathbf{\Gamma}}\}$$

We may think of the given set as represented by the resultant force and couple, in the sense that they summarize the capabilities of the given set. If it happens that the following equation holds,

(11.1) $$\bar{\mathbf{F}} \cdot \bar{\mathbf{\Gamma}} = 0$$

a reduction to a force *or* a couple is always possible. If $\bar{\mathbf{F}}$ is zero, then only the couple is left. If $\bar{\mathbf{\Gamma}}$ is zero, then $\bar{\mathbf{F}}$ alone is the resultant force. If both $\bar{\mathbf{F}}$ and $\bar{\mathbf{\Gamma}}$ are zero, then the system which they represent is equivalent to a null set of forces, and equilibrium reigns. But if neither $\bar{\mathbf{F}}$ nor $\bar{\mathbf{\Gamma}}$ is zero, then it is interesting to point out that the force $\bar{\mathbf{F}}$ at an arbitrary $\mathbf{P}$ and the couple $\bar{\mathbf{\Gamma}}$ can be replaced by an equivalent single force $\bar{\mathbf{F}}'$ suitably displaced from $\bar{\mathbf{F}}$. This merely reverses the procedure in Sec. 10.4 by which a force was replaced by a displaced force and a couple. This situation is represented in Figs. 11.1 and 11.2. Since the only significant thing about the couple $\bar{\mathbf{\Gamma}}$ is its moment, we may take the couple $\bar{\mathbf{\Gamma}}$ as made up of two forces of any desired magnitude, as long as we take care to preserve the moment magnitude. Let us then replace the couple by two forces $\{\bar{\mathbf{F}}', -\bar{\mathbf{F}}\}$ with $-\bar{\mathbf{F}}$ acting at $\mathbf{P}$. The

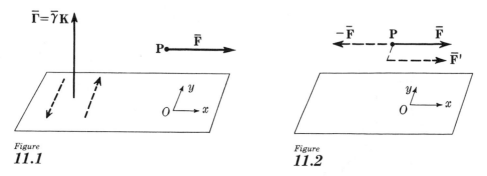

Figure
11.1

Figure
11.2

magnitude of the moment will still be equal to $\bar{\gamma}$ if we take care to have the line of action of $\bar{\mathbf{F}}'$ at a distance d from the line of action of $-\bar{\mathbf{F}}$ given by

(11.2)
$$d = \frac{\bar{\gamma}}{\bar{f}}$$

as in Fig. 11.2. Since $-\bar{\mathbf{F}}$ and $\bar{\mathbf{F}}$ annul each other, it is now apparent that our original system of forces is in fact equivalent to the single force $\bar{\mathbf{F}}'$. This maneuver is often very advantageous. One form of this conclusion may be stated as follows:
   (11.3) *A set of forces for which* $\bar{\mathbf{F}} \cdot \bar{\mathbf{\Gamma}} = 0$ *always has either a single force or a single couple as a resultant.*
   As a first application of Proposition (11.3), suppose that all the forces under consideration lie in the *xy* plane. Then, if we pick our reference point **P** in this plane, $\bar{\mathbf{\Gamma}}$ is normal to the plane, while of course $\bar{\mathbf{F}}$ lies in the plane; thus (11.1) is satisfied. Hence
   (11.4) *A set of forces in a plane always has either a single force or a single couple as a resultant.*

Example I

   Given three forces as in Fig. 11.3: $10/0°$ lb at (2,2) ft; $15/-120°$ at $(-2,2)$ ft; $10/-45°$ at $(0,-4)$ ft.
   a. Find an equivalent force (at the origin) and couple.
   b. Reduce to a single force or couple.

Solution

   a. The single force at the origin is

$$\bar{\mathbf{F}} = (10 - 15 \cos 60° + 10 \cos 45°)\mathbf{I} + (-15 \cos 30° - 10 \cos 45°)\mathbf{J}$$
$$= 9.6\mathbf{I} - 20.1\mathbf{J} = 22.3/-64.5° \text{ (lb)}$$

Now take moments about the origin to get the moment of the couple

$$\bar{\mathbf{\Gamma}} = (-20 + 15 + 26 + 28.3)\mathbf{K} = 49.3\mathbf{K} \qquad \text{(ft-lb)}$$

   b. Now, using the method just outlined, we displace $\bar{\mathbf{F}}$ by an amount

$$d = 49.3/22.3 = 2.2 \text{ ft}$$

where, as in Fig. 11.4, it is a suitable resultant for the given system. Note that one point on its line of action is at a distance $d/\cos 64.5° = 5.1$ ft below the origin on the *y* axis. This same result may be obtained without using Eq. (11.2). We wish to

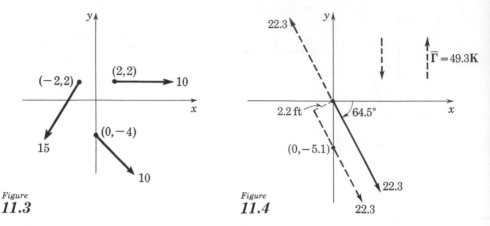

Figure
11.3

Figure
11.4

find a line of action for $\bar{\mathbf{F}}$ such that its moment about **O** will be equal to $\bar{\mathbf{\Gamma}}$. Let $\mathbf{R} = x\mathbf{I} + y\mathbf{J}$ be any point on this line of action. Then

$$\mathbf{R} \times \bar{\mathbf{F}} = \bar{\mathbf{\Gamma}}$$

or

$$(x\mathbf{I} + y\mathbf{J}) \times (9.6\mathbf{I} - 20.1\mathbf{J}) = 49.3\mathbf{K}$$

or, equating coefficients of **K**,

$$20.1x + 9.6y + 49.3 = 0$$

is an equation of the resultant. When x is set equal to zero, we get

$$y = -49.3/9.6 = -5.1 \text{ ft}$$

as before.

Example 2

What single force is equivalent to the force and couple shown in Fig. 11.5 applied to a rectangular plate 5 by 12 ft?

Solution

According to the conclusions of this section, the resultant is a 15-lb force parallel to the given force but displaced by an amount $\bar{y}/\bar{f} = (12)(5)/15 = 4$ ft, as indicated by the dotted lines in the figure.

As an alternative approach, consider Fig. 11.6, where the x and y axes are chosen and the given force resolved into its x and y projections. Now, using the fact that moments about **O** (or about the z axis) must be the same for the resultant as for the given set of forces,

$$13.0y = (5)(13) - (12)(5) = 5 \qquad y = 5/13$$

Hence the 15-lb resultant crosses the axis at a distance 0.38 ft above the origin.

The preceding solution is based on a special aspect of the geometry. More generally, let (x,y) be any point on the line of action of the resultant. Again, taking moments about the z axis,

$$13.0y - 7.5x = (5)(13) - (12)(5) = 5$$

which is an equation for the line of action of the resultant.

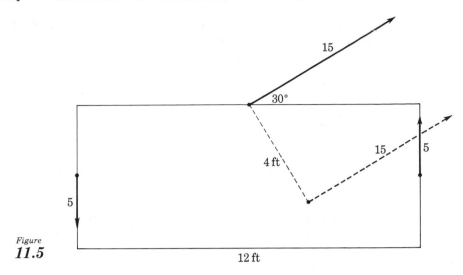

15

30°

4 ft

15   5

5

Figure
11.5

12 ft

A second interesting special case is that of parallel forces not necessarily con-
fined to a plane. Suppose we have a family of forces $f_1\mathbf{J}, f_2\mathbf{J}, \ldots, f_n\mathbf{J}$, all parallel
to the y axis. By the reduction theorem (10.19) this system is equivalent to a force
at the origin

$$\bar{\mathbf{F}} = (\Sigma f_i)\mathbf{J}$$

together with a couple

$$\bar{\boldsymbol{\Gamma}} = \Sigma\, \mathbf{R}_i \times f_i\mathbf{J} = (\Sigma f_i \mathbf{R}_i) \times \mathbf{J}$$

This last equality is justified by the laws governing multiplication of scalars and
distribution with respect to addition in vector products. Since the vector product

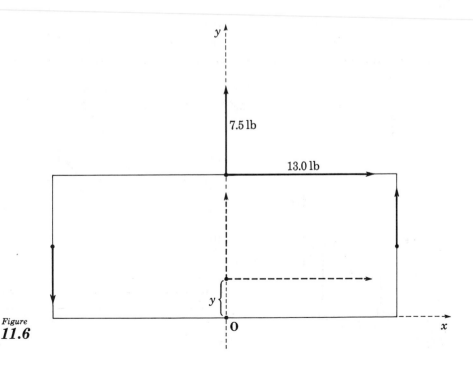

y

7.5 lb

13.0 lb

y

0   x

Figure
11.6

of any vector times $\mathbf{J}$ is perpendicular to $\mathbf{J}$, it is clear that again we have $\bar{\mathbf{F}} \cdot \bar{\boldsymbol{\Gamma}} = 0$; thus the conclusions of (11.3) are again valid:

(11.5) *A set of parallel forces always has either a single force or a single couple as a resultant.*

Example 3

Find the resultant of the following three parallel forces: $5\mathbf{J}$ at $(0,0,2)$, $-4\mathbf{J}$ at $(3,0,3)$, and $-8\mathbf{J}$ at $(6,0,0)$, as shown in Fig. 11.7.

Solution

The resultant will, by (10.19), be a force equal to the vector sum of the given forces:

$$\bar{\mathbf{F}} = (5 - 4 - 8)\mathbf{J} = -7\mathbf{J}$$

By (10.20), the moment sum about the x axis and the z axis must be the same for the resultant as for the original system. Taking $(x,0,z)$ as a point on the resultant, we have then

$$\Sigma \gamma_x = -(5)(2) + (4)(3) = -(-7)(z)$$
$$\Sigma \gamma_z = -(4)(3) - (8)(6) = +(-7)(x)$$

Thus the resultant acts at $(\frac{60}{7}, 0, \frac{2}{7})$. If the vector sum of the forces had been zero, the resultant would have been a couple with moment equal to the moment sum about the origin of the given system.

Example 4

A rectangular plate 6 by 12 ft is subject to forces normal to its plane as shown in Fig. 11.8. Dots indicate forces in the positive z direction, crosses in the negative z direction. Find the resultant.

Solution

The vector sum of the seven given forces is

$$\bar{\mathbf{F}} = 15\mathbf{K} + 25\mathbf{K} - 30\mathbf{K} + 5\mathbf{K} - 10\mathbf{K} + 15\mathbf{K} - 20\mathbf{K} = \mathbf{O}$$

Hence the resultant is a single couple. To find its moment, take moments about the x and y axes:

$$\gamma_x = 6(25) - 6(30) + 3(15) + 6(5) = 45 \text{ ft-lb}$$
$$\gamma_y = 6(30) - 6(15) - 6(15) - 12(5) + 12(10) = 60 \text{ ft-lb}$$

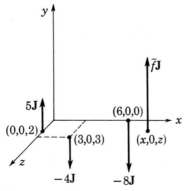

Figure
11.7

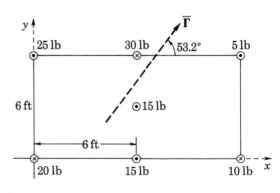

Figure
11.8

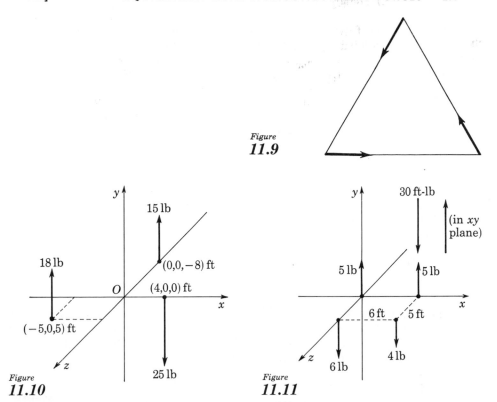

Figure
11.9

Figure
11.10

Figure
11.11

Hence the resultant couple has moment $\bar{\Gamma} = 45\mathbf{I} + 60\mathbf{J} = 75\underline{/53.2°}$ ft-lb. Thus the net instantaneous effect of the seven forces is that of a 75-ft-lb torque twisting about a line in the xy plane inclined at 53.2° to the x axis.

EXERCISES

1. Equal forces of magnitude f act along the sides of an equilateral triangle as shown in Fig. 11.9. Construct the resultant force or couple.
2. Given in the xy plane: the forces $10\underline{/-45°}$ lb at (0,3) ft, $6\underline{/-135°}$ lb at (5,5) ft, and $8\underline{/180°}$ lb at (0,−5) ft. (a) Reduce to a force at (5,5) and a couple. (b) Reduce to a single force or a couple.
3. Find the resultant of the following forces (units are pounds and feet): $-6\mathbf{I}$ at (0,3,0); $7\mathbf{I}$ at (0,5,0); $5\mathbf{I}$ at (0,7,0); $10\mathbf{I}$ at (0,10,0).
4. Use the methods of this section to verify Eqs. (3.6).
5. Find the resultant of the forces shown in Fig. 11.10.
6. Find the resultant of the forces shown in Fig. 11.11.
7. In our main reduction theorem (10.19) **P** was *any* point. Show that **P** may always be chosen so that $\bar{\mathbf{F}}$ and $\bar{\Gamma}$ are parallel (Poinsot's theorem). (HINT: Resolve $\bar{\Gamma}$ into components parallel and perpendicular to $\bar{\mathbf{F}}$.)

11.2. EQUILIBRIUM WITH NONCONCURRENT FORCES

In Sec. 3.6 we adopted as a postulate the common-sense proposition that a particle or rigid body is in equilibrium if and only if the forces acting on it from the outside

are equivalent to no forces.   This postulate, based on Newton's treatment of mechanics and substantiated by experiment, has been used in Chaps. 3 and 4 as a means
of handling problems concerning the equilibrium of particles.   In the preceding
chapter we found that any set of forces is effectively as simple as a resultant set
consisting of one force $\bar{\mathbf{F}}$ equal to the vector sum of the forces, together with a
couple $\bar{\boldsymbol{\Gamma}}$ equal to the vector sum of the moments of the forces about some point on
the line of action of $\bar{\mathbf{F}}$.   In Sec. 10.7 this result was applied briefly to equilibrium
problems.   Let us state the criteria here:

(11.6) *For a rigid body to be in equilibrium, it is necessary that the vector sum of
the forces acting on it be zero.*

(11.7) *For a rigid body to be in equilibrium, it is necessary that the moment about
any point or axis of the set of forces acting on it be zero.*

Using Postulate (3.10) and the reduction theorem (10.19), a converse proposition
might be stated.   Combining these in a single statement, we have

(11.8) *A rigid body is in equilibrium if and only if the vector sum and the moment
sum about any one point of the forces acting on it are both zero.*

In equation form, the condition for equilibrium is

(11.9) $\Sigma \mathbf{F} = \mathbf{O} \qquad \Sigma \boldsymbol{\Gamma} = \mathbf{O}$

Other special forms are possible.   For instance, $\bar{\mathbf{F}}$ is zero if its x, y, and z components
are zero [as already noted in (3.15)].   Similarly, the vector $\bar{\boldsymbol{\Gamma}}$ is zero if its corresponding components are zero.   We have, however, seen that these components are
merely the moments about the axes; thus, along with

(11.10) $\Sigma f_x = 0 \qquad \Sigma f_y = 0 \qquad \Sigma f_z = 0$

we may write

(11.11) $\Sigma \gamma_x = 0 \qquad \Sigma \gamma_y = 0 \qquad \Sigma \gamma_z = 0$

Let us see how these general ideas may be applied systematically to specific types
of problems.

Parallel Forces.   Suppose that the forces may all be expressed in the form $f\mathbf{J}$.
Then it is clearly superfluous to use the conditions involving x and z components
of the forces or y components of the moments.   We are left, then, with the equations

(11.12) $\Sigma f_y = 0 \qquad \Sigma \gamma_x = 0 \qquad \Sigma \gamma_z = 0$

The latter two equations are with respect to axes through any desired origin.   The
only limitation is that these axes be perpendicular to $\mathbf{J}$.

Example I

A 100-lb uniform plank is supported horizontally at its ends, as shown in Fig.
11.12.   A 200-lb load rests at a point one-third of the way from one end.   What are
the forces required to support the plank?

Solution

As in problems involving particles, the first step is to isolate something.   Suppose
that we first isolate the load (see Fig. 11.13).   Two forces act on it: its weight $\mathbf{W}$
(200 lb, downward) and the contact reaction $\mathbf{C}$ with the beam.   The equilibrium
condition $\Sigma \mathbf{F} = \mathbf{O}$ here yields

$$\mathbf{W} + \mathbf{C} = \mathbf{O} \qquad \text{or} \qquad \mathbf{C} = -\mathbf{W}$$

Figure
11.12

Figure
11.13

Hence the contact reaction is 200 lb upward.   Now isolate the beam (see Fig. 11.14).
By the reaction postulate (3.1), a force equal but opposite to **C**, that is, a force equal
to **W**, acts on the plank because of the load.   Thus we could have just as well introduced the weight of the load as a force acting on the beam.   (This device would be
invalid were the beam not in equilibrium.)   Another force acting on the beam is
gravity.   Since the plank is uniform, the weight **W'** may be thought of as acting at
its center.   (Justification for this statement appeared in Sec. 10.8.)   Now consider
the reactions at the ends.   Let them be resolved into horizontal components **D** and
E and vertical components **A** and **B**.   By the condition $\Sigma f_x = 0$, we get $d - e = 0$,
or $d = e$.   Nothing further may be said.   **D** and **E** might be pushes or pulls of any
magnitude whatever.   The forces in this case are said to be *statically indeterminate*
since a complete solution cannot be achieved simply by applying the conditions of
equilibrium.   If enough information were available about the internal state of the
plank, a solution would be possible.   Since nothing in the statement of the problem
suggested that the beam was under compression or tension, we shall assume that
D = **E** = **O**.   Then, using $\Sigma f_y = 0$, we may write (referring to Fig. 11.15)

$$a - w - w' + b = 0$$

From this and the data of the problem we infer that

$$a + b = 300 \text{ lb}$$

Let us now choose our z axis as perpendicular to the figure and outward through the
left end of the plank.   Using the condition $\Sigma \gamma_z = 0$ and denoting the length of the
beam by $6s$, we get

$$(0)(a) - (2s)(w) - (3s)(w') + (6s)(b) = 0$$

From this we conclude that $b = 116.7$ lb, so that $a = 183.3$ lb.   Our choice of a
z axis was arbitrary: we could just as well have chosen a parallel one through the
center, other end, or even a random point of the plank.   As the student gets practice
in solving statics problems, he will develop facility in choosing suitable axes or points
of reference.   A useful check on numerical work may be obtained by substituting
values in such an alternative equation.   Here, for example, let us take moments
about the center of the plank:

$$-(3s)(183.3) + (s)(200) + (3s)(116.7) = 0$$

This equation is valid within the limits of accuracy of the data and of slide-rule
computation.

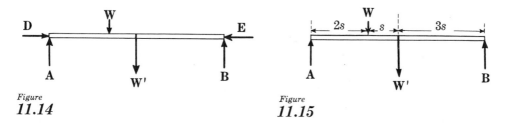

Figure
11.14

Figure
11.15

Example 2

The position of a load **W** on a symmetrical three-legged table is shown in Fig. 11.16. Find the corresponding vertical forces transmitted by the legs.

Solution

Isolate the table.   Apply the condition $\Sigma\, \mathbf{F} = \mathbf{O}$:

$$\mathbf{A} + \mathbf{B} + \mathbf{C} + \mathbf{W} = \mathbf{O}$$

Apply the condition $\Sigma\, \gamma = 0$, taking moments about the axis **AC** in the figure,

$$-3w \sin 45° + 6b \sin 60° = 0$$

so

$$b = 0.408w$$

Now take moments about axis **AB**:

$$3w \sin 15° - 6c \sin 60° = 0$$

so

$$c = 0.149w$$

Using the first equation, $a + b + c - w = 0$, a can be found also:

$$a = w - 0.408w - 0.149w = 0.443w$$

A check might be obtained by taking moments about **BC**.

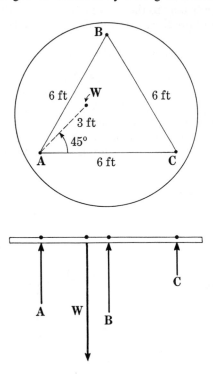

Figure
11.16

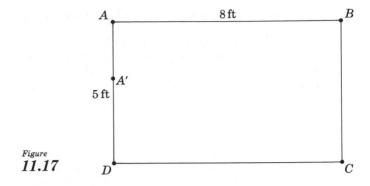

Figure
11.17

EXERCISES

8. A uniform rectangular concrete slab lies at rest on a smooth surface. It is shown from above in Fig. 11.17. The slab is 5 by 8 ft and weighs 5,000 lb. A vertical force at A (i.e., normal to the slab) is gradually increased until two corners are lifted from the supporting surface. Which two corners remain at rest on the surface—or is this a matter of chance? Explain. What forces do these corners experience?

9. Repeat the preceding exercise, assuming that the lifting force is now applied at A', 2 ft from A on the edge AD.

10. In Fig. 11.18 a single force acting at $(\bar{x},0,\bar{z})$ is sufficient to produce equilibrium. How large is this force, and what are the values of $\bar{x}$ and $\bar{z}$?

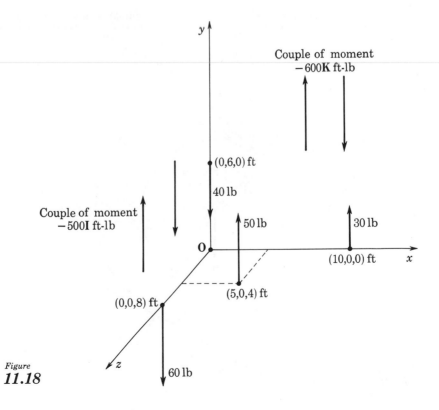

Figure
11.18

11.3. EQUILIBRIUM WITH PLANE FORCES

Time and time again it will be found that the forces acting on a body may be considered as lying in a single plane, as was shown, for example, in the alternative solution to the example in Sec. 10.7. For convenience, take this as the xy plane. Then each force may be expressed in the form $f_x\mathbf{I} + f_y\mathbf{J}$. For such forces the sums Σf_z, $\Sigma \gamma_x$, $\Sigma \gamma_y$ are clearly of no interest. The useful conditions of equilibrium are then

$$(11.13) \qquad \Sigma f_x = 0 \qquad \Sigma f_y = 0 \qquad \Sigma \gamma_z = 0$$

Example 1

A metal spool consists of two disks of radius 15 in., joined by an axle of radius 9 in. The total weight is 36.8 lb. It rests on a ramp inclined at 30° to the horizontal and is held in place by a rope wrapped around the axle, coming off its upper side, and directed 20° above the ramp. If the spool is held in equilibrium, find the tension in the rope and the frictional force between spool and plane.

Solution

Figure 11.19 represents the isolated spool and the forces acting on it. It is assumed that the forces are located symmetrically, so the reactions between the two disks and the ramp are replaced by single resultant forces $\mathbf{N}$ and $\mathbf{F}$ in the normal plane through the center of the spool. Resolve $\mathbf{T}$, the tension in the rope, into components parallel and perpendicular to the ramp, and then take moments about the line of contact between spool and plane:

$$\Sigma \gamma = 0$$

or

$$-t \cos \phi(r + r' \cos \phi) - t \sin \phi(r' \sin \phi) + w \sin \theta\, r = 0$$

or

$$t = w \frac{r \sin \theta}{r \cos \phi + r'} = 36.8 \frac{15 \times 0.50}{14.1 + 9} = 11.9 \text{ lb}$$

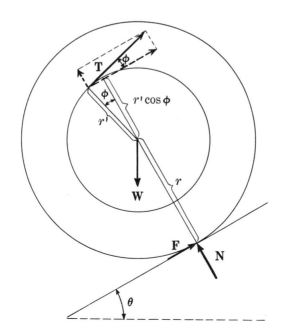

Figure
11.19

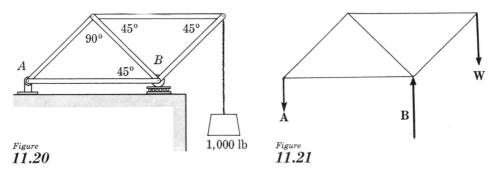

Figure
11.20

1,000 lb

Figure
11.21

Now let us take moments about the axis of the spool, again setting the sum of these moments equal to zero,

$$-tr' + fr = 0$$

or

$$f = t\frac{r'}{r} = 11.9 \times \frac{9}{15} = 7.2 \text{ lb}$$

As a check let us compute the sum of the components parallel to the ramp:

$$t \cos \phi - w \sin \theta + f \overset{?}{=} 0$$

or

$$11.9 \times 0.94 - 36.8 \times 0.50 + 7.2 = 11.2 - 18.4 + 7.2 = 0$$

Thus a check is obtained.

Example 2

In Sec. 4.4 some attention was given to simple structures composed of light rigid members subject only to compressions and tensions. At that stage of our study it was convenient to have all external forces specified in advance. Now we can do a more thorough piece of work on such problems, for the method of moments allows us to isolate the whole structure and to find relations between external forces.

Consider the simple truss shown in Fig. 11.20. The left ground attachment is rigid. The right contact is on rollers in order that thermal stresses may be minimized. Such stresses, due to the thermal expansion or contraction of member AB, might otherwise cause the member to be in a state of tension or compression quite apart from the load. The solution then would be statically indeterminate. First isolate the whole frame, as in Fig. 11.21. Taking moments about B, it is clear that A has magnitude 500 lb, whence B has magnitude 1,500 lb. The forces in the beams may now be determined by isolating the hinge pins in successive joints as in previous examples. This is left for the student.

EXERCISES

11. A packing box uniformly loaded is 6 ft high and 4 ft square (see Fig. 11.22). It weighs 200 lb. If the box rests on a horizontal floor against a cleat which prevents its sliding, what is the maximum perpendicular force **P** along the upper face which the box can sustain without tipping? What force must the cleat provide in this case?

12. A uniform ladder 13 ft long, weighing 20 lb, rests against a smooth vertical wall 12 ft above a smooth horizontal floor. It is kept from slipping along the floor by means of a string running from the middle of the ladder horizontally to a hook on the wall.

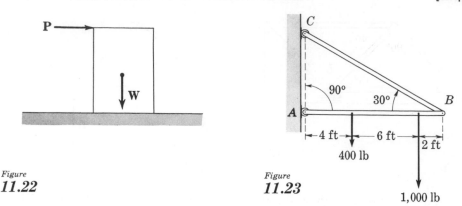

Figure
11.22

Figure
11.23

A 180-lb man climbs the ladder very cautiously, but nevertheless the string breaks just as he reaches the halfway rung. What is the breaking strength of the string?

13. A 100-lb uniform beam is hinged at the lower end to a vertical wall at an angle of 45°. A 5-ft rope goes from the upper end of the beam to a point 3 ft higher on the wall (i.e., higher than the upper end of the beam). When a load of 500 lb is attached to the upper end of the beam, (a) what is the tension in the rope, and (b) what are the horizontal and vertical components of the reaction force at the hinge?

14. The joints of the wall bracket shown in Fig. 11.23 are smooth pins. The weights of the rods may be neglected. Find (a) the tension in CB; (b) the magnitude and direction of the force exerted on beam AB by the pin at A.

15. A steel hoop 4 ft in diameter and weighing 20 lb is hung, as shown in Fig. 11.24, on two small smooth pegs 3 ft apart and determining a vertical line. What force is exerted on each peg?

16. A simple truss has five light members as shown in Fig. 11.25. Find the tensions or compressions (state which) in each of the five members.

17. Find the force in each member of the truss shown in Fig. 11.26. Neglect weights of the beams. Each acute angle is either 30° or 60°.

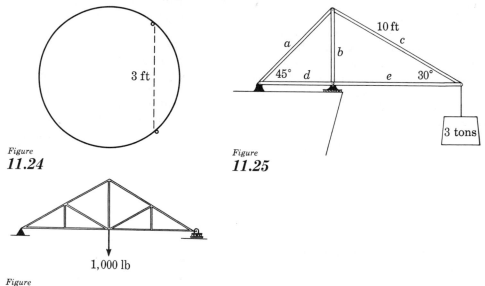

Figure
11.24

Figure
11.25

Figure
11.26

11.4. SHEARING FORCE AND BENDING MOMENT

In dealing with solid bodies we have paid little attention to internal forces.   Yet it is quite possible to isolate a portion of a body and thus bring to light the forces acting across the boundary between the isolated portion and the rest of the body.   This approach will be used in the present section.   It affords an interesting application of the principles of statics and at the same time gives us concepts for use in a later chapter.

This new point of view will be applied here to a very special class of problems. We shall consider the internal forces of horizontal beams.   Suppose that a beam is in equilibrium subject to various external forces, such as gravity, pier reactions, and weight of loads.   We shall assume that all the external forces act in the vertical plane through the beam's axis.   As a boundary, imagine a plane normal to the beam. The position of this plane section can be specified by giving the coordinate x of the corresponding point on an axis parallel to the beam, as in Fig. 11.27.   If we isolate the portion, say, to the left of the boundary, we may ask, What is the resultant of the system of forces by which the right portion acts on the left portion?   Such a system, according to Sec. 10.6, can always be reduced to a force $\mathbf{F}_s$ and a couple $\mathbf{\Gamma}_b$.   For the cases which we are considering, $\mathbf{F}_s$ is normal to the beam and its magnitude f_s is called the *shearing force*.   The magnitude of $\mathbf{\Gamma}_b$, γ_b is called the *bending moment*.   Figure 11.28 shows the directions which will be treated as positive for either a left or a right end isolation.   Note that these are the actual directions to be expected for a small left-hand portion of a simple unloaded beam supported at its ends.

Both f_s and γ_b may have negative values.   In such a case the actual forces across the boundary are directed oppositely to those of Fig. 11.28.

Example I

A light uniform beam 10 ft long is held in horizontal position by simple supports (such as knife-edges) 1 ft from either end as in Fig. 11.27.   It sustains a load of 1,000 lb 3 ft from one end.   Find the shearing force and bending moment at the center.

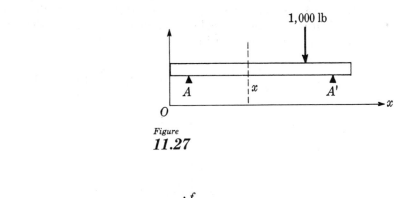

Figure
11.27

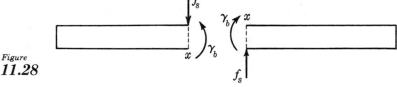

Figure
11.28

Solution

First we isolate the whole beam to find the forces of support at A and A'. Taking moments about A, we have

$$8a' - 6(1,000) = 0$$

so

$$a' = 750 \text{ lb} \qquad a = 250 \text{ lb}$$

Now isolate the left half of the beam. We have for equations of equilibrium (taking moments about an axis in the plane of section in order to leave f_s out of the equation)

$$\Sigma f_y = 0: \qquad\qquad 250 - f_s = 0 \qquad f_s = 250 \text{ lb}$$

$$\Sigma \gamma = 0: \qquad\qquad -(4)(250) + \gamma_b = 0 \qquad \gamma_b = 1,000 \text{ ft-lb}$$

Alternative Solution

Let us now isolate the right half of the beam. Again we shall take moments about an axis in the plane of section.

$$f_s + 750 - 1,000 = 0 \qquad f_s = 250 \text{ lb}$$

$$-\gamma_b - (2)(1,000) + (4)(750) = 0 \qquad \gamma_b = 1,000 \text{ ft-lb}$$

The two approaches give the same answers, of course. Ordinarily, one should isolate the portion giving the simpler equations of equilibrium.

Example 2

Find equations for shearing force and bending moment of a uniform slender beam of mass m and length l which has simple knife-edge supports at the ends.

Solution

Letting a positive x axis run along the beam as in Fig. 11.29, the possible plane sections may be described by values of x from 0 to l. Isolate the portion from 0 to x. The weight of this portion is $mg(x/l)$ acting at the middle, where the coordinate is $x/2$. Each support carries half the load. The force equation of equilibrium is

$$\frac{mg}{2} - \frac{mgx}{l} - f_s = 0 \qquad f_s = \frac{mg}{2}\left(1 - \frac{2x}{l}\right)$$

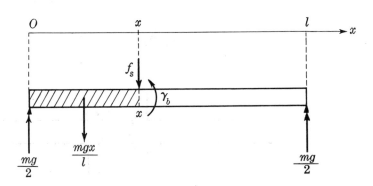

Figure
11.29

The moment equation, taking moments about the right end of the isolated portion, is

$$-\frac{mg}{2}x + \frac{mgx}{l}\left(\frac{x}{2}\right) + \gamma_b = 0 \qquad \gamma_b = \frac{mgx}{2}\left(1 - \frac{x}{l}\right)$$

Graphically, these results appear as in Fig. 11.30.

Interrelationships. Suppose that the weight per length (linear weight density) of a beam is $q(x)$ at the point x. Let us isolate a section of the beam carrying no additional load. Let the section extend from $x - \Delta x$ to $x + \Delta x$. For x, the shearing force and bending moment are f_s and γ_b. For the ends of this section, the approximate values are $f_s \pm (df_s/dx)\,\Delta x$, $\gamma_b \pm (d\gamma_b/dx)\,\Delta x$, as shown in Fig. 11.31. Isolating the section, we have for a first approximate equilibrium equation

$$2\frac{df_s}{dx}\Delta x + 2q(x)\,\Delta x = 0$$

Dividing by Δx and taking the limit as Δx approaches zero (so that our approximate equation gets more and more exact), we get

(11.14) $$\frac{df_s}{dx} = -q(x)$$

This may be checked with Fig. 11.30, where $q(x)$ is a constant and the slope is $-(mg/l)$, as predicted by the equation.

For a moment equation, taking moments around the center,

$$2\frac{d\gamma_b}{dx}\Delta x - 2f_s\,\Delta x = 0$$

Dividing by Δx and taking limits as Δx approaches zero,

(11.15) $$\frac{d\gamma_b}{dx} = f_s$$

This too may be checked with Fig. 11.30.

These two results are valid except at points where concentrated loads appear. For such points, the shearing force changes instantaneously by an amount equal to the load, and the bending moment has a corresponding discontinuity in slope.

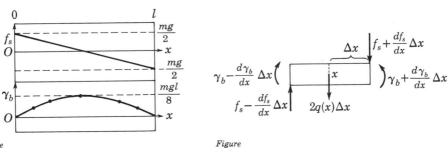

Figure
11.30

Figure
11.31

Example 3

A uniform slender beam of mass m and length l is supported as shown in Fig. 11.32. A load of $2mg$ is applied at the right end. Investigate the shearing force and bending moment.

Solution

Assigning coordinates as previously, we isolate the region from 0 to x where $x < l/2$. The forces on the isolated portion appear in Fig. 11.33. The equations for equilibrium are

$$2mg + \frac{mgx}{l} + f_s = 0 \quad \text{or} \quad f_s = -mg\left(2 + \frac{x}{l}\right)$$

$$2mgx + \frac{mgx^2}{2l} + \gamma_b = 0 \quad \text{or} \quad \gamma_b = -mgx\left(2 + \frac{x}{2l}\right)$$

Now, using Fig. 11.34, let us isolate the portion from 0 to x for $\frac{l}{2} < x < l$. The equations now are

$$5mg - 2mg - \frac{mgx}{l} - f_s = 0 \qquad f_s = 3mg - \frac{mgx}{l}$$

$$2mgx + \frac{mgx^2}{2l} - 5mg\left(x - \frac{l}{2}\right) + \gamma_b = 0$$

or

$$\gamma_b = 3mgx - \frac{mgx^2}{2l} - \frac{5mgl}{2}$$

The first of these equations shows that the value of f_s jumps by $5mg$ at the point of support.

A graphical summary appears in Fig. 11.35.

Alternative Solution

A more analytical and somewhat shorter approach makes use of Eqs. (11.14) and (11.15). We start with

$$\frac{df_s}{dx} = -\frac{mg}{l}$$

We integrate and use the fact that at the left support the shearing force (provided by the support) is $-2mg$. We get

$$f_s = -\frac{mg}{l}x + c \qquad -2mg = 0 + c \qquad f_s = -2mg - \frac{mg}{l}x$$

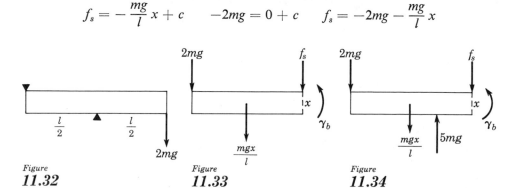

Figure
11.32

Figure
11.33

Figure
11.34

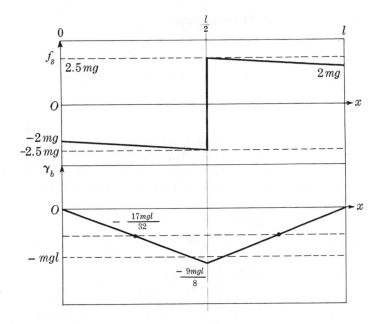

Figure
11.35

Now we may use (11.15).   Integrating again,

$$\gamma_b = -2mgx - \frac{mgx^2}{2l} + c'$$

This time our boundary condition is that $\gamma_b = 0$ at the free end $x = 0$; thus

$$\gamma_b = -mgx\left(2 + \frac{x}{2l}\right)$$

as before.   A similar procedure may be used for $x > l/2$.   For at $x = l, f_s = 2mg$ and $\gamma_b = 0$.   This time the constant of integration is given by

$$2mg = -mg + c$$

Thus

$$f_s = -\frac{mgx}{l} + 3mg$$

Integrating again, we get

$$\gamma_b = -\frac{mgx^2}{2l} + 3mgx + c'$$

Evaluating c',

$$0 = -\frac{mgl}{2} + 3mgl + c'$$

Thus

$$\gamma_b = -\frac{mgx^2}{2l} + 3mgx - \tfrac{5}{2}\,mgl$$

Bending Moment and Funicular Curves.   As a final item let us note one interesting common ground between this section and the last section of Chap 4.

From (11.15) and (11.14) together, we get

(11.16)
$$\frac{d^2\gamma_b}{dx^2} = -q(x)$$

This is to be compared with (4.9), an equation determining the shape of a funicular curve:

$$\frac{d^2y}{dx^2} = \frac{1}{h}q(x)$$

This comparison indicates that, except for constants, units, etc., the graph of γ_b is an inverted funicular curve. Thus in Fig. 11.30 we have a parabola—the curve which a cable with uniform horizontal loading assumes. And in Fig. 11.35 we have an inverted picture of a cable with a uniform horizontal load, together with a vertical force upward.

EXERCISES

18. A 250-lb 10-ft uniform beam rests horizontally on supports 8 ft apart as in Fig. 11.36, with a 600-lb load at the right end (the load is vertical).
    (a) What is the pier reaction at the left support?
    (b) What is the shearing force at the center of the beam?
    (c) What is the bending moment at the center of the beam?
19. The beam shown in Fig. 11.37 has linear weight density given by $q = q_0 + \mu x$, where μ is a constant. For simple knife-edge supports as shown, find expressions for the shearing force and bending moment at the center (i.e., at $x = l/2$).
20. A 200-lb 12-ft uniform beam rests on knife-edges at one end and 4 ft away from the other end as shown in Fig. 11.38. A 100-lb load is fastened to the unsupported end. Compute the shearing force and bending moment at the point labeled x, midway between the second knife-edge and the load.

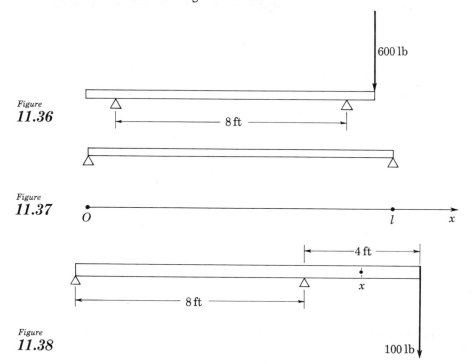

Figure
11.36

600 lb

8 ft

Figure
11.37

O l x

4 ft

x

8 ft

Figure
11.38

100 lb

21. A uniform beam weighing 1.5 lb/ft projects horizontally 20 ft from a pier to which it is rigidly fastened. Find the bending moment and shearing force at a point 10 ft from the point of support.

22. A light 10-ft beam rests on two simple knife-edge supports, one at the left end and the other 2 ft from the other end. A load of 1,000 lb is attached at the center of the beam, while a load of 500 lb is at the free end. Plot the shearing force and the bending moment.

23. Plot shearing-force and bending-moment curves for a uniform beam supported on two knife-edges, each a quarter length from the ends.

24. Plot shearing-force and bending-moment curves for a uniform horizontal beam, one end of which is set rigidly in concrete, the other end being free.

11.5. MISCELLANEOUS PROBLEMS

Methods and concepts needed for the solution of statics problems have been introduced gradually. Illustrative worked examples have been placed suggestively near the sections containing suitable methods. At the end of the present chapter you will find a melange of problems and you are invited to select any methods available. In particular, do not forget that the methods of virtual work and potential energy of Chap. 7 are applicable to rigid-body problems. Methods of finding centers of mass, and hence centers of gravity, are deferred until Chap. 15. The concepts of stress, strain, and fluid pressure are left for Chaps. 18 to 20. Thus the collection of tools useful for statics problems is by no means complete. For additional methods, examples, and problems you may wish to explore textbooks on engineering mechanics. Some good sources are given in the list of Suggested References at the end of the book.

REVIEW EXERCISES

25. A rigid uniform spherical octant is subjected to four forces as shown in Fig. 11.39:

$$\left.\begin{array}{l}\text{At } (6,0,0), \text{ a force } 10\mathbf{I} \text{ lb} \\ \text{At } (0,6,0), \text{ a force } -4\mathbf{I} \text{ lb} \\ \text{At } (0,0,6), \text{ a force } -8\mathbf{I} \text{ lb} \\ \text{At } (4,2,4), \text{ a force } 12\mathbf{I} \text{ lb}\end{array}\right\}\text{(coordinates in feet)}$$

Find at **O** an equivalent force $\bar{\mathbf{F}}$ with compensating couple $\bar{\boldsymbol{\Gamma}}$. (State results as two vectors in **IJK** form.)

26. Find a single force (state magnitude, direction cosines, and coordinates of a point in the yz plane on its line of action) equivalent to the set of forces shown in Fig. 11.40.

27. An 18-ft 120-lb uniform ladder is suspended from one end by smooth hinges H as in Fig. 11.41. It is held at an angle 60° with the vertical by resting on a smooth horizontal pipe P 6 ft from the top. At the bottom end a 200-lb athlete A hangs in equilibrium. Compute in magnitude and direction:
(a) The force exerted *on* the pipe.
(b) The force exerted *by* the hinge.

28. In Fig. 11.42 $ABCD$ is a five-member simple truss with a 2,000-lb load at pin B. The truss is supported by vertical forces at pins A and C. The distance AD is 10 ft.
(a) Find the pier reactions $\mathbf{F}_A$ and $\mathbf{F}_B$.
(b) Write in **IJ** form the three forces acting on pin D. Draw a force triangle showing how these forces are in equilibrium.
(c) Determine the forces acting on member BC. Illustrate with a diagram, isolating this member.

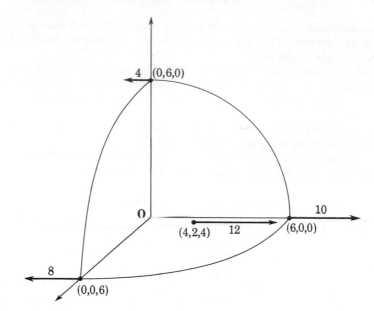

Figure
11.39

29. The trestle structure shown in Fig. 11.43 consists of three rigid members *AB*, *CD*, *BC*, with smooth pins at *B*, *C*, and *E*. The floor *AD* is smooth. A 200-lb load acts at the center of *BC*. Express in **IJ** form the force exerted by pin *B* on member *BC*. Show, with diagrams, each step in this deduction.

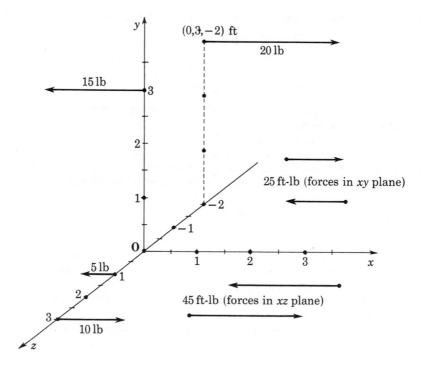

Figure
11.40

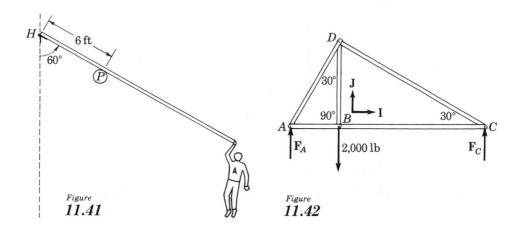

Figure
11.41

Figure
11.42

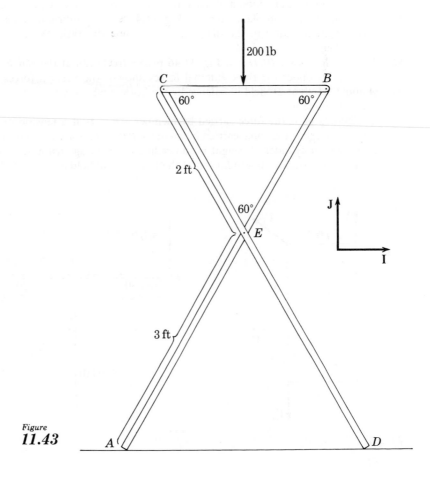

Figure
11.43

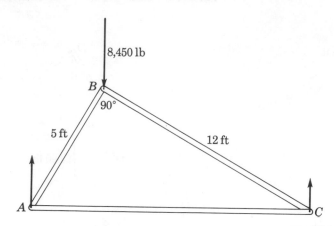

Figure
11.44

30. The triangular frame ABC in Fig. 11.44 is a simple truss supported at pins A and C by vertical pier reactions. An 8,450-lb vertical load is applied at pin B. Members AB and BC are, respectively, 5 and 12 ft long. The angle at B is 90°.

(a) Find in direction and magnitude the force exerted by member AB on pin A, and state whether AB is in a state of compression or tension.

(b) Determine in direction and magnitude the force exerted by pin A on member AC.

31. The rectangular rigid plane object in Fig. 11.45 is in equilibrium under the five forces shown (not to scale) in the diagram. Determine the ratio $|\mathbf{V}|/|\mathbf{H}|$. Justify briefly steps taken.

32. The simple truss $ABCDA$ in Fig. 11.46 pivots freely about the pin B. It is now in equilibrium under the three external forces shown: the vertical forces of 1,500 lb at A and 3,200 lb at D, held in balance by the horizontal force $\mathbf{F}$ at C.

(a) Determine $\mathbf{F}$.

(b) How large is the force carried by member AB? Is it a tension or compression?

(c) How large is the force carried by member BD? Is it a tension or a compression?

33. A horizontal cylinder of weight w and radius r is held against a vertical smooth wall by a slanting smooth board hinged at the bottom and held at an angle θ with the wall

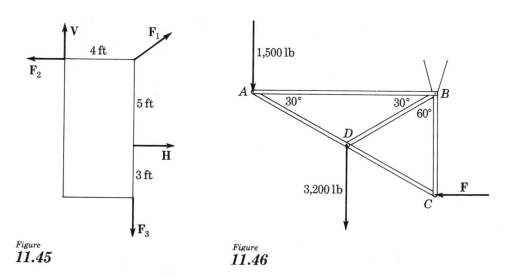

Figure
11.45

Figure
11.46

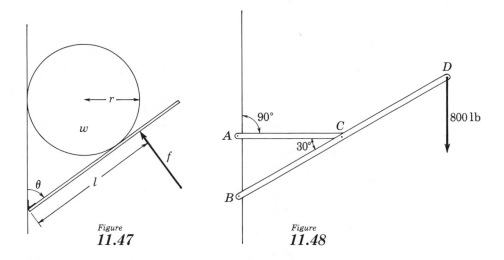

Figure
11.47

Figure
11.48

by a normal force f at a distance l from the hinge (see Fig. 11.47).   Express f in terms of w, r, l, and θ.

34. In Fig. 11.48, BD is a uniform beam weighing 100 lb, 20 ft long.   The beam supports at its outer end D a load (vertical) of 800 lb. AC is a strut of negligible weight.   The joints at A, B, and C are made with smooth pins. C is the center of BD.
(*a*) What is the tension in the strut AC?
(*b*) What are the horizontal and vertical components of the force exerted by the pin at B?

35. A uniform 20-ft beam is subject, as shown in Fig. 11.49, to three forces.   This set of forces is equivalent to a single force $\bar{F}$ at P (5 ft from right end) together with a compensating couple $\bar{\Gamma}$.   Regarding the figure as in the xy plane as shown:
(*a*) Express $\bar{F}$ in **IJK** form.
(*b*) Express $\bar{\Gamma}$ in **IJK** form.
(*c*) Where along the beam (state coordinate x relative to left end as origin) could a single force equivalent to the original three-force system be applied?

36. The power wheels of an empty lumber truck (see Fig. 11.50) carry a total load of 2,500 lb.   When the truck is loaded, half the additional weight is supported by the power wheels.   The truck is unloaded by chaining the load to a tree and then driving

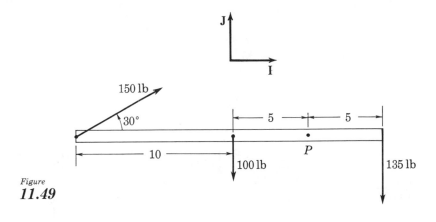

Figure
11.49

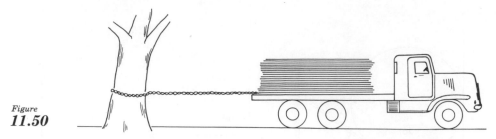

Figure
11.50

out from under the load.   If the coefficient of friction between load and truck is 0.41 and between tires and icy ground is 0.15, how large a load can be handled in this way? Make the details of your analysis clear.

37. A flat uniform board of weight w has the shape of a rectangle twice as long as it is wide.   It is hung on a horizontal nail by means of a light screw eye at one corner. What must be the weight of an object hung on an adjacent corner to make the rectangle's edges inclined at 45°?

38. Each of a pair of braces for staging consists of two metal bars, one 2 ft long, the other 1.5 ft long, with a hinged joint between them.   It is used, as in Fig. 11.51, on a ladder with rungs 15 in. apart.   The end of the long bar has a hook to go over one round; the other bar ends in a U-shaped piece which fits over the second rung below.   The load, say, the weight of a 180-lb man, is supported by a bar attached to the hinges of the two braces.   Find the reaction at each rung when the ladder makes an angle of 70° with the horizontal.

39. A 3- by 7-ft door weighing 80 lb is supported by two hinges 6 in. from top and bottom. (a) Neglecting friction, discuss the possible range of hinge reactions both in direction and magnitude.

(b) Describe the locus of the points of intersection of the possible pairs of hinge forces.

40. Referring to Fig. 11.52, the lever is 17 in. long and weighs 0.5 lb.   It is smoothly pivoted at a point 4 in. from one end.   At B, 12 in. from the pivot, is attached a cord sustaining a tension of 1 lb.   The lever is held at an angle of 45° with the horizontal by a peg A 3 in. from the pivot.   What force does the peg A withstand?

41. Two small weights, w and $2w$, connected by a light flexible cord of length r, are hung over a smooth cylinder of radius r.   Find the position of equilibrium.   (Find the angle θ which the radius to the smaller weight makes with the vertical.)

42. The top of a uniform 20-ft ladder weighing 50 lb rests against a smooth vertical wall at a point 16 ft from the floor.   The ladder is kept from slipping by a string tied to its base and to a point on the wall 5 ft from the floor.   The coefficient of friction between

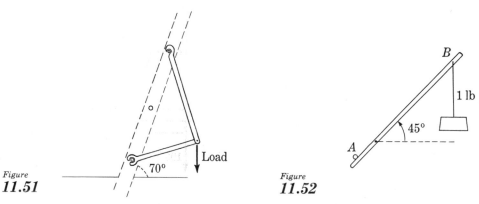

Figure
11.51

Figure
11.52

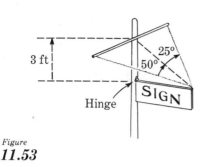

Figure
11.53

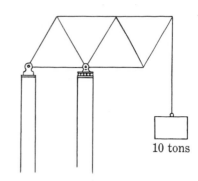

Figure
11.54

floor and ladder is 0.1.   The string will break under a tension of 52 lb.   How far may a 200-lb man ascend the ladder with safety?

43. One end of an 800-lb sign 4 ft long is hinged to a post.   On the post 3 ft above the sign and at right angles to it is a horizontal bar.   The other end of the sign is attached by light chains running to the ends of the bar.   These chains make angles of 25° and 50°, respectively, with the plane of the sign and post as shown in Fig. 11.53.   Find the tensions in the chains and the force sustained by the hinge.

44. Find the forces sustained by each of the members of the truss in Fig. 11.54.   Assume that the joints consist of simple frictionless pins and that the weights of the beams are to be neglected.   The triangles are all equilateral.

45. The top D of a light tripod is 8 ft from the horizontal plane of the feet A, B, C.   The triangle ABC is isosceles: $AC = BC$, and legs AD and BD are both 10 ft long. CD is 16 ft long.   Angle $ADB = 45°$.   If a 200-lb vertical load is applied at D, what is the corresponding thrust in each leg?

46. In Fig. 11.55 the pivots A, B, C are frictionless pins. AD is a single rigid member. Neglect weight of beams.
(*a*) What thrust is exerted by the brace CB?
(*b*) What is the reaction at bearing C, in both direction and magnitude?

47. The simple truss shown in Fig. 11.56 is anchored in such a way that the force transmitted to the pier at B is vertical.

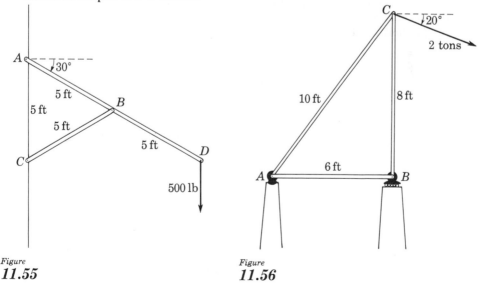

Figure
11.55

Figure
11.56

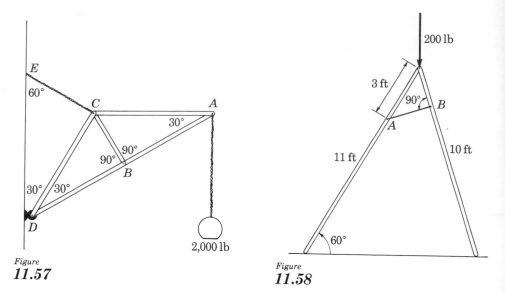

Figure
11.57

Figure
11.58

(a) How large is this vertical force?
(b) How large is the horizontal component of the pier reaction at A?
(c) How great is the tension in the member AC?

48. The truss shown in Fig. 11.57 is supported by the smooth pivot D and the rope EC. Find the force (state whether tension or compression) sustained by each of the five members. Also find the tension in the rope.

49. The legs of a stepladder (see Fig. 11.58) are, respectively, 11 and 10 ft long. The angle of the long leg with the floor (horizontal and smooth) is 60°. The brace AB meets the long leg at a point 3 ft from the top and is perpendicular to the other leg. When a 200-lb man stands on the top, what is the tension in the support AB, and what are the reaction forces at the floor?

50. The framework shown in Fig. 11.59 is held in equilibrium by the cable AB when the 1,000-lb force is applied at E. Find:
(a) The tension at AB.
(b) The horizontal and vertical forces exerted by the hinge C.

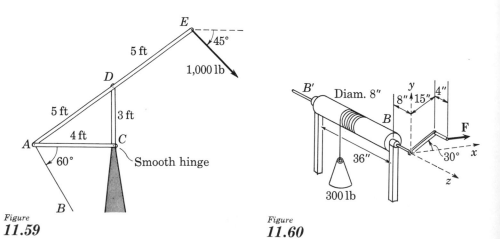

Figure
11.59

Figure
11.60

51. A hand-operated windlass supports a 300-lb load as shown in Fig. 11.60. The diameter of the horizontal drum is 8 in. The distance between the bearings B' and B is 3 ft. The load hangs halfway between the bearings. The axle extends 8 in. beyond the bearing B. A 15-in. crank is rigidly attached at right angles to the end of the axle. A horizontal force **F** acts on the handle of the crank at a point 4 in. from its base. **F** is perpendicular to the axle. When the crank makes an angle of 30° with the horizontal (x axis in the figure), the system is in equilibrium. The z axis is taken along the axle, and the y axis vertical.

(*a*) Find the magnitude of **F**, neglecting bearing friction.

(*b*) Find in **IJ** form the forces exerted by the bearings B' and B (these forces may be assumed to act parallel to the xy plane).

52. A mast AB, shown in Fig. 11.61, is 10 ft tall. The lower end is held by a fixed pivot. Guy wires CE and CD make angles of 30° with the horizontal, where C is 2 ft from the top. At B a force **F** given by

$$\mathbf{F} = -600\mathbf{I} - 400\mathbf{K} \qquad \text{lb}$$

is applied.

(*a*) Find the corresponding tensions in the two guy wires.

(*b*) Find in **IJK** form the reaction force at A.

53. A cable under a tension of 1,800 lb makes an angle of 20° with the horizontal at the top of the structure shown in Fig. 11.62. The seven members of the structure are pinned at the ends, forming a simple truss. This truss is pinned firmly at d, but at e the rollers ensure a normal reaction.

(*a*) How large is the reaction force at e?

(*b*) What angle with the vertical is made by the reaction force at d? (Show in a diagram.)

(*c*) How large is the reaction force at d?

(*d*) Find the force sustained by member ab. (State whether a tension or compression.)

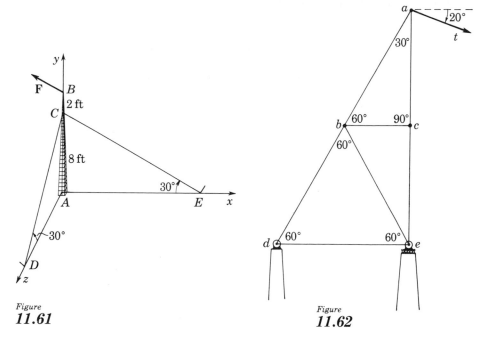

Figure
11.61

Figure
11.62

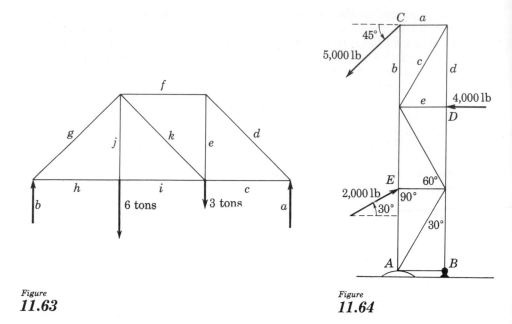

Figure
11.63

Figure
11.64

Similarly, specify the forces sustained by the other members of the structure:

(*e*) In *ac*.   (*f*) In *bc*.   (*g*) In *db*.
(*h*) In *ec*.   (*i*) In *eb*.   (*j*) In *ed*.

54.   Figure 11.63 represents a simple truss composed of four congruent right isosceles triangles. It is supported at the ends by vertical-pier reactions *a* and *b*. The loads of 3 and 6 tons are indicated.
(*a*) Find the pier reactions *a* and *b*.
(*b*) Find the tension or compression (state which) for each of the nine members of the truss.

55.   (*a*) By isolating the whole simple truss shown in Fig. 11.64, find the forces exerted on the truss at *A* (vertical) and at *B*.
(*b*) Compute the tension or compression (state which) sustained by the five members labeled *a* to *e*.

MOMENT of MOMENTUM and PARTICLE ORBITS

Thus far we have concerned ourselves mainly with specific applied forces acting on idealized objects. In much of the remaining work we shall emphasize properties that can be associated with the very space in which events happen. Gravitational forces are an example. Any object near the earth is apparently subject to a downward pull. This pull obviously depends on no actual contact. Even the moon is held in its orbit by just such a force. We feel confident in predicting that a rocket will experience gravitational forces corresponding to various positions near the earth. The force then is a *function of position*.

As a particle moves in a region under the influence of such a variable force, its motion is limited and regulated according to a number of laws derived from the postulates of Newtonian mechanics. If its kinetic energy varies, we know that equivalent work has been done by the force. If its momentum alters, there is a corresponding impulse exerted by the force. If the force is conservative, then we may apply the principle of energy conservation. If there should be a zero net impulse, then momentum must be conserved. In the present chapter all these concepts will be useful. In addition we shall apply the concept of moment of a force to dynamics, deriving for particles a new conservation principle.

The conclusions developed in this chapter provide information concerning particle orbits and hence have applications to atomic physics, astronomy, and space physics.

12.1. MOMENT OF MOMENTUM

In Chaps. 10 and 11 the vector product operation has been useful in handling moments of forces. We use it now to define moment of momentum. Let a particle at position $\mathbf{R}$ have momentum $m\mathbf{V}$. Then the moment of momentum of the particle about the point of position vector $\mathbf{Q}$ is defined to be equal to

$$(\mathbf{R} - \mathbf{Q}) \times m\mathbf{V}$$

In particular, the moment of momentum about the origin is equal to

$$\mathbf{R} \times m\mathbf{V}$$

This concept is very close to angular momentum as defined in elementary physics. Consider, for instance, a particle of mass m traveling in the x direction along a straight line at a distance y from the origin as shown in Fig. 12.1. Its moment of momentum is equal to

$$\mathbf{R} \times m\mathbf{V} = (x\mathbf{I} + y\mathbf{J}) \times mv\mathbf{I} = -ymv\mathbf{K}$$

But $x = y \tan \theta$; hence $v = \dot{x} = y(\sec^2 \theta)\dot{\theta}$. Substituting $\sec \theta = r/y$, we have the equality

$$(12.1) \qquad\qquad ymv = (mr^2)\dot{\theta}$$

The quantity mr^2 is the instantaneous *moment of inertia* about the origin of the particle, and hence Eq. (12.1) expresses for this example the equality in magnitude of moment of momentum and angular momentum. Incidentally, the concept of moment of inertia receives an extended treatment in Chap. 15.

To see the dynamical use of moment of momentum, let us again consider a particle of momentum $m\mathbf{V}$ subject to a variable force $\mathbf{F}$. For convenience, we take moments about the origin. We may start with Newton's second law in the form

$$\mathbf{F} = \frac{d}{dt}(m\mathbf{V})$$

Taking moments, we have

$$\mathbf{R} \times \mathbf{F} = \mathbf{R} \times \frac{d}{dt}(m\mathbf{V})$$

We now observe that

$$\frac{d}{dt}(\mathbf{R} \times m\mathbf{V}) = \mathbf{V} \times m\mathbf{V} + \mathbf{R} \times \frac{d}{dt}(m\mathbf{V})$$

Hence we have

$$(12.2) \qquad\qquad \mathbf{R} \times \mathbf{F} = \frac{d}{dt}(\mathbf{R} \times m\mathbf{V})$$

so the rate of change of moment of momentum is equal to the moment of the force.

Suppose that at time t_0 the particle is at $\mathbf{R}_0$ and has velocity $\mathbf{V}_0$ and at t_1 the velocity is $\mathbf{V}_1$ at $\mathbf{R}_1$. Then we may integrate to get

$$\int_{t_0}^{t_1} \mathbf{R} \times \mathbf{F}\, dt = \mathbf{R}_1 \times m\mathbf{V}_1 - \mathbf{R}_0 \times m\mathbf{V}_0 = \Delta(\mathbf{R} \times m\mathbf{V})$$

The left member is defined to be the *angular impulse* about $\mathbf{O}$ exerted by the force $\mathbf{F}$ during the interval t_0 to t_1. Note that we have an angular analogue of the impulse-momentum principle:

For a particle the change of moment of momentum about any fixed center during a time interval is equal to the net angular impulse exerted on the particle.

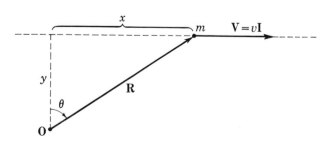

Figure
12.1

12.2. CONSERVATION OF MOMENT OF MOMENTUM

For a single particle the law of conservation of momentum is not very revealing. Essentially, at first, it seems to restate Newton's first law that a particle subject to no external forces continues in uniform motion in a straight line. Clearly, if a particle is subject to no forces, it is subject to no impulses, and hence to no momentum change. But the net impulse exerted on a particle may be null even if the force is non-null. Consider a particle in an orbit tracing out the same path periodically. The force holding the path in the orbit is non-null, but because the pattern is repetitive, the net impulse must vanish for each period τ: $\int_{t_0}^{t_0+\tau} \mathbf{F}\,dt = \mathbf{O}$ for each time t_0.

The corresponding law of *conservation of moment of momentum* for a single particle has much more content. If angular impulse is null, moment of momentum is unchanged. In the next section we shall see important consequences of this law.

Suppose now that one has an aggregate of particles. Relative to a reference point, say, the origin $\mathbf{O}$, the moment of momentum is defined to be the sum of the corresponding quantities, particle by particle. Thus for n particles the moment of momentum may be written

$$\sum_{i=1}^{n} \mathbf{R}_i \times m_i \mathbf{V}_i$$

If for each particle we write an equation like (12.2), where we replace $\mathbf{F}$ by $\bar{\mathbf{F}}_i + \bar{\mathbf{F}}_i'$, letting $\bar{\mathbf{F}}_i$ be the resultant of external forces acting on the ith particle and $\bar{\mathbf{F}}_i'$ the resultant of internal forces as in Sec. 6.6, we get

$$\sum_{i=1}^{n} \mathbf{R}_i \times \bar{\mathbf{F}}_i + \sum_{i=1}^{n} \mathbf{R}_i \times \bar{\mathbf{F}}_i' = \sum_{i=1}^{n} \frac{d}{dt}(\mathbf{R}_i \times m_i \mathbf{V}_i)$$

Now assume that the internal forces between two particles act oppositely along the line joining them. The set of forces $\{\bar{\mathbf{F}}_i'\}$ can then be arranged as equal and opposite pairs. Such pairs have zero moments about any point, so the contribution of internal forces vanishes. Thus we have for an aggregate, corresponding to (12.2) for one particle,

$$(12.3) \qquad \sum_{i=1}^{n} \mathbf{R}_i \times \bar{\mathbf{F}}_i = \frac{d}{dt} \sum_{i=1}^{n} (\mathbf{R}_i \times m_i \mathbf{V}_i)$$

If this is integrated with respect to time, we get an equation of the form

$$(12.4) \qquad \Sigma \int_{t_0}^{t_1} \mathbf{R} \times \mathbf{F}\,dt = \Delta(\Sigma \mathbf{R} \times m\mathbf{V})$$

In words, it may be stated:

(12.5) *The change during a time interval in moment of momentum of an aggregate of particles is equal to the net angular impulse exerted by the external forces during this interval.*

An immediate special case is the *law of conservation of moment of momentum*.

(12.6) *The moment of momentum about a fixed point* $\mathbf{O}$ *is constant as long as the net external angular impulse about* $\mathbf{O}$ *is zero.*

Example. Ballistic Pendulum

As was described in Sec. 7.14, the velocity of a bullet may be found by firing it into a heavy pendulum whose deflection can readily be measured (see Fig. 12.2). The bullet and the pendulum bob may be taken as a two-particle aggregate. The

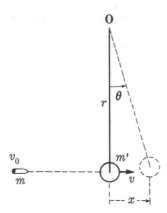

Figure
12.2

only external forces at the instant of impact are gravity and the tension in the string, neither of which has a moment about the point of support **O**. Consequently, moment of momentum is conserved. Taking magnitudes only,

$$rmv_0 = r(m + m')v$$

A similar equation was derived in Sec. 7.14, Example 1.
This equation could, of course, have been deduced equally well from the linear momentum relationships. We have, then, v_0 in terms of v:

$$v_0 = \left(1 + \frac{m'}{m}\right)v$$

The joint speed v of the particles after impact may be computed in terms of the angular displacement θ by energy methods:

$$\tfrac{1}{2}(m + m')v^2 = (m + m')gr(1 - \cos\theta)$$

In practice, it is usually more feasible to measure the horizontal displacement x rather than the angle θ. Using the approximation, for small θ, given in Sec. 7.11,

$$1 - \cos\theta = \frac{\theta^2}{2} = \frac{x^2}{2r^2}$$

We have, then,

$$v^2 = \frac{gx^2}{r}$$

Thus, assuming that m' is much larger than m, we get as a working formula

$$v_0 = \frac{m'}{m}\sqrt{\frac{g}{r}}\,x$$

It should be pointed out that by taking components in, say, the z direction, one may obtain results analogous to (12.5) and (12.6) for moments about an axis.
Thus far in this section moments have been taken about a point **O** (or an axis) fixed in an inertial frame of reference. Other points might be used. For instance, using the center of mass of the aggregate as reference point, we may derive

$$\Sigma\,\mathbf{R}' \times \mathbf{F} = \Sigma\,\mathbf{R}' \times m\frac{d\mathbf{V}'}{dt}$$

Pursuing the same sort of argument as before, we arrive at, instead of (12.4),

$$\Sigma \int_{t_0}^{t_1} \mathbf{R'} \times \mathbf{F}\, dt = \Delta\, (\Sigma\, \mathbf{R'} \times m\mathbf{V'})$$

Our main propositions can be rephrased for this case as follows (see Exercise 58):

(12.7) *The change during a time interval in moment of relative momentum about the center of mass of an aggregate of particles is equal to the net angular impulse about the center of mass exerted by external forces during this interval.*

The moment of relative momentum about the center of mass is constant as long as the net external angular impulse about the center of mass is zero.

This latter pair of theorems will be especially useful for rigid bodies.

EXERCISES

1. A rod of length r hangs vertically from a horizontal pivot through one end. A force of constant magnitude f is applied at the other end and is maintained normal to the rod while it rotates through a small angle θ. Taking the angular speed as ω during this displacement, find (a) the angular impulse and (b) the moment about the pivot of the linear impulse regarding this net impulse as acting at the point of initial application. Show that the ratio of these two is $\theta : \sin \theta$.

2. Regard the planets, moons, asteroids, comets, etc., around our sun as an aggregate of particles. Assume that each particle experiences a force of attraction toward each of the others and toward the sun. Show that the moment of momentum about the sun is constant.

3. A ballistic pendulum consists of a 10-kg bob on a 3-m rope. A 50-g bullet aimed 15° below the horizontal strikes the pendulum and produces a deflection of 35°. Find the velocity of the bullet.

4. The position, mass, and velocity of three particles are given below:

R, m	m, kg	V, m/sec
O	2	$\mathbf{I} - 4\mathbf{J} + 2\mathbf{K}$
5I	3	$3\mathbf{J} - \mathbf{K}$
2I − 4J	5	$-\mathbf{I} + \mathbf{J} - \mathbf{K}$

Compute the following: (a) the momentum of the aggregate, (b) the velocity of the center of mass, (c) the position of the center of mass, (d) the moment of momentum about the origin, (e) the moment of momentum about the center of mass.

12.3. CENTRAL FORCES

We now return to the main theme of this chapter: the motion of a single particle subject to a force varying with position. If a particle is subject to a force which is always directed through (or away from) a fixed point or *center*, the force is said to be *central*. For convenience we consider forces having the origin as center. For such a force $\mathbf{F}$ the position vector $\mathbf{R}$ of the particle is either parallel or antiparallel to $\mathbf{F}$; hence $\mathbf{R}$ must satisfy the equation (see Fig. 12.3)

$$\mathbf{R} \times \mathbf{F} = \mathbf{O}$$

so that the angular impulse exerted by **F** always vanishes. Consequently, for a central force, by Eq. (12.2) or by the conservation law, the moment of momentum is a constant vector, which we write $m\mathbf{H}$:

$$\mathbf{R} \times m\mathbf{V} = m\mathbf{H}$$

or

(12.8) $$\mathbf{R} \times \mathbf{V} = \mathbf{H}$$

If **H** happens to be a null vector, the path goes directly through **O**, for in that case **R** and **V** are parallel. If **H** is not a null vector, we can at least observe that *the path of the particle lies in a plane*, for both **R** and **V** are perpendicular to **H**.

A second conclusion concerning central-force motion of a particle is this: The rate at which the position vector **R** sweeps out area in the plane of the motion is constant; this is known as the *law of areas*. To prove it, we seek an expression for the rate of area sweeping. For the moment an intuitive vector demonstration is given. In the following section a standard analytic expression will appear. Observe that for a very small displacement $d\mathbf{R}$ the area swept out is essentially that of a triangle bounded by vectors **R**, $d\mathbf{R}$, and $\mathbf{R} + d\mathbf{R}$ (see Fig. 12.4). Now recall that the area of a triangle is half the magnitude of the cross product of two of the bounding vectors.

$$da = \tfrac{1}{2} |\mathbf{R} \times d\mathbf{R}|$$

If this equation is divided, member by member, by dt, we have the desired result

(12.9) $$\frac{da}{dt} = \tfrac{1}{2} \left| \mathbf{R} \times \frac{d\mathbf{R}}{dt} \right|$$
$$= \tfrac{1}{2} |\mathbf{R} \times \mathbf{V}| = \tfrac{1}{2} |\mathbf{H}| = \tfrac{1}{2}h, \text{ a const}$$

For an alternative approach, compare Chap. 5, Exercise 112.

A useful and easily remembered property of central-force motion is *Newton's theorem*. It has been shown that

$$|\mathbf{R} \times \mathbf{V}| = h$$

This may be rewritten (see Fig. 12.5) as

$$rv \sin \psi = h$$

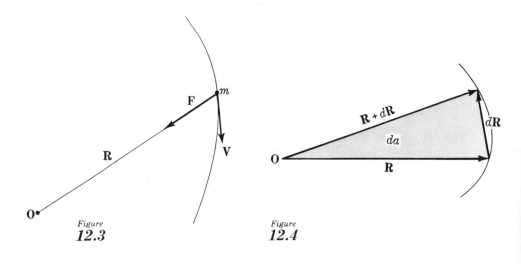

Figure
12.3

Figure
12.4

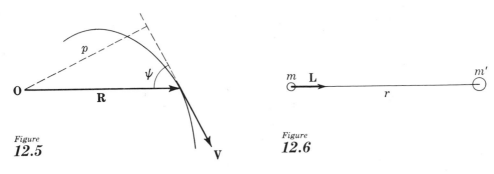

Figure
12.5

Figure
12.6

Let p denote the perpendicular distance from **O** to the tangent to the trajectory; that is, $p = r \sin \psi$. We have, then,

(12.10)
$$pv = h$$

EXERCISES

In these exercises consider the motion of a particle of mass m attracted toward a fixed point **O** by a force proportional to the distance:

$$\mathbf{F} = -mn^2\mathbf{R}$$

5. Prove that the field is conservative.
6. Prove that the potential energy of the particle (with respect to **O**) when at a distance r from **O** is $\frac{1}{2}n^2mr^2$.
7. Prove that
$$v^2 + n^2r^2 = \text{const}$$

12.4. INVERSE-SQUARE FORCES

According to Newton's law of universal gravitation (1672), between any two mass particles there is a force of attraction proportional to the product of the masses and inversely proportional to the square of the distance of separation. Referring to Fig. 12.6, the force on the particle of mass m is given by

(12.11)
$$\mathbf{F} = \frac{\gamma mm'}{r^2} \mathbf{L}$$

where γ is the gravitational constant, experimentally determined, having the value 6.67×10^{-11} in the mks system. Similarly, if we isolate the other particle it is subject to a force

(12.12)
$$\mathbf{F'} = -\frac{\gamma mm'}{r^2} \mathbf{L}$$

To make sure that this force is conservative, let us derive a work formula, using the following equations developed somewhat earlier:

$$d\mathbf{R} = d(r\mathbf{L}) = dr\,\mathbf{L} + r\,d\mathbf{L}$$
$$\mathbf{L} \cdot \mathbf{L} = 1 \qquad \mathbf{L} \cdot d\mathbf{L} = 0$$
$$\int_{\mathbf{R_1}}^{\mathbf{R_2}} \mathbf{F'} \cdot d\mathbf{R} = -\gamma mm' \int_{\mathbf{R_1}}^{\mathbf{R_2}} \frac{\mathbf{L} \cdot (dr\,\mathbf{L} + r\,d\mathbf{L})}{r^2}$$
$$= -\gamma mm' \int_{r_1}^{r_2} \frac{dr}{r^2} = \gamma mm' \left[\frac{1}{r_2} - \frac{1}{r_1}\right]$$

This value is independent of the path; therefore the force is conservative.

Suppose now that we regard the particle of mass m as fixed at the origin of our coordinate system. Then the potential energy of the particle of mass m' when at position **R** is given by

$$(\text{p.e.})_b = -\gamma mm' \left[\frac{1}{r} - \frac{1}{b} \right]$$

where b is the magnitude of the position vector **B** of the point used arbitrarily as a reference for calculation of potential energy. Clearly, the simplest formula occurs when the reference point is very far away ($b = \infty$). This potential-energy formula is used most often with inverse-square forces:

$$(12.13) \qquad \text{p.e.} = \frac{-\gamma mm'}{r}$$

In Chap. 17 we shall study inverse-square situations in more detail. For the moment it will suffice to anticipate the result that a particle outside of a uniform spherical shell experiences a gravitational force as if the mass of the shell were concentrated at its center. A particle inside such a shell experiences no gravitational force whatever. Our planet may be regarded roughly as a collection of concentric spherical shells; hence particles near it are attracted toward its center as if its whole mass were there.

In the study of electricity, inverse-square forces play an important role. Two electrically charged particles *in vacuo* are attracted or repelled by an electrostatic force given by the equation

$$(12.14) \qquad \mathbf{F} = \frac{qq'}{4\pi\epsilon_0 r^2} \mathbf{L}$$

For like charges q and q' (both positive or both negative) this is a force of repulsion. For unlike charges it is an attraction. In the mks system of units charge is measured in coulombs and the constant ϵ_0, the permittivity of free space, has the value 8.854×10^{-12} farad/m.

Many types of examples might be developed to illustrate a principle as prevalent as the inverse-square law. Since this chapter aims particularly at orbits, let us consider a few elementary properties of orbits near an idealized spherical earth.

Example 1. Acceleration of Gravity

Let $\bar{g}$ denote the acceleration of gravity at the earth's surface and $\bar{r}$ the earth's radius. Then what is the acceleration at a distance r from the earth's center? At each distance the force on a particle of mass m may be written in two ways:

$$\bar{f} = m\bar{g} = \frac{\gamma mm'}{\bar{r}^2} \qquad f = mg = \frac{\gamma mm'}{r^2}$$

Hence

$$\bar{g}\bar{r}^2 = gr^2$$

or

$$(12.15) \qquad g = \bar{g}\left(\frac{\bar{r}}{r}\right)^2$$

Note that the first equation allows us to equate $\gamma m'$ and $\bar{g}\bar{r}^2$, so that near the earth the inverse-square force and potential energy may be written

$$(12.16) \qquad \mathbf{F} = -m\bar{g}\left(\frac{\bar{r}}{r}\right)^2 \mathbf{L}$$

$$(12.17) \qquad \text{p.e.} = -\frac{m\bar{g}\bar{r}^2}{r}$$

Example 2. Circular Satellite Orbits

For a circular orbit of radius r the equation of motion of a particle subject only to gravity is very simple. The force mg is centripetal, and the acceleration is normal to the path. Using a circle as subscript for speed in a circular path, the normal acceleration is v_0^2/r. Hence

$$mg = \frac{mv_0^2}{r} \quad \text{or} \quad v_0^2 = gr$$

Using the result of Example 1,

(12.18)
$$v_0^2 = \frac{\bar{g}\bar{r}^2}{r} = \bar{v}_0^2 \frac{\bar{r}}{r}$$

The speed $\bar{v}_0$ is the *skimming speed* for an orbit very close to the earth but neglecting friction. Its numerical value, to slide-rule accuracy, is easily computed from $\bar{v}_0 = (\bar{g}\bar{r})^{\frac{1}{2}}$ to be about 17,700 mph. For a satellite at a more realistic altitude, say, about 370 miles, $v_0 = 16,900$. At $r = 239,000$ miles, $v_0 = 3,230$ miles/hour. For circular orbits we have seen that orbital speed varies inversely as the square root of the radius. An observer concerned with the frequency of satellite passages is more interested in the angular speed $\omega = v_0/r$. Using the equations above, we find

(12.19)
$$\omega = \bar{\omega} \left(\frac{\bar{r}}{r}\right)^{\frac{3}{2}}$$

This conclusion is very close, for the special circular case, to Kepler's third law, which is developed in the next section.

Example 3. Escape Speed

Suppose that a projectile subject only to the earth's gravitational force has speed v_1 when its distance from the earth's center is r_1. What speed will it have at distance r_2? As a direct application of energy conservation we may write

$$\tfrac{1}{2}mv_1^2 - \frac{m\bar{g}\bar{r}^2}{r_1} = \tfrac{1}{2}mv_2^2 - \frac{m\bar{g}\bar{r}^2}{r_2}$$

This equation may be solved for any one of the four variables r_1, r_2, v_1, v_2 in terms of the other three. Particularly interesting is the case where v_2 is set equal to zero and r_2 is taken as very large so that the projectile will barely have escaped the earth's pull. For each radial distance r, a corresponding critical or escape speed v_e is determined:

$$\frac{v_e^2}{2} - \frac{\bar{g}\bar{r}^2}{r} = 0$$

or

(12.20)
$$v_e^2 = \frac{2\bar{g}\bar{r}^2}{r} = 2v_0^2$$

So at any given position near the earth, the kinetic energy required for escape is just twice the kinetic energy for a circular orbit. Note that the potential energy at radial distance r may be written

(12.21)
$$\text{p.e.}(r) = -\tfrac{1}{2}mv_e^2$$

Example 4. Effect of Friction on a Circular Orbit

The total energy for a circular orbit is

$$\tfrac{1}{2}mv_0^2 - \tfrac{1}{2}mv_c^2 = -\tfrac{1}{2}mv_0^2 = \frac{-m\bar{g}\bar{r}^2}{2r}$$

If the energy of a satellite is sapped by friction, r must correspondingly grow smaller. By the results of Example 2, this requires that the speed increase.

EXERCISES

8. A space ship at a distance r from the center of the earth requires an initial kinetic energy u to escape from the earth's gravitational field in a free flight. What initial energy would it require in a free flight:
    (a) To double its distance from the center of the earth?
    (b) To establish a circular orbit at a distance r from the center of the earth?
9. The Venusians plan to "liberate" our moon (this is pure supposition). What percentage increase in kinetic energy, as computed relative to the earth, must the moon experience in order to make its escape?
10. How much faster would the earth have to rotate in order that gravity would barely suffice to keep a man on the ground at the equator? State answer in this form: "n times as fast as at present." Assume that the earth's gravitational attraction for the man is as at present.

12.5. PLANETARY MOTION

After arduous study of observed data, Kepler, in the early seventeenth century, enunciated three conclusions about the motion of planets.

I. *The orbit of a planet is an ellipse with the sun as focus.*

II. *The area swept out by the radius from the sun to the planet is traversed at a constant rate.*

III. *The square of the time in which a planet traces out its orbit is proportional to the cube of its mean distance from the sun.*

Newton used these results in arriving at the law of gravitation. In this course we shall reverse the order and see how Kepler's laws are a consequence of the law of gravitation.

Polar Coordinate Equations for Conics. The vectorial approach to the first law leads to a polar coordinate equation of a conic. As a mathematical preliminary let us review this item from analytical geometry. Suppose that in a plane we have given a fixed point **O** called a *focus* and a fixed line λ called a *directrix*. Then any point **R** of the plane has a *focus distance* r, where r is the distance from the focus **O** to the point **R**. The point **R** also has a *directrix distance* y between the point **R** and the line λ. In particular, the focus distance of **O** is 0, and we denote the directrix distance of **O** by d. Now we can define *conic*: for each non-negative constant e (called the *eccentricity* of the conic), the set of points in the plane such that the ratio of focus distance to directrix distance is e is said to constitute the conic of eccentricity e, focus **O**, and directrix λ. Working from this definition it is easy to write an equation for such a conic. Using polar coordinates r (the length of the position vector **R** relative to an origin at the focus as in Fig. 12.7) and θ (measured counterclockwise from a line through **O** parallel to λ), we have

$$y = d + r \sin \theta$$

But by our definition, $r/y = e$; hence $y = r/e$.

Figure
12.7

Substituting and simplifying, $r = ed + er \sin \theta$, or, except when $\sin \theta = 1/e$,

$$r = \frac{ed}{1 - e \sin \theta}$$

The value of r for $\theta = 0°$ is called the *semilatus rectum* of the conic.   When e satisfies $0 \leq e < 1$, the conic is called an ellipse.   When $e = 1$, it is a parabola, and when $e > 1$, it is a hyperbola.

Proof of the First Law.   If in the equation $\mathbf{R} \times \mathbf{V} = \mathbf{H}$ we substitute

$$\mathbf{R} = r\mathbf{L} \quad \text{and} \quad \mathbf{V} = \dot{r}\mathbf{L} + r\dot{\theta}\mathbf{M}$$

and simplify, we get

(12.22) $$\mathbf{H} = r^2\dot{\theta}(\mathbf{L} \times \mathbf{M}) = r^2\dot{\theta}\mathbf{K}$$

The scalar form of this equation,

(12.23) $$h = r^2\dot{\theta}$$

is easily identified as a form of the law of areas:

$$\frac{d}{dt}(\text{area}) = \tfrac{1}{2} r^2\dot{\theta} = \frac{h}{2}$$

The fact that the force acting on a planet of mass m at a distance r from the sun satisfies the usual inverse-square law of gravitation may be expressed thus:

$$\mathbf{F} = -\frac{\gamma mm'}{r^2}\mathbf{L}$$

It follows that the acceleration of a planet at a distance r from the sun is given by

(12.24) $$\dot{\mathbf{V}} = \frac{\mathbf{F}}{m} = -\left(\frac{k}{r^2}\right)\mathbf{L}$$

where in this case $k = \gamma m'$.

Equations (12.22) and (12.24) represent in useful form the information available about central forces and about gravitation.   To get something we can integrate, multiply, member by member, (12.24) by (12.23):

(12.25) $$h\dot{\mathbf{V}} = -k\dot{\theta}\mathbf{L}$$

This may be integrated directly, for we already know that $\dot{\mathbf{M}} = -\dot{\theta}\mathbf{L}$.   We get

(12.26) $$h\mathbf{V} = k(\mathbf{M} + \mathbf{E})$$

where $k\mathbf{E}$, the constant of integration, is a constant vector in the plane of motion. Substituting again for $\mathbf{V}$ in (12.8), we get

$$\mathbf{R} \times \mathbf{V} = \mathbf{H} = r\mathbf{L} \times \frac{k}{h}(\mathbf{M} + \mathbf{E})$$

Hence

(12.27)
$$h\mathbf{K} = \frac{rk}{h}(\mathbf{L} \times \mathbf{M} + \mathbf{L} \times \mathbf{E})$$

The vector product $\mathbf{L} \times \mathbf{E}$ may be evaluated from Fig. 12.8 by using Chap. 9, Exercise 13, or by expanding $(\mathbf{M} \times \mathbf{K}) \times \mathbf{E}$:

$$\mathbf{L} \times \mathbf{E} = (\mathbf{M} \times \mathbf{K}) \times \mathbf{E} = (\mathbf{M} \cdot \mathbf{E})\mathbf{K} - (\mathbf{K} \cdot \mathbf{E})\mathbf{M} = (\mathbf{M} \cdot \mathbf{E})\mathbf{K} = -e \sin \theta \mathbf{K}$$

where e is the magnitude of $\mathbf{E}$.

Since all the vectors are multiples of $\mathbf{K}$, we may rewrite (12.27) as

$$h = \frac{rk}{h}(1 - e \sin \theta)$$

Solving for r, we get

(12.28)
$$r = \frac{h^2/k}{1 - e \sin \theta}$$

which we identify as a conic of eccentricity e. Since planetary orbits are obviously closed, parabolas and hyperbolas can be ruled out. The orbit then has to be an ellipse, as is claimed in Kepler's first law. Later we shall use the results of this derivation for other situations, some of which will require conics other than ellipses.

The significance of $\mathbf{E}$, the constant of integration, can be pictured vividly by applying Eq. (12.28) to Fig. 12.8 for $\theta = -90°$ and $+90°$.

Proof of the Second Law. The second law is precisely the law of areas derived for all central-force fields.

Proof of the Third Law. The period τ of a planet's description of its orbit may be expressed as the area of the orbit divided by the constant rate at which area is swept out. That rate is given in (12.9) as $0.5h$.

(12.29)
$$\tau = \frac{\text{area}}{0.5h}$$

We can use the equation of the orbit to relate h to the mean distance. The mean distance a is defined as the average of the maximum and minimum distances (see Fig. 12.9):

$$a = \tfrac{1}{2}(r_2 + r_1)$$

These extreme differences may be found by putting $\theta = -90°, 90°$ in (12.28),

$$r_1 = \frac{h^2/k}{1+e} \qquad r_2 = \frac{h^2/k}{1-e} \qquad a = \left(\frac{h^2}{k}\right)(1 - e^2)^{-1}$$

so that

(12.30)
$$h = \sqrt{ak(1 - e^2)}$$

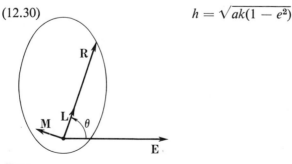

Figure
12.8

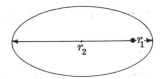

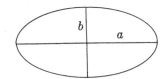

Figure
12.9

The area of the ellipse is πab (b is the semiminor axis) or $\pi a^2 \sqrt{1 - e^2}$; thus (12.29) becomes

$$\tau = \frac{\pi a^2 \sqrt{1 - e^2}}{0.5 \sqrt{ak(1 - e^2)}} = \frac{2\pi a^{\frac{3}{2}}}{k^{\frac{1}{2}}}$$

or

(12.31)
$$\frac{\tau^2}{a^3} = \frac{4\pi^2}{k} = \frac{4\pi^2}{\gamma m'}$$

The right member is the same for every planet; thus the law is proved. The discussion thus far has postulated an unaccelerated sun. Modifications will be suggested in a later section.

EXERCISES

The earth's eccentricity is 0.0167, and the mean distance from the sun is 92.9 million miles.

11. What is the ratio of the maximum to the minimum speed of the earth in its orbit?
12. Saturn takes 29.5 years to complete its orbit. What is its mean distance from the sun?
13. For how many days in the year is the earth's distance from the sun greater than the mean distance?
14. The number of days spent by the planetoid Eros in each quadrant of its elliptical orbit are, respectively, as follows: 138.0, 183.6, 183.6, 138.0. Find the eccentricity of the orbit and the mean distance from the sun. (Take the corresponding distance for the earth as 92.9 million miles.)

12.6. ENERGY CRITERIA FOR ORBITS IN AN INVERSE-SQUARE FIELD

The potential energy of a particle of mass m moving freely under the gravitational influence of a spherical mass m' taken with respect to a point at infinity is

(12.32)
$$\text{p.e.} = -\frac{\gamma m m'}{r} = -\frac{km}{r}$$

Since a field of this type is conservative, the total energy (kinetic plus potential) is constant.

(12.33)
$$\text{t.e.} = \text{k.e.} + \text{p.e.} = \tfrac{1}{2}mv^2 - \frac{km}{r} = \text{const}$$

Note that for this total energy to be zero,

(12.34)
$$v = v_c = \sqrt{\frac{2\gamma m'}{r}} = \sqrt{\frac{2k}{r}}$$

This *critical speed* is the *escape speed*, i.e., the speed which would enable the particle to escape from the influence of the field (compare Sec 12.4, Example 3).

To evaluate v in terms of r we square (12.26) of the preceding section:

$$h^2 \mathbf{V} \cdot \mathbf{V} = k^2(1 + 2\mathbf{M} \cdot \mathbf{E} + e^2)$$
$$= k^2[2(1 + \mathbf{M} \cdot \mathbf{E}) + e^2 - 1]$$

Now $\mathbf{M} \cdot \mathbf{E} = -e \sin \theta$, so, substituting in the previous equation,

$$v^2 = \left(\frac{k}{h}\right)^2 [2(1 - e \sin \theta) + (e^2 - 1)]$$

and now substituting the orbit equation (12.28),

$$v^2 = \left(\frac{k}{h}\right)^2 \left[2\left(\frac{h^2}{kr}\right) + (e^2 - 1)\right]$$
$$= \frac{2k}{r} + \left(\frac{k}{h}\right)^2 (e^2 - 1)$$

or

(12.35)
$$v^2 = v_c^2 + \left(\frac{k}{h}\right)^2 (e^2 - 1)$$

Hence

$$\text{t.e.} = \tfrac{1}{2}m\left[\frac{2k}{r} + \frac{k^2}{h^2}(e^2 - 1)\right] - \frac{km}{r}$$

or

(12.36)
$$\text{t.e.} = \tfrac{1}{2}m\frac{k^2}{h^2}(e^2 - 1)$$

The following conclusions may now be drawn:

If $v > v_c$, then t.e. > 0, $e > 1$, and the orbit is hyperbolic.
If $v = v_c$, then t.e. $= 0$, $e = 1$, and the orbit is parabolic.
If $v < v_c$, then t.e. < 0, $e < 1$, and the orbit is elliptic.

Example. Energy in an Elliptical Orbit

The formula for the total energy in the case of an elliptical orbit may be written, using formula (12.30), as follows:

(12.37)
$$\text{t.e.} = -\frac{km}{2a}$$

This points up the remarkable fact that the total energy in an elliptical orbit based on an inverse-square force depends only on the major axis of the ellipse! Also, it indicates that for a satellite losing energy by friction, the orbit grows smaller (as indicated for circular orbits in Sec. 12.4, Example 4).

EXERCISES

15. A comet has speed 5×10^4 m/sec when at a distance 2×10^{11} m from the sun (mass 2×10^{30} kg).   Will the orbit be elliptic, parabolic, or hyperbolic?
16. What are the maximum and minimum speeds of a parabolic comet whose nearest approach to the sun is 1 million miles?

12.7. APPLICATIONS TO SATELLITE ORBITS

In this section we shall use previous results to determine a few orbit properties having to do with eccentricity. Letting, as in Sec. 12.5, r_1 stand for the radius at perigee (point of closest approach to the earth), r_2 for the radius at apogee, and a the semimajor axis, we can conclude that $r_1 = a(1 - e)$, $r_2 = a(1 + e)$, and hence $e = (r_2 - r_1)/(r_2 + r_1)$. If the corresponding speeds are v_1 and v_2, we know from the law of areas that $v_1 r_1 = v_2 r_2$, and hence that

(12.38)
$$\frac{v_1}{v_2} = \frac{1 + e}{1 - e}$$

We have seen that at each point exterior to the earth a satellite of mass m may be described by r, its distance from the center, v_0, the speed at that point required for a circular orbit, v_c, the speed required for escape, the potential energy $-\frac{1}{2}mv_c^2 = -mv_0^2$. We shall let $(v_0)_1$ denote the speed required for a circular orbit at the point of nearest approach (perigee) and $(v_0)_2$ at apogee. Then, by energy conservation,

$$v_1^2 - 2(v_0)_1^2 = v_2^2 - 2(v_0)_2^2$$

From Sec. 12.4, Example 2, we know that $(v_0)_1^2/(v_0)_2^2 = r_2/r_1 = (1 + e)/(1 - e)$. Eliminating v_2 and $(v_0)_2$, the energy equation just given becomes

$$v_1^2 - 2(v_0)_1^2 = v_1^2\left(\frac{1 - e}{1 + e}\right)^2 - 2(v_0)_1^2\frac{1 - e}{1 + e}$$

which leads to

(12.39)
$$v_1^2 = (1 + e)(v_0)_1^2$$

Similarly,

(12.40)
$$v_2^2 = (1 - e)(v_0)_2^2$$

The preceding relationships throw considerable light on the shape of elliptical orbits. Imagine a projectile at a distance r from the earth's center being given a velocity at right angles to that radius vector. If its kinetic energy is exactly $u_0 = \frac{1}{2}mv_0^2$, where v_0 is the circular orbit speed for r, the orbit is a circle. If it is exactly $2u_0$, the orbit is a parabola. If the kinetic energy is greater than $2u_0$, the orbit is a hyperbola. If the kinetic energy satisfies $u_0 <$ k.e. $< 2u_0$, then the path is elliptical with eccentricity (k.e./u_0) $- 1$. If k.e. $< u_0$, then the orbit is still elliptical, but now the launching point is at apogee rather than perigee and the eccentricity is $1 -$ (k.e./u_0). These conclusions are immediate consequences of the equations just derived, together with results from Sec. 12.6.

As an application of (12.39) and (12.40), consider what happens to the orbit of a satellite, initially in a circular path, which suddenly undergoes a change in speed from v_0 to $v_0(1 - \delta)$, where δ is a small positive fraction. According to one of the relations just derived, the energy having dropped from u_0 to $u_0(1 - \delta)^2$ or approximately $u_0(1 - 2\delta)$, the eccentricity becomes

$$e = 1 - \frac{u_0(1 - 2\delta)}{u_0} = 2\delta$$

Now the speed ratio calculated at the beginning of this section shows that the maximum speed (at perigee) will be equal to $(1 - \delta)v_0(1 + e)/(1 - e)$. But for the new orbit, $e = 2\delta$ and, since δ is small, $(1 - 2\delta)^{-1}$ is approximately $1 + 2\delta$. Hence the new maximum speed is

$$(1 - \delta)v_0(1 + 2\delta)^2, \text{ or approximately } v_0(1 + 3\delta)$$

Thus diminishing the minimum speed of the satellite has the effect of increasing the maximum speed by a larger factor.

EXERCISES

17. Verify the formula $(v_c)_1/(v_c)_2 = [(1 + e)/(1 - e)]^{\frac{1}{2}}$.
18. Verify the formula t.e. $= -\frac{1}{2}m(1 - e)(v_o)_1^2$.
19. Show that for any particular orbit in an inverse-square field the quantity $v^2 - 2v_o^2$ is a constant.

12.8. A PROPERTY OF PLANETARY KINETIC ENERGY

In this section we shall endure a rather arduous calculation for the sake of a result interesting in its own right and also important in certain applications. First, let us note that the kinetic energy of a particle in plane motion can easily be expressed as the sum of a radial term and a transverse term. For

$$\mathbf{V} = \dot{r}\mathbf{L} + r\dot{\theta}\mathbf{M}$$

Therefore

$$\mathbf{V} \cdot \mathbf{V} = \dot{r}^2 + (r\dot{\theta})^2$$

Thus

$$\text{k.e.} = \tfrac{1}{2}m\mathbf{V} \cdot \mathbf{V} = \tfrac{1}{2}m\dot{r}^2 + \tfrac{1}{2}m(r\dot{\theta})^2$$

Writing

(12.41) $$(\text{k.e.})_r = \tfrac{1}{2}m\dot{r}^2 \qquad (\text{k.e.})_t = \tfrac{1}{2}m(r\dot{\theta})^2$$

we shall compare the average values of k.e. and $(\text{k.e.})_t$.

First we look at $\overline{\text{k.e.}}$, defined as

(12.42) $$\overline{\text{k.e.}} = \frac{m}{2\tau} \int_0^\tau v^2 \, dt$$

where τ is the time over which the averaging takes place. For us it will be the period of orbital motion. From (12.23) we get

(12.43) $$dt = \frac{r^2}{h} \, d\theta$$

and using (12.28),

(12.44) $$dt = \frac{(h^3/k^2) \, d\theta}{(1 - e \sin \theta)^2}$$

In Sec. 12.6 a formula for v^2 was obtained equivalent to

(12.45) $$v^2 = \frac{k^2}{h^2} (1 - 2e \sin \theta + e^2)$$

Now let (12.44) and (12.45) be substituted in (12.42):

$$\overline{\text{k.e.}} = \frac{hm}{2\tau} \int_0^{2\pi} \frac{1 - 2e \sin \theta + e^2}{(1 - e \sin \theta)^2} \, d\theta$$

or

$$\overline{\text{k.e.}} = \frac{hm}{2\tau} \int_0^{2\pi} \left[1 + \frac{e^2 \cos^2 \theta}{(1 - e \sin \theta)^2} \right] d\theta$$

Integrating by parts and simplifying, this reduces to

$$\overline{\text{k.e.}} = \frac{hm}{2\tau} \int_0^{2\pi} \frac{d\theta}{1 - e \sin \theta} = \frac{hm}{\tau} \int_{-\pi/2}^{\pi/2} \frac{d\theta}{1 - e \sin \theta}$$

Using the standard substitution $z = \tan \frac{1}{2}\theta$, $d\theta = 2\,dz/(1 + z^2)$, $\sin \theta = 2z/(1 + z^2)$, the integral is readily transformed into

$$\overline{\text{k.e.}} = \frac{2hm}{\tau} \int_{-1}^{1} \frac{dz}{(z - e)^2 + (1 - e^2)} = \frac{2hm}{\tau\sqrt{1 - e^2}} \left[\tan^{-1} \frac{z - e}{\sqrt{1 - e^2}} \right]_{-1}^{1}$$

$$= \frac{2hm}{\tau\sqrt{1 - e^2}} \left[\tan^{-1}\left(\frac{1 - e}{1 + e}\right)^{\frac{1}{2}} + \tan^{-1}\left(\frac{1 + e}{1 - e}\right)^{\frac{1}{2}} \right]$$

$$= \frac{2hm}{\tau\sqrt{1 - e^2}} \frac{\pi}{2} = \frac{\pi hm}{\tau\sqrt{1 - e^2}}$$

Using the fact that for an ellipse

$$b = a\sqrt{1 - e^2}$$

we may write

(12.46) $$\overline{\text{k.e.}} = \frac{\pi hma}{\tau b}$$

The other average is easier to compute:

$$(\overline{\text{k.e.}})_t = \frac{m}{2\tau} \int_0^{\tau} (r\omega)^2 \, dt$$

As in (12.43),

$$r^2\omega = h$$

Therefore

$$(\overline{\text{k.e.}})_t = \frac{hm}{2\tau} \int_0^{\tau} \omega \, dt = \frac{hm}{2\tau} \int_0^{2\pi} d\theta$$

Hence

(12.47) $$(\overline{\text{k.e.}})_t = \frac{\pi hm}{\tau}$$

The main result of this section, valid for any elliptical motion due to an inverse-square law, is contained in the following equation:

(12.48) $$\frac{(\overline{\text{k.e.}})_t}{\overline{\text{k.e.}}} = \frac{b}{a}$$

EXERCISES

20. Show that the average kinetic energy of a planet is given by the formula

$$\overline{\text{k.e.}} = \tfrac{1}{2}m \left(\frac{h}{b}\right)^2$$

21. Use Newton's law for central-force motion to prove that the actual kinetic energy of a planet at the ends of the minor axes of its orbit is equal to the average kinetic energy for the whole orbit.

22. What are the dimensions of h and k?

12.9. MECHANICS OF THE BOHR HYDROGEN ATOM

In many branches of physics it has been found natural and advantageous to explain phenomena in terms of mechanical models. It is not always possible to devise simple models which lead to results verified by experiment. The Bohr theory of the atom was an unusual success, particularly for simpler atoms, because of its simplicity and because of the remarkable agreement between spectrographic data and the results of the theory.   Modern theories of the atom are more complex, but the simple model is still very helpful.   According to this theory the hydrogen atom consists of a "sun" (proton) having a positive electrical charge of 1.60×10^{-19} coulomb and a "planet" (electron) having an equal negative charge.   The mass of the proton is roughly 1,800 times that of the electron; therefore we shall assume the proton to be at rest with the electron coursing about it.

Using Coulomb's law, the force of attraction is (in newtons)

$$(12.49) \qquad \mathbf{F} = \frac{-q^2}{4\pi\epsilon_0 r^2}\mathbf{L} = m\frac{d\mathbf{V}}{dt}$$

where q is the electronic charge and ϵ_0 the permittivity of free space (8.854×10^{-12} farad/m).   This falls at once into the framework of our planetary-motion studies.

$$(12.50) \qquad \frac{d\mathbf{V}}{dt} = -\frac{k}{r^2}\mathbf{L}$$

where

$$k = \frac{q^2}{4\pi\epsilon_0 m}$$

By Sec. 12.5, then, we say immediately that Kepler's laws are obeyed by the electron in its travels around the proton.   The difficulty with this model thus far is that such an atom is a miniature antenna and should, according to the classical theory, radiate energy.   This would be at the expense of potential energy: the electron would spiral into the nucleus.

The first step in the Bohr solution is to suppose that the electron may travel in certain *permissible* orbits without radiating.   These orbits are described by *quantum conditions*.   We shall here take the liberty of stating these conditions in a form that fits the discussion of Sec. 12.8.   Ordinarily action or angular momentum are quantized.   We shall describe orbits as permissible if their *average kinetic energies* satisfy the following two equations.   (Only one quantum number was used in the original theory.)

$$(12.51) \qquad \overline{\text{k.e.}} = \frac{nh}{2\tau}$$

$$(12.52) \qquad \overline{(\text{k.e.})_t} = \frac{n_t h}{2\tau}$$

where n and n_t (not greater than n) are integers known, respectively, as *principal quantum number* and *azimuthal quantum number*. τ is the period of the electron in its orbit. h is Planck's constant (6.62×10^{-34} joule-sec).   From the results of Sec. 12.8, it is apparent that only those ellipses are permissible orbits for which

$$(12.53) \qquad \frac{b}{a} = \frac{n_t}{n} = \sqrt{1 - e^2}$$

Consequently, only certain values of the eccentricity are possible (see Exercise 25), and the axes of the orbits are in whole-number ratios.

The total energy associated with a given orbit is, by (12.36),

$$\text{t.e.} = \tfrac{1}{2}m\frac{k^2}{h^2}(e^2 - 1) = -\tfrac{1}{2}m\frac{k^2}{h^2}\frac{n_t^2}{n^2}$$

Now

$$\overline{(\text{k.e.})}_t = \frac{n_t h}{2\tau} = \frac{\pi h m}{\tau}$$

(from Sec. 12.8); thus, substituting for k its value in (12.50), we have

(12.54)
$$(\text{t.e.})_n = \frac{-mq^4}{8\epsilon_0^2 h^2 n^2}$$

Observe that this value depends on the principal quantum number, but not the azimuthal.

There are, then, according to the Bohr theory, strictly defined permissible orbits in which an electron can remain with constant total energy. The second step in the Bohr theory is the assumption as to what takes place when an electron changes its orbit. When an electron passes from one permissible orbit to another of lower energy, radiation takes place at a frequency v such that the energy loss is precisely hv. It is possible to compute the values of orbital energy to considerable accuracy, and hence to predict those frequencies at which radiation may occur. These computed frequencies check remarkably well with the lines of the hydrogen spectrum. Figure 12.10 shows the relationship between electron transitions for orbits of low quantum number and wavelengths of lines in the hydrogen spectrum. [One angstrom unit (1 A) is equal to 1×10^{-10} m.]

The discovery of the Balmer series, the conclusion that frequencies in such a series can be expressed in the form

$$v = \text{const}\left(\frac{1}{n^2} - \frac{1}{n'^2}\right)$$

and the theoretical confirmation by means of the Bohr theory make a fascinating story. The student is referred to any good elementary text on atomic physics for information of this sort.

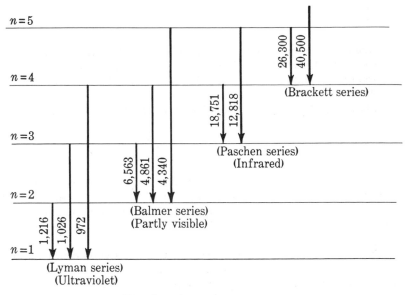

Figure
12.10

(Wavelengths in angstrom units)

EXERCISES

Constants

Mass of electron .... 9.11×10^{-31} kg
Mass of proton .... 1.67×10^{-27} kg
Velocity of light (c)....... 2.998×10^8 m/sec

23. Show that the semiaxes of an electron orbit of principal quantum number n and azimuthal quantum number n_t are

$$a = \frac{n^2 h^2 \epsilon_0}{\pi m q^2} \qquad b = \frac{n n_t h^2 \epsilon_0}{\pi m q^2}$$

24. Compute a in meters for $n = 1$.
25. Complete the following table, where n is the principal quantum number, n_t is the azimuthal quantum number, e is the eccentricity of the orbit, a, b are the semimajor and semiminor axes of the orbit, and a_1, b_1 are these semiaxes for the case $n = 1$.

Orbit	n	n_t	e^2	a/a_1	b/b_1
i	1	1	0	1	1
ii	2	1			
iii	2	2			
iv	3	1			
v	3	2			
vi	3	3			

26. Sketch to scale for a fixed proton the six orbits described in Exercise 25.
27. According to the Bohr theory, radiation takes place at frequency ν given by

$$h\nu = \frac{hc}{\lambda} = (\text{t.e.})' - \text{t.e.}$$

when an electron goes from an orbit of energy (t.e.)′ to one of energy t.e. What should be the wavelength λ of radiation resulting from a transition: (*a*) From orbit v to orbit ii (notation of Exercise 25)? (*b*) From orbit ii to orbit i (notation of Exercise 25)?
28. Show that the period of revolution of an electron in the hydrogen atom is given by

$$\tau = \frac{4n^3 h^3 \epsilon_0^2}{m q^4}$$

29. The mechanical frequency of revolution for principal quantum number n can be computed from the preceding result. Call it f. The frequency of radiation for a transition to the orbit with principal quantum number equal to $n - 1$ is given by the procedure of Exercise 27. Call it ν. Find the ratio f/ν. What is its limit for large n?
30. Show that the quantum conditions used in this section can be expressed in terms of angular momentum; for example, $n_t h = 2\pi m h$.
31. Replot Fig. 12.10 with energy levels spaced to scale.
32. Show that Eq. (12.54) has the form t.e. $= -km/2a$.

12.10. BOMBARDMENT OF HEAVY NUCLEI BY α PARTICLES

The kinetic theory of gases shows atoms to behave like elastic spheres of radius approximately 10^{-10} m. This also is the order of magnitude of inner Bohr orbits. To see how large a part of this space is devoid of mass, attempts were made to probe the atom. Rutherford used α particles the mass of which (6.64×10^{-27} kg) is too great to permit deflections by electrons in the orbits. It was observed that some of these particles when shot through gold foil were deflected through large angles, indicating collision with a massive nucleus. It is our aim to calculate the nearest approach to the center of the atom in terms of the amount that the projectile is deflected. The α particle consists of two protons and two neutrons; therefore its charge is $+2q$. The nucleus of the target atom has a positive charge also denoted by zq, where z is the atomic number (see Fig. 12.11). Using Coulomb's law, the equation of motion is

$$\mathbf{F} = \frac{2zq^2}{4\pi\epsilon_0 r^2}\mathbf{L} = m\frac{d\mathbf{V}}{dt}$$

This is a force of repulsion, but the equation can again be put in the form

(12.55)
$$\frac{d\mathbf{V}}{dt} = -\frac{k}{r^2}\mathbf{L} \qquad k = -\frac{zq^2}{2\pi\epsilon_0 m}$$

Consequently, the orbit is a conic with the target as focus. From the speed equation

$$v^2 = \frac{k^2}{h^2}\left(\frac{2h^2}{kr} + e^2 - 1\right)$$

it is apparent that $e > 1$, since k is negative. The orbit then is *hyperbolic*. Note that the firing speed, taken for $r = \infty$, is

(12.56)
$$v_0 = \frac{-k}{h}\sqrt{e^2 - 1}$$

From the geometry of the hyperbola, it is clear that (see Fig. 12.12)

(12.57)
$$\sqrt{e^2 - 1} = \cot\frac{\varphi}{2}$$

where φ is the angle of deflection, and that

$$p = ae\cos\frac{\varphi}{2} = a\sqrt{e^2 - 1}$$

By Newton's law for central forces,

(12.58)
$$h = pv_0 = av_0\sqrt{e^2 - 1}$$

Eliminating h between (12.56) and (12.58), we get

(12.59)
$$a = -\frac{k}{v_0^2}$$

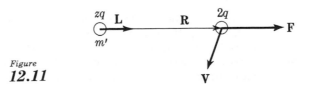

Figure
12.11

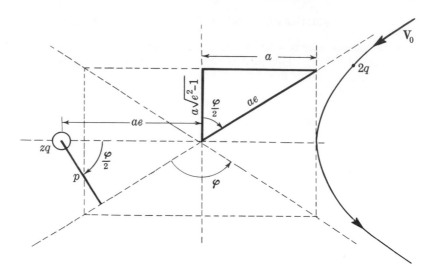

Figure
12.12

Hence, substituting the value for k in (12.55),

(12.60)
$$a = + \frac{zq^2}{2\pi\epsilon_0 mv_0^2}$$

The distance of nearest approach to the nucleus is (see Fig. 12.12)

(12.61)
$$d = a + ae = a\left(1 + \csc\frac{\varphi}{2}\right)$$

As φ approaches $180°$, d approaches a minimum. Actual angles of scattering up to $150°$ were observed when α particles of speed $0.064c$ (c denotes speed of light) were used with gold ($z = 79$). For these values,

$$d = \frac{zq^2[1 + \csc(\varphi/2)]}{2\pi\epsilon_0 mv_0^2} = \frac{79(1.6 \times 10^{-19})^2(1 + 1.04)}{2\pi(8.854 \times 10^{-12})(6.64 \times 10^{-27})(0.064)^2(9 \times 10^{16})}$$

$$= 3.0 \times 10^{-14} \text{ m}$$

This result showed the relative emptiness of the atom and thus made the Bohr theory seem more tenable.

EXERCISES

33. Prove that

$$\tan\frac{\varphi}{2} = \frac{zq^2/4\pi\epsilon_0 p}{\frac{1}{2}mv_0^2}$$

34. In the numerical case worked out in the preceding section, what is the speed of the α particle at the point of deepest penetration? After its escape from the nucleus?

35. What is the eccentricity of the orbit of an α particle deflected through $90°$?

36. A hyperbolic comet passes close enough to the sun to have its course changed by $60°$. What is the maximum percentage change in speed?

12.11. THE TWO-BODY PROBLEM

In the examples of central fields examined thus far, the center was assumed to be a fixed point. This assumption was justified by the comparatively large mass of the sun, the hydrogen nucleus, and the gold nucleus. We now consider, particularly for the gravitational case, the consequences of removing this restriction. This constitutes the famous "problem of two bodies," which was solved by Newton. The system of two particles is subjected to no external forces; therefore the center of mass $\bar{\mathbf{R}}$ experiences no acceleration. Let $\bar{\mathbf{R}}$ be the origin (see Fig. 12.13). Then the equations of motion are

$$\frac{d\mathbf{V}_1}{dt} = -\frac{\gamma m m'}{m r^2}\mathbf{L}$$

and

$$\frac{d\mathbf{V}_2}{dt} = \frac{\gamma m m'}{m' r^2}\mathbf{L}$$

where

$$r = r_1 + r_2 = r_1 + \frac{m}{m'}r_1$$

so, for the particle of mass m, for instance,

$$\frac{d^2\mathbf{R}_1}{dt^2} = -\frac{\gamma m'}{[1 + m/m']^2 r_1^2}\mathbf{L}$$

Similarly for the other particle. Hence
    (12.62) *Each of the particles describes a conic with $\bar{\mathbf{R}}$ as focus.*
    In contemplating planetary motion, we are more interested in motion with respect to the sun:

(12.63) $$\frac{d\mathbf{V}}{dt} = \frac{d}{dt}(\mathbf{V}_1 - \mathbf{V}_2) = \frac{d\mathbf{V}_1}{dt} - \frac{d\mathbf{V}_2}{dt} = -\frac{\gamma(m + m')}{r^2}\mathbf{L}$$

This is to be compared with previous result (12.24):

$$\frac{d\mathbf{V}}{dt} = -\frac{\gamma m'}{r^2}\mathbf{L} = -\frac{k}{r^2}\mathbf{L}$$

It is apparent that Kepler's third law must now be written with $k = \gamma(m + m')$.

(12.64) $$\frac{\tau^2}{a^3} = \frac{4\pi^2}{k} = \frac{4\pi^2}{\gamma(m + m')}$$

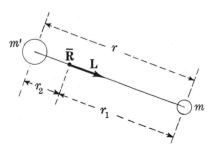

Figure
12.13

In the case of the Bohr hydrogen atom, a similar adjustment is made.   From

$$\frac{d\mathbf{V}_1}{dt} = -\frac{q^2}{4\pi\epsilon_0 m r^2}\mathbf{L}$$

and

$$\frac{d\mathbf{V}_2}{dt} = \frac{q^2}{4\pi\epsilon_0 m' r^2}\mathbf{L}$$

we get

$$\frac{d\mathbf{V}}{dt} = \frac{d\mathbf{V}_1}{dt} - \frac{d\mathbf{V}_2}{dt} = -\frac{q^2}{4\pi\epsilon_0 r^2}\left(\frac{1}{m} + \frac{1}{m'}\right)\mathbf{L} = -\frac{q^2}{4\pi\epsilon_0 r^2}\left(\frac{1}{\mu}\right)\mathbf{L}$$

where μ is the *reduced mass* of the satellite. μ should be substituted for m in the formulas derived for the hydrogen atom.   The theory of α particle scattering for light nuclei would be equally appropriate here.   The other examples have been elected because of their relative simplicity.

EXERCISES

37.   If the mass of the earth were equal to that of the sun, the relative orbit being as at present, how long would a year be?

38.   Compute the reduced mass of the planetary electron in the hydrogen atom.

39.   Two particles have masses m_1 and m_2.   Their center of mass has velocity $\bar{\mathbf{V}}$.   Prove that

$$\frac{\bar{\mathbf{V}}}{\mu} = \frac{\mathbf{V}_1}{m_2} + \frac{\mathbf{V}_2}{m_1}$$

40.   Two particles collide elastically (coefficient of restitution is 1).   The x axis is normal to the surface of contact.   Show that the amount of energy gained by one particle and lost by the other is equal to $2\mu\bar{v}_x(v_{2_x} - v_{1_x})$, where $\bar{v}_x$ is the x component of the velocity of the center of mass.

REVIEW EXERCISES

41.   Two particles have masses m_1 and m_2.   Let their velocities be $\mathbf{V}_1$ and $\mathbf{V}_2$ and their velocities relative to their center of mass be $\mathbf{V}_1'$ and $\mathbf{V}_2'$.   Letting $\mathbf{V}_r = \mathbf{V}_1 - \mathbf{V}_2$, derive the equations

$$m_1\mathbf{V}_1' = \mu\mathbf{V}_r \qquad \mathbf{V}_1 = \bar{\mathbf{V}} + \left(\frac{\mu}{m_1}\right)\mathbf{V}_r$$

State and prove analogous equations for $\mathbf{V}_2'$ and $\mathbf{V}_2$.

42.   Between the moon and the earth is a null point where the gravitational fields due to earth and moon just cancel each other.   How high is this point above the surface of the moon?   With what speed would an object falling from rest at the null point strike the moon?   The diameter of the moon is 2,163 miles.   Its mass is 0.0123 times that of the earth.   Its distance from the earth is 239,000 miles.

43.   The derivation of Eq. (12.28) is invalid when $\sin\theta = 1/e$.   What sort of physical limitation, if any, is involved here?

44.   The mean translational kinetic energy of a molecule of a gas at temperature θ is $\frac{1}{2}m\bar{v}^2 = \frac{3}{2}k\theta$, where $\bar{v}$ is the root mean square (rms) speed, k is the Boltzmann constant 1.38×10^{-23} joule/deg, and θ is the absolute temperature.   At what temperature would the rms speed of oxygen equal the escape speed at the surface of the earth?

45.   A particle subject to a force $\mathbf{F(R)}$ toward $\mathbf{O}$ describes an ellipse with *center* $\mathbf{O}$.   If $\mathbf{A}$ and $\mathbf{B}$ are position vectors as shown in Fig. 12.14, show that $|\mathbf{F(A)}|/|\mathbf{F(B)}| = a/b$.

Figure
12.14

46. Show that the total energy (p.e. + k.e., with p.e. $= 0$ at $r = \infty$) for:
     (a) A vertical trajectory attaining height h is $-\frac{1}{2}mv_c^2$ (where v_c is evaluated at the top of the orbit).
     (b) A circular orbit at height h is $-\frac{1}{4}mv_c^2$.
47. At an altitude h a satellite is given a horizontal speed 10 per cent greater than the speed v_0 for that point. What is the eccentricity of the resulting orbit?
48. The *orbit* of a moving particle is the curve traced by the position vector $R(t)$. The *hodograph* of the same particle is the curve for which the position vector is the velocity $V(t)$ of the particle. For inverse-square central motion we have seen that the orbit is a conic. Show that the corresponding hodograph is a circle of radius k/h. Show in a diagram how a selection of velocity vectors for an elliptical orbit fit such a circle.
49. Show that Proposition (12.7) is valid relative to a point Q (not the center of mass), provided that the acceleration vector for Q is directed toward (or away from) the center of mass throughout the interval.
50. In Exercise 41 show that $V_1' \times V_2' = O$.
51. Prove that a satellite in an elliptical orbit has, at the end of its minor axis, exactly enough speed for a circular orbit through that point.
52. Show that the speed of a planet at a distance r from the sun is given by $v^2 = k(2/r - 1/a)$, where a is the mean distance.
53. An alpha particle is scattered by a heavy nucleus through an angle of 60°. Find the maximum percentage change of speed which the particle experiences. Include full details of your analysis of the problem and of the computation.
54. A particle P travels in an elliptical orbit with the center of the force field at the focus F.
     For the position shown in Fig. 12.15 the polar coordinates of P are

$$r = 6 \times 10^7 \text{ miles} \qquad \theta = 60°$$

and the speed $v_1 = 2 \times 10^3$ mph. The velocity vector V_1 is parallel to the major axis of the ellipse.

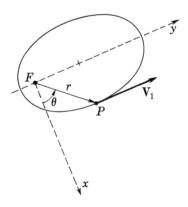

Figure
12.15

(a) According to the law of areas, area is swept out at a constant rate. Evaluate this rate in square miles per hour.

(b) How does the speed v_1 compare with the maximum speed for the orbit? (State answer as a percentage.)

55. The orbit around the earth of Lunik III had altitude (above the earth's surface) at perigee of 25,500 miles. Its period was 15.3 days. (Compare the moon: mean distance 239,000 miles, period 27.3 days.) Use Kepler's three laws to compute further information about the orbit: mean distance from the center of the earth, eccentricity, areal speed, maximum orbital speed, distance at apogee, minimum orbital speed.

56. A free projectile passes to one side of the moon (mass of moon: 7.35×10^{22} kg, mean radius of moon: 1.74×10^6 m). In the position of nearest approach the projectile is 4.00×10^5 m above the surface of the moon traveling horizontally at 2,850 m/sec. For this situation Eq. (12.35) is to be applied. Compute numerical values in mks units for:

      (a) k.   (d) e.

      (b) h.   (e) The angle of scattering if a hyperbola; the maximum distance above the moon's surface if an ellipse.

      (c) v_c.   (f) The minimum speed.

The gravitational constant γ may be taken as 6.67×10^{-11} mks units.

57. According to Poincaré's model, the Milky Way is a uniform spherical cluster of sparsely distributed stars. This means that a star at a distance r from the center of the galaxy is attracted toward the center with a gravitational force determined by the distance r and the mass in the sphere of radius r.

(a) Show that stars in this cluster move on elliptical paths with the center of the galaxy *at the center of each ellipse*.

(b) Show that stars in circular orbits move with an angular speed which is *independent of the size of the circle*. Show that this angular speed may be written $(\gamma m/\rho^3)^{\frac{1}{2}}$, where ρ and m are the radius and mass of the galaxy and γ is the gravitational constant given in the preceding exercise.

58. Give a detailed derivation, starting from first principles, of Proposition (12.7).

CHAPTER THIRTEEN

RIGID-BODY KINEMATICS

Our study of motion has to date been limited to objects behaving like particles or swarms of particles. Among the various types of particle aggregates the rigid bodies are of particular interest and importance. Many of the objects of engineering or of the physics laboratory are regarded as rigid bodies whenever deformations can be neglected: wheels, pistons, lenses, ladders, and various vehicles. Furthermore, we treat reference frames as rigid bodies, so any systematic study of particle motion relative to moving frames necessitates an understanding of the motion of rigid bodies.

13.1. TRANSLATION AND ROTATION OF A RIGID BODY

The motion even of a rigid body at first seems to offer a variety of complexities. It is easy to imagine twistings and spiralings which appear far from simple. In this section let us study briefly motions that are admittedly simple though distinctly important. We shall regard the motion of a rigid body as completely specified at any instant if we can compute the velocity and the position of every point of the body. In the simplest motion, *translation*, this is easily done. For *in translation, all points have identical velocities at any given time*. Suppose that $\mathbf{P}$ is a reference point in the body and $\mathbf{R}$ is any other representative point of the body (see Fig. 13.1). Then the formula for $\mathbf{V}$ at any time is simply

$$(13.1) \qquad\qquad \mathbf{V} = \mathbf{V}_P$$

Both members of this equation are functions of time; thus $\mathbf{V}$ may have any pattern already studied for a single point. Over any time interval any two points of a body in translation have the same displacement. Thus the simplifying fact of translation is that the paths traced out by different points are geometrically congruent (see Fig. 13.2). It follows that the orientation of the body is constant under translation. For instance, a steady compass needle set to rotate freely about a vertical axis maintains a fixed orientation even when carried along a curved path. This is an example of curvilinear translation. More frequently encountered is motion along a straight path without change of orientation.

The second elementary motion of a rigid body is motion with one line of the body (or rigid extension thereof) fixed. Such motion is called *rotation*. For the fixed line the velocity of every point is, of course, zero. The motion of the body as a whole is best described in terms of angular displacements. Let us take the fixed line as, say, the z axis and consider the section of the body cut out by the xy plane. Let $\mathbf{P} = p \underline{/\theta}$ be a typical point of this section (see Fig. 13.3). Then θ may be thought of as a function of the time as the body rotates, it being understood that the axes do not rotate. If an angular displacement $\Delta\theta$ takes place during the time interval Δt, then the quotient $\Delta\theta/\Delta t$ is the average or *effective angular speed*. The instantaneous angular speed ω is defined by the equation

$$(13.2) \qquad \omega = \lim_{\Delta t \to 0} \frac{\Delta\theta}{\Delta t} = \frac{d\theta}{dt} = \dot\theta$$

It is left for Exercise 7 to show that ω is independent of the choice of $\mathbf{P}$.

Similarly, the rate of increase of angular speed, the scalar *angular acceleration*, is defined by

$$(13.3) \qquad \alpha = \frac{d\omega}{dt} = \omega\frac{d\omega}{d\theta}$$

These equations are entirely analogous to (5.46) and (5.47) concerning rectilinear motion. The corresponding variables are seen at once to be x and θ, v and ω, a and α, t and t.

Example I

A wheel initially rotating at 120 rpm is subject to a deceleration given by $\alpha = -0.5\omega^2$. How long will it take for the wheel to halve its speed?

Solution

It is given that $d\omega/dt = -0.5\omega^2$, and initially

$$\omega = 4\pi \text{ rad/sec}$$

Integrating, we get

$$t = \int_0^t dt = \int_{4\pi}^{2\pi} \frac{d\omega}{-0.5\omega^2} = \frac{2}{\omega}\Big|_{4\pi}^{2\pi} = \frac{1}{2\pi} = 0.16 \text{ sec}$$

As is illustrated in Fig. 13.3, just as an application of the usual definition of the radian measure of an angle, $s = p\theta$. Since the perpendicular radius p is constant, successive differentiation yields similar relations between the angular velocity and the curvilinear speed of the point $\mathbf{P}$ as well as between the angular acceleration and

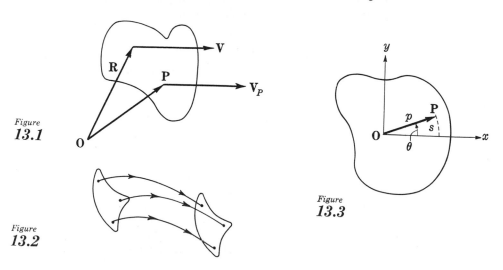

Figure
13.1

Figure
13.2

Figure
13.3

the tangential acceleration of **P**. These equations, listed below, enable one to compute the speed and acceleration imparted to each point of a rigid body by its rotation around a fixed axis.

(13.4) $p\dot\theta = \dot s$ or $\omega p = v$

(13.5) $p\dot\omega = \dot v$ or $\alpha p = a_T$

Example 2

At a given moment a rigid body rotating about a fixed axis has an angular velocity of 2 rad/sec and an angular acceleration of 3 rad/sec². Find the magnitude of the total acceleration of a point of the body situated 20 cm from the axis of rotation.

Solution

$$a_T = p\alpha = 20 \times 3 = 60 \text{ cm/sec}^2$$

$$a_N = \frac{v^2}{\rho} = \frac{(20 \times 2)^2}{20} = 80 \text{ cm/sec}^2$$

Thus $\mathbf{A} = 60\mathbf{T} + 80\mathbf{N}$ and $a = 100$ cm/sec².

EXERCISES

1. State and derive for θ and ω equations relating them to α and t subject to the assumption that α is constant.

2. A wheel rotates according to the pattern $\theta + 4\alpha = 0$. Assuming that ω is equal to zero when $\theta = 1$ rad, what is the maximum angular speed, and how soon is it attained?

3. A wheel uniformly accelerated changes from a counterclockwise rotation at 10 rad/sec to a clockwise rotation of 10 rad/sec in 2 min. What is the angular acceleration and the effective angular speed for this time interval?

4. The angular speed of a wheel varies according to $\omega = 2\theta^{\frac{1}{2}}$. What is the time required for a displacement from $\theta = 4$ to $\theta = 9$ rad? What is the angular acceleration?

5. A wheel rotates according to the law $\alpha = 3t^2 - 2t$. If it starts rotating at 2 rad/sec, through what angle will it turn in the first 2 sec?

6. An angular rotation is subject to a deceleration given by $\alpha = -3\omega$. Through how great an angle does the wheel turn as the angular speed diminishes from 20 to 10 rad/sec?

7. Show that ω in (13.2) is independent of the choice of **P**.

8. A particle travels from rest about a circle of radius 3 cm at an angular speed given by $\omega = 3t$ rad/sec. Through what angle must it move before the total acceleration has magnitude 15 cm/sec²?

9. The wheel of a gyroscope which is 2 ft in radius is spinning about its fixed axis at the rate of 1,000 rpm. What is the total acceleration of a point on the outside rim of the wheel?

10. A particle travels around a circle of radius 10 ft with an angular acceleration of 3 rad/sec². At the moment when its angular speed is 2 rad/sec, what are the magnitude and direction of its acceleration vector? Draw a circle to show direction.

11. Prove that in any motion of a rigid body the velocities of any pair of points have equal components in the direction of the line joining them.

$$\left[\text{HINT}: \frac{d}{dt}(\mathbf{R} \cdot \mathbf{R}) = 0\right]$$

13.2. ANGULAR VELOCITY AS A VECTOR

In the preceding section the angular speed of rotation about an axis was defined. We define now an associated *angular velocity vector* $\boldsymbol{\Omega}$ (see Fig. 13.4) directed along the axis of rotation (the z axis) in the sense given by the right-hand rule and of magnitude ω; thus

(13.6) $\mathbf{\Omega} = \omega\mathbf{K}$

Just as in Sec. 5.8 we omitted the $\mathbf{I}$ in all equations, so in Sec. 13.1 it was not a disadvantage to deal with ω rather than $\mathbf{\Omega}$.   But even in the simple case of a fixed axis of rotation vectors may be used to get expressions of helpful generality.

Taking our origin $\mathbf{O}$ on the axis of rotation, let $\mathbf{R}$ be the position vector of a representative point in the body as in Fig. 13.5. Let $\mathbf{\Omega}$ denote the instantaneous angular velocity. $\mathbf{V}$ will denote the instantaneous velocity of the point $\mathbf{R}$. Now consider the vector product $\mathbf{\Omega} \times \mathbf{R}$. Its magnitude is $\omega r \sin \phi$, which we recognize as the speed of $\mathbf{R}$. The direction of $\mathbf{\Omega} \times \mathbf{R}$, perpendicular to the plane of $\mathbf{\Omega}$ and $\mathbf{R}$, is that of $\mathbf{T}$, the unit tangent vector for the circular path traced out by the point $\mathbf{R}$. Our conclusion is then

(13.7) $\mathbf{V} = \mathbf{\Omega} \times \mathbf{R}$

This is a very vital kinematic formula. It should be understood, of course, that calling the rotation axis the z axis was merely a matter of convenience. Any fixed axis might be the rotation axis.

Vector Addition of Angular Velocities. One feels uneasy about representing quantities by vectors unless one has ascertained that, at least under favorable circumstances (such as concurrence for forces), the quantities combine like vectors—by the parallelogram rule. At first glance it is not at all obvious that angular velocities can reasonably be combined in this way. As a heuristic approach to this question let us suppose that a rigid body instantaneously has angular velocity $\mathbf{\Omega}_1 = \omega_1\mathbf{I}$ about the x axis and $\mathbf{\Omega}_2 = \omega_2\mathbf{J}$ about the y axis. This effect could, for instance, be obtained by rotating a spinning wheel and its support about an axis perpendicular to the spin axis. Let us compute the resulting behavior of the point $\mathbf{R} = (x,y)$ in the xy plane. Because of rotation about the x axis, it has an upward velocity $\omega_1 y\mathbf{K}$; because of rotation about the y axis the velocity is $-\omega_2 x\mathbf{K}$. We have (for instance, in Sec. 5.4) already accepted the vector nature of linear velocity, so at once we add to get

$$\mathbf{V} = (\omega_1 y - \omega_2 x)\mathbf{K}$$

but this is precisely equal to

$$\mathbf{\Omega} \times \mathbf{R} = (\omega_1\mathbf{I} + \omega_2\mathbf{J}) \times (x\mathbf{I} + y\mathbf{J})$$

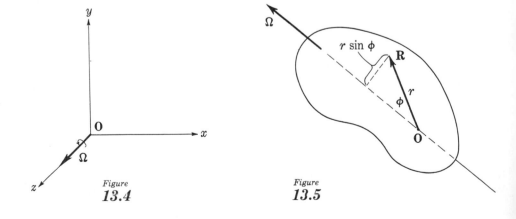

Figure
13.4

Figure
13.5

so that the instantaneous velocity of every point of the plane is equal to that for the rotation associated with the vector $\boldsymbol{\Omega}$ determined by

$$\boldsymbol{\Omega} = \boldsymbol{\Omega}_1 + \boldsymbol{\Omega}_2$$

The derivation just outlined brings us close to the facts, but it is too long, on the one hand, and insufficiently general, on the other.   Referring now to Fig. 13.6, let us consider a general vector treatment.   The equations only are given, since the main intentions of the argument are the same as before.

$$\mathbf{V} = \mathbf{V}_1 + \mathbf{V}_2 = \boldsymbol{\Omega}_1 \times \mathbf{R} + \boldsymbol{\Omega}_2 \times \mathbf{R} = (\boldsymbol{\Omega}_1 + \boldsymbol{\Omega}_2) \times \mathbf{R}$$

In other words, the behavior of an arbitrary point $\mathbf{R}$ is precisely that which would be induced by a rotation $\boldsymbol{\Omega}$ given by

$$\boldsymbol{\Omega} = \boldsymbol{\Omega}_1 + \boldsymbol{\Omega}_2$$

In Chap. 2 we saw how linear displacements add as vectors.   In Sec. 5.4 we saw that velocities add as vectors.   The above equation $\mathbf{V} = \mathbf{V}_1 + \mathbf{V}_2$ can be interpreted as a sum of a frame velocity plus a relative velocity by attaching a frame of velocity $\mathbf{V}_1$ to the point $\mathbf{R}$ and then regarding $\mathbf{V}_2$ as a velocity relative to that frame.   The roles of $\mathbf{V}_1$ and $\mathbf{V}_2$ can of course be reversed.   We can therefore conclude that infinitesimal angular displacements add as vectors:

$$\boldsymbol{\Omega} \, dt = \boldsymbol{\Omega}_1 \, dt + \boldsymbol{\Omega}_2 \, dt$$

But angular displacements do not in general add according to the parallelogram rule.   To convince yourself of this fact place a square sheet of printed cardboard initially in the first quadrant of the xy plane.   Rotate it first through 90° about the x axis (into the xz plane).   Then rotate it 90° about the y axis (into another quadrant of the xz plane).   If these angular displacements added as vectors, a rotation of 127.3° about the line $x = y$ would have produced the same effect.

Example.   Components of the Earth's Angular Velocity Vector

Another evidence of the vector nature of angular velocity is found in the local rotation of the earth's surface.   Suppose that during the short time interval Δt the earth turns about its axis through an angle $\Delta\theta$.   This means that meridian circle a in Fig. 13.7 turns into the position previously occupied by circle b.   At a latitude λ

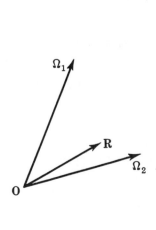

Figure
13.6

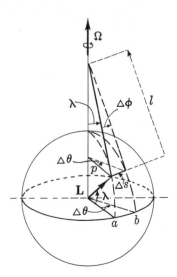

Figure
13.7

how much of this rotation is experienced as a rotation? From the diagram it is clear that the direction of north (tangent to the meridian) has changed by an angle $\Delta\phi$. This is a rotation about an axis which is vertical at the point under consideration. For small enough angles, the arc Δs will do for determining the radian measure of either $\Delta\phi$ or $\Delta\theta$. Thus

$$\Delta\theta = \frac{\Delta s}{p} \qquad \Delta\phi = \frac{\Delta s}{l}$$

Hence

$$\frac{\Delta\phi}{\Delta\theta} = \frac{p}{l} = \sin\lambda = \cos(90° - \lambda)$$

Consequently,

$$\frac{\Delta\phi}{\Delta t} = \frac{\Delta\theta}{\Delta t}\cos(90° - \lambda)$$

or in the limit, as Δt approaches zero,

$$\frac{d\phi}{dt} = \frac{d\theta}{dt}\cos(90° - \lambda)$$

Otherwise expressed,

(13.8) $\omega_\lambda = \mathbf{\Omega} \cdot \mathbf{L}$

This is the desired result, for it shows that the local rotation is the component in that direction of the total angular velocity vector. Furthermore, this effect can be checked experimentally by means of a Foucault pendulum. The theory of this type of pendulum is given in Chap. 14.

EXERCISES

12. A rigid body rotates at 100 rad/sec about an axis with direction cosines $(0.707, 0, -0.707)$. With respect to an origin on the axis, the point **P** at a given instant has coordinates (3,4,5). Find the magnitude and direction cosines of the velocity of **P**. It is understood that the reference axes do not rotate but are fixed.

13. With respect to a fixed origin in a rigid body, point **A** of the body has coordinates (2,0,1) ft and velocity vector $-\mathbf{I} + \mathbf{J} + 2\mathbf{K}$ ft/sec. **B**, a point in the yz plane, has velocity $2\mathbf{J} + 2\mathbf{K}$ ft/sec. Find the direction cosines of the instantaneous axis of rotation, the angular speed, and the coordinates of **B**.

14. What is the angular speed due to the earth's rotation about a vertical axis of a field at latitude 45°N?

13.3. ANGULAR VELOCITY AS AN OPERATOR FOR DIFFERENTIATION

We have already seen how, for a position vector **R**, the rate of change induced by rotation about a fixed axis is given by

(13.9) $\dfrac{d\mathbf{R}}{dt} = \mathbf{\Omega} \times \mathbf{R}$

This relationship has far wider application than at first appears. Let the vector **B** (drawn from **P** to **Q** in Fig. 13.8) be any vector fixed in a rigid body. Let us compute the rate of change of **B** due to rotation of the body about a fixed axis:

$$\frac{d\mathbf{B}}{dt} = \frac{d}{dt}(\mathbf{Q} - \mathbf{P}) = \frac{d\mathbf{Q}}{dt} - \frac{d\mathbf{P}}{dt}$$

But both **P** and **Q** are vectors drawn from a point on the axis of rotation; thus (13.9) is applicable.   Therefore

$$\frac{d\mathbf{B}}{dt} = \boldsymbol{\Omega} \times \mathbf{Q} - \boldsymbol{\Omega} \times \mathbf{P}$$

Now using the distributive law for vector products, we get the desired result

$$\frac{d\mathbf{B}}{dt} = \boldsymbol{\Omega} \times (\mathbf{Q} - \mathbf{P}) = \boldsymbol{\Omega} \times \mathbf{B}$$

(13.10) *Any vector* **B**, *constant with respect to a rigid body which is rotating with an angular velocity* $\boldsymbol{\Omega}$, *has induced by the rotation a rate of change given by*

$$\frac{d\mathbf{B}}{dt} = \boldsymbol{\Omega} \times \mathbf{B}$$

Both the symbols d/dt and $\boldsymbol{\Omega} \times$ can be regarded as *operators* acting on suitable vectors.   When d/dt "operates" on the vector **B**, the result is the vector $d\mathbf{B}/dt = \dot{\mathbf{B}}$. When $\boldsymbol{\Omega} \times$ acts on **B**, the result is the vector $\boldsymbol{\Omega} \times \mathbf{B}$.   An operator is said to be *linear* if the result of operating on a linear combination of vectors is the same linear combination of the results of the operator's acting on the given vectors.   This is more easily expressed in symbols.   If L is a linear operator, then

$$L(c\mathbf{A} + d\mathbf{B}) = cL(\mathbf{A}) + dL(\mathbf{B})$$

where c and d are any scalars, **A** and **B** are any suitable vectors, and $L(\mathbf{A})$ is the result of applying the operator L to the vector **A**, etc.   Clearly, d/dt and $\boldsymbol{\Omega} \times$ are both linear operators, for

$$\frac{d}{dt}(c\mathbf{A} + d\mathbf{B}) = c\frac{d\mathbf{A}}{dt} + d\frac{d\mathbf{B}}{dt}$$

$$\boldsymbol{\Omega} \times (c\mathbf{A} + d\mathbf{B}) = c(\boldsymbol{\Omega} \times \mathbf{A}) + d(\boldsymbol{\Omega} \times \mathbf{B})$$

Proposition (13.10) may be considered as a conclusion about operators acting on vectors constant relative to a rigid body.   This conclusion may be written symbolically thus:

(13.11)
$$\frac{d}{dt} = \boldsymbol{\Omega} \times$$

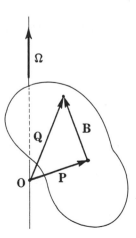

Figure
13.8

Acceleration due to Rotation. As an application of (13.10), we shall find an expression for the acceleration of the point **R** of Fig. 13.5 for the case where $\boldsymbol{\Omega}$ is constant. The velocity vector **V** is then constant with respect to the body; thus

$$\mathbf{A} = \frac{d\mathbf{V}}{dt} = \boldsymbol{\Omega} \times \mathbf{V} = \boldsymbol{\Omega} \times (\boldsymbol{\Omega} \times \mathbf{R})$$

Here you must recall that we have adopted the convention of using the same symbol for a point as for its position vector.

For the sake of completeness, we shall include cases where $\boldsymbol{\Omega}$ is not constant. For this we need to define a *vector angular acceleration*, denoted by $\mathfrak{A}$ (read as capital alpha),

(13.12)
$$\mathfrak{A} = \frac{d\boldsymbol{\Omega}}{dt}$$

In the present case $\boldsymbol{\Omega}$ varies only in magnitude, since **K** is constant. Differentiating (13.6), we get

$$\mathfrak{A} = \frac{d}{dt}(\omega\mathbf{K}) = \frac{d\omega}{dt}\mathbf{K} = \alpha\mathbf{K}$$

Now let us differentiate (13.7) in order to find an acceleration formula:

$$\mathbf{A} = \frac{d\mathbf{V}}{dt} = \frac{d}{dt}(\boldsymbol{\Omega} \times \mathbf{R}) = \mathfrak{A} \times \mathbf{R} + \boldsymbol{\Omega} \times \mathbf{V}$$

or

(13.13)
$$\mathbf{A} = \mathfrak{A} \times \mathbf{R} + \boldsymbol{\Omega} \times (\boldsymbol{\Omega} \times \mathbf{R})$$

The student should convince himself that for circular motion Eq. (5.42) specializes to an equation equivalent to (13.13). In particular, the second term of (13.13) is the centripetal acceleration.

Example. Precession

Figure 13.9 shows a gyroscope rotating with angular velocity

$$\boldsymbol{\Omega} = \omega\mathbf{E}$$

Suppose now that **E** rotates with an angular velocity $\boldsymbol{\Omega}'$. Then we have $\boldsymbol{\Omega}$ varying in direction. The angular acceleration, according to (13.12), is

$$\mathfrak{A} = \frac{d}{dt}(\omega\mathbf{E}) = \frac{d\omega}{dt}\mathbf{E} + \omega\frac{d\mathbf{E}}{dt}$$

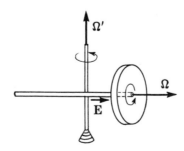

Figure
13.9

Since **E** is a vector of constant length, we can apply (13.10):

$$\frac{d\mathbf{E}}{dt} = \mathbf{\Omega}' \times \mathbf{E}$$

Thus

(13.14) $\mathfrak{A} = \alpha\mathbf{E} + \mathbf{\Omega}' \times \mathbf{\Omega}$

EXERCISES

15. A body rotates around the z axis uniformly at 20 rad/sec. Find the velocity and acceleration vectors for the point $\mathbf{I} - 2\mathbf{J} + 3\mathbf{K}$ ft.
16. A gyro rotating at a speed of 1,000 rad/sec about the x axis precesses about the y axis at 3 rad/sec. Find the angular acceleration vector.
17. For a particle in plane motion whose position vector is $\mathbf{R} = r\mathbf{L}$, show that the velocity vector may be written

$$\mathbf{V} = \frac{dr}{dt}\mathbf{L} + \mathbf{\Omega} \times \mathbf{R}$$

18. **B** is any vector of constant length. Prove or disprove the statement: If **B** varies in direction, then for an infinite number of vectors $\mathbf{\Omega}$, one can write

$$\frac{d\mathbf{B}}{dt} = \mathbf{\Omega} \times \mathbf{B}$$

13.4. VELOCITY PATTERNS FOR A RIGID BODY

In Chap. 5 we have learned how at every instant to assign to a moving point or particle a velocity vector relative to a given reference frame. A body, rigid or deformable, is regarded as an aggregate of such particles. Hence, at each instant, the motion of such a body is represented by an array of velocity vectors. This array of velocity vectors, one for each point in the body, we shall refer to as a *velocity pattern*. Later on (Chap. 17) the mathematical nature of vector patterns will be looked into: there we might say that velocity is a function of position or that the velocity pattern constitutes a vector field. The simplest velocity pattern for a body is that for a body at rest relative to the given frame of reference. Then every velocity vector is a null vector.

   In Sec. 13.1 we examined two elementary motions of a rigid body. Translation has a velocity pattern in which all the vectors are equal. Figure 13.10a shows such a pattern for a selection of points of a wheel in translation. A translation pattern can be summarized by a single equation,

$$\mathbf{V} = \mathbf{V}_L$$

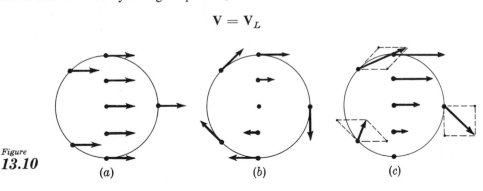

Figure
13.10
          (a)   (b)   (c)

where $\mathbf{V}_P$ is the velocity of any representative point $\mathbf{P}$. The equation expresses the fact that *every* point has the same velocity as $\mathbf{P}$. When a rigid body rotates about a fixed axis, an entirely different velocity pattern results. For a wheel rotating about a fixed axis the pattern can be summarized by an equation of the form

$$\mathbf{V} = \mathbf{\Omega} \times \mathbf{R}$$

This shows that every point has a velocity vector at right angles to its position vector relative to a point on the fixed axis, its magnitude satisfying the elementary relation (13.4). Part of such a pattern is shown in Fig. 13.10*b*, which represents a wheel rotating about a fixed axis.

   We now turn to less circumscribed motions of a body. Any single point of a rigid body may have an arbitrarily complicated motion. It can dash and spiral along any sort of trajectory. But once the motion of such a single point has been specified, the very fact that the body is rigid places stringent limitations on the motions attainable by other points of the body. Let us examine mathematically the limitations placed on velocity patterns by the condition of rigidity. Relative to an origin $\mathbf{O}$ in a definite reference frame, let $\mathbf{P}$ and $\mathbf{Q}$ be the position vectors of two points of the body as in Fig. 13.11. If the body is rigid, the distance between these points remains constant during the motion. Hence we may write

$$(\mathbf{Q} - \mathbf{P}) \cdot (\mathbf{Q} - \mathbf{P}) = \text{const}$$

Differentiating and simplifying, this yields

(13.15) $$(\mathbf{Q} - \mathbf{P}) \cdot \mathbf{V}_P = (\mathbf{Q} - \mathbf{P}) \cdot \mathbf{V}_Q$$

This equation is readily interpreted: The velocities of $\mathbf{P}$ and $\mathbf{Q}$ have equal components in the direction of the segment between them. This probably is not an unexpected result since it merely indicates that in a rigid body points cannot fly apart or together. It remains to ask how complicated such a pattern may become. The answer is gratifyingly simple: The most complicated possible velocity pattern for a rigid body can always be regarded as a rotation superimposed on a translation. In the succeeding sections this proposition will be demonstrated. It is illustrated in Fig. 13.10*c*.

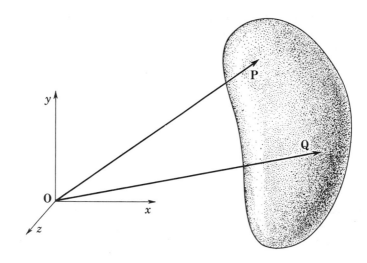

Figure
13.11

19. Let us define a rigid body as one for which the distance between any two points is a constant. Let the origin **O** be a point of the body, and let **P** and **Q** be any other points of the body. Prove that the scalar product **P · Q** is a constant.

20. A, B, and C are points of a rigid body. These three points form a triangle. For a velocity pattern such that $\mathbf{V}_A = \mathbf{V}_B = \mathbf{V}_C = \mathbf{V}$, prove that every point on the segment AB has velocity **V**.

21. For the pattern described in Exercise 20, prove that every point inside the triangle ABC has velocity **V**.

22. For the pattern described in Exercise 20, prove that every point inside the body has velocity **V**.

13.5. VELOCITY PATTERNS AND REFERENCE FRAMES

In Sec. 5.4 we studied velocities relative to a moving reference frame, our principal conclusion being stated in Eq. (5.17):

$$\mathbf{V} = \mathbf{V}_f + \mathbf{V}'$$

Suppose that a reference frame with origin **O′** is moving in translation relative to our "fixed" or laboratory frame. Then, by (13.1), for every point,

$$\mathbf{V}_f = \mathbf{V}_{O'}$$

so that the velocity pattern of a body viewed from the moving frame is related to the corresponding pattern as seen from the laboratory frame by

(13.16) $$\mathbf{V}' = \mathbf{V} - \mathbf{V}_{O'}$$

This provides an easy way to go from one pattern to another for the same state of motion.

In particular, suppose that **O′** is picked as a point of the body itself (see Fig. 13.12). The moving frame will still be in translation; i.e., its axes will always have the same direction relative to the laboratory frame. For this particular frame it is clear that the pattern must have one simplifying aspect: the vector assigned to **O′**

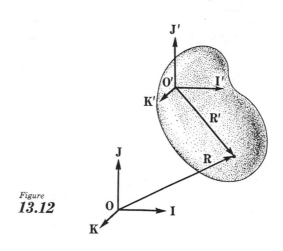

Figure
13.12

must be null. This is easy to see if one thinks about what the velocity of $\mathbf{O}'$ in the new frame really is. It also follows from (13.16):

$$\mathbf{V}'_{O'} = \mathbf{V}_{O'} - \mathbf{V}_{O'} = \mathbf{O}$$

For any body, then, rigid or not, the most complicated velocity pattern is a translation pattern superimposed on a pattern having at least one null vector.

EXERCISE

23. Show graphically the sort of pattern which one gets by superimposing [according to Eq. (5.17)] the two velocity patterns in the xy plane given by (a) $\mathbf{V}_R = 6\mathbf{I}$ and (b) $\mathbf{V}_R = \mathbf{K} \times (\mathbf{R} - 2\mathbf{J})$. Use the same scale for both distance and speed. In particular, what are the coordinates of the single point in the plane having null velocity?

13.6. MOTION OF A RIGID BODY WITH ONE POINT FIXED

We now consider what sort of velocity pattern is instantaneously possible for a rigid body having one point at rest. We wish to show that there must be a unique vector $\mathbf{\Omega}$ such that the whole pattern is described by (13.7),

$$\mathbf{V} = \mathbf{\Omega} \times \mathbf{R}$$

where it is understood that the origin for position vectors is the fixed point itself. Relative to this frame of reference consider any two points $\mathbf{P}$ and $\mathbf{Q}$. Since the body is rigid, we know, as in Sec. 13.4, not only that $(\mathbf{P} - \mathbf{Q})^2$ is a constant, but also that $\mathbf{P} \cdot \mathbf{P}$ and $\mathbf{Q} \cdot \mathbf{Q}$ are constants. It follows easily (cf. Exercise 19) that

(13.17) $$\mathbf{P} \cdot \mathbf{Q} = \text{const}$$

By differentiating and rearranging, we get

(13.18) $$\mathbf{V}_P \cdot \mathbf{Q} = -\mathbf{V}_Q \cdot \mathbf{P}$$

This is an example of an *anticommutative operation* on $\mathbf{P}$ and $\mathbf{Q}$, one in which permuting variables cause a change in sign. Like all such operations, when the variables are equal, the operation yields a null result,

(13.19) $$\mathbf{V}_P \cdot \mathbf{P} = \mathbf{O}$$

for any point $\mathbf{P}$ of the body.

Let us now suppose that we are confronted with a particular velocity pattern such that $\mathbf{V}_O = \mathbf{O}$. Let N denote the set of points $\mathbf{R}$ for which $\mathbf{V}_R = \mathbf{O}$. N is not empty, for $\mathbf{O}$ is in it. We assume that the body is not at rest, so it is possible to pick a point $\mathbf{A}$ not on N. Applying (13.18) to $\mathbf{A}$ and any point $\mathbf{R}$ of N, we get

(13.20) $$\mathbf{V}_A \cdot \mathbf{R} = -\mathbf{V}_R \cdot \mathbf{A} = 0$$

This shows that N is contained in the plane through $\mathbf{O}$ having $\mathbf{V}_A$ as normal (compare Sec. 2.12, Example 6). By (13.19) $\mathbf{A}$ lies on this plane. Since we deal with a three-dimensional body, we can find a point $\mathbf{B}$ not on the plane, and hence with a non-null velocity $\mathbf{V}_B$.

(13.21) $$\mathbf{V}_B \neq \mathbf{O} \qquad \mathbf{V}_A \cdot \mathbf{B} \neq 0$$

We now are in a position to express the vector $\mathbf{\Omega}$ for which we seek. Since N lies in the plane through the origin with $\mathbf{V}_A$ as normal and also, by the same argument, in the plane through the origin with $\mathbf{V}_B$ as normal, it lies in the line of intersection of the two planes, and hence is perpendicular to both their normals. Thus, if a suitable vector $\boldsymbol{\Omega}$ exists, it must be parallel to $\mathbf{V}_A \times \mathbf{V}_B$. Let us inquire whether every point on the line of intersection is at rest. Let $\mathbf{C} = k\mathbf{V}_A \times \mathbf{V}_B$ be such a point. That the three vectors $\mathbf{A}$, $\mathbf{B}$, $\mathbf{C}$ are independent is apparent geometrically, but should be proved algebraically in Exercise 25. We now show that $\mathbf{V}_C \cdot \mathbf{A} = 0$, $\mathbf{V}_C \cdot \mathbf{B} = 0$, $\mathbf{V}_C \cdot \mathbf{C} = 0$, so that, by (9.27), $\mathbf{V}_C = \mathbf{O}$. First, using the anticommutative property,

$$\mathbf{V}_C \cdot \mathbf{A} = -\mathbf{V}_A \cdot \mathbf{C} = -\mathbf{V}_A \cdot k\mathbf{V}_A \times \mathbf{V}_B$$

The last member vanishes because of the repeated factor $\mathbf{V}_A$. Similarly,

$$\mathbf{V}_C \cdot \mathbf{B} = -\mathbf{V}_B \cdot \mathbf{C} = -\mathbf{V}_B \cdot k\mathbf{V}_A \times \mathbf{V}_B = 0$$

Also $\mathbf{V}_C \cdot \mathbf{C} = 0$ by (13.19). We can conclude, then, that the set N of points instantaneously at rest consists exactly of the points on the line through $\mathbf{O}$ parallel to $\mathbf{V}_A \times \mathbf{V}_B$.

We proceed to show that a suitable vector $\boldsymbol{\Omega}$ is in fact given by

$$(13.22) \qquad \boldsymbol{\Omega} = \left(\frac{1}{\mathbf{V}_A \cdot \mathbf{B}}\right)(\mathbf{V}_A \times \mathbf{V}_B) = \left(\frac{1}{\mathbf{V}_B \cdot \mathbf{A}}\right)(\mathbf{V}_B \times \mathbf{V}_A)$$

The equality of these two expressions for $\boldsymbol{\Omega}$ follows at once from the anticommutative property (13.18).

One must now ascertain whether this vector $\boldsymbol{\Omega}$ has the desired property set forth in (13.7). Let us try it on $\mathbf{A}$ and $\mathbf{B}$. Are the relations

$$(13.23) \qquad \boldsymbol{\Omega} \times \mathbf{A} = \mathbf{V}_A \qquad \boldsymbol{\Omega} \times \mathbf{B} = \mathbf{V}_B$$

actually true? These relations may be verified directly by substituting (13.22). If you then expand the expressions using the basic identity for vector triple products (9.24) along with the previous relations of this section, you should have no difficulty in checking these equations. Details are left as Exercise 26.

We can so far conclude that, for points $\mathbf{A}$ and $\mathbf{B}$, the vector $\boldsymbol{\Omega}$ plays the stipulated role. This is not enough, for $\boldsymbol{\Omega}$ was defined in terms of these points. Let us again pick a third point $\mathbf{C}$ such that $\mathbf{C} = k'\boldsymbol{\Omega}$. As before, the three vectors $\mathbf{A}$, $\mathbf{B}$, $\mathbf{C}$ are independent. Then, according to the results of Sec. 9.7, *any* vector $\mathbf{R}$ can be expressed as a linear combination of $\mathbf{A}$, $\mathbf{B}$, $\mathbf{C}$:

$$\mathbf{R} = s_1\mathbf{A} + s_2\mathbf{B} + s_3\mathbf{C}$$

for the right scalars s_1, s_2, s_3. Differentiating with respect to t,

$$\mathbf{V}_R = s_1\mathbf{V}_A + s_2\mathbf{V}_B + s_3\mathbf{V}_C$$

Query: Why are the s's constant? We have seen that $\mathbf{V}_C = \mathbf{O}$, and it is obvious that $\boldsymbol{\Omega} \times \mathbf{C} = \mathbf{O}$ since $\boldsymbol{\Omega}$ and $\mathbf{C}$ are parallel. Hence we have

$$\mathbf{V}_R = s_1\boldsymbol{\Omega} \times \mathbf{A} + s_2\boldsymbol{\Omega} \times \mathbf{B} + s_3\boldsymbol{\Omega} \times \mathbf{C}$$

Rearranging,

$$\mathbf{V}_R = \boldsymbol{\Omega} \times (s_1\mathbf{A} + s_2\mathbf{B} + s_3\mathbf{C}) = \boldsymbol{\Omega} \times \mathbf{R}$$

We have previously seen that such an equation typifies the velocity pattern for a rigid rotation. We can then conclude:

(13.24) *Any velocity pattern of a rigid body with one point instantaneously at rest is a rotation about an axis through that point.*

Example

In the case of a precessing gyro, for instance, the motion might be thought of as two rotations superimposed or as a single instantaneous rotation about an axis between the spin axis and the precession axis as in Fig. 13.13.

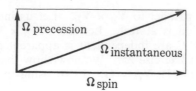

Figure
13.13

One bit of business is still unfinished. At the beginning of this section we started to look for a *unique* vector Ω. Our defining equation for Ω was stated in terms of A and B. Suppose we had chosen A' and B' instead, and thus had been led to a vector Ω' which had the desired properties. Then we could write for all points R:

$$V_R = \Omega' \times R$$

From the equation $\Omega \times R = \Omega' \times R$ we cannot immediately conclude that $\Omega = \Omega'$. No such cancellation law is valid. It would be just as reasonable to claim $B = B'$ in (9.8). The desired conclusion is not elusive, however. Rewriting (13.22),

$$V_A \times V_B = (V_A \cdot B)\Omega$$

But

$$V_B = \Omega' \times B$$

So

$$V_A \times V_B = V_A \times (\Omega' \times B) = (V_A \cdot B)\Omega' - (V_A \cdot \Omega')B$$

The second term vanishes, for

$$V_A \cdot \Omega' = \Omega' \times A \cdot \Omega' = 0$$

Hence

$$V_A \times V_B = (V_A \cdot B)\Omega = (V_A \cdot B)\Omega'$$

and canceling the scalar $V_A \cdot B$, which by (13.21) is not zero, we get

$$\Omega = \Omega'$$

Uniqueness may also be demonstrated by use of Chap. 9, Exercise 37*a*.

EXERCISES

24. Give further examples of anticommutative operations:
   (*a*) At least two from arithmetic or scalar algebra.
   (*b*) At least two from vector algebra.
25. Show that the three vectors A, B, C selected in this section are independent.
26. Verify (13.23) by direct substitution, expansion, etc.

13.7. GENERAL MOTION OF A RIGID BODY

If the results of Secs. 13.5 and 13.6 are combined, one has the final conclusion that any rigid-body motion is instantaneously a rotation superimposed on a translation. Hence the velocity pattern for any rigid-body motion may always be summarized by an equation like the following:

(13.25) $$V_R = V_{O'} + \Omega \times R'$$

The vector addition in the right member symbolizes the point-by-point superposition of two velocity patterns, one translational and the other rotational.

In the preceding paragraph $\mathbf{O}'$ is any reference point of the body itself.   Relative to $\mathbf{O}'$ the position vector $\mathbf{R}'$ of a typical point $\mathbf{R}$ is given by $\mathbf{R}' = \mathbf{R} - \mathbf{O}'$, as in Fig. 13.14.   Thus (13.25) actually means

$$(13.26) \qquad \mathbf{V}_R = \mathbf{V}_{O'} + \boldsymbol{\Omega} \times (\mathbf{R} - \mathbf{O}')$$

If we pick a different point $\mathbf{O}''$ of the body as reference point, we may use

$$(13.27) \qquad \mathbf{V}_R = \mathbf{V}_{O''} + \boldsymbol{\Omega} \times (\mathbf{R} - \mathbf{O}'')$$

The surprising thing about this new equation is that the same $\boldsymbol{\Omega}$ is used as appeared in (13.26).   Linear velocities for a rigid body usually vary from point to point.   But at each instant the body has a single unique angular velocity.   This may be seen by substituting $\mathbf{O}''$ for $\mathbf{R}$ in Eq. (13.26) and then subtracting the result term by term from (13.26).

This unique angular velocity vector $\boldsymbol{\Omega} = \omega\mathbf{E}$ determines a direction with respect to which the velocity pattern has peculiar properties.   It follows immediately from (13.26) that

$$(13.28) \qquad \mathbf{V}_R \cdot \mathbf{E} = \mathbf{V}_{O'} \cdot \mathbf{E}$$

In words,

(13.29) *All velocity vectors of a velocity pattern which is possible for a rigid body have equal components in the direction of the angular velocity vector.*

Of course, if $\boldsymbol{\Omega} = \mathbf{O}$, $\mathbf{E}$ is not specified, but in that case, according to (13.25), we have translation, and hence (13.28) is valid for any unit vector $\mathbf{E}$.

The components perpendicular to $\boldsymbol{\Omega}$ also are somewhat restricted, as will next appear.   The equation

$$(13.30) \qquad \mathbf{R} = \mathbf{O}' + s\mathbf{E}$$

for a scalar parameter s is an equation for the line through $\mathbf{O}'$ parallel to $\boldsymbol{\Omega}$ (see Fig. 13.15).   (Compare Appendix 2, Sec. A2.1.)

Substituting for $\mathbf{R}$ in (13.26) the expression just given, one concludes:

$$\mathbf{V}_R = \mathbf{V}_{O'}$$

That is, all points on this line have the same velocity!   This is equally true for any line drawn in the body parallel to $\boldsymbol{\Omega}$.   In other words,

(13.31) *A rigid body may be instantaneously regarded as a bundle of rigid lines each of which is in translation.*

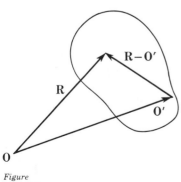

Figure
13.14

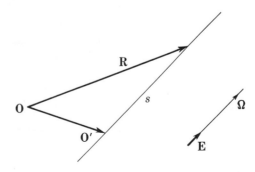

Figure
13.15

Again the proposition is trivially correct if $\mathbf{\Omega} = \mathbf{O}$, but we shall assume in what follows that $\mathbf{\Omega} \neq \mathbf{O}$, so that $|\mathbf{\Omega}| \equiv \omega \neq 0$.

It may happen that one such line is at rest, as in the case of rotation about a fixed axis. If no points are at rest, there is always one line moving parallel to $\mathbf{\Omega}$. This line is the *axis* of the motion. To prove this let us start by assuming it, and hence ascertaining where such an axis must be if it exists. Then we can check on its properties. According to (13.31), it seems reasonable to consider only one point on each line of the bundle, so consider a plane section (see Fig. 13.16) normal to $\mathbf{\Omega}$ through whatever $\mathbf{O}'$ we happen to be using. *If* there is a point $\mathbf{C}$ of this plane whose velocity is parallel to $\mathbf{\Omega}$, one would have

$$\mathbf{E} \times \mathbf{V}_C = \mathbf{O}$$

or, by (13.26),

$$\mathbf{E} \times [\mathbf{V}_{O'} + \mathbf{\Omega} \times (\mathbf{C} - \mathbf{O}')] = \mathbf{O}$$

Expanding, we get

$$\mathbf{E} \times \mathbf{V}_{O'} + [\mathbf{E} \cdot (\mathbf{C} - \mathbf{O}')]\mathbf{\Omega} - (\mathbf{E} \cdot \mathbf{\Omega})(\mathbf{C} - \mathbf{O}') = \mathbf{O}$$

But $\mathbf{C} - \mathbf{O}'$ lies in a plane normal to $\mathbf{E}$, so $\mathbf{E} \cdot (\mathbf{C} - \mathbf{O}') = 0$. Writing $\mathbf{E} \cdot \mathbf{\Omega} = \omega$, we get

$$(13.32) \qquad \mathbf{C} = \mathbf{O}' + \frac{\mathbf{E} \times \mathbf{V}_{O'}}{\omega}$$

Note that the magnitude of $\mathbf{E} \times \mathbf{V}_{O'}$ is equal to the component of $\mathbf{V}_{O'}$ normal to $\mathbf{\Omega}$. This formula gives us a definite point in the plane as long as $\omega \neq 0$. When ω approaches zero, $\mathbf{C}$ gets farther from $\mathbf{O}'$.

Now let us compute the velocity of $\mathbf{C}$ to make sure that it is indeed parallel to $\mathbf{\Omega}$. By (13.26), again,

$$\mathbf{V}_C = \mathbf{V}_{O'} + \mathbf{\Omega} \times \left(\frac{\mathbf{E} \times \mathbf{V}_{O'}}{\omega}\right)$$

or

$$(13.33) \qquad \mathbf{V}_C = (\mathbf{E} \cdot \mathbf{V}_{O'})\mathbf{E}$$

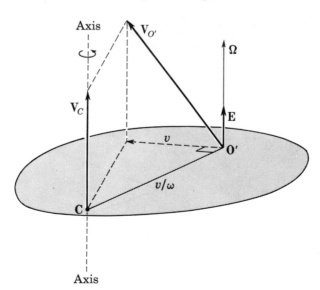

Figure
13.16

Axis

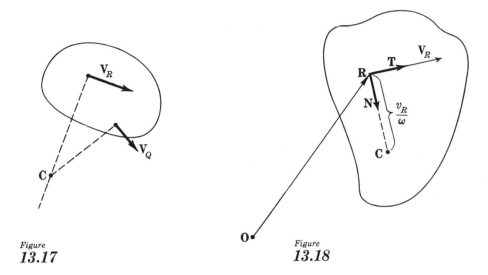

Figure
13.17

Figure
13.18

This gives us the desired check. From this result, together with (13.29), we may conclude:

(13.34) *Any rigid body motion is instantaneously either a translation* $(\mathbf{\Omega} = \mathbf{O})$, *a rotation* $(\mathbf{\Omega} \cdot \mathbf{V}_{O'} = 0$, *so that* $\mathbf{V}_C = \mathbf{O})$, *or a spiraling motion about the axis given by* (13.32).

In the second case, where $\mathbf{\Omega} \cdot \mathbf{V}_{O'} = 0$, the motion is, by (13.28), instantaneously parallel to any plane with $\mathbf{\Omega}$ as normal. In each normal plane $\mathbf{C}$ is called the *instantaneous center of rotation*. An equation for $\mathbf{C}$ has been developed in (13.32). Thus, from any point of the plane $\mathbf{R}$ whose velocity is known, we can draw a line perpendicular to its velocity vector (see Fig. 13.17), since $\mathbf{E} \times \mathbf{V}_R$ is perpendicular to $\mathbf{V}_R$. If two such lines intersect, $\mathbf{C}$ is determined. Otherwise one may measure off the distance v_R/ω from $\mathbf{R}$. The latter interpretation appears vividly if we write (see Fig. 13.18)
$$\mathbf{V}_R = v_R\mathbf{T} \qquad \mathbf{\Omega} = \omega\mathbf{E} \qquad \mathbf{E} \times \mathbf{T} = \mathbf{N}$$

Then substitution in (13.32) gives as a working formula

(13.35)
$$\mathbf{C} = \mathbf{R} + \frac{\mathbf{E} \times v_R\mathbf{T}}{\omega} = \mathbf{R} + \frac{v_R}{\omega}\mathbf{N}$$

In summary,

(13.36) *Any plane motion of a rigid body can instantaneously be analyzed as either a translation or as a rotation about an instantaneous axis.*

Example 1

The velocity pattern for a wheel rolling without slipping in Fig. 13.10 showed clearly that the instantaneous axis of rotation is the contact axis at the ground. In the light of the ideas of this section it is interesting to note that all the velocity vectors are perpendicular to the line to this center $\mathbf{C}$ (in the plane of the wheel) and also that they are in length proportional to their distance from the center $\mathbf{C}$.

Example 2

A wheel of radius 1.5 ft (see Fig. 13.19) spinning at 2.5 rad/sec moves forward at only 2 ft/sec. Where is the instantaneous center of rotation? What is the speed of the points at the ends of horizontal and vertical diameters?

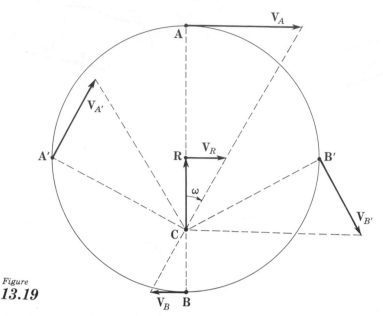

Figure
13.19

Solution

The velocity of the center point **R** is known. By Eq. (13.35) the distance from **R** to **C** is $v_R/\omega = 2/2.5 = 0.8$. Hence the position of **C** is approximately as shown in the figure. The angle labeled ω is a measure of the angular speed. Since ω is the same for all points of the body, any velocity vector drawn to scale at the corresponding point subtends the same angle ω. Thus, for example, in Fig. 13.19, the dashed lines show how velocity vectors are constructed at **A** and **B**, **A′** and **B′**. Note that, once **C** has been located, the velocity pattern is the usual one for rotation with **C** as center.

Numerical values of the speed are computed using **R** as reference point. For example, for **B′**, taking conventional **I, J, K**,

$$\mathbf{V}_R = 2\mathbf{I} \qquad \mathbf{\Omega} = -2.5\mathbf{K} \qquad \mathbf{B'} - \mathbf{R} = 1.5\mathbf{I}$$

$$\mathbf{V}_{B'} = \mathbf{V}_R + \mathbf{\Omega} \times (\mathbf{B'} - \mathbf{R}) = 2\mathbf{I} - 2.5\mathbf{K} \times 1.5\mathbf{I} = 2\mathbf{I} - 3.75\mathbf{J} \qquad \text{ft/sec}$$

which agrees with the graphical result in Fig. 13.19.

EXERCISES

27. Draw diagrams showing for several representative points how Eq. (13.25) adequately describes velocities of points on a wheel rolling without slipping (*a*) when **O′** is taken as the point instantaneously at the rear end of the horizontal diameter and (*b*) when **O′** is taken as the point instantaneously in contact with the ground.

28. A wheel of 30-in. diameter spins at 60 rad/sec while the vehicle advances at 30 mph. Find instantaneous velocities for points at the ends of the horizontal and vertical diameters.

29. A propeller of length 10 ft rotates at 1,000 rpm while being moved in the direction of its axis at 100 ft/sec. Find the speed of a point near the end of the propeller.

30. An automobile wheel is braked so that the velocity vector of the uppermost point is parallel to that of the lowest point and twice as large. Find the velocities of the points at the ends of a horizontal diameter.

31. The center of a wheel of diameter 4 ft rotating about the z axis moves in the x direction at 20 ft/sec. At the same moment the leading point of the wheel has a speed of 35 ft/sec. What is the angular speed?

32. Find the instantaneous axis of rotation for the wheel of Exercise 28.

33. Find the instantaneous center of rotation for the wheel of Exercise 30.

34. A ladder resting on a horizontal floor and against a vertical wall makes an angle of 60° with the horizontal. If it starts to slip, where is the instantaneous axis of rotation?

35. The center of a wheel of radius 2 ft rotating about the z axis moves in the x direction at 10 ft/sec. The lowest point of the wheel moves twice as fast in the opposite direction. Find the instantaneous center.

REVIEW EXERCISES

36. At a given moment the point Q of a rigid body has velocity zero. Prove that the velocity of any other point P of the body satisfies the equation

$$\mathbf{V}_P \cdot \mathbf{P} = \mathbf{V}_P \cdot \mathbf{Q}$$

where $\mathbf{P}$ and $\mathbf{Q}$ are position vectors with respect to an arbitrary origin.

37. $\mathbf{M}$ is the mid-point of the segment $\mathbf{AB}$, all three being points of a rigid body. $\mathbf{A}$ has velocity $10\mathbf{J}$, $\mathbf{B}$ has velocity $-4\mathbf{J}$. What is the velocity of $\mathbf{M}$? Prove your result.

38. A wheel of radius 6 in. rolls without slipping around the outside of a fixed circle also of radius 6 in. How many complete trips per second must it make in order that the angular speed of the wheel be 20 rad/sec?

39. A wheel of radius 1 in. rolls without slipping around the inside of a fixed circle of radius 1 ft twice a second. What is the angular speed of the small wheel?

40. A rigid body rotates at angular speed

$$\omega = 3t^2 - 2t$$

about a fixed axis whose direction cosines are $(0.6, -0.8, 0.0)$. Relative to an origin on this axis, a point $\mathbf{R}$ of the body has at time $t = 2$ sec the position $\mathbf{R} = 7\mathbf{I} - \mathbf{J}$. For that moment find for the point $\mathbf{R}$ the magnitude and direction cosines of

(a) $\mathbf{V}$.   (b) $\mathbf{T}$.   (c) $\mathbf{A}$.   (d) $\mathbf{N}$.

41. A particle travels around a circle of radius 10 ft with an angular acceleration of 3 rad/sec². At the moment when its angular speed is 2 rad/sec, what are the magnitude and direction of its acceleration factor? (Draw a diagram to show direction.)

42. The angular displacement from equilibrium, θ, of a torsion pendulum follows the pattern of simple harmonic motion:

$$\theta = \theta_m \sin \omega t$$

If the amplitude of such an oscillation is 0.82 rad and the period is 3.58 sec:
(a) What is the maximum angular speed?
(b) What is the angular displacement when the angular speed is one-fourth of the maximum?

43. A wheel of diameter 2 ft rolls along horizontal ground, slipping. The center of the wheel has velocity of $+5\mathbf{I}$ ft/sec (i.e., parallel to the positive x axis which is horizontal). The point in contact with the ground has velocity $+3\mathbf{I}$ ft/sec.
(a) What is the angular speed?
(b) What in $\mathbf{IJK}$ form is the velocity of the uppermost point of the wheel? (Take y axis as vertical, upward.)
(c) What is the speed of the foremost point of the wheel (i.e., of the forward end of the horizontal diameter)?

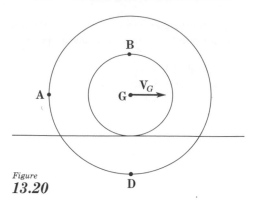

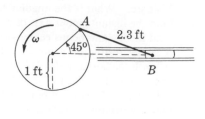

Figure
13.20

Figure
13.21

44. The hub of a wheel has a diameter which is equal to the radius of the wheel. This hub rolls without slipping along a horizontal track as indicated in Fig. 13.20. The velocity vector of the center **G** is drawn to scale.

(a) Copy the figure approximately, and draw to the same scale velocity vectors for the points **A**, **B**, **D**. Show how the construction is carried out.

(b) The equation $\mathbf{V}_R = \mathbf{V}_A + \boldsymbol{\Omega} \times (\mathbf{R} - \mathbf{A})$ is valid for any point **R** of the wheel. To illustrate this at **G** in the diagram, draw to scale the vectors $\mathbf{V}_A$ and $\boldsymbol{\Omega} \times (\mathbf{G} - \mathbf{A})$.

45. A discus is thrown with a velocity whose horizontal and vertical components are initially **80I** and **40J** ft/sec, respectively. In addition, the discus spins with a constant angular velocity given by

$$\boldsymbol{\Omega} = 120(2\mathbf{J} + \mathbf{K}) \qquad \text{rad/sec}$$

At the time $t = 1$ sec, what in **IJK** form is the velocity of the point of the discus 4 in. behind the center, measured horizontally (i.e., in the negative x direction)?

46. A wheel of radius 10 in. rolls, skidding, on a horizontal plane surface. Its center travels at 2 ft/sec while the wheel spins at 3 rad/sec. Which points of the wheel instantaneously have a vertical velocity?

47. What is the instantaneous center of rotation for the wheel described in Exercise 43?

48. A spinning disk moves in the xy plane. At the moment when the center of the disk happens to be at the origin, the point $(-5,0)$ ft has velocity $4\mathbf{I} + 2\mathbf{J}$ ft/sec and the disk has angular velocity $-2\mathbf{K}$ rad/sec.

(a) What is the velocity at the same instant of the point of the disk at the origin?

(b) The instantaneous center of rotation is (x,y). Find x and y.

49. **B** is any vector of constant length. Prove that, for the vector $\boldsymbol{\Omega}$, given by

$$\boldsymbol{\Omega} = \frac{\mathbf{B} \times (d\mathbf{B}/dt)}{\mathbf{B} \cdot \mathbf{B}}$$

it is true that $\boldsymbol{\Omega} \times \mathbf{B} = d\mathbf{B}/dt$.

50. Derive and interpret a formula for acceleration analogous to (13.25).

51. Find the instantaneous center of rotation for the connecting rod AB in Fig. 13.21 for the position shown.

52. The paddle wheel of an excursion steamer rotates at 25 rpm while the ship moves at 4 mph. How far and in what direction from the axis of the wheel is the instantaneous axis of rotation?

53. The loci of instantaneous axes and centers of rotation are an interesting subject, often pursued in studies in kinematics. Find the locus as viewed from a fixed set of axes (*space centrode*) and the locus as viewed from axes fixed in the moving body (*body centrode*) of the center of rotation of the ladder described in Exercise 34. Note that the motion can be described as the rolling of the body centrode on the space centrode.

CHAPTER FOURTEEN

RELATIVE MOTION
of a PARTICLE

Descriptions of motion are based on reference frames. Usually, we have assumed a preferred reference frame so that statements about displacement, velocity, or acceleration were unambiguous. Occasionally, as in Sec. 5.4, in Exercise 109 of Chap. 7, and in Sec. 13.5, we have compared motions as observed from different reference frames. Each such frame may be regarded as a rigid body. Thus far we have considered only reference frames whose axes were parallel, so that each frame has been in translation relative to the other. In this chapter we consider frames in relative motion of a more general sort. This extension of our study is particularly important since we live on a rotating planet and since the devices of engineering so often involve rotating parts. We also shall look into some of the dynamic, as well as kinematic, manifestations of relative motion.

14.1. VELOCITIES VIEWED FROM A MOVING REFERENCE FRAME

In Sec. 5.4 our discussion of relative motion was limited to the simple but important case where the moving axes remained always parallel to the fixed axes. Now that we have had some experience in dealing with rotations, let us attempt a more general attack on the problem. What we need is a systematic way of relating natural descriptions of apparent motion based on different reference frames. Most of our coordinate frames are attached to the earth. Relative to such a frame the moon obviously rises and sets, describing a closed orbit around the earth. But if we take the point of view of a frame attached to the sun, with axes set by the directions of familiar constellations, then the moon's orbit is a fancy variation of the earth's own elliptical path. We say that the moon's motion about the earth is superimposed on the earth's motion about the sun. We wish to show that in such a case, instantaneously, the velocities add as vectors. In Sec. 5.4 this conclusion was achieved quite easily. We must start again at the beginning, allowing for general motion of a moving frame.

It is still possible to resolve any displacement into two parts: a frame displacement and a relative displacement. The *frame displacement*, as before, is the displacement which a point would acquire by merely holding fixed coordinates in the

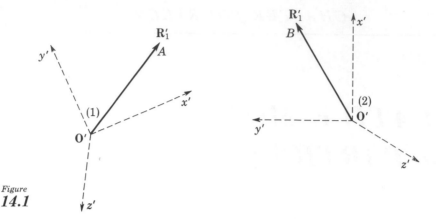

Figure
14.1

moving frame of reference.   In Fig. 14.1 a moving reference frame is depicted by
$O'x'y'z'$.   Only two positions of this frame are shown: an initial position (1) and a
final position (2).   This displacement of the moving frame is observed from a frame
treated as "fixed," which we may regard as attached to the page on which the figure
is printed.   If you identify your own point of view with that of the preferred or fixed
frame, you can imagine the moving frame in the figure as it gently soars and twists
from position (1) to position (2).   Now, in both of the pictures of the frame $O'x'y'z'$
is drawn a position vector $\mathbf{R}'_1$.   Note that, from the point of view of the moving frame
this vector remains constant: its x', y', and z' components are the same at (2) as at (1).
But from the point of view of the preferred frame, the tip of vector $\mathbf{R}'_1$ has moved
from point A to point B.   The vector AB is the frame displacement for *any* point
initially at $\mathbf{R}'_1$, regardless of its final position.

The *relative displacement* is the apparent displacement as observed with reference
to the moving frame.   Thus, in Fig. 14.2, a particle originally at point A is finally
at point C, so that the displacement which we observe from our preferred frame is
AC.   But from the point of view of the moving frame, the original position vector
was $\mathbf{R}'_1$ and the final position vector was $\mathbf{R}'_2$, so the relative displacement is BC or
$\Delta\mathbf{R}'$.   Figure 14.3 shows all these aspects of the displacement in a single figure.   The
displacement AC of the moving point is labeled $\Delta\mathbf{R}$, where, as usual for a displacement, $\Delta\mathbf{R} = \mathbf{R}_2 - \mathbf{R}_1$, a change in position vector.   Similarly, from the point of
view of the moving frame, the observed displacement BC is given by $\Delta\mathbf{R}' = \mathbf{R}'_2 - \mathbf{R}'_1$.

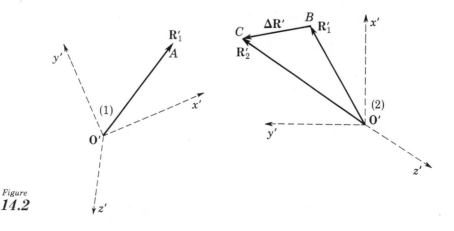

Figure
14.2

But the triangle ABC represents the vector addition

$$AC = AB + BC$$

where AB is the frame displacement previously discussed.   Hence we can write

(14.1) $$\Delta \mathbf{R} = \Delta \mathbf{R}_f + \Delta \mathbf{R}'$$

as in Sec. 5.4.   If the time interval between situation (1) and situation (2) is Δt, we can multiply through by the scalar $1/\Delta t$ and take limits as Δt approaches zero to get, as before,

(14.2) $$\mathbf{V} = \mathbf{V}_f + \mathbf{V}'$$

(When such a relation is used with x, y, z components, components relative to the *same* set of axes must, of course, be used for all three terms.)   This time the moving frame is not necessarily in simple translation; thus $\mathbf{V}_f$ is to be regarded as a function of position rather than instantaneously as a constant.   Fortunately, we can express it in a general way by applying (13.25).   We merely regard the moving frame of reference as a rigid body:

(14.3) $$\mathbf{V}_f = \mathbf{V}_{O'} + \boldsymbol{\Omega} \times \mathbf{R}'$$

Here $\boldsymbol{\Omega}$ is the angular velocity vector representing instantaneously the rotation of the moving frame.   The combined equation is thus

(14.4) $$\mathbf{V} = \mathbf{V}_{O'} + \boldsymbol{\Omega} \times \mathbf{R}' + \mathbf{V}'$$

Example I

We have previously had occasion to consider plane motion of a particle in terms of the unit vectors $\mathbf{L}$ and $\mathbf{M}$.   Regarding them as fixed in our rotating body, we have

$$\mathbf{O} = \mathbf{O}' \qquad \mathbf{V}_{O'} = \mathbf{O}$$

$$\mathbf{R} = \mathbf{R}' = r\mathbf{L} \qquad \mathbf{V}' = \frac{d\mathbf{R}'}{dt} = \frac{dr}{dt}\mathbf{L}$$

$$\mathbf{V}_f = \boldsymbol{\Omega} \times \mathbf{R}'$$

or

$$\mathbf{V}_f = \omega\mathbf{K} \times r\mathbf{L} = \omega r\mathbf{M}$$

Hence

$$\mathbf{V} = \frac{dr}{dt}\mathbf{L} + \omega r\mathbf{M}$$

which is equivalent to (5.41).

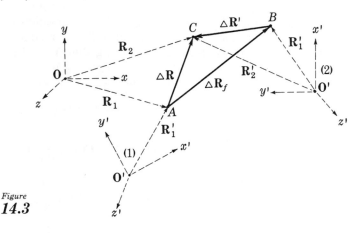

Figure
14.3

Example 2

Taking into account the earth's daily rotation, what is the absolute speed of a car heading north at 80 mph at a point of latitude 45°N?

Solution

Pick origin at center of earth, x axis along radius toward point in question, xy plane to include the North Pole.   Then $\mathbf{R}' = 4{,}000\mathbf{I}$ miles, $\mathbf{V}' = 80\mathbf{J}$ mph.   To find the angular velocity vector $\boldsymbol{\Omega}$, we observe that the angular speed is $\pi/12$ rad/hr, or 0.26 rad/hr, and that a unit vector in the right direction is $0.707\mathbf{I} + 0.707\mathbf{J}$.   We have, then,

$$\boldsymbol{\Omega} = 0.18(\mathbf{I} + \mathbf{J})$$

and

$$\mathbf{V} = \mathbf{V}' + \boldsymbol{\Omega} \times \mathbf{R}' = 80\mathbf{J} - 720\mathbf{K}$$

which is a vector of magnitude 724 (mph).

EXERCISES

1. Four airplanes leave a flying field at the equator to fly, respectively, north, east, south, and west at 100 mph.   Find an absolute velocity vector for each, taking into account the earth's spin on its axis.

2. A wheel of radius 80 cm rotates at 100 rad/sec.   A second wheel, mounted on the circumference of the first, has a parallel angular velocity vector.   Its radius is 20 cm, and it rotates at 400 rad/sec relative to the first wheel.   Let $\mathbf{P}$ be a point on the circumference of the smaller wheel.   Find its speed when it is (a) nearest to the center of the large wheel, (b) farthest from the center of the large wheel.   Illustrate with diagrams

3. In a reference frame $\mathbf{O}xyz$, a particle moves with uniform speed v along the x axis, so that its coordinates are given by $x = vt$, $y = 0$, $z = 0$.   Suppose that a second reference frame $\mathbf{O}x'y'z'$ has the same origin and same z axis as the first frame, but that the $x'y'$ plane rotates, relative to the first frame, about the z axis at uniform angular speed ω. Give a detailed analysis of the particle's velocity with respect to the second frame.   In particular, determine whether the position vector of the particle has uniform angular speed relative to the rotating frame.

14.2. DERIVATIVES RELATIVE TO ROTATING FRAMES

In Sec. 13.3 we found that the derivative of a vector $\mathbf{B}$ fixed in a moving frame has a time derivative given by $(d/dt)\,\mathbf{B} = \boldsymbol{\Omega} \times \mathbf{B}$, where $\boldsymbol{\Omega}$ is the angular velocity of the moving frame.   We now consider how to compute the derivative of any vector which is not necessarily fixed in the moving frame.   As before, we specify the vector by its initial and terminal points $\mathbf{P}$ and $\mathbf{Q}$. $\mathbf{P}$ is the position vector relative to our preferred or "fixed" frame of the initial point of $\mathbf{B}$.   Similarly, $\mathbf{Q}$ designates the terminal point.   We shall apply (14.4), remembering that $\mathbf{V}'$ is, by definition, given by

(14.5)
$$\mathbf{V}' = \lim_{\Delta t \to 0} \frac{\Delta \mathbf{R}'}{\Delta t} = \frac{d'\mathbf{R}'}{d't}$$

where the symbols $d'/d't$ play the same role for the moving frame as d/dt does for the preferred or fixed frame.   We get

$$\frac{d}{dt}\mathbf{P} = \mathbf{V}_{O'} + \boldsymbol{\Omega} \times (\mathbf{P} - \mathbf{O}') + \frac{d'}{d't}(\mathbf{P} - \mathbf{O}')$$

and

$$\frac{d}{dt}\mathbf{Q} = \mathbf{V}_{O'} + \boldsymbol{\Omega} \times (\mathbf{Q} - \mathbf{O}') + \frac{d'}{d't}(\mathbf{Q} - \mathbf{O}')$$

Subtracting and using the linearity of the operators d/dt, $d'/d't$, and $\Omega \times$ (cf. Sec. 13.3), we get

$$\frac{d}{dt}(\mathbf{Q} - \mathbf{P}) = \Omega \times (\mathbf{Q} - \mathbf{P}) + \frac{d'}{d't}(\mathbf{Q} - \mathbf{P})$$

or, since $\mathbf{B} = \mathbf{Q} - \mathbf{P}$, we have

(14.6)
$$\frac{d}{dt}\mathbf{B} = \Omega \times \mathbf{B} + \frac{d'}{d't}\mathbf{B}$$

Since this holds for any vector $\mathbf{B}$ for which the use of $d'/d't$ is appropriate, we have another operator identity, extending Eq. (13.11):

(14.7)
$$\frac{d}{dt} = \Omega \times + \frac{d'}{d't}$$

Such a bare expression should be fortified with words:

(14.8) *The derivative (with respect to time), viewed from a fixed frame, of any vector function of time is equal to the sum of the corresponding derivative as viewed from a moving frame plus, if the moving frame is rotating, the derivative induced by the rotation* [cf. (13.10)].

The preceding result may be obtained more directly. It is obvious that $\mathbf{R} = \mathbf{O}' + \mathbf{R}'$, at any instant. Differentiating with respect to time, taking the point of view of the fixed system, we have

(14.9)
$$\mathbf{V} = \mathbf{V}_{O'} + \frac{d\mathbf{R}'}{dt}$$

This, too, is a valid equation. Now let us recall the significance of $\mathbf{V}'$; it is the derivative of $\mathbf{R}'$ with respect to t as seen from the moving frame of reference:

(14.10)
$$\mathbf{V}' = \frac{d'\mathbf{R}'}{d't}$$

The primes are to emphasize that the derivative is as viewed from the moving system. If we substitute (14.10) in (14.4) and compare with (14.9), we conclude:

(14.11)
$$\frac{d}{dt}\mathbf{R}' = \Omega \times \mathbf{R}' + \frac{d'}{d't}\mathbf{R}'$$

as would be predicted by (14.8).

14.3. ACCELERATIONS VIEWED FROM A MOVING REFERENCE FRAME

In Sec. 14.1 we study the relationship between apparent velocities as observed from two different frames in relative motion. Taking the point of view of one frame, every point has at each instant a frame velocity associated with the other frame. This frame velocity was found to be equal to the vector difference between the velocities as observed from the two frames:

$$\mathbf{V}_f = \mathbf{V} - \mathbf{V}'$$

One might be tempted to conjecture that a frame acceleration defined analogously would be equal to a similar difference of observed accelerations.

We can define *frame acceleration* $\mathbf{A}_f$ in a natural way as the acceleration a point would have if it merely remained at a fixed position in the moving frame, i.e., for which $\mathbf{V}' = \mathbf{O}$. Since a moving frame may be regarded as a rigid body, we can easily write down a formula for frame acceleration. Differentiating with respect to time equation (14.3), we get

$$\mathbf{A}_f = \mathbf{A}_{O'} + \frac{d\boldsymbol{\Omega}}{dt} \times \mathbf{R}' + \boldsymbol{\Omega} \times \frac{d}{dt}\mathbf{R}'$$

But by (14.8)

$$\frac{d}{dt}\mathbf{R}' = \boldsymbol{\Omega} \times \mathbf{R}' + \mathbf{V}' = \boldsymbol{\Omega} \times \mathbf{R}'$$

since $\mathbf{V}' = \mathbf{O}$, so

(14.12) $$\mathbf{A}_f = \mathbf{A}_{O'} + \mathfrak{A} \times \mathbf{R}' + \boldsymbol{\Omega} \times (\boldsymbol{\Omega} \times \mathbf{R}')$$

This shows that the acceleration of a point on a moving body or reference frame can be written as the vector sum of three accelerations. $\mathbf{A}_{O'}$ is the usual acceleration of the reference point or origin $\mathbf{O}'$ on the moving object. The other two terms have to do with the instantaneous rotation of the body about an axis through $\mathbf{O}'$: the first term $\mathfrak{A} \times \mathbf{R}'$ is the tangential part, and $\boldsymbol{\Omega} \times (\boldsymbol{\Omega} \times \mathbf{R}')$ is the centripetal part.

The definition of *relative acceleration* $\mathbf{A}'$ is immediate; this is the usual acceleration as computed on the basis of displacements relative to the moving frame:

(14.13) $$\mathbf{A}' = \frac{d'\mathbf{V}'}{d't} = \frac{d'}{d't}\left(\frac{d'\mathbf{R}'}{d't}\right)$$

To demonstrate that the possible conjecture suggested in the first paragraph of this section is not valid, let us consider a simple example.

Example

A turntable or carrousel rotates at angular speed ω. A bullet or ball is projected just above the turntable in such a way that it passes at uniform speed v directly over the center $\mathbf{O}'$ as indicated by the dashed line in Fig. 14.4. Let $t = 0$ for the instant when the projectile crosses $\mathbf{O}'$. On the turntable we select $\mathbf{O}'$ as origin and the direction of the dotted line at $t = 0$ as x' direction. At $t = 0$ the apparent velocity is $\mathbf{V}' = v\mathbf{I}'$. But at a later time t the projectile is, relative to the $\mathbf{O}'x'y'$ frame, at a point with polar coordinates $vt/{-\omega t}$. Relative to the turntable, its trajectory is not a straight line but a curve, in fact a spiral; for the projectile that started at $t = 0$ along the x' axis appears to veer to the right as indicated in Fig. 14.5. You can check this by a crude experiment. Fasten a piece of cardboard to

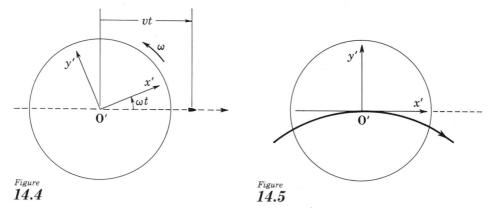

Figure
14.4

Figure
14.5

a magazine with a thumbtack lightly set. Rotate the cardboard and simultaneously draw, relative to your desk, a straight line across the cardboard. The curve should resemble at least vaguely the one shown in Fig. 14.5. Using standard formulas from calculus books, it is easy to show that at $\mathbf{O}'$ the radius of curvature of the spiral is given by $\rho = v/2\omega$. At the point $\mathbf{O}'$ we have $\mathbf{V}_f = \mathbf{O}$ and $\mathbf{A}_f = \mathbf{O}$, for $\mathbf{O}'$ is at rest and $\mathbf{R}'$ is a null vector at $t = 0$. The acceleration $\mathbf{A}$ is null since the projectile travels its straight course at uniform speed. The relative acceleration, however, is not null. At $\mathbf{O}'$, since $\mathbf{V}_f = \mathbf{O}$, $v' = v$. By symmetry the apparent tangential acceleration is zero. So we have

$$a' = \frac{v'^2}{\rho} = \frac{v^2}{v/2\omega} = 2\omega v$$

This example disproves the naïve conjecture of the first paragraph. We next develop a correct general formula.

14.4. THE THEOREM OF CORIOLIS

To get a more complete view of acceleration when rotation axes are involved, let us apply (14.8) to the velocity formula

$$\mathbf{V} = \mathbf{V}_{O'} + \mathbf{\Omega} \times \mathbf{R}' + \mathbf{V}'$$

We get by straight differentiation

$$\frac{d}{dt}\mathbf{V} = \frac{d}{dt}\mathbf{V}_{O'} + \frac{d}{dt}\mathbf{\Omega} \times \mathbf{R}' + \mathbf{\Omega} \times \frac{d}{dt}\mathbf{R}' + \frac{d}{dt}\mathbf{V}'$$

and using (14.8) to express the derivatives of $\mathbf{R}'$ and $\mathbf{V}'$,

$$\mathbf{A} = \mathbf{A}_{O'} + \mathbf{\mathfrak{A}} \times \mathbf{R}' + \mathbf{\Omega} \times [(\mathbf{\Omega} \times \mathbf{R}') + \mathbf{V}'] + \mathbf{\Omega} \times \mathbf{V}' + \mathbf{A}'$$

From the discussion in the preceding paragraph we can identify $\mathbf{A}_f$ and $\mathbf{A}'$, the frame acceleration and the relative acceleration. We then can write

(14.14) $\mathbf{A} = \mathbf{A}_f + \mathbf{A}_c + \mathbf{A}'$

where $\mathbf{A}_c$, called the *Coriolis acceleration* or the *complementary acceleration*, is given by

(14.15) $\mathbf{A}_c = 2\mathbf{\Omega} \times \mathbf{V}'$

Equation (14.14) is often called the *theorem of Coriolis*. This concept is vital in engineering kinematics and in long-range ballistics. Observe that it is zero if there is no rotation, if the relative motion is parallel to the angular velocity, or if the point merely has its frame velocity. Full interpretation is perhaps most easily given from the dynamical point of view to be developed next, but some simple applications are in order at this time.

Example I

First let us consider the implications for the example in Sec. 14.3. There we found $\mathbf{A} = \mathbf{O}$, $\mathbf{A}_f = \mathbf{O}$, $\mathbf{A}' = -2\omega v\mathbf{J}$. Now for $\mathbf{A}_c$

$$\mathbf{\Omega} = \omega\mathbf{K} \qquad \mathbf{V}' = v\mathbf{I}$$

Hence

$$\mathbf{A}_c = 2(\omega\mathbf{K}) \times (v\mathbf{I}) = 2\omega v\mathbf{J}$$

Note that $\mathbf{A}_c = -\mathbf{A}'$ is necessary for the theorem of Coriolis.

The preceding simple example shows how rotation of reference frames causes apparent curvilinear motion, and hence an apparent centripetal acceleration, quite different from the usual centripetal acceleration that depends on the distance from an axis of rotation. This phenomenon is especially significant for inhabitants of a rotating planet. We saw in Sec. 13.2 that each locality of the earth can be regarded as rotating about a vertical axis with angular speed $\omega_\lambda = \omega \sin \lambda$, λ being the latitude. This means, for example, that, except at the equator, apparent accelerations must appear for horizontal motions like the one studied in Example 1. Because the reference frame (i.e., the landscape) rotates under a particle in motion, its path appears curved, and hence accelerated. For motions which are not horizontal, the vector machinery of this section will usually be needed for adequate analysis.

Example 2

A particle moves with constant relative speed v' around the rim of a wheel of radius r. The wheel rotates in the opposite sense about its fixed axis at constant angular speed ω. Taking the wheel as a frame of reference, compute and diagram the components of velocity and acceleration.

Solution

For the choice of axes shown in Fig. 14.6,

$$\mathfrak{A} = \mathbf{O} \qquad \mathbf{A}_{O'} = \mathbf{O} \qquad \mathbf{O} = \mathbf{O}' \qquad \mathbf{V}_{O'} = \mathbf{O}$$

Then we have

$$v = \omega r - v' \qquad a' = \frac{v'^2}{r} \qquad a_c = 2\omega v' \qquad a_f = \omega^2 r$$

Thus

$$a = \omega^2 r - 2\omega v' + \frac{v'^2}{r}$$

As a check on this analysis, observe that from the overall view we have clockwise circular motion at a speed of $v' - \omega r$. Then the acceleration (centripetal) should be

$$\frac{(v' - \omega r)^2}{r} = \frac{v'^2}{r} - 2\omega v' + \omega^2 r$$

as already found.

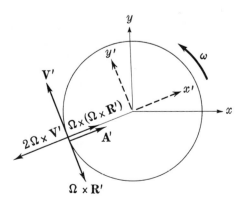

Figure
14.6

EXERCISES

4. Use the methods of this section to derive Eq. (5.42). (The first example of Sec. 14.1 may be taken as a model.)

5. To reinforce the student's comprehension of our analysis of acceleration a more formal partially analytical approach may be helpful. Let us consider the special case where the origins of the two reference frames coincide and where the moving frame rotates uniformly about an axis through the common origin. Starting with

$$\mathbf{R} = x'\mathbf{I}' + y'\mathbf{J}' + z'\mathbf{K}' = \mathbf{R}'$$

differentiate and regroup terms to show that

$$\mathbf{V} = \mathbf{\Omega} \times \mathbf{R}' + \mathbf{V}'$$
$$\mathbf{A} = \mathbf{\Omega} \times (\mathbf{\Omega} \times \mathbf{R}') + 2\mathbf{\Omega} \times \mathbf{V}' + \mathbf{A}'$$

For instance,

$$\frac{d(x'\mathbf{I}')}{dt} = \frac{dx'}{dt}\mathbf{I}' + x'\mathbf{\Omega} \times \mathbf{I}' \ldots$$

6. A particle moves with constant relative speed v' outward along a spoke of a wheel rotating at uniform angular speed ω about a fixed axis. When its distance from the center is r, find expressions for the magnitude of the velocity and the acceleration. Illustrate with a diagram showing directions of the various components.

7. A particle moves with constant relative speed v' around the rim of a wheel of radius r; the wheel rolls along a straight line with uniform speed v. Taking the wheel as a frame of reference, find the Coriolis acceleration. Draw this and the other accelerations in a diagram.

8. How great is the Coriolis acceleration for an airplane traveling north and also for an airplane traveling east at 150 mph at points on the equator?

9. In what regions of the earth may the Coriolis acceleration for surface travel be vertical? Is this effect independent of the direction of travel?

10. In what regions of the earth is the horizontal component of the Coriolis acceleration a maximum for a given surface speed?

11. Prove that in the Northern Hemisphere all horizontal projections of the Coriolis acceleration are to the right or to the left (state which) of the direction of travel on the surface.

12. In Fig. 14.7 the whole $x'y'$ plane rotates about the z axis counterclockwise at 2 rad/sec. A particle **P** moves clockwise at 30 ft/sec (relative to the $x'y'$ plane) around the circle

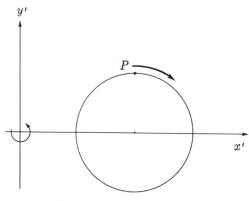

Figure
14.7

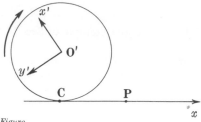

Figure
14.8

of radius 5 ft whose center is (12,0,0) ft.   For the moment when **P** is at (12,5,0) ft, plot to scale, labeling with magnitudes, $\mathbf{V'}$, $\mathbf{V}_f$, $\mathbf{A}_f$, $\mathbf{A}_c$, $\mathbf{A'}$, $\mathbf{A}$, $\mathbf{V}$.

13.   A wheel of radius 3 ft rolls without slipping along the positive x axis with angular speed 5 rad/sec.   The axes $x'y'O'$ are fixed on the wheel and rotate with it. **C** is the point of contact between wheel and axis.   **P** is a fixed point 4 ft from **C** at the moment shown in Fig. 14.8.   Although **P** is fixed in space, it has an apparent motion as seen from the moving frame.   Draw to scale and label with symbols and magnitudes the vectors $\mathbf{V}_{O'}$, $\mathbf{V'}$, $\mathbf{A}_f$, $\mathbf{A}_c$.

14.   Repeat Exercise 12 with the motions unchanged but with the moving origin **O'** at the center of the circle and with the $x'y'$ axes rotating with **P** so that its coordinates are constantly (0,5).

14.5. PARTICLE DYNAMICS IN MOVING FRAMES

The basic dynamical equation

(14.16) $$\bar{\mathbf{F}} = \Sigma\,\mathbf{F} = m\mathbf{A}$$

has meaning only in conjunction with the reference frame with respect to which **A** is reckoned.   It was remarked in Sec. 3.6 that Newton's laws are not valid with respect to all frames.   Frames for which they are valid are called *inertial frames*. Since a relation such as (14.16) is subject to experimental check, it seems reasonable to assume that inertial frames do exist.   Let $\mathbf{O}xyz$ be such a frame and $\mathbf{O'}x'y'z'$ be a frame in motion with respect to the first frame.   Let the acceleration of **O'** relative to the first frame be $\mathbf{A}_{O'}$ and the angular velocity and acceleration be $\boldsymbol{\Omega}$ and $\mathfrak{A}$. If a particle of mass m subject to forces of resultant $\bar{\mathbf{F}}$ has an acceleration $\mathbf{A'}$ relative to the moving frame, then, by the preceding section, its acceleration **A** in the inertial frame is

$$\mathbf{A} = \mathbf{A}_f + \mathbf{A}_c + \mathbf{A'}$$

It is now obvious that the equation

(14.17) $$\bar{\mathbf{F}} = \Sigma\,\mathbf{F} = m\mathbf{A'}$$

is not valid in general.   In fact, we may say:

(14.18) *A frame accelerated with respect to an inertial frame is not an inertial frame.*

A frame rotating with respect to an inertial frame is not an inertial frame.

Now it is often desirable to solve mechanics problems with respect to such frames of reference.   In fact, any frame rigidly attached to the earth presumably has an angular velocity of approximately one revolution per day with respect to some inertial frame.   The aim of this section is to point out means of adapting (14.17) for use in a noninertial frame.   The expedient is direct, even naïve.   First we substitute (14.14) into (14.16):

$$\Sigma \, \mathbf{F} = m\mathbf{A}_f + m\mathbf{A}_c + m\mathbf{A}'$$

Next we transfer the undesirable terms from right to left:

$$\Sigma \, \mathbf{F} - m\mathbf{A}_f - m\mathbf{A}_c = m\mathbf{A}'$$

Then we pretend that, in addition to the usual external forces included in $\Sigma \, \mathbf{F}$, there are also a *frame force* $\mathbf{F}_f$ and a *Coriolis force* $\mathbf{F}_c$ given by

(14.19) $$\mathbf{F}_f = -m\mathbf{A}_f$$

(14.20) $$\mathbf{F}_c = -m\mathbf{A}_c$$

If now we reinterpret the resultant $\bar{\mathbf{F}}$ as

$$\bar{\mathbf{F}} = \Sigma \, \mathbf{F} + \mathbf{F}_f + \mathbf{F}_c$$

we may write quite accurately

(14.21) $$\bar{\mathbf{F}} = m\mathbf{A}'$$

Example I

What is the acceleration of free fall relative to a railway coach accelerated at 6 ft/sec²?

Solution

Isolate a particle free to fall as shown in Fig. 14.9.   The frame acceleration to the right corresponds to a frame force to the left.   The resultant force $\bar{\mathbf{F}}$ determines the acceleration $\mathbf{A}'$ which is desired:

$$a' = \sqrt{(32.2)^2 + (6.0)^2} = 32.8 \text{ ft/sec}^2$$

at an angle θ given by

$$\tan \theta = 6.0/32.2 \qquad \theta = 106.°$$

Example 2

Whenever a particle is in motion on a rotating body, its behavior relative to that body is as if it were acted on by a Coriolis force (as well as a frame force).   It is, for instance, an observable fact that rivers in the Northern Hemisphere erode their right banks more than the left.   The opposite effect is found in the Southern Hemisphere.   Navigators use tables based on latitude and speed to determine corrections due to Coriolis forces acting on bubble sextants.   Another such example is the *geostrophic wind*, which tends to blow along lines of constant pressure (with the high-pressure area on the right, low-pressure area on the left, in the Northern Hemisphere)

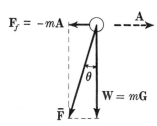

Figure
14.9

at such a speed that forces due to pressure differences are counterbalanced by Coriolis forces.   When the lines of constant pressure are curved, centrifugal forces enter the picture.

Example 3

To get an idea of the magnitude of the Coriolis force, let us compute it for a 10-lb projectile traveling east horizontally at 2,000 ft/sec at a point of latitude 45°N.

Solution

Pick axes locally fixed to surface of earth: x axis east, y axis north, and z axis vertical.   Then $\omega = \pi/12$ rad/hr, or

$$\omega = 7.27 \times 10^{-5} \text{ rad/sec}$$

(If allowance is made for the earth's annual journey around the sun, this value must be corrected slightly.)

$$\mathbf{\Omega} = 0.707\omega(\mathbf{J} + \mathbf{K})$$
$$\mathbf{V}' = 2,000\mathbf{I}$$

$$|\mathbf{F}_c| = |-2m\mathbf{\Omega} \times \mathbf{V}'| = \left|-2 \times \frac{10}{32.2} \times 7.27 \times 10^{-5} \times 2,000\right| = 0.09 \text{ lb}$$

Such a force may not seem large, but it is enough to cause a trajectory to be influenced. In practical long-range ballistics the Coriolis deviation is allowed for.

Centrifugal Force.   Under the category of frame forces, the most familiar special case, occurring particularly for uniform rotation, is one of the form

$$-m\mathbf{\Omega} \times (\mathbf{\Omega} \times \mathbf{R}')$$

which is called centrifugal force.   Like the Coriolis force and other frame forces, this is purely fictitious.   Like the others, it is merely a device to make the basic Newtonian law of motion, $\mathbf{\bar{F}} = m\mathbf{A}$, valid in a noninertial frame.

Example 4

If a railway coach takes at 60 mph a curve of radius 500 ft, at what angle will the chandeliers hang?   The coach is not an inertial frame; thus the "equilibrium position" must be computed as due to both the weight and the centrifugal force:

$$-m\omega^2 r = -m\frac{v^2}{r} = -m\frac{88^2}{500} = -15.5m$$

The angle θ for equilibrium (see Fig. 14.10) is given by

$$\tan \theta = 15.5/32.2$$
$$\theta = 25.7°$$

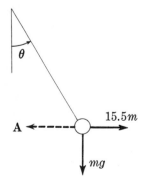

Figure
14.10

EXERCISES

15. What is the period of a simple pendulum 24 in. long suspended from the ceiling of a railway coach traveling at 45 mph along a straight horizontal track?

16. A cannon mounted on a tank with its bore horizontal and its muzzle a distance h above the ground may be turned to fire in any direction. The muzzle speed when the tank is at rest is v_0. Suppose that the tank moves ahead at speed u. (a) Investigate the locus of points on the ground (assumed level) which could be hit by a projectile fired at a given moment. (b) If the tank continues to move at uniform speed u, how far from the tank may such a projectile land?

17. What is the period of a simple pendulum of length 24 in.: (a) On an elevator accelerating upward at 16 ft/sec²? (b) On an elevator accelerating downward at 16, 32, 64 ft/sec²? (c) On a train accelerating at 32 ft/sec² on a straight level track?

18. A train accelerates at 8 ft/sec² uniformly along a level track. If a trainman standing on a boxcar throws a missile forward at an elevation of 30° with an initial speed of 100 ft/sec, where will the missile return to the level from which it was thrown?

19. At what angular speed will a man stick to the wall of a spinning cylindrical room of radius 10 ft if the coefficient of friction is 0.2?

20. A particle of mass m moves with constant relative speed v' around the rim of a wheel of radius r. The wheel rotates about a fixed axis at constant angular speed ω. Taking the wheel as a frame of reference, derive formulas for the magnitudes of the Coriolis force and the centrifugal force acting on the particle.

21. A particle of mass m moves with constant relative speed v' outward along a spoke of a wheel rotating about a fixed axis at constant angular speed ω. For the moment when its distance from the center is r, find formulas for the magnitudes of the Coriolis force and the centrifugal force relative to a frame rigidly attached to the wheel.

14.6. EFFECTS OF THE EARTH'S ROTATION

The Plumb Line. It is customary to consider gravitational forces near the earth as acting in the direction of a plumb line. Let us see to what extent this direction is influenced by the centrifugal force associated with the earth's rotation. Let us suppose that at a locality of latitude λ we have a plumb bob of mass m hanging at rest at the end of a string. Relative to a frame of reference rigidly hitched to the earth at this locality (see Fig. 14.11), the bob is in equilibrium subject to three forces: the tension which just balances the apparent gravitational force, $\mathbf{T} = -m\mathbf{G}$; the purely gravitational force $m\mathbf{G}'$; and the centrifugal force $\mathbf{F}_f$ of magnitude

$$m\omega^2(\rho \cos \lambda) = m\omega^2 p$$

where ρ is the radius of the earth (considered as a sphere). Since ω^2 is so small, we shall draw approximate quantitative conclusions directly from a vector diagram relating these three forces. By inspection of Fig. 14.12 we get

$$\phi = \frac{y}{mg} \quad \text{where } y = m\omega^2 p \sin \lambda$$

so

(14.22) $$\phi = \Delta\lambda = \frac{\omega^2 p \sin \lambda \cos \lambda}{g}$$

Also

$$x = m(g' - g) = m\omega^2 p \cos \lambda$$

Thus

(14.23) $$\Delta g = \omega^2 \rho \cos^2 \lambda$$

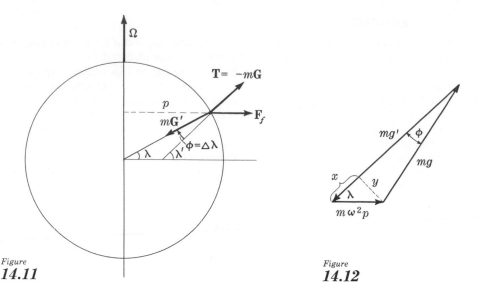

Figure
14.11

Figure
14.12

At the equator this variation amounts to about 0.4 ft/sec². Other numerical conclusions are left for Exercises 25 and 26.

A plumb line tends to be normal to the earth's surface (especially over oceans); therefore the conclusions just noted are qualitatively consistent with the equatorial bulge of the earth.

Effect of the Earth's Rotation on the Trajectory of a Projectile. We shall consider motion near one locality on the earth's surface. The forces acting on a projectile are the gravitational force plus centrifugal force, combined as $m\mathbf{G}$; the Coriolis force; and any further external forces of resultant $\bar{\mathbf{F}}$. Consequently,

$$(14.24) \qquad \bar{\mathbf{F}} + m\mathbf{G} - 2m\mathbf{\Omega} \times \mathbf{V'} = m\mathbf{A'}$$

Here for simplicity's sake we shall neglect air friction and other external forces except gravity. We have, then,

$$(14.25) \qquad \mathbf{A'} = \mathbf{G} - 2\mathbf{\Omega} \times \mathbf{V'}$$

We integrate this, assuming that the projectile initially left the origin with velocity $\mathbf{V_0'}$,

$$(14.26) \qquad \mathbf{V'} - \mathbf{V_0'} = \mathbf{G}t - 2\mathbf{\Omega} \times \mathbf{R'}$$

Integrating again,

$$(14.27) \qquad \mathbf{R'} = \mathbf{V_0'}t + \tfrac{1}{2}\mathbf{G}t^2 - 2\mathbf{\Omega} \times \int_0^t \mathbf{R'}\, dt$$

In order to evaluate the integral in this equation, we shall substitute (14.27) into itself, but since ω^2 is very small indeed, we shall do so only partly. The resulting approximate expression, good for moderate values of t, is

$$\mathbf{R'} = \mathbf{V_0'}t + \tfrac{1}{2}\mathbf{G}t^2 - 2\mathbf{\Omega} \times \int_0^t (\mathbf{V_0'}t + \tfrac{1}{2}\mathbf{G}t^2)\, dt$$

or

$$(14.28) \qquad \mathbf{R'} = \mathbf{V_0'}t + \tfrac{1}{2}(\mathbf{G} - 2\mathbf{\Omega} \times \mathbf{V_0'})t^2 - \tfrac{1}{3}(\mathbf{\Omega} \times \mathbf{G})t^3$$

Numerical applications to problems involving falling particles and projectiles will be assigned as exercises.

Foucault's Pendulum. At a given point **O** of latitude λ, let the unit vertical vector be **K** (see Fig. 14.13). Then the xy plane may be considered as a tangent plane at the origin **O**. If a simple pendulum is set up just over **O** and released from rest in a displaced position of polar coordinates (r, θ), it would, were it not for the earth's rotation, describe a simple harmonic motion over the line through **O** at constant angle θ (see Fig. 14.14). The equation of motion would be, for a pendulum of length l,

$$-\frac{mg}{l} r = m \frac{d^2r}{dt^2}$$

or, multiplying by the unit radial vector **L**,

$$(14.29) \qquad -\frac{mg}{l} \mathbf{R} = m \frac{d^2\mathbf{R}}{dt^2}$$

The Coriolis force, acting transversely, might be expected to alter the character of the motion. Since the motion, for an inextensible string and for small displacements, is bound to be nearly plane, we shall take account only of the component parallel to the plane, i.e. (using Chap. 9, Exercise 27),

$$\mathbf{F}_{c(\text{horizontal})} = -2m\mathbf{K} \times [(\mathbf{\Omega} \times \mathbf{V}') \times \mathbf{K}] = 2m\mathbf{K} \times [\mathbf{K} \times (\mathbf{\Omega} \times \mathbf{V}')]$$

$$= 2m\mathbf{K} \times [(\mathbf{K} \cdot \mathbf{V}')\mathbf{\Omega} - (\mathbf{K} \cdot \mathbf{\Omega})\mathbf{V}']$$

$$= -2m\omega \sin \lambda (\mathbf{K} \times \mathbf{V}')$$

Let us add this force to the left member of (14.29), realizing now that the oscillation will probably no longer take place along a fixed straight line.

$$-2m\omega \sin \lambda (\mathbf{K} \times \mathbf{V}') - \frac{mg}{l} \mathbf{R} = m \frac{d^2\mathbf{R}}{dt^2}$$

Everything will now be expressed in terms of the unit radial and transverse vectors **L** and **M**. By (5.42),

$$\frac{d^2\mathbf{R}}{dt^2} = \left[\frac{d^2r}{dt^2} - r\left(\frac{d\theta}{dt}\right)^2\right]\mathbf{L} + \left[2\frac{dr}{dt}\frac{d\theta}{dt} + r\frac{d^2\theta}{dt^2}\right]\mathbf{M}$$

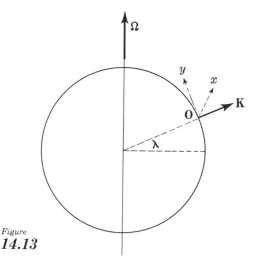

Figure
14.13

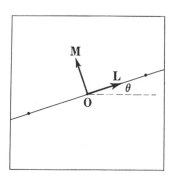

Figure
14.14

Using (5.41),

$$\mathbf{K} \times \mathbf{V}' = \mathbf{K} \times \left[\frac{dr}{dt} \mathbf{L} + r \frac{d\theta}{dt} \mathbf{M} \right] = \frac{dr}{dt} \mathbf{M} - r \frac{d\theta}{dt} \mathbf{L}$$

Substituting these expressions and equating coefficients of $\mathbf{M}$, we get

$$-2\omega \sin \lambda \frac{dr}{dt} = 2 \frac{dr}{dt} \frac{d\theta}{dt} + r \frac{d^2\theta}{dt^2}$$

This may be rewritten as

$$-2 \frac{dr}{dt} \left(\omega \sin \lambda + \frac{d\theta}{dt} \right) = r \frac{d}{dt} \left(\omega \sin \lambda + \frac{d\theta}{dt} \right)$$

which easily integrates to give

$$r^2 \left(\omega \sin \lambda + \frac{d\theta}{dt} \right) = \text{const}$$

Since the pendulum repeatedly goes through equilibrium position, the constant is zero and

(14.30) $$\frac{d\theta}{dt} = -\omega \sin \lambda$$

Equating coefficients of $\mathbf{L}$ with this value of $d\theta/dt$ gives us

$$-2 \frac{d\theta}{dt} \left(-r \frac{d\theta}{dt} \right) - \frac{gr}{l} = \frac{d^2r}{dt^2} - r \left(\frac{d\theta}{dt} \right)^2$$

From this it is clear that if we can neglect (as previously) ω^2, the equation of motion is still (14.29) but that the plane of the oscillation rotates opposite to that of the earth at a rate $(-)\omega \sin \lambda$. This result is observable. As originally performed by Foucault in 1851, it is one of the great historical experiments of physics, giving evidence of the rotation of the earth and also of the vector nature of angular velocity.

EXERCISES

22. An ice floe weighing 1 million tons floats in the vicinity of the North Pole moving west at 4 miles per day. Find the Coriolis force.
23. Where can the Coriolis force due to the earth's rotation be horizontal? How? Where can it be vertical? How?
24. Evaluate the Coriolis force for a 200-lb projectile fired northward at an elevation of 45° with a speed of 2,500 ft/sec at a place of latitude 45°N.
25. At what latitude is the direction of a plumb line most affected by the earth's rotation? How large is this maximum effect?
26. At what latitude is the magnitude of the tension in a plumb line most affected by the earth's rotation? How large is this maximum effect for a pendulum of mass 1 kg?

REVIEW EXERCISES

27. A wheel of radius 10 in. rotates about its fixed axle at 20 rad/sec. A particle moves around the circumference in the opposite sense at 150 in./sec relative to the wheel. Find the magnitude of $\mathbf{A}_c$ and $\mathbf{A}$. Illustrate with a diagram.
28. A wheel of 30 in. diameter rolls, spinning, along an icy road. The velocity of the

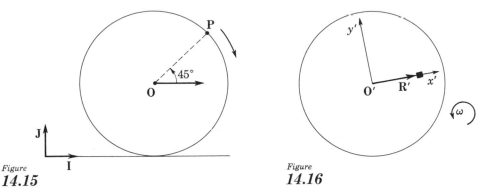

Figure
14.15

Figure
14.16

center is constant at 30 mph, while the angular speed is at a given moment 60 rad/sec, with an angular acceleration of 10 rad/sec². Taking **I** as a unit vector in the direction of the road and **J** vertically up, find, in **IJK** form:

(*a*) The velocity vector for the point **P** on the upper circumference whose inclination with **I** is 45°, as shown in Fig. 14.15.

(*b*) The acceleration vector for the point **P** of (*a*).

(*c*) The position vector relative to the center **O** of the wheel of the instantaneous center of rotation.

29. A wheel rotates at angular speed ω (see Fig. 14.16). A collar moves radially along a spoke of the wheel in such a way that its distance from the center is given by

$$r' = a + bt + ct^2$$

where a, b, c are constants. $x'O'y'$ is a reference frame attached to the wheel so that the collar moves on the x' axis. Thus, relative to the moving frame, the position vector **R'** of the collar is given by $\mathbf{R'} = r'\mathbf{I'}$.

For the moving frame as specified, determine in **I'J'** form the following vectors: **V**, **V'**, **A**, **A$_c$**, **A**. Your answers will be in terms of some of the following: a, b, c, ω, t. (NOTE: **O'** is at rest.)

30. At time $t = 1$ sec the axes $x'O'y'$ rigidly attached to a carrousel rotating with angular velocity

$$\Omega = (2t^2 - 0.5)\mathbf{K}$$

are, respectively, parallel to the axes xOy fixed on the ground as indicated in Fig. 14.17. The moving origin **O'** is 10 ft from the center of the rotating body. At $t = 1$ a boy on the ground has coordinates $x' = 4$, $y' = -3$ (ft) (relative to the moving axes) while his velocity and acceleration (relative to the fixed axes) are $\mathbf{V} = 10\mathbf{I}$ ft/sec and $\mathbf{A} = 5\mathbf{I}$ ft/sec². Compute in **IJK** form his velocity **V'** and acceleration **A'** *relative to the moving axes*. Show all steps in the computation.

31. A cam is pivoted at a point Q 3.0 cm from the center O of a wheel which rotates clockwise at 20 rad/sec. The point P of the cam, 2 cm from Q, describes a counterclockwise circle in the plane of the wheel. The speed of P relative to the wheel is 15 cm/sec.

Evaluate each of the following for the moment when Q and P occupy the positions shown in Fig. 14.18. The moving frame is to be taken as rigidly attached to the wheel. Express all answers in **IJK** form.

(*a*) **V**$_f$ (*b*) **V'**   (*c*) **V**   (*d*) **A**$_f$ (*e*) **A**$_c$ (*f*) **A'**   (*g*) **A**

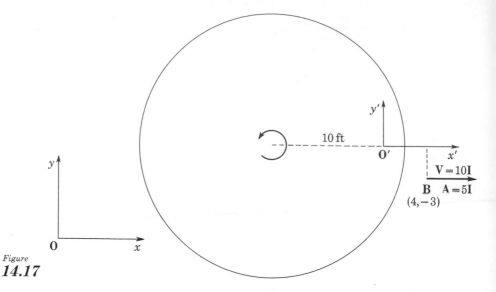

Figure
14.17

32. An airplane traveling at 600 mph pulls out of a dive with a centripetal acceleration of 5g.
    (a) What is the angular speed?
    (b) What is the radius of curvature of the path?
    (c) If the pilot reaches forward quickly to the controls, what is the magnitude of the Coriolis acceleration of his hand?   Take the speed of his hand as 10 ft/sec.
    (d) In the preceding what is the direction of the Coriolis force to which his hand is subject?

33. Compute the magnitude (in pounds) of the total initial Coriolis force acting on a 2-ton projectile fired due east with an initial elevation of 30° and initial speed of 1,800 ft/sec.   The latitude is 60°N.

34. Apply Lamy's theorem (Chap. 3, Exercise 25) to Fig. 14.12, and thence derive (14.22) and (14.23).

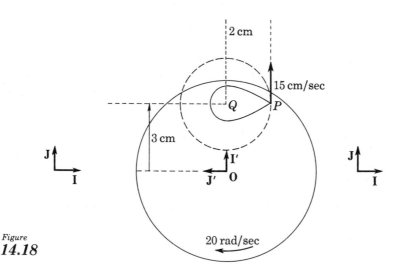

Figure
14.18

35. Consider motion relative to a reference frame rotating with constant angular velocity Ω. (a) Is the centrifugal force on a particle for such a frame conservative? If so, derive a formula for potential energy. (b) Reply to the same inquiry for the Coriolis force.

36. Discuss the motion of a particle free to slide on an inclined plane when the plane is subjected to a horizontal acceleration.

37. Show that a particle projected at 727 ft/sec on a smooth horizontal plane surface at a point of latitude 30° tends to trace out a circular arc of radius 10^7 ft.

38. If a train of mass 2,000 tons heads northeast at 60 mph on a straight level track, what is the horizontal reaction on the rails? (Latitude is 50°N.)

39. Taking your origin at the starting point (latitude λ), your y axis as vertical upward (direction of a plumb line), your x and z axes as east and south (horizontal), respectively, write three scalar equations equivalent to (14.28), expressing the position (x',y',z') of the projectile in terms of the direction cosines l, m, n of the initial velocity, the magnitude of the initial velocity v_0, and g, ω, λ, and t.

40. A particle is dropped from rest from a height of 1 mile above a point of latitude 40°N. How far from the point directly below it (plumb line) will it land? (Neglect ω^2.)

41. A bullet is fired upward at an initial speed of 1,600 ft/sec at a point of latitude 60°N. Neglecting air resistance and higher powers of the angular speed of the earth, find where the bullet will land.

42. A cannon elevated at 45° is fired first north and then south from a point of latitude 45°N. The muzzle velocity is 800 m/sec. How far from the meridian plane do the projectiles land in each case?

43. Foucault's historic pendulum experiment was performed in Paris (48°50′N). With what angular speed did the plane of his pendulum presumably rotate?
    Could places be found where the angular speed would be twice as great? Explain.
    Could places be found where the angular speed would be half as great? Explain.

44. In air navigation a correction for Coriolis force has to be applied to sextant readings. (a) In a plane traveling at 400 mph at latitude 70°N, by what angle in radians does a spirit level aligned transverse to the plane miss the true horizontal?
    (b) Taking the radius of the earth as 3,950 miles, by how many miles would this angular error change one's estimated position?

45. Describe and discuss the Coriolis-force pattern for an automobile wheel turning a corner.

CHAPTER FIFTEEN

MASS CENTER
and GYRATION RADIUS

This chapter is devoted to methods of calculating suitable mean positions frequently useful in mechanics. The center of mass of an aggregate of particles has already appeared (see, for instance, Sec. 6.6) as a point whose behavior epitomizes the overall translatory motion of the aggregate. This conclusion can be applied to extended bodies, for such bodies can be regarded as aggregates of particles which are tightly bound together. For our purposes at present, atoms and molecules are much too small to be of interest. The particles we speak of are merely arbitrarily small chunks which are imagined to fit together smoothly. In this way we can talk about mathematical limits as dimensions approach zero without encountering the manifold complexity which appears *physically* when dimensions approach zero. In large-scale mechanics we can properly substitute the smooth continuous pictures given us by our deceptive senses for the quite different atomic pictures which are so necessary for the study of small-scale phenomena. For rigid bodies the radius of gyration, as we shall see in Chap. 16, provides for rotational motion an analogous mean distance. The problem of computing mean distances is essentially a problem in integral calculus. Consider a uniform rod with one end at the origin, the other at $(l,0,0)$. The center of mass is given by the single coordinate

$$\bar{x} = \frac{1}{l} \int_0^l x \, dx = \frac{l}{2}$$

The radius $\bar{\bar{x}}$ of gyration is given by

$$\bar{\bar{x}}^2 = \frac{1}{l} \int_0^l x^2 \, dx = \frac{l^2}{3}$$

Similar calculations involving different mass distributions or greater geometrical complications are standard exercises in calculus courses. While some routine integrations will be included here, the emphasis will be on general conclusions of a unifying nature.

344

15.1. CENTER OF MASS

The ideas of Sec. 6.6 can easily be applied to a rigid body. Let the body be divided into small elements. The mass of a typical element is Δm_i. The position vector of a point in this element is $\mathbf{R}_i$, as in Fig. 15.1. If the elements are small enough, the expression

$$\frac{\Sigma\, \Delta m_i\, \mathbf{R}_i}{\Sigma\, \Delta m_i}$$

is a good approximation of what we should desire to call the position vector of the center of mass of the body. To make the definition unique, we take the limit as the elements approach zero in size and mass. (If we let $\mathbf{R}_i$ denote the center of mass of the element, then passing to the limit is necessary only as a device for summation.) The equation is then

(15.1) $$\bar{\mathbf{R}} = \lim_{\Delta m_i \to 0} \frac{\Sigma\, \Delta m_i\, \mathbf{R}_i}{\Sigma\, \Delta m_i} = \frac{1}{m} \int_m \mathbf{R}\, dm$$

The introduction of the notation of definite integral over the whole body comes naturally from similar discussions in Sec. 5.10. m, as usual, is a symbol for the mass of the body:

$$m = \Sigma\, \Delta m_i = \int_m dm$$

As usual, the one vector equation is equivalent to a set of three scalar equations such as the following:

(15.2) $$\bar{x} = \frac{1}{m}\int_m x\, dm \qquad \bar{y} = \frac{1}{m}\int_m y\, dm \qquad \bar{z} = \frac{1}{m}\int_m z\, dm$$

In actual numerical applications it is often convenient to express dm in some form in terms of coordinates as, for instance,

$$dm = \delta\, dx\, dy\, dz$$

where δ is the density. Then Eqs. (15.2) become triple integrals over appropriate ranges of x, y, and z. Computations of this sort are normally performed in courses in calculus and will be omitted here. Simpler computations will be presented,

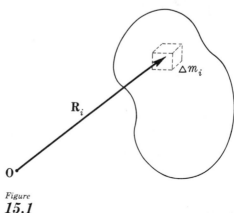

Figure
15.1

however. From simple properties of the definite integral the following results (analogous to Chap. 5, Exercise 63), will be stated:

(15.3) *If a body of uniform density has a plane or line of symmetry, the center of mass lies on this line or plane.*

For reference we also state a conclusion already recorded in Sec. 5.10.

(15.4) *The center of mass of a solid, uniform in density, coincides with its centroid.*

Another very useful result which is an easy conclusion from elementary properties of definite integrals (already met in part in Chap. 5, Exercise 64) is the following:

(15.5) *If a body is composed of n parts whose centers of mass are* $\bar{\mathbf{R}}_1, \ldots, \bar{\mathbf{R}}_n$ *and whose masses are* $m_1, \ldots, m_n$, *then the center of mass of the whole is given by*

$$\bar{\mathbf{R}} = \frac{\Sigma m_i \bar{\mathbf{R}}_i}{\Sigma m_i}$$

Example I

Find the center of mass of a uniform solid right cone.

Solution

From the symmetry, the center of mass lies on the axis (taken as x axis as shown in Fig. 15.2). It remains to compute $\bar{x}$. Take as elements disks of thickness dx and mass dm [all points in such an element have x coordinates approximately the same; thus we are in effect applying (15.5) in a limiting case, using integration for the summation]. Then

$$dm = \delta \pi\, y^2\, dx$$

Since $y = x \tan \theta$, we have

$$\bar{x} = \frac{\delta \pi \tan^2 \theta}{m} \int_0^h x^3\, dx = \frac{1}{4} \frac{\delta \pi \tan^2 \theta}{m} h^4$$

Now we compute the mass of the cone:

$$m = \delta \pi \tan^2 \theta \int_0^h x^2\, dx = \tfrac{1}{3}\delta \pi \tan^2 \theta\, h^3$$

Substituting this, we get

$$\bar{x} = \tfrac{3}{4}h$$

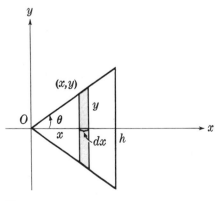

Figure
15.2

Example 2

Find the center of mass of a uniform hemispherical shell of radius r.

Solution

In Fig. 15.3, a plane section of the hemispherical shell is shown. The quarter circle shown in the first quadrant will, when rotated about the y axis, sweep out the surface of the hemisphere. At the same time the arc element of length $r\,d\theta$ sweeps out a band of circumference $2\pi r \cos\theta$, and hence of area $2\pi r^2 \cos\theta\,d\theta$. The mass of this element can be expressed in terms of an area density,

$$\sigma = m/2\pi r^2 \qquad dm = 2\pi r^2 \sigma \cos\theta\,d\theta$$

or, to save steps, we can exploit the fact that the density is uniform and use area a in place of mass m:

$$\bar{y} = \frac{1}{2\pi r^2}\int_0^{\pi/2}(r\sin\theta)(2\pi r^2\cos\theta\,d\theta)$$

$$= r\int_0^{\pi/2}\sin\theta\cos\theta\,d\theta = r\left[\frac{\sin^2\theta}{2}\right]_0^{\pi/2} = \frac{r}{2}$$

Example 3

Find the center of mass of a uniform wire bent into the shape of a quarter circle.

Solution

The first quadrant of Fig. 15.3 may be used again. Let the total mass of the wire be m. Then the mass of the element of length $r\,d\theta$ is $m(r\,d\theta)/(\pi r/2)$. Then

$$\bar{y} = \frac{1}{m}\int_0^{\pi/2}(r\sin\theta)\,\frac{2m\,d\theta}{\pi} = \frac{2r}{\pi}[-\cos\theta]_0^{\pi/2} = \frac{2r}{\pi}$$

Similarly,

$$\bar{x} = \frac{2r}{\pi}$$

Example 4

A semicircular disk of mass m and radius r has a density which varies radially:

$$\sigma(x) = \sigma_0 + kx$$

where $\sigma(x)$ is the area density (i.e., the mass per area) at a distance x from the center O, and k is a constant. Find the center of mass.

Solution

We use the general idea expressed in (15.5), extended to integrals. The disk is divided into semicircular bands, as shown in Fig. 15.4. A typical band (shaded

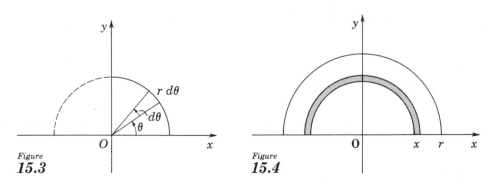

Figure
15.3

Figure
15.4

in the figure) has radius x, width dx, area $\pi x\, dx$, mass $dm = \pi x \sigma(x)\, dx$. The y coordinate for such a band is, by the preceding example, equal to $2x/\pi$. The center of mass of the disk is, by (15.5), given by

$$\bar{y} = \frac{1}{m} \int_0^r \frac{2x}{\pi}\, dm$$

Substituting for dm we have

$$\bar{y} = \frac{1}{m} \int_0^r \frac{2x}{\pi}\, \pi x\, (\sigma_0 + kx)\, dx$$

$$= \frac{2}{m} \int_0^r (\sigma_0 x^2 + kx^3)\, dx$$

$$= \frac{2}{m} \left(\frac{\sigma_0 r^3}{3} + \frac{kr^4}{4} \right)$$

The mass is given by

$$m = \int_0^r \pi x(\sigma_0 + kx)\, dx = \pi \left(\frac{\sigma_0 r^2}{2} + \frac{kr^3}{3} \right)$$

Hence

$$\bar{y} = \frac{4\sigma_0 + 3kr}{3\sigma_0 + 2kr}\, \frac{r}{\pi}$$

EXERCISES

1. A narrow cylindrical bar of length 1 m has a variable density given by

$$\delta = 8{,}000(1 + 0.5x)\, \frac{kg}{m^3} \qquad \text{for } 0 \le x \le 1$$

Find the center of mass.

2. A truncated cone is made of uniform material and has radii 25 and 40 cm. Its altitude is 40 cm. Find the center of mass.

3. Find the center of mass of a triangular frame consisting of three uniform rods whose lengths are, respectively, 5, 12, and 13 ft.

4. Find the center of mass of a triangular frame consisting of three uniform rods whose lengths are, respectively, 10, 10, and 5 ft.

5. A capital letter L is cut out of a piece of sheet metal 8 by 10 in. by removing a rectangle of dimensions 6 by 8 in. Find the center of mass.

6. Masses of 5, 7, and 9 g are placed at points with coordinates (0,3), (0,0), and (4,0). Find the center of mass.

7. Find a formula for the center of mass of a solid cone having the shape described in Example 1 but the density function given in Example 4.

15.2. THEOREMS OF PAPPUS

Two famous theorems are useful tools in solving for centroids or for centers of mass of uniform bodies. Given first a plane curve and an axis as in Fig. 15.5. Let the curve be rotated about the axis through an angle θ. Then a typical element of length Δs sweeps out a band of radius y whose area Δa is given by

$$\Delta a = \Delta s\, y\theta$$

Summing over the whole curve and passing to the limit as Δs becomes small, we get

$$\text{Area} = \theta \int y\, ds$$

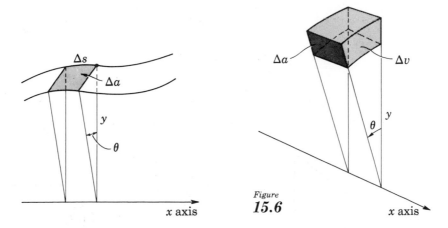

Figure
15.5
x axis

Figure
15.6
x axis

But, assigning uniform linear density to the original curve, its center of mass (or just its centroid) may be located by

$$\bar{y} = \frac{\int y \, ds}{l}$$

where l is the length of the curve.   Our conclusion is then

(15.6)   Area $= \bar{y}\theta l$

Similarly, given a plane area Δa and an axis (see Fig. 15.6), a rotation about the axis through an angle θ yields an element of volume

$$\Delta v = \Delta a \, y\theta$$

for which an integration gives

$$v = \theta \int y \, da$$

But from

$$\bar{y} = \frac{\int y \, da}{a}$$

we get

(15.7)   Volume $= \bar{y}\theta a$

where a is the whole area rotated.

Equations (15.6) and (15.7) epitomize the theorems of Pappus:

(15.8) *When a homogeneous plane curve (region) is rotated about an axis in the plane, the area (volume) swept out is equal to the product of the length (area) of the curve (region) times the length of the path traced out by the centroid or center of mass of the curve (region).*

Example I

Find the center of mass of a wire of length 8 in. bent in the shape of Fig. 15.7.

Solution

Rotate about the x axis through an angle of 360°.   The area swept out is

$$\tfrac{1}{2} \times 5 \times 2\pi \times 3 + \pi 3^2 = 24\pi$$

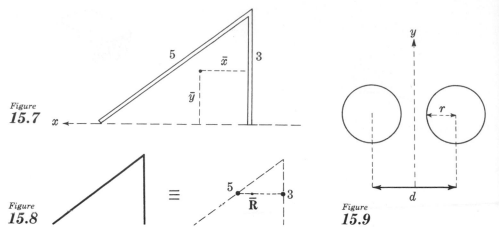

Figure
15.7

Figure
15.8

Figure
15.9

Thus

$$8 \times 2\pi \bar{y} = 24\pi \qquad \bar{y} = 1.5 \text{ in.}$$

Likewise, rotating about the y axis,

$$\text{Area} = \tfrac{1}{2} \times 5 \times 2\pi \times 4 = 20\pi.$$

Thus

$$8 \times 2\pi \times \bar{x} = 20\pi \qquad \bar{x} = 1.25 \text{ in.}$$

This particular example is inserted just to illustrate procedure. It may be more easily done by other methods (15.3 and 15.5). The two segments may be treated as particles concentrated at their centers of mass, as shown in Fig. 15.8. From this figure the results are obvious.

Example 2

Use the theorem of Pappus to compute the volume of a torus (doughnut) whose cross-sectional picture is given in Fig. 15.9.

Solution

Rotating one of the circles about the y axis, we have, by (15.8),

$$\text{Volume} = 2\pi \times \frac{d}{2} \times \pi r^2 = \pi^2 \, d \, r^2$$

EXERCISES

8. Find the center of mass of a semicircular flat plate cut from uniform sheet metal.
9. Find the center of mass of a wire bent to form a semicircular arc.
10. Find the center of mass of a solid hemisphere.
11. Find the center of mass of a plane figure cut out of sheet metal having the shape of a square of side 1 ft surmounted by a semicircle of diameter 1 ft.
12. An isosceles trapezoid has bases b and $3b$. The base angles are 45°. Find the center of mass.

15.3. MOMENT OF INERTIA AND RADIUS OF GYRATION

The moment of inertia of a rigid body about an axis is, qualitatively speaking, a measure of rotational inertia just as mass is a measure of translational inertia. Consider as in Fig. 15.10 a particle of mass m free to rotate at a perpendicular distance

p from a fixed axis. If a force of magnitude f is applied, tangential to the circle, the particle experiences an acceleration $a_T = \alpha p$, so that $f = m\alpha p$. The translational inertia m is equal to f/a_T. A corresponding rotational inertia could be taken as the ratio of torque to angular acceleration:

$$(15.9) \qquad \frac{\gamma}{\alpha} = \frac{fp}{f/mp} = mp^2$$

This same quantity appeared also in (12.1). The conclusion of (15.9) is sufficient motivation for defining the moment of inertia of a collection of particles or of an extended body. We assume that the moment of inertia of a collection of particles is the sum of the moments of inertia of the constituent particles. The appropriateness of this assumption will evolve naturally in the next chapter. In symbols, then, the moment of inertia, denoted by i, is given for a finite aggregate of n particles by a summation

$$(15.10) \qquad i = i_1 + i_2 + \cdots + i_n$$

where each i_k is given as in (15.9) or for an extended body by an integration

$$(15.11) \qquad i = \int di$$

where $di = p^2\, dm$. Thus, in Fig. 15.11, we write for the moment of inertia about the z axis

$$(15.12) \qquad i_z = \int_m p^2\, dm = \int_m (\mathbf{K} \times \mathbf{R})^2\, dm$$

To justify the last expression observe that $|\mathbf{K} \times \mathbf{R}| = r \sin \theta = p$, where θ is the angle between $\mathbf{K}$ and $\mathbf{R}$. For an axis through the origin $\mathbf{O}$ parallel to any unit vector $\mathbf{E}$, the *moment of inertia* is thus defined to be

$$i = \int_m (\mathbf{E} \times \mathbf{R})^2\, dm$$

Example I

As a trivial application of the definition, consider a uniform hoop of mass m and radius r. What is its moment of inertia about a normal axis through its center?

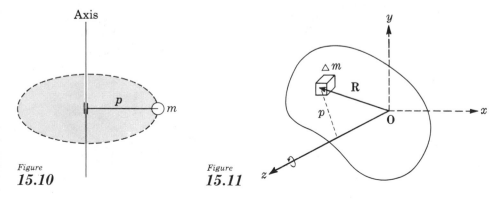

Figure **15.10**   *Figure* **15.11**

Imagine the hoop to be divided into small segments of mass Δm (see Fig. 15.12). Treating each segment as a particle, its moment of inertia is $r^2 \Delta m$. Applying (15.10),

$$i = \Sigma p^2 \Delta m$$

Since for each segment the perpendicular distance p from the axis is r, we have

$$i = \Sigma r^2 \Delta m = r^2 \Sigma \Delta m = mr^2$$

Alternatively, applying (15.11),

$$i = \int p^2 \, dm = r^2 \int dm = r^2 m$$

Example 2

To find the moment of inertia of a sphere about a diameter, say, the x axis in Fig. 15.13.

Solution

Let us divide the sphere into elements each of which has a fixed distance from the axis, i.e., into cylindrical-shell elements of radius $y = r \sin \theta$ and thickness $dy = r \cos \theta \, d\theta$. The mass of such an element, taking δ as the uniform density, is

$$dm = \delta \, 4\pi xy \, dy$$

and its moment of inertia is

$$di = \delta \, 4\pi xy^3 \, dy = 4\pi \, \delta r^5 \sin^3 \theta \cos^2 \theta \, d\theta$$
$$= 4\pi \, \delta r^5 \cos^2 \theta \sin \theta \, d\theta - 4\pi \, \delta r^5 \cos^4 \theta \sin \theta \, d\theta$$

Integrating for θ from 0 to $\pi/2$, we get

$$i = \frac{8\pi \, \delta r^5}{15}$$

The total mass m of the sphere is known:

$$m = \tfrac{4}{3}\pi \, \delta r^3$$

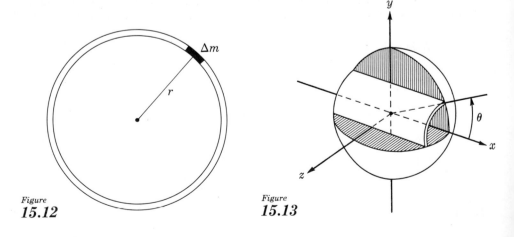

Figure
15.12

Figure
15.13

Thus i may be written

$$i = \tfrac{2}{5}mr^2$$

Note that a sphere of mass m and radius r has the same moment of inertia as a hoop of mass m and radius $\bar{p}$ given by

$$\bar{p}^2 = \tfrac{2}{5}r^2$$

This convenient approach to problems of rotational inertia leads to defining the *radius of gyration* $\bar{p}$ of a rigid body about a particular axis by

(15.13)
$$\bar{p}^2 = \frac{i}{m}$$

or

$$m\bar{p}^2 = \int_m p^2 \, dm$$

The radius of gyration is the distance from the axis at which the mass of a body can be regarded as concentrated without altering its rotational inertia. In the case of the hoop (Example 1), the radius of gyration for the stated axis is equal to the actual radius r, for the mass *is* all concentrated at this distance from the axis.

Example 3

Find the radius of gyration of a solid cylinder about its axis (see Fig. 15.14).

Solution

As in the last example, let us divide the cylinder into shells of radius x, thickness dx, and hence of moment of inertia

$$di = 2\pi \, \delta l x^3 \, dx$$

Integrating,

$$i = 2\pi \, \delta l \int_0^r x^3 \, dx = \tfrac{1}{2}\pi \, \delta l r^4$$

Dividing by $m = \pi r^2 l \delta$, we get

$$\bar{p}^2 = \tfrac{1}{2}r^2$$

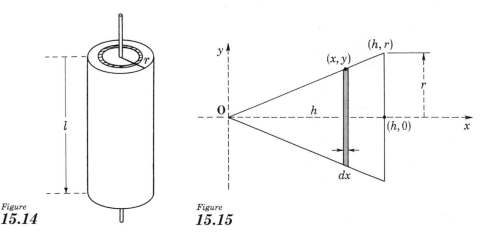

Figure
15.14

Figure
15.15

Example 4

Find the radius of gyration for rotation about a perpendicular axis of symmetry of a thin uniform rod of length $2r$.

Solution

We may write, canceling out factors involving density and cross section,

$$\bar{p}^2 = \frac{1}{2r} \int_{-r}^{r} x^2 \, dx = \frac{1}{2r} \left[\frac{x^3}{3} \right]_{-r}^{r} = \tfrac{1}{3} r^2$$

Example 5

What is the radius of gyration about its axis of symmetry of a homogeneous isosceles triangle?

Solution

Regard the triangle as made up of adjacent parallel rods, a typical one of which is shaded in Fig. 15.15. By Example 4, the rod shown has radius of gyration $\bar{p}$ given by $\bar{p}^2 = \tfrac{1}{3} y^2$. Its mass is $2\sigma y \, dx$, where σ is the area density m/rh, m being the mass of the triangle. Hence the moment of inertia of the rod is

$$di = \tfrac{2}{3} \sigma y^3 \, dx$$

But $y = rx/h$, so we have

$$i = \int di = \tfrac{2}{3} \frac{m}{rh} \left(\frac{r}{h} \right)^3 \int_0^h x^3 \, dx$$

$$= \tfrac{1}{6} m r^2 \quad \text{and} \quad \bar{p}^2 = \frac{r^2}{6}$$

Note that this problem may be solved in other ways. For instance, the triangle can be thought of as divided into horizontal strips:

$$i = 2\sigma \int_0^r y^2 (h - x) \, dy = 2\sigma \int_0^r \left[y^2 h - \left(\frac{h}{r} \right) y^3 \right] dy$$

$$= \tfrac{1}{6} \sigma r^3 h = \tfrac{1}{6} m r^2$$

or multiple integration may be used.

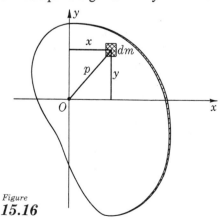

Figure
15.16

EXERCISES

13. Four 5-lb balls are situated at the corners of a square 1 yd to a side. Compute the moment of inertia about (a) a diagonal; (b) an edge; (c) an axis normal to the square at its center; (d) an axis normal to the square at a corner. Treat the balls as particles.
14. Compute the radius of gyration about a diameter of a uniform circular disk of radius a.
15. A cylinder of the size shown in Fig. 15.14 has a radial density function $\delta = \delta_0 + kx$. Compute the radius of gyration for rotation about the axis of the cylinder.
16. A uniform isosceles trapezoid of parallel bases b and b' and of altitude h is rotated about its axis of symmetry. Find the radius of gyration.

15.4. THE PERPENDICULAR-AXIS THEOREM

Consider a plane figure lying in the xy plane as in Fig. 15.16. Its moment of inertia about the z axis may be written

$$i_z = \int_m p^2 \, dm = \int_m (x^2 + y^2) \, dm = \int_m x^2 \, dm + \int_m y^2 \, dm$$

or, since these terms are the moments of inertia about the y and x axes, respectively,

(15.14) $$i_z = i_x + i_y$$

The relationship stated in (15.14) constitutes what is known as the perpendicular-axis theorem for plane figures.

Example 1

Find the radius of gyration of a circular disk about a diameter.

Solution

By the result on cylinders, $i_z = \tfrac{1}{2}mr^2$. (This implies that the disk lies in the xy plane with the origin at its center.) Assuming that the disk is uniform, one diameter is as good as another; thus, by the symmetry, $i_x = i_y$. Using the perpendicular axis result,

$$i_x + i_y = 2i_x = i_z$$

or

$$i_x = \tfrac{1}{4}mr^2 \qquad \bar{p}^2 = \tfrac{1}{4}r^2$$

Example 2

To find the radius of gyration of a plane rectangle of dimensions $2a$ by $2b$ rotated about a perpendicular axis through its center. Choosing axes as shown in Fig. 15.17, i_x is easily evaluated in terms of the previous result concerning a rod, for the whole rectangle can be thought of as composed of rods of length $2b$ laid side by side. Hence

$$i_x = \tfrac{1}{3}mb^2$$

Similarly,

$$i_y = \tfrac{1}{3}ma^2$$

By (15.14), we have

$$i_z = \tfrac{1}{3}m(a^2 + b^2) \qquad \bar{p}^2 = \frac{a^2 + b^2}{3}$$

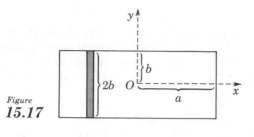

Figure
15.17

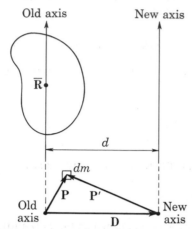

Figure
15.18

15.5. THE PARALLEL-AXIS THEOREM

In most of the examples so far we have computed moments of inertia for axes through the center of mass. For symmetrical bodies this is manifestly advantageous. We shall now introduce a theorem which enables one to use these simpler results in other circumstances without repeating computations. The statement of the result is

(15.15) *For rotation about an axis not through its center of mass, the radius of gyration $\bar{p}'$ of a rigid body is given by*

$$\bar{p}'^2 = \bar{p}^2 + d^2$$

where $\bar{p}$ is its radius of gyration about a parallel axis through the center of mass and d is the distance between the two parallel axes.

PROOF. For each element of mass, consider the plane through this element and perpendicular to the two axes. Let **P** and **P′** be the vectors to the element dm from the points where the axes meet the plane and let **D** be the vector between these points in the sense shown in Fig. 15.18, so that

$$\mathbf{P}' = \mathbf{P} - \mathbf{D}$$

This relationship is diagramed in Fig. 15.18. Then the new moment of inertia i' is given by

$$i' = \int_m p'^2 \, dm = \int_m (\mathbf{P}' \cdot \mathbf{P}') \, dm = \int_m (\mathbf{P} - \mathbf{D}) \cdot (\mathbf{P} - \mathbf{D}) \, dm$$

$$= \int_m (\mathbf{P} \cdot \mathbf{P}) \, dm - 2 \int_m (\mathbf{P} \cdot \mathbf{D}) \, dm + \int_m (\mathbf{D} \cdot \mathbf{D}) \, dm$$

$$= \int_m p^2 \, dm - 2\mathbf{D} \cdot \int_m \mathbf{P} \, dm + d^2 \int_m dm$$

Now the first term on the right is at once recognizable as i. The integral in the second term must vanish since it gives the mass times the perpendicular distance from the old axis to the center of mass. Rewriting,

$$i' = i + d^2 m$$

or, dividing by m,

$$\bar{p}'^2 = \bar{p}^2 + d^2$$

Example 1

The moment of inertia of a sphere about a diameter is $0.4mr^2$. How far from the center of the sphere must an axis be placed in order to increase the moment of inertia by 50 per cent?

Solution

$$0.6mr^2 = 0.4mr^2 + md^2 \qquad 0.2r^2 = d^2$$

Thus

$$d = 0.45r$$

Example 2

What is the radius of gyration of a uniform bar of length l about one end?

Solution

Using Sec. 15.3, Example 4, together with the parallel-axis theorem,

$$\bar{p}^2 = \frac{1}{3}\left(\frac{l}{2}\right)^2 + \left(\frac{l}{2}\right)^2 = \frac{l^2}{3}$$

Note that this result could have been regarded as obvious since l in this example corresponds to r in Example 4 just referred to. Example 4 consists of two symmetrical parts, each similar to the bar of the present example! We could use this example to compute the radius of gyration for a right triangle about a leg, using a calculation substantially identical with that of Sec. 15.3, Example 5.

EXERCISES

17. Find the moment of inertia of a uniform bar of length $4r$ and mass m about a perpendicular axis at a distance r from the center.
18. Find the radius of gyration of a circular disk of radius r about a tangent line.
19. The mass of a hoop is 5 kg. Its radius is 0.6 m. Find its moment of inertia (a) about a diameter; (b) about a tangent.
20. A half disk or semicircular plate is rotated about an axis through its center of mass and parallel to the bounding diameter. Find the radius of gyration.
21. A homogeneous plane quarter circle of radius r is rotated about a bounding diameter. Find the radius of gyration.
22. A uniform plane figure having the shape of a square surmounted by a semicircle is rotated about (a) the base; (b) the axis of symmetry. If the square has edge $2r$ and the circle has radius r, find the two radii of gyration.

15.6. ADDITIONAL METHODS FOR COMPUTING MOMENTS OF INERTIA

It is quite possible to associate long and happily with moments of inertia without meeting explicitly the two topics of this section. They are, however, rather interesting, and they will be welcomed by students who like to learn "rules of thumb" which make unnecessary tedious integrations.

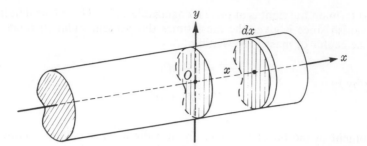

Figure
15.19

The Cylinder Theorem. We shall here apply the name cylinder to any solid generated by moving a plane figure perpendicular to itself along a straight line. Thus the ordinary cylinder may be thought of as generated by moving a thin circular disk. We shall try to compute an expression for the moment of inertia about some axis (in Fig. 15.19, the y axis) perpendicular to the generators (such as the x axis in the figure) of the cylinder. Taking as an element a slice of thickness dx and mass dm, we can write first its moment of inertia about a parallel axis through its center of mass $\bar{\mathbf{R}}$

$$di'' = \bar{p}''^2 \, dm$$

About a parallel axis, in the slice, which cuts the x axis, the moment of inertia of the slice is (see Fig. 15.20)

$$di' = \bar{p}''^2 \, dm + \bar{z}^2 \, dm$$

And finally, about the y axis itself:

$$di = \bar{p}''^2 \, dm + \bar{z}^2 \, dm + x^2 \, dm$$

This may be integrated over the whole mass.

$$i_y = \int \bar{p}''^2 \, dm + \int \bar{z}^2 \, dm + \int x^2 \, dm$$

Now p'' and $\bar{z}$ are the same for each element; thus they may be taken outside the integration symbol:

$$i_y = m\bar{p}''^2 + m\bar{z}^2 + \int x^2 \, dm$$

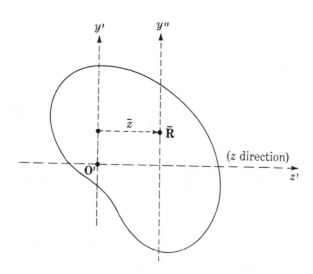

Figure
15.20

Each term has its own significance. $m\bar{p}''^2$ is the moment of inertia of a disk having the shape of the slices we have taken as elements and possessing the entire mass of the cylinder. It is, however, the moment of inertia about a parallel axis through the center of mass. $m\bar{p}''^2 + m\bar{z}^2$ is the moment of inertia of such a disk located in the yz plane taken about the y axis. Finally, $\int x^2\, dm$ is the moment of inertia about the y axis of a rod of mass m lying along the x axis. We write, then,

$$(15.16) \qquad\qquad i_{\text{cylinder}} = i_{\text{disk}} + i_{\text{rod}}$$

In words, if a cylinder is parallel to the x axis, its moment about the y axis is the sum of (a) the moment about the y axis of the disk obtained by projecting the whole cylinder into the yz plane and (b) the moment about the y axis of the rod obtained by projecting the whole cylinder into the x axis. [Note that "y axis" may be replaced by "z axis" in the above statement. Equation (15.16) is also true for moments about the x axis; but the result is less meaty in this case.]

Example 1

Find the moment of inertia of an ordinary solid cylinder of length $2l$ and radius r about a perpendicular axis through the center (see Fig. 15.21).

Solution

Using the terminology of (15.16),

$$i_{\text{disk}} = \tfrac{1}{4}mr^2$$

$$i_{\text{rod}} = \tfrac{1}{3}ml^2$$

i_{cylinder} is the sum of these two terms.

Example 2

Find the moment of inertia of a rectangular box about an axis of symmetry.

Solution

The result previously obtained about a rectangular plate can be extended to this problem. Here, however, for the present, let us use the cylinder theorem (see Fig. 15.22).

$$i_{\text{disk}} = \tfrac{1}{3}mc^2 \qquad i_{\text{rod}} = \tfrac{1}{3}ma^2$$

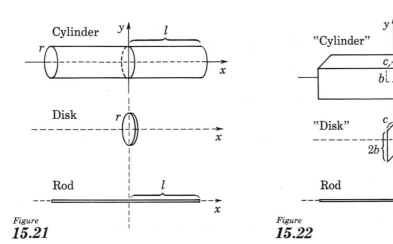

Figure
15.21

Figure
15.22

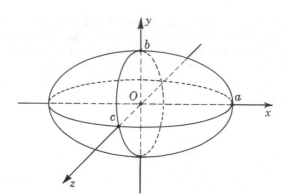

Figure
15.23

Hence, for the "cylinder,"

$$i_y = \tfrac{1}{3}m(a^2 + c^2)$$

Similarly,

$$i_x = \tfrac{1}{3}m(b^2 + c^2)$$

Routh's Rule. The results on radii of gyration for certain simple figures have been summarized by Routh in a way that is easy to remember.

(15.17) *The square of the radius of gyration for rotation about an axis of symmetry of a solid body having rectangular, elliptical, or ellipsoidal symmetry is equal to the sum of the squares of the semiaxes of symmetry perpendicular to the rotation axis divided by 3, 4, or 5, respectively.*

The student should observe that this rule includes previous results on the disk (elliptical), the sphere (ellipsoidal), the rod (rectangular), as well as for rectangular shapes. In particular, the results just obtained for a solid box are given by it.

Example 3

What are the radii of gyration about the coordinate axes of the ellipsoid (see Fig. 15.23)

$$\frac{x^2}{a^2} + \frac{y^2}{b^2} + \frac{z^2}{c^2} = 1$$

Solution

By Routh's rule,

$$\bar{p}_x^2 = 0.2(b^2 + c^2)$$

$$\bar{p}_y^2 = 0.2(a^2 + c^2)$$

$$\bar{p}_z^2 = 0.2(a^2 + b^2)$$

For the case where $a = b = c$, this example degenerates into the sphere (previously handled).

EXERCISES

23. Find the radius of gyration of a solid cone of altitude h and radius of base r about its axis of symmetry.

24. A cube of edge s is rotated about one edge. Find the radius of gyration.

25. An elliptical disk bounded by a curve which, with respect to the axes of symmetry, has the equation

$$\frac{x^2}{a^2} + \frac{y^2}{b^2} = 1$$

is rotated about the line $x = a$. Find the radius of gyration.

26. Find the radius of gyration of a solid cone of altitude h and radius of base r about a diameter of its base.

15.7. NOTE ON PRINCIPAL AXES OF INERTIA

The study of moments of inertia might be pursued much further. Here we shall have to be content with a cursory inquiry into slightly more general ideas.

Given a rigid body and axes $\mathbf{O}xyz$, we have so far defined three *moments of inertia*:

$$i_x = \int_m (\mathbf{I} \times \mathbf{R})^2 \, dm = \int_m (y^2 + z^2) \, dm$$

$$i_y = \int_m (\mathbf{J} \times \mathbf{R})^2 \, dm = \int_m (z^2 + x^2) \, dm$$

$$i_z = \int_m (\mathbf{K} \times \mathbf{R})^2 \, dm = \int_m (x^2 + y^2) \, dm$$

(A vector squared denotes the scalar product with itself.) Three other inertia constants are often used. These are the *products of inertia*:

$$i_{xy} = -\int_m (\mathbf{I} \times \mathbf{R}) \cdot (\mathbf{J} \times \mathbf{R}) \, dm = \int_m xy \, dm$$

$$i_{yz} = -\int_m (\mathbf{J} \times \mathbf{R}) \cdot (\mathbf{K} \times \mathbf{R}) \, dm = \int_m yz \, dm$$

$$i_{zx} = -\int_m (\mathbf{K} \times \mathbf{R}) \cdot (\mathbf{I} \times \mathbf{R}) \, dm = \int_m zx \, dm$$

The coordinate axes are called *principal axes of inertia relative to* $\mathbf{O}$ if these products are zero. (That is, if i_{xy} and i_{zx} are both zero, then the x axis is such an axis, etc.) It is easy to show, for instance, that a line of symmetry or a line normal to a plane of symmetry is such an axis. (In the latter case the origin is taken in the plane.)

We now consider the moment of inertia about a random axis through the origin. Let its direction be given by the unit vector

$$\mathbf{E} = l\mathbf{I} + m\mathbf{J} + n\mathbf{K}$$

Then we have

$$i = \int_m p^2 \, dm = \int_m (\mathbf{E} \times \mathbf{R})^2 \, dm$$

Substituting the value for $\mathbf{E}$, this may be expanded since

$$(\mathbf{E} \times \mathbf{R})^2 = l^2 (\mathbf{I} \times \mathbf{R})^2 + m^2 (\mathbf{J} \times \mathbf{R})^2 + n^2 (\mathbf{K} \times \mathbf{R})^2$$
$$+ 2lm(\mathbf{I} \times \mathbf{R}) \cdot (\mathbf{J} \times \mathbf{R}) + 2mn(\mathbf{J} \times \mathbf{R}) \cdot (\mathbf{K} \times \mathbf{R}) + 2nl(\mathbf{K} \times \mathbf{R}) \cdot (\mathbf{I} \times \mathbf{R})$$

Using the values for the six inertia constants given earlier, this means

$$(15.18) \qquad i = l^2 i_x + m^2 i_y + n^2 i_z - 2lm i_{xy} - 2mn i_{yz} - 2nl i_{zx}$$

A matrix form of this equation will be found in Appendix 4, Sec. A4.4, Example 5.

This equation shows how any moment of inertia is expressible in terms of the six basic inertia constants relative to a given set of axes if the axis is through the origin.

The last equation suggests that the inertia constants might be used to define a quadric surface with points at a distance from the origin correlated with radius of gyration about an axis in that direction. This suggestion leads to the fascinating theory of the *ellipsoid of inertia*, which the student is encouraged to read about elsewhere.

In this course, our use of (15.18) will be brief and to the point. Picking co-ordinate axes in coincidence with axes of symmetry of simple bodies, we can easily compute moments of inertia about skew axes.

Example 1

Given a cylinder of length $2l$ and radius r, pick the origin at the center and the x axis along the axis of the cylinder. Then an axis through the center at an angle θ with the axis of symmetry (i.e., the x axis) may be described by

$$\mathbf{E} = \cos \theta \mathbf{I} + \sin \theta \mathbf{J}$$

All three coordinate axes are axes of symmetry; thus the products of inertia vanish giving

$$i = m\left[\cos^2 \theta \frac{r^2}{2} + \sin^2 \theta \left(\frac{l^2}{3} + \frac{r^2}{4}\right)\right]$$

Example 2

Given a cube, let us pick origin at the center and axes parallel to the edges. Then the coordinate axes are axes of symmetry, and hence principal axes of inertia. Also because of the symmetry,

$$i_x = i_y = i_z$$

Using (15.18), we get

$$i = l^2 i_x + m^2 i_y + n^2 i_z$$
$$= (l^2 + m^2 + n^2) i_x$$
$$= i_x$$

Thus for a uniform cube the moment of inertia is the same for any axis through the center.

EXERCISES

27. Perform in detail the vector manipulations leading to (15.18).
28. Find the radius of gyration of a disk of radius r about an axis through its center and making an angle of 45° with the normal.
29. Find the radius of gyration of a rectangle of dimensions $2a \times 2b$ about a diagonal.
30. In view of (15.18) can you extend the "cylinder theorem" (15.16) to a skew axis through the center? Reinforce your answer by details.

REVIEW EXERCISES

31. The positions and masses of four particles are as follows:
   (i) Mass, 10 g; position vector, $6\mathbf{I}$ ft.
   (ii) Mass, 15 g; position vector, $4\mathbf{I} + 4\mathbf{J}$ ft.
   (iii) Mass, 20 g, position vector, $3\mathbf{I} + 2\mathbf{J} - 3\mathbf{K}$ ft.
   (iv) Mass, 30 g; position vector, at origin.
   Find the position vector of the center of mass.

32. A jar, the interior of which is of the form of a uniform cylinder of depth 6 in., weighs 3 lb empty and 5 lb filled with water. When filled with water the center of gravity is 3.3 in. below the top. How far from the top is the center of gravity when the jar is empty?

33. A square piece of sheet metal 4 in. on a side has a hole of 3 in. diameter cut through its center. How far from the center of the circle is the center of mass of the figure remaining after the removal of one corner quarter as shown in Fig. 15.24?

34. A uniform wire bent in the shape of a J as shown in Fig. 15.25 consists of a semicircle of radius r, one side being continued a distance x. When the figure balances on a knife-edge shown in cross section at A, the segment of length x is horizontal. Find x in terms of r.

35. The perpendicular distance from a fixed plane for a typical mass element dm of a body is denoted by p and for the center of mass of the body is $\bar{p}$. Derive the formula

$$m\bar{p} = \int p \, dm$$

36. A vector perpendicular to a fixed axis and extending from the axis to a typical mass element dm of a body is denoted by $\mathbf{P}$ and for the center of mass of the body is $\bar{\mathbf{P}}$. Derive the formula

$$m\bar{\mathbf{P}} = \int \mathbf{P} \, dm$$

37. A uniform metal plate in the shape of a right triangle has altitude h and base b. What is its radius of gyration for rotation about the vertical edge?

38. Compute the radius of gyration of a uniform block of steel 3 by 4 by 5 in. about one of the longest edges.

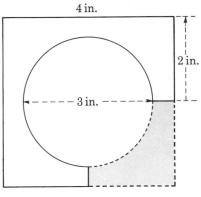

Figure
15.24

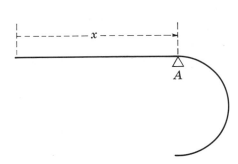

Figure
15.25

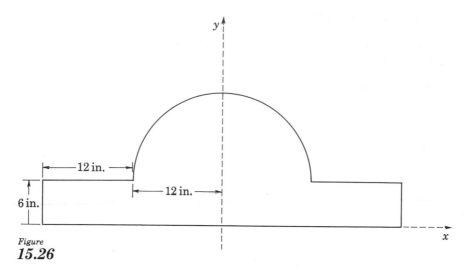

Figure
15.26

39. A uniform wire 5 ft long is bent into the shape of a square 15 in. on the side. Find the radius of gyration about an axis normal to the square and through one corner.
40. Find the center of mass of a uniform plane quarter circle of radius a.
41. What is the radius of gyration of the figure described in Exercise 40 about an axis perpendicular to its plane and through the center of mass?
42. A plane thin metal part of mass 1.2 lb/ft² has the shape shown in Fig. 15.26: a rectangle 4 ft by 6 in. surmounted by a semicircle of radius 1 ft. Find:
   (a) The y coordinate of the center of mass.
   (b) The moment of inertia for rotation about the y axis.
43. What is the radius of gyration of a uniform spherical shell of radius r for rotation about a diameter?
44. Consider a plane figure for which both the x and y axes are axes of symmetry. Let θ be the angle between the x axis and an axis of rotation through the origin and in the plane of the figure. Show that the moment of inertia is given by an expression of the form
$$i = \mu_1 + \mu_2 \sin^2 \theta$$
Identify the constants μ_1, μ_2.
45. Using the nomenclature of the preceding exercise, plot the reciprocal of the radius of gyration $(i/m)^{-\frac{1}{2}}$ as a function of θ in a polar coordinate graph:
   (a) For a rectangle 2 by 4 ft.
   (b) For a rod 5 ft long.
   (c) For an ellipse $x^2/4 + y^2/16 = 1$.
46. Suppose that we regard a diatomic molecule as a pair of point masses m_1 and m_2 separated by a distance r. Evaluate the moment of inertia about a normal axis through the center of mass solely in terms of r and the *reduced mass* $m_1 m_2/(m_1 + m_2) = \mu$.

CHAPTER SIXTEEN

APPLICATIONS: RIGID-BODY MECHANICS

In this chapter we combine our knowledge of particle dynamics, moments of forces, and rigid-body kinematics to handle basic problems in rigid-body dynamics. Such considerations are essential for many branches of engineering. Many devices of the physics laboratory also require a knowledge of the mechanics of rigid bodies.

16.1. CENTER OF MASS IN STATICS PROBLEMS

In Sec. 10.8 it was shown that for an aggregate of particles the resultant of the weights passes through the center of mass as long as gravity is uniform. This fact applies to rigid bodies; therefore we may say:

(16.1) *The gravitational forces on a rigid body (in a region of uniform gravity) have as resultant a single force (the weight) acting through the center of mass.*

We have assumed this to be true when dealing with symmetrical bodies.

Example I

A uniform triangular board of sides 3, 4, and 5 ft is suspended by the corner having the smallest angle. What angle does the longest side make with the vertical when the board is in equilibrium?

Solution

It is easy to show that the center of mass is at the point shown in Fig. 16.1. For equilibrium the line $\mathbf{O\bar{R}}$ must be vertical; therefore β is the desired angle. From the figure we see that

$$\tan(\alpha + \beta) = \tfrac{3}{4} \qquad \alpha + \beta = 36.8°$$
$$\tan \alpha = \tfrac{3}{8} \qquad \alpha = 20.6°$$

Thus

$$\beta = 16.2°$$

In physics and engineering one is likely to encounter forces whose actions are distributed over a body but which are not uniform, gravity being an example. In such cases the center of action may not be the center of mass. Such problems may

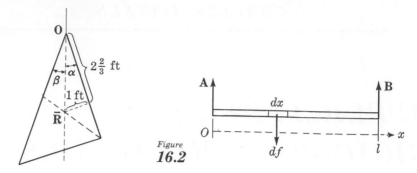

Figure
16.1

Figure
16.2

be handled by replacing the previous conditions for equilibrium by

(16.2) $$\int d\mathbf{F} = \mathbf{O} \qquad \int d\boldsymbol{\Gamma} = \mathbf{O}$$

Example 2

A uniform bar of weight w and length l is supported horizontally by vertical forces **A**, **B** at the ends, as in Fig. 16.2. A vertical downward force in addition to gravity varies according to the rule

$$df = kx\,dx$$

where k is a constant. Find **A** and **B**.

Solution

Using (16.2),

$$a + b - w - \int_0^l kx\,dx = 0$$

or

$$a + b = w + \tfrac{1}{2}kl^2$$

Also

$$bl - w\frac{l}{2} - \int_0^l kx^2\,dx = 0$$

or

$$b = \frac{w}{2} + \frac{kl^2}{3}$$

Whence

$$a = \frac{w}{2} + \frac{kl^2}{6}$$

EXERCISES

1. A uniform triangular board weighs 10 lb. Its edges have lengths 18, 24, and 30 in. It is supported, with the largest edge horizontal, by two vertical strings, one at each end of the largest edge. Find the tensions.

2. A uniform triangular plate of weight w is supported horizontally by vertical threads through the corners. The angles of the triangle are α, β, and γ. Find the tension in each of the threads.

3. A uniform semicircular plate is supported in a horizontal position by three vertical threads, one at each end of the bounding diameter and one on the circumference at the middle of the bounding semicircle. If the plate weighs 1.75 newtons, what is the tension in each of the threads?

4. A uniform bar (like the one in Fig. 16.2) is subject to a variable normal force per unit length given by

$$\frac{d\mathbf{F}}{dx} = (a + bx^2)\mathbf{J}$$

Find the magnitude and location of the resultant.

16.2. DYNAMICS OF A RIGID BODY IN TRANSLATION

In Chap. 13 rotation and translation were discussed as the principal modes of motion of a rigid body. We now turn to the dynamics of pure translation. First let us recall that in translation all points have the same velocity and hence the same acceleration

(16.3) $$\mathbf{V} = \bar{\mathbf{V}} \qquad \mathbf{A} = \bar{\mathbf{A}}$$

Using the results of Sec. 13.7, we might equally well describe the motion by

$$\Omega = \mathbf{O} \qquad \mathfrak{A} = \mathbf{O}$$

We might immediately consider any rigid body of mass m as an aggregate of particles and then apply earlier conclusions to the case at hand. It may, however, be more illuminating to proceed right from the theory concerning single particles; thus let us now regard the body as consisting of many small elements, a typical one having mass Δm (see Fig. 16.3). Let $\mathbf{R}$ be a point within such an element. For each element Δm, $\mathbf{F}$ denotes the resultant of external forces, $\mathbf{F}'$ of internal forces. Then

$$\mathbf{F} + \mathbf{F}' = \mathbf{A} \, \Delta m$$

(Subscripts are now omitted deliberately for the sake of simplicity of notation. Any student wishing to do so is hereby authorized to insert any such trimmings.) It is to be remembered that $\mathbf{A}$ is the same for each Δm. Adding all such equations, member by member, the $\mathbf{F}'$'s add up to zero, since they are present in equal and opposite pairs, and the result is

(16.4) $$\bar{\mathbf{F}} = \Sigma \, \mathbf{F} = \Sigma \, \mathbf{A} \, \Delta m = \mathbf{A}[\Sigma \, (\Delta m)] = m\mathbf{A} = m\bar{\mathbf{A}}$$

This is merely a reaffirmation of the statement made previously about aggregates in general: The center of mass moves like a single particle subjected to the same external forces. Except for the emphasis on the circumstance that $\mathbf{A}$ is the same for all elements, this result makes no statement applying uniquely to translation. The negative point of view that translation is absence of rotation may be expressed by resorting to expressions involving moments. Taking moments about a random origin $\mathbf{O}$, we get for each element

$$\bar{\mathbf{\Gamma}}_O = \Sigma \, \mathbf{R} \times \mathbf{F} = \Sigma \, \mathbf{R} \times \mathbf{A} \, \Delta m = (\Sigma \, \mathbf{R} \, \Delta m) \times \mathbf{A}$$

Passing to the limit as smaller and smaller Δm's are used,

$$\bar{\mathbf{\Gamma}}_O = \Sigma \, \mathbf{R} \times \mathbf{F} = \left(\int_m \mathbf{R} \, dm \right) \times \mathbf{A}$$

The notion of center of mass has again forced its way into our deliberations. Clearly, this expression is simplified by rewriting as follows:

(16.5) $$\bar{\mathbf{\Gamma}}_O = m\bar{\mathbf{R}} \times \mathbf{A} = \bar{\mathbf{R}} \times m\mathbf{A} = \bar{\mathbf{R}} \times \bar{\mathbf{F}}$$

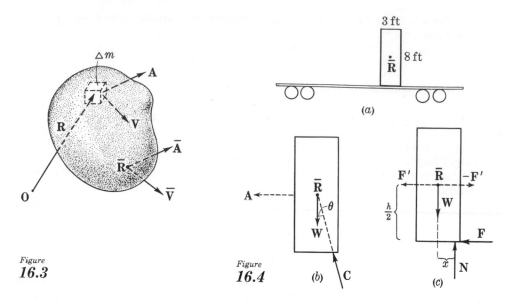

Figure
16.3

Figure
16.4   (b)

There are various ways of describing in words the results stated in Eqs. (16.4) and (16.5). One useful statement is the following:

(16.6) *For a rigid body to be in translation, the resultant of the external forces must act through the center of mass.*

A corollary is

(16.7) *If a rigid body is in translation, the moment sum of the external forces about any axis through the center of mass is zero.*

Example I

A uniformly loaded box 8 ft high and 3 ft wide (see Fig. 16.4a) rests on a flat-car which accelerates at 6 ft/sec². What angle does the resultant force of reaction between box and floor make with the vertical?

Solution

Isolate the box (see Fig. 16.4b). The only forces acting are the weight of the box **W** and the reaction **C** with the floor. Since their resultant passes through the center of mass (by 16.6), **C** as well as **W** passes through $\bar{\mathbf{R}}$. Taking horizontal components,

$$c \sin \theta = \frac{w}{g} a$$

Taking vertical components,

$$c \cos \theta - w = 0$$

Combining the two,

$$\tan \theta = \frac{a}{g} = \frac{6}{32.2} = 0.186$$

Thus

$$\theta = 10.6°$$

An alternative way of handling this problem is shown in Fig. 16.4c. Forces $\mathbf{F}'$ and $-\mathbf{F}'$, equal to and opposite to the frictional component $\mathbf{F}$, are introduced at $\bar{\mathbf{R}}$. It is clear that $w = n$; thus $\{\mathbf{W}, \mathbf{N}\}$ is a couple. By (16.7) it must be counter-balanced by an equal couple $\{\mathbf{F}, -\mathbf{F}'\}$; therefore

$$nx = f\frac{h}{2}$$

or

$$\tan\theta = \frac{x}{h/2} = \frac{f}{w} = \frac{a}{g}$$

as before.

Example 2

For what acceleration would the box in the preceding example start to tip if it did not slip?

Solution

The largest possible value of θ, if $\mathbf{C}$ is to pass through $\bar{\mathbf{R}}$, is given by

$$\tan\theta = 1.5/4.0 = 0.375$$

Using the result of the preceding example,

$$a = 0.375g = 12.1 \text{ ft/sec}^2$$

EXERCISES

5. A 150-lb man stands rigidly on the platform of a truck accelerating uniformly along a straight level road. He faces the side of the road and stands with his feet 2 ft apart. The speed of the truck increases from 15 to 30 mph in 3 sec. How much of the man's weight is on his rear foot if his center of mass is 4 ft above the floor? If he were standing with his feet close together, at what angle must he lean to avoid falling?

6. A truck has a wheel base 16 ft long. When at rest, five-eighths of the weight falls on the rear wheels. At what deceleration will the weight on the front wheels be equal to that on the rear if the center of mass is 5 ft above the ground?

7. An automobile has a wheel base of length d and width b. The center of mass is at a distance h from the ground and r from the rear wheels (measured horizontally). What coefficient of friction would theoretically enable the attainment of an acceleration so great that the front wheels would rise from the road?

8. A spool of rolling radius r and core radius r' rests on a horizontal table as shown in Fig. 16.5. Around the core of the spool is wrapped a thin tape. When the tape is

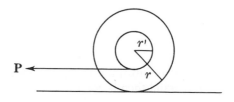

Figure
16.5

pulled horizontally, the spool slips without rolling with an acceleration of magnitude
a. What is the coefficient of friction in terms of r, r', and a?

9. A 100-lb table is 30 in. high and 6 ft long with legs at the four corners. The table is
pulled lengthwise by a symmetrically located 32-lb horizontal force at its upper edge.
If the coefficient of friction is 0.1 and if the center of mass is 2 ft above the floor, how
much of the weight rests on the front legs? For what acceleration would two-thirds
of the weight be on these legs?

10. The runners of a sled are 18 in. apart. The center of mass of the sled together with
the boy riding it is 1 ft above the ground. When the sled plus boy goes around a
level unbanked curve at 30 mph, the sled starts to tip over. No slipping to the side
occurs. Treating the motion as translational, find the radius of curvature of the path.

16.3. DYNAMICS OF A RIGID BODY IN ROTATION

In this section we shall develop a dynamical approach to the important problem of
rotation of a rigid body. Further details will appear in later sections. Suppose
that we have given a rigid body free to rotate about, say, the z axis. Let us imagine
the body to be divided up into pieces of mass Δm as in Fig. 15.11. Some of these
pieces will be subjected to external forces of resultant $\mathbf{F}$ or internal forces of resultant
$\mathbf{F}'$. For each element

$$\mathbf{F} + \mathbf{F}' = \Delta m\, \mathbf{A}$$

If we add these and take a limit, we get

$$\bar{\mathbf{F}} = m\bar{\mathbf{A}}$$

where the left member is the vector sum of the forces applied to the body from the
outside. Note that nothing is said about where the forces are applied. Taking
moments about the origin, we have for each particle

$$\mathbf{R} \times \mathbf{F} + \mathbf{R} \times \mathbf{F}' = \mathbf{R} \times \Delta m\, \mathbf{A}$$

If the sum of such equations be taken, member by member, the terms involving
internal forces will disappear, assuming that the forces of interaction between two
particles act along the line joining the particles, and we shall have, if we pass to the
limit for smaller and smaller elements,

$$\Sigma\, \boldsymbol{\Gamma} = \int_m \mathbf{R} \times \mathbf{A}\, dm$$

Now here in this section we are concerned only with rotation about the z axis;
therefore we shall take z components of each member of the equation

$$\Sigma\, \gamma_z = \int_m \mathbf{K} \cdot \mathbf{R} \times \mathbf{A}\, dm$$

For $\mathbf{A}$ let us substitute the expression derived in (13.13), using $\mathfrak{A} = \alpha\mathbf{K}$, $\boldsymbol{\Omega} = \omega\mathbf{K}$.
The integrand then becomes

$$\mathbf{K} \cdot \mathbf{R} \times [\mathfrak{A} \times \mathbf{R} + \boldsymbol{\Omega} \times (\boldsymbol{\Omega} \times \mathbf{R})]$$

The second term in brackets is a vector in the **KR** plane, so that its scalar triple product with **K** and **R** is zero. The contribution of the first term may be written as

$$\alpha(\mathbf{K} \times \mathbf{R}) \cdot (\mathbf{K} \times \mathbf{R})$$

(interchanging · and × in a triple product). Our conclusion is then

(16.8)
$$\Sigma \gamma_z = \alpha \int_m p^2 \, dm = i_z \alpha$$

where i_z is the moment of inertia about the z axis. This is a rotational analogue of equations of the form $\Sigma f_z = ma_z$. It provides us with a tool for solving problems involving rotation about a fixed axis. We first isolate the body, then add up moments about the axis of the isolating forces, and then finally apply (16.8) to discover the angular acceleration. This assumes optimistically that the moment of inertia is known. We have given some study to computations of this quantity in the preceding chapter. Sometimes it is easier to use a dynamical rather than computational solution. For instance, if we measure both the moment sum and the angular acceleration, the moment of inertia is easily found. Alternative dynamical approaches will appear as examples and exercises.

We may take the results of this section as justifying our earlier assumption (3.12) that

(16.9) *A couple is not equivalent to no forces.*

For, by (16.8), a couple properly applied to a body on an axle will produce discernible angular effects. We may also take this as a means of verifying the fact [converse of (10.3)] that

(16.10) *Two equivalent couples must have equal moments.*

For two couples are called equivalent only if they always will produce the same effect on a rigid body. Equation (16.8) assures us that under certain conditions the same effect can be expected only if the moments of the couples are equal.

Example I

A 100-lb wheel of radius 12 in. whose mass is concentrated essentially at the rim rotates about a fixed axis. When a torque of 1.2 ft-lb is applied, the wheel rotates at uniform angular speed. What angular acceleration will result if a 10-lb force is applied tangent to the rim of the wheel?

Solution

In the first instance, the angular acceleration is zero; thus the moment sum is also zero. This means that, in addition to the applied torque of 1.2 ft-lb, there must be a frictional torque of -1.2 ft-lb. The moment of inertia is merely mr^2, since the mass is concentrated at the rim. Numerically,

$$i_z = (100/32.2) \times 1^2 = 3.1 \text{ ft-lb-sec}^2$$

The 10-lb force has a moment of 10 ft-lb since the radius is 1 ft. Thus Eq. (16.8) here appears as

$$10.0 - 1.2 = 3.1\alpha$$

or

$$\alpha = 2.84 \text{ rad/sec}^2$$

Example 2. Torsion Pendulum

A torsion pendulum consists usually of a disk supported in a horizontal position by a vertical wire through its center as in Fig. 16.6.   When the disk is given an angular displacement, the twisted wire provides a restoring torque proportional to the displacement,

$$(16.11) \qquad\qquad \gamma = -k\theta$$

Applying (16.8), we have

$$-k\theta = i_z \frac{d^2\theta}{dt^2}$$

By our study of simple harmonic motion (5.60), we recognize that the period of oscillation is

$$(16.12) \qquad\qquad \tau = 2\pi \sqrt{\frac{i_z}{k}}$$

Example 3

A wheel whose moment of inertia is 6.0 kg-m² rotates about a horizontal axis (see Fig. 16.7).   The friction of the bearings produces a torque of 0.8 newton-m. The axle of the wheel has a diameter of 4 cm.   A cord wound several times around the axle has at its free end an object of mass 5.0 kg.   If this object is released from rest, how long will it take it to descend 1 m?   Neglect mass and stiffness of the cord and the inertia of the axle.

Solution

First isolate the wheel.   Let **P** be the tension produced by the cord.   Let γ_f denote the magnitude of the frictional torque.   Using (16.8),

$$pr - \gamma_f = i_z\alpha$$

Now isolate the descending object:

$$mg - p = ma$$

Assuming that the cord does not slip,

$$a = \alpha r$$

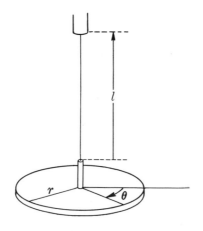

Figure **16.6**

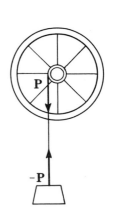

Figure **16.7**

Eliminating p, we have

$$mg - \frac{\gamma_f}{r} = \left(\frac{i}{r^2} + m\right)a$$

Substituting numerical values,

$$5.0 \times 9.8 - \frac{0.8}{0.02} = \left(\frac{6.0}{4 \times 10^{-4}} + 5.0\right)a$$

or

$$a = (9/1.5) \times 10^{-4}$$
$$= 6 \times 10^{-4} \text{ m/sec}^2$$

The distance s of drop and the time t are related by

$$s = \tfrac{1}{2}at^2$$

or

$$t = \sqrt{\frac{2}{6.0 \times 10^{-4}}} = 58 \text{ sec}$$

EXERCISES

11. A flywheel weighs 1,000 lb. Its mass may be considered as concentrated at a distance of 4 ft from the axle. Initially it is rotating at 500 rpm. A brake is applied to the outer rim at a distance of 5 ft from the axle with a normal force of 40 lb. If the coefficient of friction between brake and wheel is 0.42, how long will it take the wheel to come to rest?

12. A given wheel is free to rotate about its axis. An applied torque of 20 ft-lb is sufficient to maintain constant angular speed. A torque of 30 ft-lb produces an angular acceleration of 3 rad/sec^2. What applied torque is necessary to produce an angular acceleration of 6 rad/sec^2?

13. A wheel and axle rigidly joined together have weight 96 lb and moment of inertia 1.33 ft-lb-sec^2. The diameter of the axle is 0.5 in. The axle is supported in horizontal position by bearings whose friction may be neglected. The wheel may be braked by applying a normal force to a braking block held against the axle. The coefficient of friction between block and axle is one-third. If the wheel initially rotates at 300 rpm and if the normal force used on the brake is 100 lb, how many revolutions will the wheel make before coming to a stop? How long will it take?

14. A disk is supported horizontally by a wire through its center. When a couple of 0.5 newton-m is applied, the disk is twisted through 15°. When it is released, the period of vibration is 3.5 sec. What is the moment of inertia of the disk?

15. A homogeneous disk 1 ft in diameter and 1 in. thick is suspended horizontally by a long wire through its center, and it is used as a torsion pendulum. It has a period of 4 sec. If this first disk is replaced by another with the same dimensions but half the density, what period will result?

16.4. PHYSICAL PENDULUM

Any rigid body which can be made to oscillate freely about a fixed horizontal axis may be considered as a pendulum. Figure 16.8 shows such a body displaced from equilibrium by an angle θ. Let Q be the point where the axis intersects the plane normal to the axis and through the center of mass $\bar{R}$. Let the distance from $\bar{R}$ to Q be written h. If the friction at the axis is negligible, then the only force having

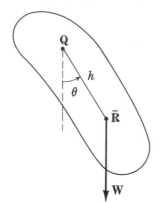

Figure
16.8

a nonzero moment about the axis is the weight. Equation (16.8) may be applied to give

(16.13)
$$-wh \sin \theta = i_z \alpha$$

If we replace α by $\omega(d\omega/d\theta)$, we can write, taking θ_0 as the amplitude,

$$-wh \int_{\theta_0}^{\theta} \sin \theta \ d\theta = i_z \int_0^{\omega} \omega \ d\omega$$

Integrating,

(16.14)
$$wh(\cos \theta - \cos \theta_0) = \tfrac{1}{2} i_z \omega^2$$

This is analogous to (6.10). Equations of this sort will be studied in Sec. 16.8.

If, as in our discussion of the simple pendulum, we agree to consider only cases where θ_0 is small, Eq. (16.13) can be rewritten as

$$-wh\theta = i_z \frac{d^2\theta}{dt^2}$$

This is an equation for simple harmonic oscillation of period given by

(16.15)
$$\tau = 2\pi \sqrt{\frac{i}{wh}} = 2\pi \sqrt{\frac{i}{mgh}}$$

If we write i in terms of the radius of gyration $\bar{p}'$, an alternative expression is

(16.16)
$$\tau = 2\pi \sqrt{\frac{\bar{p}'^2}{gh}}$$

By the parallel-axis theorem our formula may be written in terms of the corresponding radius of gyration about an axis through the center of mass:

(16.17)
$$\tau = 2\pi \sqrt{\frac{\bar{p}^2 + h^2}{gh}}$$

From this it is apparent that the point **Q** is important only as a point in the vertical plane through $\bar{\mathbf{R}}$ and normal to the desired axis at a distance h from $\bar{\mathbf{R}}$. Thus in Fig. 16.9, **Q**′ and **Q**″ are equally suitable points, as are any other points on the circle of radius h about $\bar{\mathbf{R}}$. A parallel axis through any such point would give rise to an oscillation of the same period.

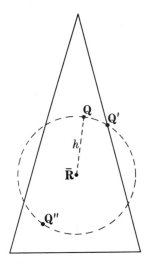

Figure
16.9

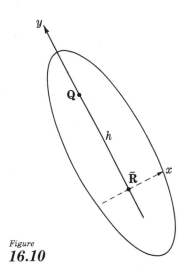

Figure
16.10

The behavior of a physical pendulum, for a given axis, may be summarized simply by saying "It has the same period as a simple pendulum of length *l*." In this case *l* is called the *equivalent length* of the physical pendulum. Combining the results just obtained with those for a simple pendulum, one gets as a formula for *l*

$$(16.18) \qquad l = \frac{\bar{p}'^2}{h} = \frac{\bar{p}^2}{h} + h$$

If we take the line $\bar{R}Q$ as in Fig. 16.10 as an axis, then h is the coordinate of **Q**. Varying h, we should expect to get different periods. In fact, the period will reach a minimum value when l is minimum. Differentiating (16.18),

$$\frac{dl}{dh} = -\frac{\bar{p}^2}{h^2} + 1$$

From this we conclude:

(16.19) *For minimum period,*

$$h = \bar{p} = \tfrac{1}{2}(l_{min})$$

A graph of l plotted against h [using Eq. (16.18)] suggests the same result and also that for other values of l the h's (of the same sign) occur in unequal pairs. Thus in Fig. 16.11 h' and h'' have the same equivalent length and hence the same period. To find interrelations, we write

$$\frac{\bar{p}^2}{h'} + h' = \frac{\bar{p}^2}{h''} + h''$$

or

$$h''\bar{p}^2 - h'\bar{p}^2 = h''^2 h' - h'^2 h''$$

Dividing out $h'' - h'$ (since $h' \neq h''$),

$$(16.20) \qquad\qquad h'h'' = \bar{p}^2$$

It is worth pointing out that

$$(16.21) \qquad\qquad h' + h'' = l$$

as a substitution of (16.20) into (16.18) reveals.

For any physical pendulum, then, if the orientation of the horizontal axis is known, and if the desired period is greater than the minimum period, there are two

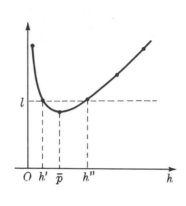

Figure
16.11

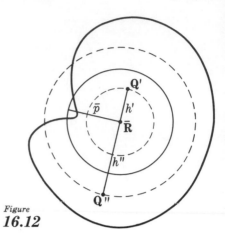

Figure
16.12

circles of points in the normal plane through $\bar{\mathbf{R}}$ through which suitable axes might be constructed to yield that period. These circles have radii h' and h'', whose sum is the length of the equivalent simple pendulum and whose geometric mean is the radius of gyration for rotation about a parallel axis through the center of mass. A pair of diametrically opposite points on the two circles (separated by a distance l) are called conjugate points (for example, $\mathbf{Q}'$ and $\mathbf{Q}''$ in Fig. 16.12).

Example 1

A square board of length s is suspended by one corner so as to oscillate about a normal horizontal axis.   Find the equivalent length.

Solution

Using Routh's rule,

$$\bar{p}^2 = \frac{1}{3}\left[\left(\frac{s}{2}\right)^2 + \left(\frac{s}{2}\right)^2\right] = \frac{1}{6}s^2$$

Now using (16.18),

$$l = \frac{\frac{1}{6}s^2}{s/\sqrt{2}} + \frac{s}{\sqrt{2}} = 0.94s$$

Example 2

If a wheel or other mechanical object is hung on a narrow horizontal support as in Fig. 16.13 and allowed to oscillate, the period may easily be observed.   The

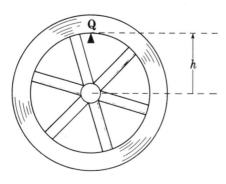

Figure
16.13

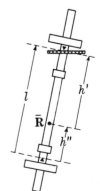

Figure
16.14

center of mass may be located by balancing; thus h may be measured. From h and τ it is easy to find the radius of gyration about a parallel axis through $\bar{\mathbf{R}}$, the center of mass of the wheel. This is a practical method for determining the moment of inertia of such an object. Numerical examples will appear among the exercises.

Example 3. Kater's Reversible Pendulum

Even the simple pendulum may be used for determining the acceleration of gravity at a given locality. More accurate determinations are made with a physical pendulum constructed with knife-edges at conjugate points (see Fig. 16.14). If the adjustable masses are moved to positions so that the period is the same, τ, for oscillation from either support, then g may be computed in terms of τ and the distance l between the points of support. Both τ and l may be measured with great precision. The full theory of Kater's pendulum, as this device is known, complete with corrections to allow for slight differences in periods, for the friction of the air, for various imperfections in the mounting, etc., is too extended for this treatment.

EXERCISES

16. A hoop of diameter 1 m and mass 2 kg hangs on a horizontal nail. With what period will it oscillate (*a*) in its own plane; (*b*) perpendicular to its own plane?

17. A wheel of inner diameter 6 ft 6 in. and weight 320 lb is hung on a normal horizontal knife-edge under the upper rim. The wheel oscillates in its own plane with a period of 2.93 sec. What is the moment of inertia about its axle?

18. A physical pendulum has a period of 2 sec when oscillating about one axis. It has the same period when oscillating about a second parallel axis twice as far from the center of mass. What is the radius of gyration about a parallel axis through the center of mass?

19. A thin uniform square board weighing 1 lb is pivoted about a horizontal axis perpendicular to the board at one corner. It oscillates as a pendulum. A diagonal of the square is 2 ft long. A simple pendulum having the same period must be how long?

20. A Kater's pendulum whose knife-edges are separated by 67.63 cm has a period of 1.651 sec. Find the acceleration of gravity.

21. When a physical pendulum of mass 3 kg oscillates about an axis 1 m from the center of mass, the period is 2.57 sec. What is the moment of inertia about a parallel axis 50 cm from the center of mass?

22. How far from the end of a meter stick may a pivot be placed in order that its period as a physical pendulum be 2 sec?

23. A ring-shaped figure of outer radius 12 in. and inner radius 4 in. is cut from a uniform thin board. It is pivoted about a normal horizontal axis 8 in. from its center. With what frequency will it oscillate as a physical pendulum?

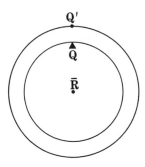

Figure
16.15

24. The ring shown in Fig. 16.15 weighs 200 lb, oscillates about the knife-edge at **Q** with a period of 3.14 sec, and has inner and outer radii of 4 and 5 ft, respectively. What is its moment of inertia about an axis through **Q′** parallel to the knife-edge?

16.5. DYNAMICS OF A RIGID BODY IN MOTION PARALLEL TO A PLANE

When a rigid body rotates about a fixed axis, all velocities are parallel to any plane which has the axis as a normal. Algebraically, the criterion may be written

$$\text{(16.22)} \qquad\qquad \mathbf{K} \cdot \mathbf{V} = 0 \qquad \text{and} \qquad \mathbf{K} \cdot \mathbf{A} = 0$$

if we select the xy plane as the favored one. Translation, too, may be an example of plane motion, assuming only that Eqs. (16.22), are satisfied continually. In this section we shall be considering any motion satisfying these equations. From Sec. 13.7 we may recall that there is always an instantaneous axis of rotation parallel to the z axis. As before, we shall let **C** denote the point of intersection between the axis and the reference plane. **R̄** will denote the center of mass. The xy plane will be picked so that it contains **R̄**.

From the dynamics of aggregates we know that the basic equation

$$\text{(16.23)} \qquad\qquad \Sigma\, \mathbf{F} = m\bar{\mathbf{A}}$$

must be satisfied. Here, as before, the left member is the vector sum of the isolating forces acting on the body. **Ā** is the acceleration of the center of mass. Since the motion is plane, this vector equation is equivalent to

$$\text{(16.24)} \qquad \Sigma\, f_x = m\bar{a}_x \qquad \Sigma\, f_y = m\bar{a}_y \qquad \Sigma\, f_z = 0$$

The z components may not appear at all. If they do occur, they are merely constraining forces which ensure that the motion does not cease to be plane.

Now taking moments about the center of mass, we have

$$\mathbf{R}' = \mathbf{R} - \bar{\mathbf{R}}$$

$$\Sigma\,\boldsymbol{\Gamma} = \Sigma\, \mathbf{R}' \times \mathbf{F} = \int_m \mathbf{R}' \times \mathbf{A}\, dm$$

Substituting

$$\mathbf{A} = \bar{\mathbf{A}} + \boldsymbol{\mathfrak{A}} \times \mathbf{R}' + \boldsymbol{\Omega} \times (\boldsymbol{\Omega} \times \mathbf{R}')$$

and taking scalar products with **K** gives us

$$\Sigma\, \gamma_z = \mathbf{K} \cdot \int \mathbf{R}'\, dm \times \bar{\mathbf{A}} + \mathbf{K} \cdot \int \mathbf{R}' \times (\boldsymbol{\mathfrak{A}} \times \mathbf{R}')\, dm + \mathbf{K} \cdot \int \mathbf{R}' \times [\boldsymbol{\Omega} \times (\boldsymbol{\Omega} \times \mathbf{R}')]\, dm$$

From the choice of origin at the center of mass, the integral in the first term is obviously zero. The integrand in the third integral is perpendicular to **K**, so that term vanishes. The second term may be rewritten as

$$\alpha \int (\mathbf{K} \times \mathbf{R}') \cdot (\mathbf{K} \times \mathbf{R}')\, dm = \alpha \int p'^2\, dm = \alpha \bar{\imath}_z$$

The conclusion is, for moments about an axis through the center of mass,

$$\text{(16.25)} \qquad\qquad \Sigma\, \gamma_z = \bar{\imath}_z \alpha$$

Equations (16.24) and (16.25) are exactly like equations previously applied to problems of translation or rotation separately. They now may be applied to other plane motions.

Example 1

With what acceleration will a uniform solid sphere roll without slipping down a plane inclined at an angle θ with the horizontal?

Solution

Isolating the sphere, the forces are the weight and the reaction of the plane, as in Fig. 16.16. This reaction force is here broken up into tangential and normal projections **F** and **N**. Let the radius be r. Then

$$\bar{a}_x = r\alpha$$

since there is no slipping. The moment of inertia for the axis through the center of mass is given by

$$i_z = \frac{w}{g}\bar{p}^2 = \frac{2}{5}\frac{w}{g}r^2$$

Applying the translation equations (16.24), we have

$$w \sin \theta - f = \frac{w}{g}\bar{a}_x \qquad w \cos \theta - n = 0$$

The rotation equation (16.25) gives us

$$fr = \frac{2}{5}\frac{w}{g}r^2\alpha \qquad \text{or} \qquad f = \frac{2}{5}\frac{w}{g}\bar{a}_x$$

Combining the two, we have

$$w \sin \theta - \frac{2}{5}\frac{w}{g}\bar{a}_x = \frac{w}{g}\bar{a}_x \qquad \text{or} \qquad \bar{a}_x = \tfrac{5}{7}g \sin \theta$$

Example 2

Find the coefficient μ of friction for which rolling without slipping becomes impossible in the preceding example.

Solution

For rolling to take place without slipping, there is required a frictional force given by (see preceding example)

$$f = w \sin \theta - \tfrac{5}{7}w \sin \theta = \tfrac{2}{7}w \sin \theta$$

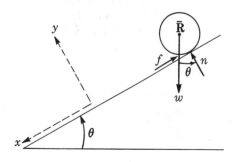

Figure
16.16

This requires a coefficient of friction at least equal to

$$\mu = \frac{f}{n} = \tfrac{2}{7} \tan \theta$$

Example 3

Find the ratio of $\bar{a}_x$ to α for the sphere of the preceding two examples when

$$\mu = k(\tfrac{2}{7} \tan \theta)$$

for some $k < 1$.

Solution

In this case slipping takes place; thus

$$f = \mu n = \frac{2k}{7} \tan \theta \,(w \cos \theta)$$

Putting this for f in the translation equation, we get

$$w \sin \theta - \tfrac{2}{7}kw \sin \theta = \frac{w}{g} \bar{a}_x$$

or

$$\bar{a}_x = g \sin \theta (1 - \tfrac{2}{7}k)$$

In the rotation equation we have

$$\tfrac{2}{7}kw \sin \theta = \frac{2}{5} \frac{w}{g} r\alpha$$

or

$$\alpha = \frac{5g \sin \theta k}{7r}$$

The ratio $\bar{a}_x/\alpha$ is then not r but the following:

$$\frac{\bar{a}_x}{\alpha} = \frac{1 - \tfrac{2}{7}k}{\tfrac{5}{7}k} r = \frac{7 - 2k}{5k} r$$

Example 4

A spool of mass m, radius of gyration $\bar{p}$, outer radius r, and inner radius r' is pulled along a rough horizontal plane surface by a force $\mathbf{F'}$ exerted on a thread rolling up on the underside of the spool, as shown in Fig. 16.17. Find the acceleration and the magnitude of the frictional force $\mathbf{F}$. Assume that no slipping occurs.

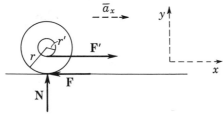

Figure
16.17

Solution

The isolating forces are shown in the figure. The translation equation gives

$$f' - f = m\bar{a}_x$$

The rotation equation gives

$$fr - f'r' = m\bar{p}^2\alpha$$

or, for no slipping,

$$f - f'\frac{r'}{r} = m\frac{\bar{p}^2}{r^2}\bar{a}_x$$

Combining the two equations to eliminate f,

$$f'\left(1 - \frac{r'}{r}\right) = \left(1 + \frac{\bar{p}^2}{r^2}\right)m\bar{a}_x$$

This may be solved for the acceleration.

To find f, we may write, from the translation equation,

$$f = f' - m\bar{a}_x = f'\left(1 - \frac{r^2 - rr'}{r^2 + \bar{p}^2}\right) = f'\left(\frac{rr' + \bar{p}^2}{r^2 + \bar{p}^2}\right)$$

Note that the quantity in parentheses has to do only with the geometry of the spool; thus the frictional force is proportional to the applied force. This means that, for f' sufficiently large, slipping will take place.

Plane Motion about Instantaneous Axis. It is interesting to see how (16.25) may be rewritten in terms of the instantaneous center **C**. Let us now use $\bar{\mathbf{R}}$ to denote the position vector of the center of mass relative to **C**. A typical force **F** acts at a point whose position vector relative to **C** is **R**, as in Fig. 16.18. As before, the point will have position vector $\mathbf{R}'$ relative to $\bar{\mathbf{R}}$; thus

$$\mathbf{R} = \bar{\mathbf{R}} + \mathbf{R}'$$

Then denoting by $\Sigma\,\boldsymbol{\Gamma}_C$ and $\Sigma\,\boldsymbol{\Gamma}$ the moment sums about **C** and $\bar{\mathbf{R}}$, respectively, and by $\bar{\mathbf{F}}$ the force sum, we have

$$\Sigma\,\boldsymbol{\Gamma}_C = \Sigma\,\mathbf{R}\times\mathbf{F} = \Sigma\,\bar{\mathbf{R}}\times\mathbf{F} + \Sigma\,\mathbf{R}'\times\mathbf{F} = \bar{\mathbf{R}}\times\bar{\mathbf{F}} + \Sigma\,\boldsymbol{\Gamma}$$

Taking only the z components,

$$\Sigma\,\gamma_C = \mathbf{K}\cdot\bar{\mathbf{R}}\times\bar{\mathbf{F}} + \Sigma\,\gamma_z = \mathbf{K}\cdot\bar{\mathbf{R}}\times m\bar{\mathbf{A}} + \Sigma\,\gamma_z$$

For a *homogeneous solid of revolution* (see Fig. 16.19) *rolling without slipping*, $\bar{a} = r\alpha$; thus, substituting (16.25) and using the parallel-axis theorem,

$$(16.26) \qquad\qquad \Sigma\,\gamma_C = (mr^2 + \bar{i}_z)\alpha = i_C\alpha$$

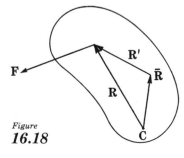

Figure
16.18

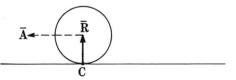

Figure
16.19

In the preceding equation it is understood that the subscript C indicates rotation about an axis through $\mathbf{C}$ and parallel to $\mathbf{K}$.

Example 5

Applying this approach to the sphere of Fig. 16.16, we have

$$\Sigma \gamma_C = wr \sin \theta = \frac{7}{5} \frac{w}{g} r^2 \alpha$$

Hence

$$\bar{a}_x = \alpha r = \tfrac{5}{7} g \sin \theta$$

as before.

Example 6

A cylindrical rod of radius r rolls in a cylindrical trough of radius r' as in Fig. 16.20.   Find the period of oscillation.

Solution

First let us relate angular displacement θ of the rod with the angular displacement ϕ along the trough.   If no slipping takes place, the arc s' along the trough is just equal to the arc s along the sphere.   We have then

$$r'\phi = s = s' = r(\theta + \phi)$$

(ϕ is added to θ in the right member to compensate for the change in direction of the normal to the trough by an angle due to its curvature.)   We may write, then,

$$r\theta = (r' - r)\phi$$

Hence, differentiating twice with respect to time,

$$r\alpha = r\frac{d^2\theta}{dt^2} = (r' - r)\frac{d^2\phi}{dt^2} = \bar{a}_T$$

[The label $\bar{a}_T$ is appropriate because the center of mass travels on a circle of radius $(r' - r)$ and hence has tangential acceleration equal to this radius times its angular acceleration magnitude.]   Using (16.26),

$$-wr \sin \phi = \frac{3}{2} \frac{w}{g} r^2 \frac{d^2\theta}{dt^2}$$

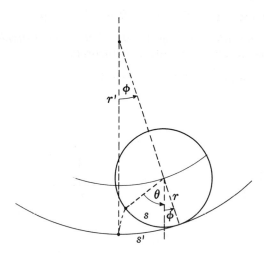

Figure
16.20

Substituting the kinematical relationship just derived and replacing sin ϕ by ϕ for small displacements, we have

$$-\phi = \frac{3}{2}\frac{r' - r}{g}\frac{d^2\phi}{dt^2}$$

This represents a simple harmonic oscillation of period

$$\tau = 2\pi\sqrt{\frac{3(r' - r)}{2g}}$$

Example 7

In Example 4 we found that the frictional force was proportional to the applied force. Now let the thread of Fig. 16.17 be pulled to the left so that the force due to the thread is exerted on the upper surface of the spool as in Fig. 16.21. This time let us inquire how r' and r must be related to $\bar{p}$ in order that the spool may roll without slipping on a *frictionless* plane.

Solution

The line of contact is the instantaneous axis of rotation, so the equations of motion may be written thus:

$$f'(r' + r) = m(\bar{p}^2 + r^2)\alpha$$
$$f' = mr\alpha$$

Hence

$$rr' + r^2 = \bar{p}^2 + r^2 \qquad \text{or} \qquad rr' = \bar{p}^2$$

This result should be compared with (16.20) and with the discussion of center of percussion in Sec. 16.11.

Application of the Method of d'Alembert. Consider a rigid body in motion parallel to the xy plane. Choose this plane so that the center of mass lies in the xy plane. The position vector of any typical point in the body is $\mathbf{R} = x\mathbf{I} + y\mathbf{J} + z\mathbf{K}$. Let $\mathbf{P}$ stand for the vector $x\mathbf{I} + y\mathbf{J}$, so that $\mathbf{P} \cdot \mathbf{K} = 0$. In order to refer the motion to the center of mass, we write also (see Fig. 16.22)

$$\mathbf{P} = \bar{\mathbf{R}} + \mathbf{P}'$$

With each element of mass dm we may associate, as in Sec. 6.7, the fictitious force $-\mathbf{A}\,dm$. Taking moments about $\mathbf{O}$,

$$\Sigma\,\mathbf{R} \times \mathbf{F} - \int \mathbf{R} \times \mathbf{A}\,dm = \mathbf{O}$$

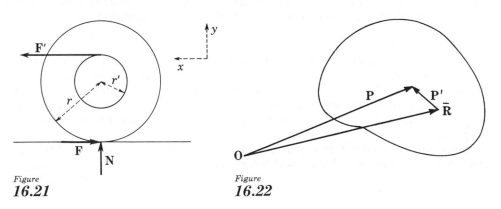

Figure
16.21

Figure
16.22

Now
$$\mathbf{A} = \bar{\mathbf{A}} + \mathfrak{A} \times (\mathbf{P'} + z\mathbf{K}) + \mathbf{\Omega} \times [\mathbf{\Omega} \times (\mathbf{P'} + z\mathbf{K})]$$
$$= \bar{\mathbf{A}} + \mathfrak{A} \times \mathbf{P'} - \omega^2 \mathbf{P'}$$
and
$$\mathbf{R} = \bar{\mathbf{R}} + \mathbf{P'} + z\mathbf{K}$$
Thus

$$\int \mathbf{R} \times \mathbf{A} \, dm = \bar{\mathbf{R}} \times m\bar{\mathbf{A}} + \bar{\mathbf{R}} \times \left(\mathfrak{A} \times \int \mathbf{P'} \, dm\right) - \bar{\mathbf{R}} \times \omega^2 \int \mathbf{P'} \, dm$$
$$+ \left(\int \mathbf{P'} \, dm\right) \times \bar{\mathbf{A}} + \mathfrak{A} \int p'^2 \, dm + \int \mathbf{P'} \times (-\omega^2 \mathbf{P'}) \, dm$$
$$+ \left(\int z \, dm\right) \mathbf{K} \times \bar{\mathbf{A}} + \mathbf{K} \times \left(\mathfrak{A} \times \int \mathbf{P'} z \, dm\right) - \mathbf{K}\omega^2 \times \int z\mathbf{P'} \, dm$$

Now since $\mathbf{P'}$ is measured from the center of mass,

$$\int \mathbf{P'} \, dm = \mathbf{O}$$

Since $\bar{\mathbf{R}}$ is in the xy plane,

$$\int z \, dm = 0$$

If we assume that the normal axis through $\bar{\mathbf{R}}$ is a principal axis of inertia, then

$$\int z\mathbf{P'} \, dm = \mathbf{I} \int zx' \, dm + \mathbf{J} \int zy' \, dm = \mathbf{O}$$

(here we have merely substituted $x' = x - \bar{x}$, $y' = y - \bar{y}$). For any plane motion with a principal axis of inertia normal to the plane through the center of mass, the conclusion, then, is
$$\Sigma \mathbf{R} \times \mathbf{F} - \bar{\mathbf{R}} \times m\bar{\mathbf{A}} - \bar{i}\mathfrak{A} = \mathbf{O}$$

This indicates that, to bring the external forces into equilibrium in the sense of d'Alembert's method, one must add $-m\bar{\mathbf{A}}$ at the center of mass, together with a couple of moment $-\bar{i}\mathfrak{A}$ (or some forces equivalent to these).

Example 8

A uniform bar of length $2r$ is free to rotate about a horizontal bearing at one end. It is released from rest in horizontal position. What instantaneously is the vertical bearing reaction, and what is the initial angular acceleration?

Solution

Using the result just derived, the bar may be regarded as in equilibrium subject to forces mar at the center of mass (the radial component $m\omega^2 r$ is zero since instantaneously the bar is at rest) and a couple of moment $\frac{1}{3}mr^2\alpha$, in addition to the horizontal and vertical bearing reactions h and v and the weight mg. These forces appear in Fig. 16.23. The minus signs are taken care of by the directions indicated as positive.

Since this is an equilibrium problem, the horizontal components have zero sum. Hence $h = 0$. Similarly, for vertical components,

$$v + mar - mg = 0$$

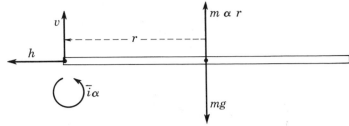

Figure
16.23

Taking moments about the center of mass, we have

$$-vr + \tfrac{1}{3}mr^2\alpha = 0$$

Eliminating α, $v - mg = -3v$ or $v = \tfrac{1}{4}mg$, and $\alpha = 3v/mr = \tfrac{3}{4}g/r$. Compare Sec. 16.8, Example 4, for another method. Further applications of the method of d'Alembert are given in Sec. 16.9.

EXERCISES

25. A solid cylinder and a cylindrical shell both roll without slipping down an inclined plane. What is the ratio of their accelerations? By the time the shell has rolled 10 ft, how far will the solid cylinder have rolled?

26. The center of mass of a 900-lb wheel of diameter 8 ft, rolling without slipping down a plane inclined at 30° to the horizontal, has an acceleration of 10 ft/sec². What is the radius of gyration? At least how great is the coefficient of friction?

27. The radius of gyration of a 36-lb wheel is 10 in. The rolling radius is 12 in. How long will it take the wheel to roll 32 ft from rest without slipping down a plane surface inclined at an angle of 30° with the horizontal?

28. A light flexible cord is wrapped around a narrow spool as in Fig. 16.24. The surface on which the cord is wound is 6 in. from the axis of the spool. The spool is allowed to fall from rest. The unwound portion of the cord is vertical, and the face of the spool moves in a fixed vertical plane. The spool falls 13.5 ft in 1.1 sec. Find the radius of gyration of the spool.

29. A solid steel cylinder 2 in. in diameter and 6 in. long is placed on an inclined plane with its axis horizontal. The angle of inclination of the plane is 60° with the horizontal. The coefficient of friction is 0.1. Starting from rest, how long will it take the cylinder to make one complete revolution? How far will the center of the cylinder travel during this time interval?

30. A wheel rolls, slipping, along level ice. The wheel has moment of inertia 13.1 kg-m², mass 50 kg, and rolling radius 0.55 m. Initially, the wheel has an angular speed of 51 rad/sec; after 10 sec it is 11 rad/sec. The only forces acting on the wheel are gravity and the contact forces with the ice. What is the coefficient of friction?

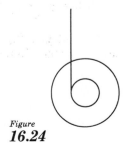

Figure
16.24

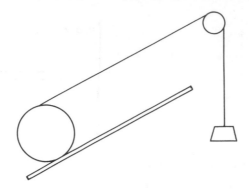

Figure
16.25

31. A wheel has weight 400 lb, moment of inertia 320 lb-ft², diameter 2 ft. The wheel is set in motion by a horizontal force of 50 lb applied at the axis in the plane of the wheel. It rolls without slipping along a horizontal plane. Find the linear acceleration of the wheel and the frictional force at the point of contact with the plane.

32. A solid cylinder of weight 20 lb and radius 6 in. has a tape wound around it, and it rests on an inclined plane with its axis horizontal. The tape passes over a smooth pulley to a 4-lb body hanging freely, as in Fig. 16.25. The inclination of the plane is 30°. Find the tension in the tape and the acceleration of the cylinder if there is no slipping.

33. With what period will a 0.25-in. ball bearing roll in a watch glass whose radius of curvature is 6 in.?

16.6. KINETIC ENERGY OF A RIGID BODY

In Sec. 7.8 we found that the kinetic energy of an aggregate of particles can be broken down into an energy associated with the center of mass plus an energy of relative motion. We shall now derive a more general result for a rigid body. As a first step we may write

$$(16.27) \qquad \text{k.e.} = \tfrac{1}{2} \int_m \mathbf{V} \cdot \mathbf{V} \, dm = \tfrac{1}{2} \int_m v^2 \, dm$$

Let $\mathbf{O'}$ be a particular point of the rigid body. We shall use it as a reference point. Then

$$\mathbf{V} = \mathbf{V}_{O'} + \mathbf{\Omega} \times \mathbf{R'}$$

where $\mathbf{R'} = \mathbf{R} - \mathbf{O'}$; that is, $\mathbf{R'}$ is the position vector of dm relative to $\mathbf{O'}$. Substituting in (16.27), we get

$$\text{k.e.} = \tfrac{1}{2} \int_m \mathbf{V}_{O'} \cdot \mathbf{V}_{O'} \, dm + \int_m \mathbf{V}_{O'} \cdot \mathbf{\Omega} \times \mathbf{R'} \, dm + \tfrac{1}{2} \int_m (\mathbf{\Omega} \times \mathbf{R'}) \cdot (\mathbf{\Omega} \times \mathbf{R'}) \, dm$$

In each integral $\mathbf{V}_{O'}$ and $\mathbf{\Omega}$ are independent of dm; thus we have, after simplifying the last integral in a manner used before in Secs. 16.3 and 16.5,

$$(16.28) \qquad \text{k.e.} = \tfrac{1}{2} m v_{O'}^2 + \mathbf{V}_{O'} \cdot \mathbf{\Omega} \times \int_m \mathbf{R'} \, dm + \tfrac{1}{2} i_{O'} \omega^2$$

where $i_{O'}$ is the moment of inertia about an axis parallel to $\mathbf{\Omega}$ and through $\mathbf{O'}$. The second term in the right member may be further interpreted. The integral is equal to $m\bar{\mathbf{R}}'$, where $\bar{\mathbf{R}}'$ is the vector from $\mathbf{O}'$ to the center of mass. But $\boldsymbol{\Omega} \times \bar{\mathbf{R}}'$ is the velocity $\bar{\mathbf{V}}'$ of the center of mass relative to a nonrotating frame with origin at $\mathbf{O}'$. Hence (16.28) may be written

$$(16.29) \qquad \text{k.e.} = \tfrac{1}{2}mv_{O'}^2 + m\bar{\mathbf{V}}' \cdot \mathbf{V}_{O'} + \tfrac{1}{2}i_{O'}\omega^2$$

We shall apply this in turn to a few important special cases.

Case I. Instantaneous Rotation with One Fixed Point. Pick $\mathbf{O}'$ as the fixed point. (If a whole axis is fixed, it may be any point on the axis.) Then $\mathbf{V}_{O'} = \mathbf{O}$, yielding

$$(16.30) \qquad \text{k.e.} = \tfrac{1}{2}i\omega^2$$

Using (15.18), one may easily show that, for coordinate axes instantaneously coinciding with principal axes of inertia, (16.30) may be rewritten

$$(16.31) \qquad \text{k.e.} = \tfrac{1}{2}i_x\omega_x^2 + \tfrac{1}{2}i_y\omega_y^2 + \tfrac{1}{2}i_z\omega_z^2$$

The details are left as Exercise 102.

Case II. Translation. Pick $\mathbf{O}'$ as a point of the body. Since $\boldsymbol{\Omega} = \mathbf{O}$, we have

$$(16.32) \qquad \text{k.e.} = \tfrac{1}{2}mv^2$$

Case III. Plane Motion in Terms of Instantaneous Center. Pick $\mathbf{O}'$ as the instantaneous center $\mathbf{C}$. Then $\mathbf{V}_{O'} = \mathbf{O}$, giving

$$(16.33) \qquad \text{k.e.} = \tfrac{1}{2}i_C\omega^2$$

Case IV. Any Motion in Terms of the Center of Mass. Pick $\mathbf{O}'$ as the center of mass $\bar{\mathbf{R}}$. Then $\bar{\mathbf{R}}'$ is null. Thus

$$(16.34) \qquad \text{k.e.} = \tfrac{1}{2}m\bar{v}^2 + \tfrac{1}{2}\bar{i}\omega^2$$

EXERCISES

34. Compute the kinetic energy of a 2-lb 2-in. uniform sphere rolling without slipping at 2 ft/sec (a) using (16.33); (b) using (16.34).
35. A uniform rod 2 m long rotates at 3 rad/sec about a perpendicular axis 40 cm from one end. Compute the kinetic energy (a) using (16.30); (b) using (16.29), with $\mathbf{O}'$ as an end of the rod (do it once for each end); (c) using (16.34).
36. A skidding 30-in. 40-lb wheel rotates at 40 rad/sec while traveling at 30 ft/sec. If the radius of gyration about the axis of the wheel is 12 in., what is the kinetic energy?
37. What solids of revolution have, for rolling without slipping, rotational kinetic energy which is 40, 50, and 100 per cent of the translational kinetic energy?
38. A car door weighing 60 lb, 2 by 4 ft, closes at 0.8 rad/sec while the car advances at 45 mph. The hinges are at the forward edge of the door. Compute the kinetic energy of the door for the moment when it is open at a 45° angle.

16.7. WORK DONE BY A COUPLE

In applying the work-energy principle to particles, we have usually computed works a force at a time. In dealing with rigid bodies, it is often convenient to calculate work done by a couple. Let our couple consist of $-\mathbf{F}$ at $\mathbf{R}$ and $+\mathbf{F}$ at $\mathbf{R} + \mathbf{D}$ as in Fig. 16.26. The point $\mathbf{R}$ has velocity $\mathbf{V}_R$. Then the point $\mathbf{R} + \mathbf{D}$ has velocity

$$\mathbf{V}_R + \boldsymbol{\Omega} \times \mathbf{D}$$

Assume that $\mathbf{\Omega} = \omega\mathbf{K}$. Then the sum of the powers exerted by these two forces is

$$\text{Power} = -\mathbf{F} \cdot \mathbf{V}_R + \mathbf{F} \cdot (\mathbf{V}_R + \mathbf{\Omega} \times \mathbf{D})$$

or

(16.35) $$\text{Power} = \mathbf{F} \cdot \mathbf{\Omega} \times \mathbf{D} = \mathbf{D} \times \mathbf{F} \cdot \mathbf{\Omega} = \mathbf{\Gamma} \cdot \mathbf{\Omega} = \gamma_z \omega$$

Corresponding work formulas are

(16.36) $$\text{Work} = \int_{t_0}^{t_1} \mathbf{\Gamma} \cdot \mathbf{\Omega} \, dt = \int_{t_0}^{t_1} \mathbf{\Gamma} \cdot \omega\mathbf{K} \, dt = \int_{\theta_0}^{\theta_1} \gamma_z \, d\theta$$

Example I

A drum 2 m in diameter is used for winding up a flexible cable of length 100 m and mass 500 kg. How much work is done in the winding? The bearing friction is 50 newton-m.

Solution

We can divide the work into two parts. First is the work of lifting the cable with a diminishing force always equal to the weight still hanging. This can be handled in a trice by noting that the center of mass is lifted 50 m.

$$\text{Work}_1 = 500 \times 9.8 \times 50 = 2.45 \times 10^5 \text{ joules (newton-m)}$$

In addition, there is the work against the frictional torque as the drum turns through an angle of 100 rad.

$$\text{Work}_2 = \gamma\theta = 50 \times 100 = 5 \times 10^3 \text{ joules}$$

The total work is clearly 2.50×10^5 joules.

An alternative approach would be to represent the torque required to turn the drum in terms of the length still hanging.

$$\gamma = 50 + (5y \ kg)(9.8 \text{ newtons/kg})(1 \text{ m})$$

or

$$\gamma = 50 + 49y \qquad \text{newton-m}$$

Moreover, $d\theta = -1 \, dy$; thus

$$\text{Work} = -\int_{100}^{0} (50 + 49y) \, dy = -50y - \tfrac{49}{2}y^2 \Big|_{100}^{0}$$

$$= 5{,}000 + 245{,}000 = 250{,}000 \text{ joules}$$

as before.

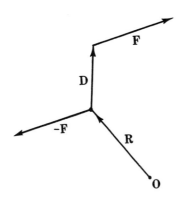

Figure
16.26

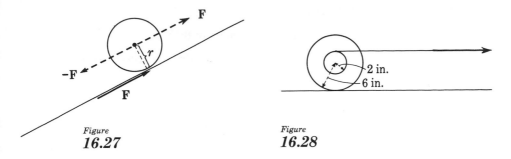

Figure
16.27

Figure
16.28

Example 2. Work Done by Friction

Let us consider a solid of revolution of radius r that is rolling on a plane as shown in Fig. 16.27. Let us add two forces $\mathbf{F}$ and $-\mathbf{F}$ at the center. Then the original force is replaced by an uphill force $\mathbf{F}$ at the center along with a couple of moment fr. For a displacement l of the center, the work done by the force is $-fl$; by the couple, $+fr\theta$. The net work is $f(r\theta - l)$. For rolling without slipping, this is zero. If the object is rolling "too slowly," and hence slipping, the value is negative. If it is rolling "too fast," and hence slipping, the direction of each arrow must be changed and still the result is negative.

EXERCISES

39. It requires a torque of 0.8 newton-m to hold a certain torsion pendulum twisted through an angle of 1.5 rad. How much work is done by the wire of the pendulum when it is allowed to untwist to equilibrium position?

40. The spool of Fig. 16.24 weighs 5 lb. What work is done during the descent of 13.5 ft: (*a*) By the tension in the cord? (*b*) By gravity?

41. A spool (see Fig. 16.28) of outer radius 6 in. and inner radius 2 in. rolls 5 ft without slipping along a horizontal plane when a cord, unrolling from its upper edge, is pulled with a 10-lb force parallel to the plane. How much work is done by this force?

42. A torque of 20 ft-lb is required to keep a shaft rotating at constant angular speed. What horsepower must be exerted to keep the shaft rotating at 55 rad/sec?

16.8. WORK-ENERGY PROBLEMS FOR A RIGID BODY

Regarding the rigid body, as usual, as merely an aggregate of particles where the members are very firmly linked, we may apply the work-energy principle:

$$(16.37) \qquad\qquad \text{Total work} = \Delta(\text{k.e.})$$

Sections 7.6 and 16.7 have provided us with ways of computing work, and Sec. 16.6 has given us ways of computing the kinetic energy. We can now illustrate the practical combination of these ideas.

Example I

How far must a cylindrical shell roll without slipping down a plane inclined at 20° in order to attain a speed of 10 ft/sec?

Solution

The kinetic energy is, since $\bar{v} = r\omega$, $\bar{p} = r$,

$$\text{k.e.} = \tfrac{1}{2}m\bar{v}^2 + \tfrac{1}{2}\bar{i}\omega^2 = m\bar{v}^2$$

The only work done is by gravity:

$$\text{Work} = wh = mgs \sin \theta$$

where s is the distance traveled along the plane and θ its inclination to the horizontal. Equating work and energy,

$$s = \frac{\bar{v}^2}{g \sin \theta}$$

or

$$s = \frac{100}{32.2 \times \sin 20°} = 9.1 \text{ ft}$$

The work-energy relationship was originally obtained by integrating the equation $\mathbf{F} = m\mathbf{A}$. We shall now obtain some special results by integrating separately the equations of motion already derived for rigid bodies.

Translational Energy of a Rigid Body. In the case of a rigid body, we know already that

$$\Sigma \mathbf{F} = m\bar{\mathbf{A}}$$

Multiplying by $d\bar{\mathbf{R}}$ and integrating, using the substitution

$$\bar{\mathbf{A}} \cdot d\bar{\mathbf{R}} = \bar{\mathbf{V}} \cdot d\bar{\mathbf{V}}$$

(16.38)
$$\Sigma \int_{\bar{\mathbf{R}}_0}^{\bar{\mathbf{R}}_1} \mathbf{F} \cdot d\bar{\mathbf{R}} = m \int_{\bar{\mathbf{V}}_0}^{\bar{\mathbf{V}}_1} \bar{\mathbf{V}} \cdot d\bar{\mathbf{V}} = \tfrac{1}{2} m \bar{v}_1^2 - \tfrac{1}{2} m \bar{v}_0^2$$

This shows that, by assigning all external forces and all mass to the center of mass of a body, we may deal with translational energies quite apart from rotation.

Example 2

Consider, for instance, as in Fig. 16.29, a solid of revolution of radius r rolling and slipping down a plane inclined at an angle ϕ. After a linear displacement s, the linear speed is $\bar{v}$. If the initial linear speed was zero, the translational-energy equation is

$$(w \sin \phi - f)s = \tfrac{1}{2} m \bar{v}^2$$

Rotational Energy of a Rigid Body in Plane Motion. A rigid body in motion parallel to the xy plane satisfies

$$\Sigma \gamma_z = \bar{i}_z \alpha$$

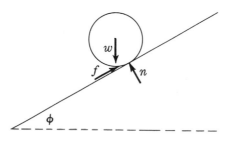

Figure
16.29

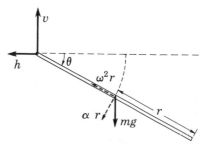

Figure
16.30

Multiplying by $d\theta$ and integrating,

(16.39) $$\Sigma \int_{\theta_0}^{\theta_1} \gamma_z \, d\theta = \bar{\imath}_z \int_{\omega_0}^{\omega_1} \omega \, d\omega = \tfrac{1}{2}\bar{\imath}_z\omega_1^2 - \tfrac{1}{2}\bar{\imath}_z\omega_0^2$$

This shows that, by considering rotational motion about an axis through the center of mass perpendicular to the plane of motion, we may deal with rotational energies quite apart from translation. It should be emphasized that the sum of (16.38) and (16.39), member by member, is merely a form of (16.37).

The division of works into translational and rotational parts may seem more plausible if first, as in Sec. 10.6, you replace each applied force by an equal force at the center of mass together with a compensating couple.

Example 3

Referring to the body in Fig. 16.29 again, if initially the angular speed is zero and if it is ω after an angular displacement of θ, then the rotational-energy equation is

$$fr\theta = \tfrac{1}{2}\bar{\imath}\omega^2$$

Example 4

A uniform bar of length $2r$ is free to rotate about a horizontal bearing at one end as in Fig. 16.30. It is released from rest in horizontal position. What are the horizontal and vertical components of the force at the bearing when the bar has descended through an angle θ?

Solution

By the time the bar has rotated through angle θ, the center of mass has descended a vertical distance $r \sin \theta$. The work-energy equation then is

$$mgr \sin \theta = \tfrac{2}{3}mr^2\omega^2 \qquad \text{so} \qquad \omega^2 r = \tfrac{3}{2}g \sin \theta$$

Differentiating with respect to time (so as to determine α),

$$2\omega\alpha r = \tfrac{3}{2}g \cos \theta \, \dot{\theta}$$

or

$$\alpha r = \tfrac{3}{4}g \cos \theta \qquad \text{since} \qquad \dot{\theta} = \omega$$

Taking horizontal and vertical components of the vector equation

$$\Sigma \mathbf{F} = m\bar{\mathbf{A}}$$

we have

$$h = m\omega^2 r \cos \theta + m\alpha r \sin \theta$$

$$= mg(\tfrac{3}{2}) \sin \theta \cos \theta + mg(\tfrac{3}{4}) \cos \theta \sin \theta$$

$$= \tfrac{9}{4}mg \sin \theta \cos \theta$$

and

$$v - mg = m\omega^2 r \sin \theta - m\alpha r \cos \theta$$

$$= mg(\tfrac{3}{2}) \sin^2 \theta - mg(\tfrac{3}{4}) \cos^2 \theta$$

Note that, for $\theta = 0°$, $v = \tfrac{1}{4}mg$ as in Sec. 16.5, Example 8.

Example 5

A physical pendulum is released from rest at an angle θ_0 with the vertical. Express the angular speed in terms of the angle θ. Investigate the bearing reaction.

Solution

The center of mass travels along a circle of radius h (see Fig. 16.31). The work done by gravity is

$$\text{Work} = wh(\cos \theta_0 - \cos \theta)$$

The kinetic energy is

$$\text{k.e.} = \frac{1}{2} i\omega^2 = \frac{1}{2} \frac{w}{g} (\bar{p}^2 + h^2)\omega^2$$

We conclude, then:

$$\omega^2 = \frac{2gh}{\bar{p}^2 + h^2} (\cos \theta_0 - \cos \theta)$$

Note that ω is maximum when $\cos \theta = -1$, or when $\theta = 180°$, as would be expected. For convenience, the bearing reaction force in Fig. 16.31 is resolved into a radial projection $\mathbf{F}_r$ and a transverse projection $\mathbf{F}_t$. Taking moments around the center of mass, we can get a rotational work-energy equation. To avoid difficult work integrations, one may evaluate the work for only a small displacement. Here let us allow a small displacement $d\theta$. The corresponding work done by $\mathbf{F}_t$ is $f_t h \, d\theta$. The change in kinetic energy is $d(\frac{1}{2} i \omega^2)$. Our rotational equation is then

$$f_t h \, d\theta = d\left(\frac{1}{2} i \omega^2\right) = i\omega \, d\omega = \frac{w}{g} \bar{p}^2 \left[\frac{gh}{\bar{p}^2 + h^2} \sin \theta \, d\theta \right]$$

Hence

$$f_t = w\left[\frac{\bar{p}^2}{\bar{p}^2 + h^2} \right] \sin \theta$$

The magnitude of $\mathbf{F}_r$ may be computed easily by using radial components of $\Sigma \mathbf{F} = m\bar{\mathbf{A}}$:

$$f_r + w \cos \theta = \frac{w}{g} \omega^2 h$$

Since ω^2 has already been found for any θ, the computation is immediate. A similar approach might have been used for finding f_t. In the above computation of f_t,

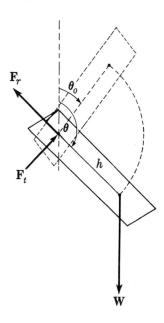

Figure
16.31

$\mathbf{F}_r$

θ_0

θ

h

$\mathbf{F}_t$

W

differentials were used.   Some students will take more comfort in an approach based on derivatives.   It is easy to show that the work-energy equation is equivalent to

$$(16.40) \qquad\qquad \text{Power} = \frac{d}{dt}(\text{k.e.})$$

(Sec. 7.7 Exercise 45).   In the rotational aspect of this example we have (relative to the center of mass)

$$\text{Power} = f_t h\omega$$

$$\frac{d}{dt}(\tfrac{1}{2}\bar{\imath}\omega^2) = \tfrac{1}{2}\bar{\imath}\frac{d}{dt}\left[\frac{2gh}{p^2+h^2}(\cos\theta_0-\cos\theta)\right]$$

so

$$\frac{d}{dt}(\text{k.e.}) = \frac{\bar{\imath}gh}{p^2+h^2}\sin\theta\,\frac{d\theta}{dt}$$

Now using (16.40), canceling ω and $d\theta/dt$, we can solve for f_t as before.

Example 6

A spool of mass m, moment of inertia $\bar{\imath}$, outer radius r, and inner radius r' rolls on a horizontal plane without slipping when pulled with a horizontal force P acting at the upper surface of the inner circumference as in Fig. 16.32.   What angular speed does it acquire in turning through an angle θ?   How large may P be without causing slipping?

Solution

For no slipping, only P actually does work.   We shall, however, first write the rotation and translation equations separately.

Rotation: $\qquad\qquad (pr'+fr)\theta = \tfrac{1}{2}\bar{\imath}\omega^2$

Translation: $\qquad\qquad (p-f)r\theta = \tfrac{1}{2}m\bar{v}^2 = \tfrac{1}{2}mr^2\omega^2$

Adding the two, we get the overall energy equation

$$p(r+r')\theta = \tfrac{1}{2}mr^2\omega^2 + \tfrac{1}{2}\bar{\imath}\omega^2$$

This may be solved for ω^2:

$$\omega^2 = \frac{2p(r+r')\theta}{mr^2+\bar{\imath}}$$

Now eliminate θ and ω^2.   This may be done, for instance, by dividing the rotation equation by the translation equation, member by member.   Solving the result for p,

$$p = f\left[\frac{\bar{\imath}+mr^2}{\bar{\imath}-mrr'}\right]$$

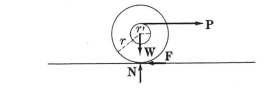

Figure
16.32

The maximum value for f is $\mu w = \mu mg$; thus p may, without causing slipping, have any value less than

$$\mu mg \left[\frac{\bar{i} + mr^2}{\bar{i} - mrr'} \right]$$

Example 7

A 20-ft ladder rests against a vertical wall with its base on horizontal ice. Initially a rope from base to wall holds it at an angle $\theta_0 = 20°$ with the vertical. The rope breaks, and the ladder slides in a vertical plane. Neglecting all friction, find:

a. The angular speed at the moment when the ladder ceases to touch the wall.

b. The angular speed as the ladder strikes the ice.

Solution

a. We shall assume that the ladder can be treated as a uniform bar of length $2l$ and mass m. As long as the ladder is in contact with both the horizontal and vertical surfaces, its center of mass describes a circle of radius l (see Fig. 16.33) and we may write $\bar{v} = l\omega$. For any position θ,

$$\text{Work} = wl \,(\cos\theta_0 - \cos\theta)$$

and

$$\text{k.e.} = \tfrac{1}{2}m\bar{v}^2 + \tfrac{1}{2}\bar{i}\omega^2 = \tfrac{1}{2}ml^2\omega^2 + \tfrac{1}{6}ml^2\omega^2$$

Equating the two, we get

$$\omega^2 = \frac{3g}{2l}\,(\cos\theta_0 - \cos\theta)$$

This is valid while the ladder touches the wall. The moment when the ladder leaves the wall can be identified as the moment when the normal reaction n' becomes zero or as the moment when the horizontal component of $\bar{v}$ becomes a maximum. Now (see Fig. 16.34)

$$\bar{v}_x = \bar{v}\cos\theta = \omega l\cos\theta$$

Thus

$$\bar{v}_x^2 = \omega^2 l^2 \cos^2\theta = \frac{3gl}{2}\,(\cos^2\theta\cos\theta_0 - \cos^3\theta)$$

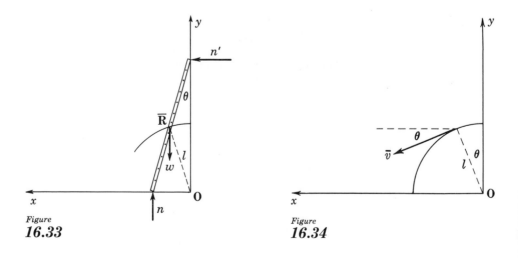

Figure
16.33

Figure
16.34

Differentiating with respect to θ and setting the result equal to zero, we have

$$\cos\theta\sin\theta\,(-2\cos\theta_0 + 3\cos\theta) = 0$$

The maximum comes then for

$$\cos\theta = \tfrac{2}{3}\cos\theta_0$$

The corresponding angular speed is given by

$$\omega^2 = \frac{3g}{2l}\,(\cos\theta_0 - \tfrac{2}{3}\cos\theta_0) = \frac{g\cos\theta_0}{2l}$$

For the values given in this example,

$$\omega = \sqrt{\frac{(32.2)(0.94)}{20}} = 1.23 \text{ rad/sec}$$

at

$$\theta = \cos^{-1}(\tfrac{2}{3}\cos\theta_0) = 51°$$

To check on the angle at which the ladder leaves the wall, let us evaluate n' in terms of θ. First we determine α by differentiating the equation for ω^2 with respect to t.

$$2\omega\alpha = \frac{3g}{2l}\sin\theta\,\omega$$

or

$$\alpha = \frac{3g}{4l}\sin\theta$$

Now taking x components of $\Sigma\,\mathbf{F} = m\bar{\mathbf{A}}$, we have (see Fig. 16.35)

$$n' = \frac{w}{g}\,(\alpha l\cos\theta - \omega^2 l\sin\theta)$$

Substituting values for α and ω^2, we get

$$n' = \frac{3w}{4}\sin\theta\,(3\cos\theta - 2\cos\theta_0)$$

For the θ found above where $\cos\theta = \tfrac{2}{3}\cos\theta_0$, we have $n' = 0$, as was expected.

    b. Once the ladder is free of the wall (after $\theta = 51°$), we have a new dynamical setup (see Fig. 16.36). Only the forces n and w now act. Our initial conditions for the new problem are $\theta_1 = 51°$, $\omega_1 = 1.23$ rad/sec.

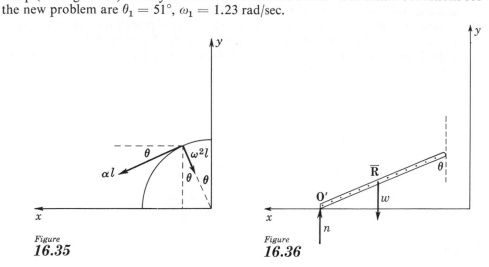

Figure
16.35

Figure
16.36

Also
$$\bar{v}_{x_1} = (1.23)(10)(\cos 51°) = 7.7 \text{ ft/sec}$$
$$\bar{v}_{y_1} = -(1.23)(10)(\sin 51°) = -9.6 \text{ ft/sec}$$

Since there is no horizontal force, $\bar{v}_x$ remains constant. Since $\mathbf{V}_{O'}$ is horizontal, we conclude from
$$\mathbf{\bar{V}} = \mathbf{V}_{O'} + \mathbf{\Omega} \times (\mathbf{O'\bar{R}})$$

that
$$\bar{v}_y = -\omega l \sin \theta$$

For the remaining displacement, $\theta = 51°$ to $\theta = 90°$, we have
$$\text{Work} = wl \cos \theta_1$$
$$\Delta(\text{k.e.}) = \tfrac{1}{2}m(\bar{v}^2 - \bar{v}_1^2) + \tfrac{1}{2}\bar{i}(\omega^2 - \omega_1^2)$$

or
$$\Delta(\text{k.e.}) = \tfrac{1}{2}m\omega^2 l^2 \sin^2 90° - \tfrac{1}{2}m(9.6)^2 + \tfrac{1}{2}\bar{i}(\omega^2 - \omega_1^2)$$

(replacing $\bar{v}^2 - \bar{v}_1^2$ by $\bar{v}_y^2 - \bar{v}_{y_1}^2$, since the x component is constant). Equating work to energy change,
$$mgl \cos \theta_1 = \tfrac{1}{2}m\omega^2 l^2 - \tfrac{1}{2}m(9.6)^2 + \tfrac{1}{6}m\omega^2 l^2 - \tfrac{1}{6}ml^2(1.23)^2$$

From this we compute ω as 2.0 rad/sec.

EXERCISES

43. A semicircular track of radius 6 in. is set opening upward in a vertical plane. A 1-in. steel ball bearing is placed on the track at a point where its tangent is inclined at 45°. It rolls without slipping. What is the maximum linear speed?

44. A wheel of mass m, radius r, and radius of gyration $\bar{p}$ is set to roll on its axle (radius r') down a plane inclined at θ (see Fig. 16.37). No slipping takes place. Find the angular speed acquired in a displacement s along the plane.

45. A 2-lb homogeneous cylinder of radius 2 in. is drawn up a plane inclined at 20° by a tape wrapped around it and passing over a light frictionless pulley to a 5-lb weight (see Fig. 16.38). Assuming that the cylinder does not slip, what speed has it acquired after moving 2 ft?

46. A wheel is caused to rotate about its fixed horizontal axis by a light flexible cord wrapped around the axle of the wheel and attached to a 640-lb load. The moment of inertia of the wheel is 2 slug-ft². The radius of the axle is 2 in. If the 640-lb load descends from rest a distance of 10 ft, its speed becomes how great?

47. A wheel of radius r, radius of gyration $\bar{p}$, and mass m is propelled by an axial couple of moment γ. If it starts from rest and does not slip, what speed will it acquire after a displacement s? How large may γ be without causing slipping if the coefficient of friction is μ?

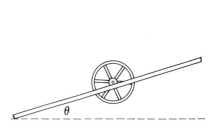

Figure
16.37

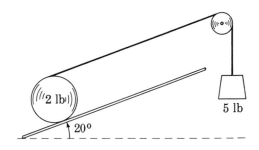

5 lb

Figure
16.38

16.9. BEARING REACTIONS BY THE METHOD OF D'ALEMBERT

In Sec. 16.5, Example 8, we used the method of d'Alembert to solve a simple problem about a bearing reaction. In the present section, similar but slightly more complicated applications are given. The basic equations for an aggregate of particles may be summarized thus:

$$(16.41) \qquad \Sigma \, \mathbf{F} - \Sigma \, m\mathbf{A} = \mathbf{0} \qquad \text{or} \qquad \Sigma \, \mathbf{F} - (\Sigma \, m)\bar{\mathbf{A}} = \mathbf{0}$$

$$(16.42) \qquad \Sigma \, \mathbf{R} \times \mathbf{F} + \Sigma \, \mathbf{R} \times (-m\mathbf{A}) = \mathbf{0}$$

The adaptation of this approach to a rigid body proceeds as in Sec. 16.5.

Example I

To illustrate the utility of this method, let us return to the problem of rotation of rigid bodies around a fixed axis. In Sec. 16.3 we obtained simple overall conclusions relating torque about the axis and the angular acceleration. We ignored, however, the important forces which compel the axis to remain fixed. Suppose, for instance, that a bar of mass m and length $2l$ is rotated about a skew axis through its center of mass at a uniform angular velocity $\mathbf{\Omega}$. What is required of the bearing B? Of course, it must provide a force to offset the weight of the bar, but we are concerned here with the forces originating with the motion. Since the center of mass is stationary, the external forces by themselves have a zero vector sum. Now let us take moments about an axis normal to the plane of the bar and the rotation axis (i.e., normal to the plane of Fig. 16.39) through the bearing B. Denote the torque exerted by the bearing itself by γ_B. To this we shall add for each element of mass dm the moment of a fictitious force: $\omega^2 x \, dm$, directed outward from the axis of rotation. Now

$$dm = \frac{m}{2l} \, ds \qquad x = s \sin \theta \qquad z = s \cos \theta$$

As an application of (16.42), we may then write

$$\gamma_B - \omega^2 \int xz \, dm = 0$$

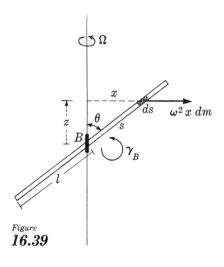

Figure
16.39

or, using the notation of Sec. 15.7,

$$\gamma_B - \omega^2 i_{zx} = 0$$

Substituting for x, z, and dm, we get

$$\gamma_B - \frac{m\omega^2 \sin \theta \cos \theta}{2l} \int_{-l}^{l} s^2 \, ds = 0$$

or

$$\gamma_B = \frac{m\omega^2 \sin \theta \cos \theta \, l^2}{3}$$

This enables us to compute the torque which the bearing must withstand for any uniform angular speed ω.

Bearing Reactions and Products of Inertia.   The preceding example showed how the method of d'Alembert may be applied to a specific problem.   Let us take a more general case.   For a body rotating at uniform speed about a fixed z axis with the bearing at the origin (see Fig. 16.40), the moment equation (for equilibrium) at a given instant is

(16.43) $$\mathbf{\Gamma}_B - \int \mathbf{R} \times \mathbf{A} \, dm = \mathbf{O}$$

Here $\mathbf{\Gamma}_B$ is the torque exerted by the bearing.   Since we are dealing with the simple case where the rotation is uniform,

$$\mathbf{A} = \mathbf{\Omega} \times (\mathbf{\Omega} \times \mathbf{R})$$

Hence

$$\mathbf{R} \times \mathbf{A} = \mathbf{R} \times [\mathbf{\Omega} \times (\mathbf{\Omega} \times \mathbf{R})] = \mathbf{R} \times [(\mathbf{\Omega} \cdot \mathbf{R})\mathbf{\Omega} - \omega^2 \mathbf{R}]$$

$$= (x\mathbf{I} + y\mathbf{J} + z\mathbf{K}) \times \omega^2 z\mathbf{K} = \omega^2 yz\mathbf{I} - \omega^2 zx\mathbf{J}$$

Substituting in (16.43), we have

(16.44) $$\mathbf{\Gamma}_B = \omega^2 \mathbf{I} \int yz \, dm - \omega^2 \mathbf{J} \int zx \, dm = \omega^2(i_{yz}\mathbf{I} - i_{zx}\mathbf{J})$$

From this it is evident that if such bearing torques are to be avoided, the products of inertia i_{yz} and i_{zx} should vanish.   This is attained if the axis of rotation is a *principal axis of inertia* with respect to an origin taken at the bearing.

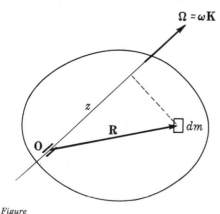

$$\Omega = \omega \mathbf{K}$$

z

$\mathbf{R}$

dm

O

Figure
16.40

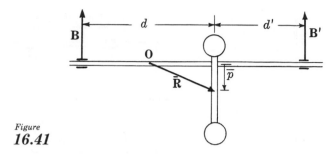

Figure
16.41

Example 2. Bearing Reactions for an Eccentric Wheel

A wheel may be set to rotate about a principal axis and yet give rise to bearing reactions associated with the motion. Figure 16.41 represents a wheel mounted so that the perpendicular distance from the axis to the center of mass is $\bar{p}$. Bearing forces **B** and **B′** are indicated in the diagram. Using the d'Alembert approach, the equation of equilibrium is

$$O = B + B' + W - m\Omega \times (\Omega \times \bar{R})$$

where **W** is the weight. For the phase of the rotation where the center of mass is lowest,

$$0 = b + b' - w - m\omega^2\bar{p}$$

$$bd = b'd'$$

Hence

$$b = \frac{m\omega^2\bar{p} + w}{1 + (d/d')}$$

It should be clearly emphasized that the problems illustrated in this section can be done without the d'Alembert approach, and also that this approach is by no means limited to problems involving bearing reactions. In so far as this section broadens the scope of Sec. 16.3, it should be pointed out that a similar extension might be given to Sec. 16.5.

EXERCISES

48. The top of a vertical axle is attached by a frictionless pin to a 30-in. uniform bar, as in Fig. 16.42. The higher the speed of rotation of the axle, the larger is the angle θ between the bar and the axle. For what constant speed is this angle 30°?

49. An 80-lb sphere, 10 in. in radius, is attached to a horizontal axle so that its center is 24 in. from the axle, as in Fig. 16.43. The bearings A and B are asymmetrically located as shown. The sphere rotates at 10 rad/sec. When $\bar{R}$ is below O, what are the bearing forces at A and B?

50. A wheel weighs 2,100 lb. Its center of mass is 0.4 in. from its geometric axis. The wheel is mounted in two bearings A and B 5 ft apart and on opposite sides, A being 2 ft from the plane of the wheel. At 200 rpm find the forces at the bearings due to the centrifugal force.

51. The uniform bar AB in Fig. 16.44 is to rotate around the axis $A'B'$. A single bearing is to be located between A' and B', the bar being connected to it by rigid struts of negligible mass. Where should this bearing be placed so that it will need to withstand no torques due to rotation?

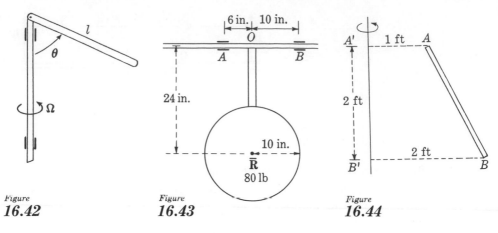

Figure
16.42

Figure
16.43

Figure
16.44

16.10. OSCILLATIONS OF A RIGID BODY

The methods introduced in Sec. 7.11 for determining periods of oscillation apply equally well to vibrations of a rigid body. This is demonstrated in the following examples.

Example I

First let us use energy methods to arrive at the period for a physical pendulum. Refer to Fig. 16.8 as before.

First Solution

The potential energy, relative to the position where $\theta = 0°$, for angle θ is

$$\text{p.e.} = mgh(1 - \cos\theta)$$

and the kinetic energy is

$$\text{k.e.} = \tfrac{1}{2}m\bar{p}'^2\omega^2$$

Hence

$$mgh(1 - \cos\theta) + \tfrac{1}{2}m\bar{p}'^2\omega^2 = \text{const}$$

Taking the time derivative,

$$mhg\sin\theta\dot{\theta} + m\bar{p}'^2\dot{\omega}\omega = 0$$

Since $\dot{\theta} = \omega$, the equation may be written, for small θ, as

$$\frac{d^2\theta}{dt^2} = -\frac{gh}{\bar{p}'^2}\theta$$

which yields the period, as before, of

$$\tau = 2\pi\sqrt{\frac{\bar{p}'^2}{gh}}$$

Second Solution

Since we have picked our reference position for potential energy so that potential energy vanishes for maximum kinetic energy, we can write

$$(\text{p.e.})_m = (\text{k.e.})_m$$

or

$$mgh(1 - \cos\theta_m) = \tfrac{1}{2}m\bar{p}'^2\omega_m^2$$

Replacing for small θ_m the expression $1 - \cos \theta_m$ by $\theta_m^2/2$, we have

$$gh\theta_m^2 = \bar{p}'^2\omega_m^2$$

Hence

$$2\pi\,\frac{\theta_m}{\omega_m} = 2\pi\sqrt{\frac{\bar{p}'^2}{gh}}$$

Example 2

Let us first return to the cylindrical rod rolling in a cylindrical trough. The problem is to find the period of the oscillation.

First Solution

Since $\theta = s/r - \phi$ (see Fig. 16.45) and $s = \phi r'$, we have

$$\omega = \left(\frac{r' - r}{r}\right)\frac{d\phi}{dt}$$

The kinetic energy is easily expressed:

$$\text{k.e.} = \tfrac{1}{2}m\bar{v}^2 + \tfrac{1}{2}\bar{\imath}\omega^2$$

Now

$$\bar{\imath} = \tfrac{1}{2}mr^2 \qquad \text{and} \qquad \bar{v} = (r' - r)\frac{d\phi}{dt}$$

Thus

$$\text{k.e.} = \tfrac{1}{2}m\left[(r' - r)^2\left(\frac{d\phi}{dt}\right)^2 + \tfrac{1}{2}r^2\left(\frac{r' - r}{r}\right)^2\left(\frac{d\phi}{dt}\right)^2\right]$$

or

$$\text{k.e.} = \tfrac{3}{4}m(r' - r)^2\left(\frac{d\phi}{dt}\right)^2 = \tfrac{3}{4}m\bar{v}^2$$

The potential energy relative to the lowest position is

$$\text{p.e.} = mg(r' - r)(1 - \cos \phi)$$

By the law of conservation of energy,

$$\tfrac{3}{4}m(r' - r)^2\left[\frac{d\phi}{dt}\right]^2 + mg(r' - r)(1 - \cos \phi) = \text{const}$$

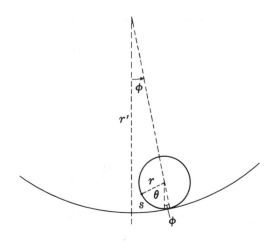

Figure
16.45

Now differentiating with respect to t and dividing out common factors,

$$\tfrac{3}{2}(r' - r)\frac{d^2\phi}{dt^2} + g \sin \phi = 0$$

For small oscillations, using the approximation (7.57), we have a simple harmonic motion of period

$$\tau = 2\pi \sqrt{\frac{3(r' - r)}{2g}}$$

as before (Sec. 16.5, Example 6).

Second Solution

Let ϕ_m denote the amplitude and $\left[\dfrac{d\phi}{dt}\right]_m$ the maximum oscillatory speed. For maximum displacement,

$$\text{p.e.} = mg(r' - r)(1 - \cos \phi_m) \qquad \text{k.e.} = 0$$

For zero displacement,

$$\text{p.e.} = 0 \qquad \text{k.e.} = \tfrac{3}{4}m(r' - r)^2 \left[\frac{d\phi}{dt}\right]_m^2$$

By the conservation law, these maximum values may be equated. Using approximation (7.58), we get

$$g\left(\frac{\phi_m^2}{2}\right) = \tfrac{3}{4}(r' - r)\left[\frac{d\phi}{dt}\right]_m^2$$

If this is rearranged in the shape of (7.59), we have

$$\tau = 2\pi \frac{\phi_m}{[d\phi/dt]_m} = 2\pi \sqrt{\frac{3(r' - r)}{2g}}$$

Example 3

The center of mass of a weighted solid of revolution of radius r is at a distance h from its center. The radius of gyration about an axis through the center of mass is $\bar{\rho}$. When the solid is displaced slightly from equilibrium position on a horizontal plane surface, it oscillates. Find the period if there is no slipping.

First Solution

The potential energy (see Fig. 16.46) for the displaced position is (relative to the equilibrium position)

$$\text{p.e.} = mgh(1 - \cos \theta)$$

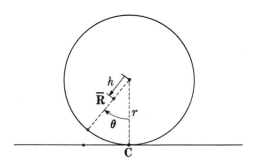

Figure
16.46

The kinetic energy may be computed with reference to the point of contact. The moment of inertia may be evaluated in terms of the distance $\bar{R}C$. Since θ is to be small, we shall use the approximate value $r - h$ for this distance:

$$\text{k.e.} = \tfrac{1}{2}m[\bar{p}^2 + (r - h)^2]\omega^2$$

By the conservation law we have

$$\text{p.e.} + \text{k.e.} = mgh(1 - \cos\theta) + \tfrac{1}{2}m[\bar{p}^2 + (r - h)^2]\omega^2 = \text{const}$$

Take the derivative with respect to time.

$$mgh \sin\theta\, \omega + m[\bar{p}^2 + (r - h)^2]\omega\,\frac{d^2\theta}{dt^2} = 0$$

With $\sin\theta$ replaced by θ for small oscillations, we have simple harmonic motion of period

$$\tau = 2\pi\sqrt{\frac{\bar{p}^2 + (r - h)^2}{gh}}$$

Second Solution

For maximum displacement,

$$\text{p.e.} = mgh(1 - \cos\theta_m) \qquad \text{k.e.} = 0$$

For zero displacement,

$$\text{p.e.} = 0 \qquad \text{k.e.} = \tfrac{1}{2}m[\bar{p}^2 + (r - h)^2]\omega_m^2$$

Using the approximation $1 - \cos\theta_m = \theta_m^2/2$, we get for the conservation equation

$$gh\theta_m^2 = [\bar{p} + (r - h)^2]\omega_m^2$$

From this we get, as before,

$$\tau = \frac{2\pi\theta_m}{\omega_m} = 2\pi\sqrt{\frac{\bar{p}^2 + (r - h)^2}{gh}}$$

EXERCISES

52. A uniform cylindrical shell of radius r rests on a cylindrical surface of radius r'. Use the methods of this section to compute the period with which it will oscillate if no slipping takes place. Use both methods explicitly.

53. Half a solid uniform cylinder (i.e., cross section is a semicircle) of radius r is placed on a concave cylindrical surface of radius r'. Compute the period with which it will rock.

54. A uniform rectangular plank 6 by 2 in. by 4 ft balances, wide face horizontal, across a cylinder of diameter 1 ft. Find the period of the tipping.

55. A 150-lb man and a 10-lb rocking chair have a center of mass 15 in. off the floor, and a radius of gyration about an axis through the center of mass is also 15 in. If the radius of curvature of the rockers is 4 ft, what is the period of rocking?

16.11. MOMENTUM RELATIONSHIPS FOR A RIGID BODY

Since we can regard a rigid body as an aggregate of particles, the equations of Secs. 7.3, 7.4, 12.1, and 12.2 can easily be adjusted to apply to a rigid body. From (7.13) and (7.17), we get

(16.45) $$\Sigma\,\mathbf{P} = \Sigma \int_{t_0}^{t_1}\mathbf{F}\,dt = \Delta\left(\int \mathbf{V}\,dm\right) = m\bar{\mathbf{V}}_1 - m\bar{\mathbf{V}}_0$$

From (12.6) and (12.7), we get, for moments about the origin,

(16.46)
$$\Sigma \int_{t_0}^{t_1} \mathbf{\Gamma}\, dt = \Delta\left(\int \mathbf{R} \times \mathbf{V}\, dm \right)$$

and for moments about the center of mass

(16.47)
$$\Sigma \int_{t_0}^{t_1} \mathbf{\Gamma}\, dt = \Delta\left(\int \mathbf{R}' \times \mathbf{V}'\, dm \right)$$

In the case of sudden impact, the duration of the angular impulse is likely to be very brief. In such a case $\mathbf{R}$ may vary negligibly during the interval. Then

$$\int_{t_0}^{t_1} \mathbf{\Gamma}\, dt = \int_{t_0}^{t_1} \mathbf{R} \times \mathbf{F}\, dt = \mathbf{R} \times \int_{t_0}^{t_1} \mathbf{F}\, dt = \mathbf{R} \times \mathbf{P}$$

or

(16.48) *A very brief angular impulse exerted by a force $\mathbf{F}$ is equal (essentially) to the moment of the linear impulse exerted by $\mathbf{F}$.*

In applying these angular results, we shall limit ourselves to special classes of problems.

First, let us assume that the rigid body is constrained to rotate around a fixed z axis. Substituting $\mathbf{V} = \mathbf{\Omega} \times \mathbf{R}$ and taking only the z components of the angular impulses, we get, from (16.46),

(16.49)
$$\Sigma \int_{t_0}^{t_1} \mathbf{K} \cdot \mathbf{\Gamma}\, dt = \Delta\left(\int \mathbf{K} \cdot \mathbf{R} \times \mathbf{V}\, dm \right)$$

(16.50)
$$\Sigma \int_{t_0}^{t_1} \gamma_z\, dt = \Delta\left[\int \mathbf{K} \cdot \mathbf{R} \times (\mathbf{\Omega} \times \mathbf{R})\, dm \right]$$

The right member may be simplified in a manner which we have met before (e.g., in Sec. 16.3):

(16.51)
$$\Sigma \int_{t_0}^{t_1} \gamma_z\, dt = \Delta(i_z \omega)$$

The quantity $i_z \omega$ is usually called the *angular momentum* [cf. (12.1)] of the body about the z axis. This conclusion is then very much analogous to (7.9).

(16.52) *The change during a time interval in the angular momentum of a rigid body free to rotate about a fixed axis is equal to the net angular impulse about that axis exerted by the external forces during this interval.*

Example 1

A wheel is mounted rigidly on a horizontal axle at whose ends are bearings. The wheel and axle together have a moment of inertia of 4.2 ft-lb-sec². The axle is 2 in. in diameter. A rope is wound several times around the axle. When the end of the rope is pulled, the wheel rotates. If the rope does not slip, what speed will the wheel attain if the rope is pulled with a 40-lb force for 3 sec?

Solution

The moment about the axle is $\frac{40}{12} = 3.33$ ft-lb, and hence the angular impulse is 10 ft-lb-sec. By (16.52), this must equal the angular momentum attained:

$$i\omega = 10$$

or

$$\omega = \frac{10}{i} = \frac{10}{4.2} = 2.38 \text{ rad/sec}$$

Now limiting ourselves to any motion of a rigid body parallel to the xy plane, we have, from (16.47), by similar arguments, for moments about an axis through the center of mass and perpendicular to the xy plane

(16.53) $$\Sigma \int_{t_0}^{t_1} \gamma_z \, dt = \Delta(\bar{\imath}_z \omega)$$

(16.54) *The change during a time interval in the angular momentum (about a normal axis through the center of mass) of a rigid body in motion parallel to a fixed plane is equal to the net external angular impulse about that axis during the interval.*

Example 2

A sphere of mass m and radius r (see Fig. 16.47) rolls and slips from rest down a plane inclined at θ, acquiring a linear speed $\bar{v}$ in t sec. Find the angular speed acquired and also the frictional force.

Solution

The linear impulse equation is

$$(mg \sin \theta - f)t = m\bar{v}$$

The angular impulse equation is

$$frt = i\omega$$

From the first,

$$f = mg \sin \theta - \frac{m\bar{v}}{t}$$

Substituting in the second,

$$\omega = \frac{frt}{i} = \frac{m(gt \sin \theta - \bar{v})r}{0.4mr^2} = \frac{2.5(gt \sin \theta - \bar{v})}{r}$$

Example 3

A sphere such as is used in bowling is given a linear speed v_0 along a horizontal plane with which it has a coefficient of friction μ. Initially, the angular speed is zero. How long before it rolls without slipping?

Solution

In general, one may say that the same constant external force f (the force of friction) provides a negative linear impulse to slow down the translation of the ball and a positive angular impulse to speed up the rotation until the critical ratio $v/\omega = r$ is reached. The linear impulse equation is

$$mv - mv_0 = -ft$$

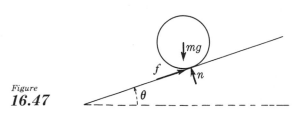

Figure
16.47

The angular impulse equation is

$$frt = \tfrac{2}{5}mr^2\omega$$

Writing $f = \mu mg$ and $v = \omega r$, we may solve for t:

$$t = \frac{2v_0}{7\mu g}$$

Example 4

A disk of radius r and mass m is mounted on a smooth horizontal pivot O on its edge as in Fig. 16.48. A sudden impulse P, horizontal and in the plane of the disk, sets the disk in motion. Find the initial angular speed and the resulting impulse P' at the pivot.

Solution

Using (16.48) and (16.52), we have, taking moments about the axis at O,

$$pr = i\omega = \tfrac{3}{2}mr^2\omega$$

Thus

$$\omega = \frac{2}{3}\frac{p}{mr}$$

The instantaneous velocity of the center of mass is then

$$\bar{v} = r\omega = \frac{2}{3}\frac{p}{m}$$

Now, using (16.45),

$$p - p' = m\bar{v} = \tfrac{2}{3}p$$

Thus

$$p' = \tfrac{1}{3}p$$

Note that the pivot has to provide an additional centripetal force

$$f = m\omega^2 r = m\frac{4p^2r}{9m^2r^2} = \frac{4p^2}{9mr}$$

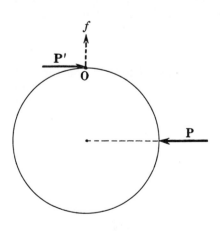

Figure
16.48

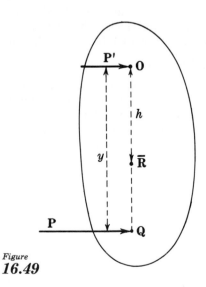

Figure
16.49

Center of Percussion. Starting with any rigid body mounted to rotate freely about a horizontal pivot **O**, i.e., a body suitable for use as a physical pendulum, let us consider the problem of eliminating the bearing impulse **P′** which occurred in the last example. Let a sudden horizontal impulse **P** (in the normal plane containing the center of mass) act on the body at **Q**, at a distance y from **O** along the line $\overline{\text{OR}}$ (see Fig. 16.49). If **Q** is located in such a way that the bearing impulse **P′** is zero, then **Q** is called the *center of percussion* relative to the axis at **O**.

The angular impulse equation, for moments about the pivot, is

$$py = i\omega$$

The linear impulse equation is

$$p + p' = m\bar{v} = m\omega h$$

Now eliminating ω and setting p' equal to zero,

$$y = \frac{i}{mh}$$

A comparison with (16.18) shows that y is equal to the *equivalent length l* of the pendulum.

(16.55) *The center of percussion of a physical pendulum is located an equivalent length below the axis of rotation.*

EXERCISES

56. An airplane propeller is 8 ft long and weighs 220 lb. Assuming that the mass of the propeller is uniformly distributed along its length, find what constant torque would give it a speed of 1,800 rpm 1 min after starting from rest.

57. A uniform spherical shell mounted on a diametrical axis has radius 0.26 m and mass 2.4 kg. A torque given by

$$\gamma = 4.8t^{\frac{1}{2}} \qquad \text{newton-m}$$

is applied. How long must it act to achieve a speed of 100 rad/sec?

58. A spool has moment of inertia i and radius r. Its weight is w. A long, light, thin, flexible tape is wound around the spool, the free end being fastened to the ceiling. The spool is released from rest with the tape taut and is allowed to fall, the tape unrolling. Find the time required for the descending spool to acquire a speed v. Find an expression for the impulse exerted by the tension in the tape during this time.

59. A uniform rod lying on ice receives at one end a normal horizontal blow of impulse p. Show that the point of impact has an instantaneous speed four times as great as would have been the case if the blow had been at the center.

60. A uniform meter stick is free to rotate in a vertical plane about a pivot at a distance d above the center. When it is struck a horizontal blow at a point at a distance d below the center, no horizontal pivot reaction results. Find d.

61. A steel pulley 2 ft in diameter slips off its fixed axle while rotating at 36 rad/sec. It travels along a concrete floor, rolling and slipping. When slipping stops, the speed of rotation has diminished to 16 rad/sec. Find the radius of gyration of the pulley.

16.12. RIGID-BODY COLLISIONS

In Sec. 7.5 we used the concept of coefficient of restitution as a means of studying impacts between spheres. It was assumed that the theory could be extended to other objects, particularly when the colliding surfaces were regular and symmetrical. The following example will illustrate this assumption.

Example

A uniform bar 3 ft long and weighing 5 lb is pivoted at one end, as shown in Fig. 16.50. It swings from rest in a horizontal position, striking squarely a 5-lb uniform solid spherical ball of diameter 1 ft when the bar is vertical. The ball is initially at rest. The point of contact is 6 in. from the end of the bar. The coefficient of restitution is 0.5. Find for the moment immediately after impact (a) the initial speed of the ball, (b) the impulse given the bar at the bearing.

Solution

Let ω_0 be the angular speed just before impact. Then the conservation-of-energy principle enables us to find ω_0.

$$\tfrac{1}{2}(\tfrac{1}{3}ml^2)\omega_0^2 = \tfrac{1}{2}mgl$$

Thus

$$\omega_0 = \sqrt{\frac{3g}{l}} = 5.7 \text{ rad/sec}$$

Let $\mathbf{P}$ and $\mathbf{P}'$ be the impulses at ball and bearing, respectively. Then the impulse-momentum principle gives

$$-p - p' = m\frac{l}{2}(\omega - \omega_0)$$

where ω is the new angular speed of the bar. For the ball (same mass) the same principle gives

$$p = mv$$

By the conservation of moment of momentum we may write

$$(\tfrac{1}{3}ml^2)\omega_0 = (\tfrac{1}{3}ml^2)\omega + mv(l - r)$$

The restitution relationship is

$$\omega(l - r) - v = -e\omega_0(l - r)$$

Eliminating ω between the last two equations, we get

$$v = \frac{\omega_0(1 + e)l^2(l - r)}{4l^2 - 6lr + 3r^2} = \frac{5.7(1.5)(9)(2.5)}{27.75} = 6.9 \text{ ft/sec}$$

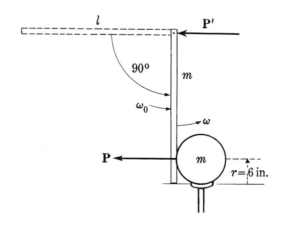

Figure
16.50

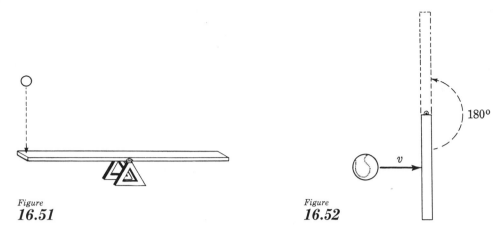

Figure
16.51

Figure
16.52

180°

v

Eliminating ω from the linear impulse equation, we get

$$p' = mv \frac{l - 3r}{2l} = \frac{5(6.9)(1.5)}{(32.2)(6)} = 0.27 \text{ lb-sec}$$

EXERCISES

62. A 10-ft plank weighing 60 lb is balanced in a horizontal position by pivots at its middle as in Fig. 16.51. A 20-lb steel ball is dropped from a height of 9 ft to strike the plank near one end. The coefficient of restitution is 0.2. Find the initial angular speed of the plank and the new velocity of the ball.

63. A 10-lb board 16 in. square is suspended from one edge about which it is free to rotate. With what horizontal velocity must a baseball weighing 9 oz strike this target in the center (as in Fig. 16.52) in order to make it rotate through 180°? The coefficient of restitution is $\frac{1}{3}$.

64. A particle weighing 0.25 lb, moving with a speed of 4 ft/sec, strikes at right angles the end of a 3-lb rod 2 ft long pivoted at the middle. If the coefficient of restitution is 0.5, find the angular speed of the rod after impact.

65. A $\frac{1}{2}$-lb yardstick lies on smooth horizontal ice. A 1-lb hockey puck, traveling at 15 ft/sec, hits one end of the rod at right angles, administering an impulse of 2.5 poundal-sec.
(a) What is the linear speed of the puck right after the impact?
(b) What is the angular speed of the yardstick right after the impact?
(c) What is the linear speed of the *opposite* end of the yardstick, right after the impact?
(d) What is the coefficient of restitution?

16.13. NOTE ON GYROSCOPIC PHENOMENA

Suppose that we have given a rigid body with one point fixed at the origin **O**. By (13.24), the motion of the body at any instant is characterized by an angular velocity vector $\boldsymbol{\Omega}$. Let us first compute the moment of momentum relative to **O**.

$$\int_m \mathbf{R} \times \mathbf{V} \, dm = \int_m \mathbf{R} \times (\boldsymbol{\Omega} \times \mathbf{R}) \, dm$$

We shall try to express this quantity in terms of x, y, and z projections. Now any vector is the sum of such projections; thus

$$\mathbf{U} = (\mathbf{U} \cdot \mathbf{I})\mathbf{I} + (\mathbf{U} \cdot \mathbf{J})\mathbf{J} + (\mathbf{U} \cdot \mathbf{K})\mathbf{K}$$

Here, likewise,

$$\int \mathbf{R} \times \mathbf{V}\, dm = \left[\int \mathbf{I} \cdot \mathbf{R} \times (\boldsymbol{\Omega} \times \mathbf{R})\, dm\right]\mathbf{I} + \left[\int \mathbf{J} \cdot \mathbf{R} \times (\boldsymbol{\Omega} \times \mathbf{R})\, dm\right]\mathbf{J}$$
$$+ \left[\int \mathbf{K} \cdot \mathbf{R} \times (\boldsymbol{\Omega} \times \mathbf{R})\, dm\right]\mathbf{K}$$

In each integrand on the right, interchange the first $\times$ with the $\cdot$.   Also replace $\boldsymbol{\Omega}$ by

$$\omega_x \mathbf{I} + \omega_y \mathbf{J} + \omega_z \mathbf{K}$$

We may write the result as follows:

$$\int \mathbf{R} \times \mathbf{V}\, dm = \left[\omega_x \int (\mathbf{I} \times \mathbf{R}) \cdot (\mathbf{I} \times \mathbf{R})\, dm + \omega_y \int (\mathbf{I} \times \mathbf{R}) \cdot (\mathbf{J} \times \mathbf{R})\, dm\right.$$
$$\left. + \omega_z \int (\mathbf{I} \times \mathbf{R}) \cdot (\mathbf{K} \times \mathbf{R})\, dm\right]\mathbf{I}$$
$$+ \left[\omega_x \int (\mathbf{J} \times \mathbf{R}) \cdot (\mathbf{I} \times \mathbf{R})\, dm + \omega_y \int (\mathbf{J} \times \mathbf{R}) \cdot (\mathbf{J} \times \mathbf{R})\, dm\right.$$
$$\left. + \omega_z \int (\mathbf{J} \times \mathbf{R}) \cdot (\mathbf{K} \times \mathbf{R})\, dm\right]\mathbf{J}$$
$$+ \left[\omega_x \int (\mathbf{K} \times \mathbf{R}) \cdot (\mathbf{I} \times \mathbf{R})\, dm + \omega_y \int (\mathbf{K} \times \mathbf{R}) \cdot (\mathbf{J} \times \mathbf{R})\, dm\right.$$
$$\left. + \omega_z \int (\mathbf{K} \times \mathbf{R}) \cdot (\mathbf{K} \times \mathbf{R})\, dm\right]\mathbf{K}$$

The integrands are now in a form which we can identify as moments of inertia and products of inertia:

$$(16.56) \quad \int_m \mathbf{R} \times \mathbf{V}\, dm = [i_x \omega_x - i_{xy} \omega_y - i_{zx} \omega_z]\mathbf{I}$$
$$+ [-i_{xy}\omega_x + i_y\omega_y - i_{yz}\omega_z]\mathbf{J} + [-i_{zx}\omega_x - i_{yz}\omega_y + i_z\omega_z]\mathbf{K}$$

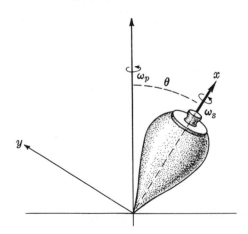

Figure
16.53

An expression of this sort can be expressed more elegantly in matrix or tensor form.
    If principal axes of the body are chosen as coordinate axes, some simplification obviously results:

$$(16.57) \qquad \int \mathbf{R} \times \mathbf{V} \, dm = i_x \omega_x \mathbf{I} + i_y \omega_y \mathbf{J} + i_z \omega_z \mathbf{K}$$

Steady Precession of a Top or Gyro.   Consider as a special case a uniform solid of revolution such as a top or gyro which rotates about an axis of symmetry and at the same time precesses about a vertical axis.   Let the coordinate axes be chosen thus: axis of spin is x axis; y axis is normal to the x axis and in the same vertical plane (as in Fig. 16.53).   Then the moment of momentum vector may be instantaneously expressed in terms of the angular velocity of spin $\boldsymbol{\Omega}_s$ and of precession $\boldsymbol{\Omega}_p$.   The total angular velocity is

$$\boldsymbol{\Omega} = \boldsymbol{\Omega}_s + \boldsymbol{\Omega}_p$$

(A special case of this was previously considered in Fig. 13.13.)   The components of the angular velocity may be expressed as follows:

$$\omega_x = \omega_s + \omega_p \cos \theta$$
$$\omega_y = \omega_p \sin \theta$$
$$\omega_z = 0$$

(One might regard the whole component ω_x as the component of spin.   In that case the following development would be carried out in terms of ω_x rather than ω_s.)   Using (16.57), we get

$$(16.58) \qquad \int \mathbf{R} \times \mathbf{V} \, dm = i_x(\omega_s + \omega_p \cos \theta)\mathbf{I} + i_y(\omega_p \sin \theta)\mathbf{J}$$

    Now relative to a fixed frame coinciding instantaneously with the rotating frame described above, the dynamical equation [generalization of (12.2)]

$$(16.59) \qquad \boldsymbol{\Gamma} = \frac{d}{dt}\left(\int \mathbf{R} \times \mathbf{V} \, dm\right)$$

is valid.   This derivative may most easily be computed by use of the operation (14.7):

$$\frac{d}{dt} = \boldsymbol{\Omega} \times \; + \frac{d'}{d't}$$

Assuming that the spin is uniform, so that $(d'/d't)(\int \mathbf{R} \times \mathbf{V} \, dm) = \mathbf{O}$,

$$\boldsymbol{\Gamma} = \frac{d}{dt}\left(\int \mathbf{R} \times \mathbf{V} \, dm\right) = \boldsymbol{\Omega}_p \times \left(\int \mathbf{R} \times \mathbf{V} \, dm\right)$$

This already brings to light the startling fact that the torque required for such a steady precession is normal to both the precession and the moment of momentum vector.
    Now let us substitute

$$\boldsymbol{\Omega}_p = \omega_p(\cos \theta \mathbf{I} + \sin \theta \mathbf{J})$$

and Eq. (1.658).   The computation is as follows.

$$\Gamma = \omega_p \begin{vmatrix} \cos\theta & \sin\theta & 0 \\ i_x(\omega_s + \omega_p \cos\theta) & i_y(\omega_p \sin\theta) & 0 \\ \mathbf{I} & \mathbf{J} & \mathbf{K} \end{vmatrix}$$

$$= (i_y\omega_p^2 \sin\theta \cos\theta - i_x\omega_p\omega_s \sin\theta - i_x\omega_p^2 \sin\theta \cos\theta)\mathbf{K}$$

$$= \omega_p\omega_s \sin\theta \left[(i_y - i_x)\frac{\omega_p}{\omega_s} \cos\theta - i_x \right]\mathbf{K}$$

$$= (\mathbf{\Omega}_s \times \mathbf{\Omega}_p)\left[(i_y - i_x)\frac{\omega_p}{\omega_s} \cos\theta - i_x \right]$$

(16.60)
$$\Gamma = (\mathbf{\Omega}_p \times i_x\mathbf{\Omega}_s)\left[1 + \left(1 - \frac{i_y}{i_x}\right)\frac{\omega_p}{\omega_s} \cos\theta \right]$$

In many important applications it happens that either $\theta = 90°$ or $\omega_s \gg \omega_p$. Then we may use

(16.61)
$$\Gamma = \mathbf{\Omega}_p \times i_s\mathbf{\Omega}_s$$

where now i_s is used to denote the moment of inertia about the axis of spin.

For the case of uniform spin where the angular momentum of spin greatly exceeds that of precession, we may proceed to (16.61) directly:

$$\Gamma = \frac{d}{dt}(i_s\mathbf{\Omega}_s) = \mathbf{\Omega}_p \times i_s\mathbf{\Omega}_s$$

Gyroscopes are of great utility as stabilizers, for, as is indicated in (16.61), the precessional response to a given torque is inversely proportional to the spin angular momentum, and the latter may be made very large.   The theory of a top precessing in a gravitational field is of importance also because of the close analogy with the performance of atomic particles precessing in magnetic fields.

EXERCISES

66. For coordinates relative to axes instantaneously coincident with principal axes of inertia, show that the kinetic energy of a rigid body moving with one point fixed is equal to one-half the scalar product of moment of momentum and angular velocity.

67. A rigid body moves with one point fixed.   Choose coordinate axes fixed in the body along principal axes.   Show from (16.57) and (16.59) that one may deduce the following (*Euler's equations of motion*):

$$\gamma_x = i_x\frac{d\omega_x}{dt} + (i_z - i_y)\omega_y\omega_z$$

$$\gamma_y = i_y\frac{d\omega_y}{dt} + (i_x - i_z)\omega_z\omega_x$$

$$\gamma_z = i_z\frac{d\omega_z}{dt} + (i_y - i_x)\omega_x\omega_y$$

68. Use Euler's equations (Exercise 67) to establish the constancy of kinetic energy for a rigid body in motion with one point fixed and with external forces having zero moment about the fixed point.   [HINT: Multiply each equation by the proper component of $\mathbf{\Omega}$, add, and integrate.   Compare with (16.31).]

69. A top consists of a thin disk 12 cm in diameter weighing 200 g together with a pin of negligible mass mounted normal to the disk through its center.   The point of the

pin is 3 cm from the disk. The top spins with the point fixed and precesses at an angular speed of 2 rad/sec, while the pin makes an angle of 20° with the vertical. Find the rate of spin.

70. Show that, for a top spinning with its point stationary,

$$\omega_x^2 i_x + \omega_y^2 i_y + \omega_z^2 i_z + 2mgl \cos \theta = \text{const}$$

71. For a top of mass m, having its center of mass at a distance h from the fixed tip, in steady precession where $\omega_s \gg \omega_p$, show that

$$\omega_p = \frac{hmg}{i_s \omega_s}$$

REVIEW EXERCISES

72. A spool of weight w, rolling radius r, and axle radius r' rests on a horizontal plane. A thread coming off the lower surface of the axle is pulled horizontally. The spool does not rotate at all, but slides horizontally with an acceleration a. Express in terms of w, r, r', a, and g the magnitude of the force exerted on the thread and the coefficient of friction.

73. A uniformly loaded cubical packing case set squarely on a truck (against cleats on the floor at the base of the case) tips forward as the truck decelerates uniformly while going down a hill inclined at 15° with the horizontal. State a minimum possible value for the deceleration.

74. A 200-lb packing case 4 ft square and 5.3 ft high is pushed by a force **P** as shown in Fig. 16.54. When |**P**| is 40 lb, the case slides at a uniform speed. If |**P**| is increased to 100 lb, assuming the same friction:
(*a*) What acceleration will result?
(*b*) How far from the center will the resultant normal reaction **N** be?
(*c*) For how large a value of **P** would the case start to tip?

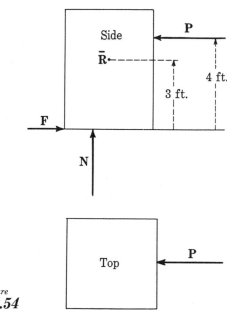

Figure
16.54

75. A 16-ft pole is dragged behind a truck. One end initially drags on the ground. The other end is fastened by a light rope 10 ft long to a point on the rear of the truck 10 ft above the ground. At what uniform acceleration would the pole and the rope form a straight line?

76. A physical pendulum is set up on a railway coach so that its plane of motion is the vertical plane in the direction of motion. If the track is straight, what angle with the vertical will specify the *equilibrium position* of the pendulum when the acceleration of the coach is a?

77. A heavy packing case 8 by 4 by 4 ft stands on the back of a truck on its square base with sides parallel to those of the vehicle. The truck accelerates down a 30° slope, causing the case to tip over. If the mass of the case is uniformly distributed, state a minimum possible value for the acceleration.

78. A double-torsion pendulum as in Fig. 16.55 consists of a wire and two disks held rigidly at a fixed distance apart. The period is τ_0. When a uniform wheel of known moment of inertia i_1 is centered on the lower disk, the period is τ_1. When a symmetric wheel of unknown moment of inertia is placed on the lower disk instead of the other, the period is τ_2. Find in terms of τ_0, τ_1, τ_2, and i_1 the unknown moment of inertia.

79. A uniform 16-lb disk of radius 9 in. is suspended horizontally by a uniform wire attached to its center. A torque of 1 ft-lb will hold the disk turned into a position 90° from its equilibrium position. When released, it oscillates as a torsion pendulum.
(a) Find the period.
(b) If the mid-point of the suspending wire in part (a) is held fast so that the pendulum is only half as long, what will be the period?
(c) If a thin hoop weighing 4 lb is fitted to the circumference of the disk in part (a), what will be the period? (The wire is full length.)

80. A uniform solid disk 60 cm in diameter and 1 cm thick is free to oscillate in a vertical plane about a horizontal axis at a point on its circumference. The center of the disk is displaced 3 cm from its equilibrium position, held there at rest, and then released.
(a) What is the period of the oscillation?
(b) What is the maximum angular speed?

81. A uniform rod weighing 2 kg and 2 m long is suspended as a compound or physical pendulum about a point 40 cm from one end. It is given a displacement of 10° from its position of stable equilibrium and then released.

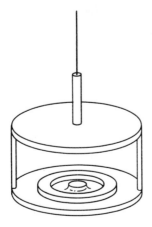

Figure
16.55

(*a*) With what period will it oscillate?

(*b*) What will be its maximum angular speed?

82. A uniform rod suspended from a knife-edge 4 ft from one end has the same period as a simple pendulum 8 ft long. How long is the rod?

83. Two physical pendulums designed to oscillate about a common axis are clamped together to form a new pendulum of mass m, period τ, with center of mass at a distance h from the axis. If m', h', and τ' and m'', h'', and τ'' are the corresponding values for the original pendulums taken separately, show that the new period is given by

$$\tau^2 = \frac{m'\tau'^2h' + m''\tau''^2h''}{m'h' + m''h''}$$

84. A meter stick oscillates freely as a physical pendulum about a horizontal axis at a distance d from its center. The period is 2.156 sec. Find d.

85. A semicircular plate of radius r is cut of uniform material. It is mounted so as to be free to oscillate about a perpendicular horizontal axis through one corner. Find the period.

86. Derive Eqs. (16.20) and (16.21) algebraically by considering h' and h'' as the roots of the quadratic equation (16.18).

87. A small hole is drilled through a uniform meter stick of mass 200 g at the 90 cm mark. When a tiny knife-edge is inserted to support the stick, it oscillates in a vertical plane with period t_0 sec. It will, of course, have the same period for a hole at the 10 cm mark.

(*a*) Find the period t_0.

(*b*) Find two other scale positions on the meter stick for which the period is t_0.

88. Three meter sticks are pinned together at the 25- and 75-cm marks as shown in Fig. 16.56. One of the pins serves as a pivot about which the triangular frame oscillates as a physical pendulum in a vertical plane. Find the period of oscillation.

89. A uniform cubical block of length 10 in. is set up to oscillate as a pendulum about a horizontal axis along one edge. Find the period.

90. A uniform circular aluminum disk is allowed to oscillate as a physical pendulum about an axis normal to its plane. How far from the center should this axis be located for minimum period? Compute this minimum period in terms of the radius r of the disk and the acceleration g of gravity.

91. Find the equivalent length of each of the following:

(*a*) A spring-and-bob combination such that the spring is 10 in. shorter when the bob is removed than when it is supporting the bob in equilibrium.

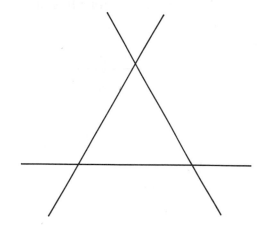

Figure
16.56

(b) A wooden cylinder which floats and oscillates vertically with 4 ft of its length submerged when at the equilibrium position.

(c) A circular hoop of diameter 30 in. hung on a nail and oscillating in its own plane.

92. A solid steel cylinder 10 cm in radius is placed with its axis horizontal on an inclined plane. The angle of inclination with the horizontal is θ. The coefficient of friction is 0.1. Find the ratio of linear to angular acceleration for the cases where θ is equal to 20°, 40°, 60°, and 80°.

93. A circular hoop of diameter d and mass m rolls from rest without slipping down an incline of constant slope and length s in t sec. Find the angle of inclination of the hill.

94. A sphere rolls without slipping down a roof inclined at an angle of 30°. If it starts from rest at a point 17.5 ft from the edge of the roof and the edge of the roof is 26 ft above the ground, where is the point where it will strike the ground?

95. A plane table is tilted at an angle of 20° with the horizontal. A spherical ball bearing of diameter 1 in. and mass 66.3 g is rolled up the plane with an initial speed v_0. There is no slipping. If the ball is to return to the starting point in exactly 3 sec, how large should v_0 be?

96. A solid uniform sphere is allowed to roll down a plane inclined at an angle θ with the horizontal. The coefficient of friction is $\mu = 0.20$. What is the greatest angle θ at which this rolling will take place without slipping?

97. Figure 16.57 represents a uniform circular solid 100-lb cylinder set in motion by a 25-lb applied force **P**. The diameter of the cylinder is 1 ft. The motion is parallel to the plane section shown. It must *not* be assumed that the motion is rolling without slipping.

(a) If the contact with the plane on which the cylinder rests is smooth, find the magnitude of the acceleration of the center of mass and of the angular acceleration.

(b) Suppose the contact is not smooth, but that the angular acceleration is 12 rad/sec². Find the acceleration of the center of mass.

98. A uniform steel sphere (specific gravity = 7.8, diameter = 1 in.) is rolled directly up a plane inclined at 20° with the horizontal. If its speed at the bottom is 6 ft/sec and if it rolls without slipping, how many feet up the plane will it go before stopping?

99. A spool of mass m, rolling radius r, and winding radius r' slides without rolling down a plane inclined at an angle θ. The thread goes (see Fig. 16.58) from the upper edge of the winding surface, parallel to the plane, over a small frictionless pulley to a load of mass m'. The acceleration of the center of mass of the spool is of magnitude $\bar{a}$. The coefficient of friction between spool and plane is μ. For the correct value of m', rotation is prevented. It is then possible to find the acceleration $\bar{a}$ which will result.

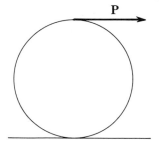

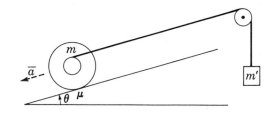

Figure
16.57

Figure
16.58

(a) Express $\bar{a}$ in terms of g, θ, r, r', μ.

(b) Express m' in terms of g, θ, r, r', μ, $\bar{a}$, m.

100. A boy rolls his hoop along level pavement by pushing horizontally with a stick at the rear end of a horizontal diameter. The stick slides as the hoop rotates, but no slipping takes place at the pavement. The hoop is a yard in diameter, and it weighs 2 lb. The coefficient of friction between hoop and stick is $\frac{1}{3}$.

(a) Compute the linear acceleration when the horizontal component of the applied force is 1.5 lb.

(b) For the situation described in (a), at least how great is the coefficient of friction at the pavement (in order that no slipping occur there)?

101. A large spherical homogeneous steel ball bearing is initially at rest on the level floor of an otherwise empty boxcar. When the train starts, accelerating uniformly, the bearing rolls without slipping toward the rear, moving a distance of 17.5 ft (along the car) in 7.0 sec. What is the acceleration of the train?

102. A rigid body moves with one point fixed. Instantaneously, the axis of rotation has direction cosines l, m, and n. (a) Derive an expression for the kinetic energy in terms of ω_x, ω_y, ω_z, i_x, i_y, i_z, i_{yz}, i_{zx}, i_{xy}. (b) Verify (16.31).

103. Show that the work done by external forces on a rigid body moving parallel to the xy plane can be broken up into translational and rotational aspects thus:

$$\text{Work} = \sum \int_{\bar{R}_0}^{\bar{R}_1} \mathbf{F} \cdot d\bar{\mathbf{R}} + \sum \int_{\theta_0}^{\theta_1} \gamma_z \, d\theta$$

104. How much work is done in hoisting a bucket containing $\frac{1}{2}$ ton of ore to the top of a mine shaft 2,000 ft deep if the cable weighs 2 lb/ft?

105. In a magnetic field of intensity $\mathbf{H}$, the force on a pole of strength ϕ is $\mathbf{H}\phi$. A bar magnet may be considered as composed of two poles ϕ, $-\phi$ separated by a relative position vector of constant length $\mathbf{D}$. How much work does the field do on the magnet as the vector changes from $\mathbf{D}_0$ (parallel to $\mathbf{H}$) to some other orientation $\mathbf{D}_1$? (Use scalar products to express your answer.)

106. A uniform chain lies on a rough horizontal table perpendicular to the smooth edge with a length y_1 overhanging. As it slips until an amount y_2 overhangs, show that the amount of work done by friction is equal to the displacement $(y_2 - y_1)$ times the coefficient of friction μ times the mean weight of chain on the table $(w_1 + w_2)/2$.

107. One end of a 100-lb 100-ft cable is attached to a 100-lb load. The rest of the cable is wound around a steel horizontally mounted winding drum in the shape of a cylindrical shell of radius 1 ft and weight (empty) 100 lb whose bearings have negligible friction. Initially, the cable is all wound up and the system is at rest. If released, with what speed will the load be descending when the amount of cable out is 50 ft?

108. A narrow pipe weighing 40 lb falls vertically from rest 100 ft and pierces the ground to a depth of 10 in. What is the average force of resistance?

109. A uniform rod (see Fig. 16.59), with a smooth bearing at one end, has weight w. It can oscillate freely in a vertical plane. It is released from rest in a vertical (up) position. When it goes through its horizontal position ($\theta = 90°$), what will be the horizontal and vertical components of the total force exerted on the rod by the hinge?

110. A solid uniform semicylinder (see Fig. 16.60) of radius r and mass m rocks without slipping. When it goes through equilibrium position, the angular speed is ω. Letting O' be the center of curvature for a central cross section, it is clear that $v_{O'} = r\omega$. What is the kinetic energy of the object?

111. In an experiment on the curving of baseballs, a ball was projected at 100 ft/sec with

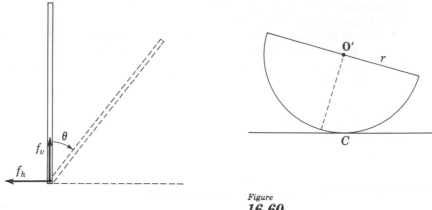

Figure
16.59

Figure
16.60

a spin of 1,800 rpm. What fraction of the kinetic energy was rotational? Take the diameter of the ball as 3 in.

112. A flexible chain 10 m long of linear density 0.5 kg/m is wound around a uniform solid cylinder of mass 5.0 kg and radius 20 cm. The cylinder is equipped with bearings so that it can rotate about its horizontal axis. The bearing friction constitutes a constant torque of 0.40 newton-m impeding rotation. Initially, the cylinder is at rest and the unwound portion of the chain is 1 m long. How fast will the cylinder be rotating after 5 m of the chain is unwound (i.e., when the total portion unwound is 5 m) if the chain does not slip on the cylinder?

113. A uniform rod weighing 20 lb is pivoted about a point 2 ft from its center. The length of the rod is 8 ft. The rod, initially at rest in a horizontal position, is released and swings freely about the pivot. After it has moved through an angle of 30°, what are the vertical and horizontal components of the bearing reactions?

114. A uniform bar 16 ft long and weighing 40 lb is pivoted about a horizontal axis at a point 4 ft from the center. If it falls from rest when horizontal, find the radial and transverse components of the bearing reactions when the angle is 45°.

115. A 10-lb uniform disk 2 ft in diameter is pivoted about a normal horizontal axis at the circumference. It is released from rest at its highest position. What is the maximum speed attained? What is the bearing reaction when the diameter through the pivot is horizontal?

116. A uniform rod 3 ft long is placed with one end on a smooth horizontal table and it is allowed to fall from rest. Initially it is inclined at 60° with the horizontal. What is the speed of the center of mass at the moment when the rod becomes horizontal?

117. A uniform rod initially standing vertically on end on a horizontal table tips and falls. It does not slip until its inclination is 45°. What is the coefficient of friction?

118. A tripod consisting of three uniform legs 6 ft long hinged freely at the top is placed on perfectly smooth ice with the legs vertical. They slip outward, and the tripod flattens. With what speed does the top hit the ice?

119. A rigidly attached smooth post stands vertically on a laboratory table. Beside it is placed vertically a uniform rod a meter long. The top of the rod is hinged flexibly to a light ring which slides freely on the post. The bottom of the rod rests on the smooth table. The rod slips and falls, its ring sliding down the post.
    (a) At what angle of inclination does the ring withstand no force due to the rod?
    (b) At what angle of inclination does the rod cease to press down on the table?

120. A uniform 2-lb bar 12 in. long is held vertically at rest against the interior of a smooth

sphere of radius 10 in.   It is then released.   When the upper end crosses the horizontal equator of the sphere:

(a) What is the speed of the center?

(b) What are the reaction forces at the ends?

121. An 8-ton trailer, uniformly loaded, is 40 ft by 10 ft wide.   It is attached to a 4-ton tractor by a single central pivot.   The tractor has brakes and chains for all wheels. The effective coefficient of friction is 0.4.   The trailer has no chains, so for it the friction is negligible.   After riding steadily along a level icy road at 25 ft/sec, the tractor's brakes are locked, with the result that the speed diminishes to 20 ft/sec while traveling 12 ft.   The trailer, skidding, swings about its pivot, getting 30° out of line in the 12-ft displacement of the tractor (see Fig. 16.61).   Find its angular speed at this moment.   Assume that braking is maximum.   Neglect lateral skidding of tractor.

122. In Exercise 120, with what period would the bar oscillate about its equilibrium position?

123. A uniform bar of length d has at one end a screw eye through which passes a taut, perfectly smooth horizontal wire.   With what period will the bar oscillate:

(a) In the vertical plane including the wire?

(b) In the vertical plane normal to the wire?

124. A uniform bar 4 ft long, weighing 8 lb, has a smooth horizontal pivot at one end.   It is released from rest in a vertical upward position.   When it reaches the position making an angle of 30° with the downward vertical, what are the magnitude and the direction of the net bearing reaction (i.e., resultant bearing reaction)?

125. A uniform chain ABC of mass m and length πr is in unstable equilibrium along the upper semicircumference of a smooth horizontal cylinder of radius r as shown in Fig. 16.62.   A light strong cord ADC completes the circumference.   The chain slips from its initial position and slides around the cylinder.

(a) During the motion the center of mass of the chain moves on a circle.   What is the radius of this circle?

(b) What is the radius of gyration for the motion described?

(c) What maximum angular speed does the chain attain?

(d) What is the period of oscillation about the position of stable equilibrium?

126. A semicylindrical shell has radius r.   With what period will it rock at low amplitude on a plane horizontal surface?

(a) Assume no slipping.

(b) Assume no friction.

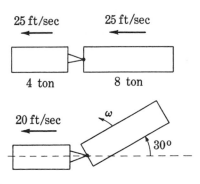

Figure
16.61

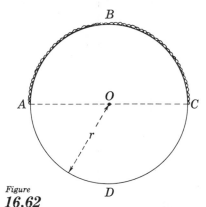

Figure
16.62

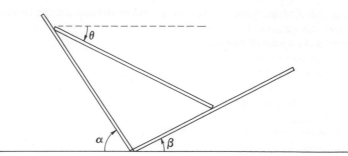

Figure
16.63

127. Two smooth horizontal boards make angles α, β with the horizontal as shown in Fig. 16.63. A third uniform horizontal board in equilibrium makes angle θ with the horizontal resting on the given two boards. Express θ in terms of α and β.

128. A uniform circular disk of moment of inertia i is supported in horizontal position by three equally spaced vertical strings attached to the circumference. When a small torque is applied, the trifilar suspension twists through an angle θ about its vertical axis to a new equilibrium position. If d, the length of the supports, is much greater than the radius of the disk, show that

$$\gamma = \frac{2gi \sin \theta}{d}$$

129. (a) If the trifilar suspension in Exercise 128 is twisted through a large angle θ_m and released from rest, what maximum angular speed does it attain?
(b) If the device is allowed to make small oscillations about its equilibrium position, what is the period?

130. A homogeneous disk of mass m and radius r is mounted to swing freely about a horizontal axis through a point A. The distance to A from the center O of the disk is r' as in Fig. 16.64. A string of length l attaches an object of mass m' to the point

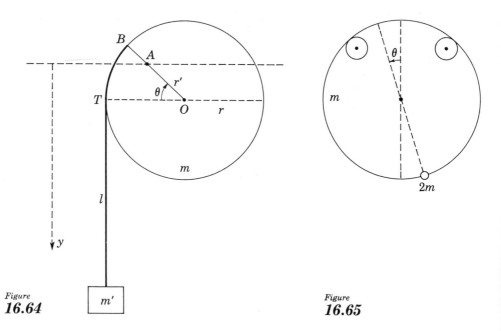

Figure
16.64

Figure
16.65

B on the circumference of the disk. OAB is a straight line, and the string lies on the curve of the disk from B to the point of tangency T.   When the system is in equilibrium, the angle between OB and the horizontal is θ.   (The angle θ is positive.)

(a) In terms only of r, r', l, θ, express the vertical distance y from the point of support A to the suspended object.

(b) In terms only of m, m', r, r', θ, express the potential energy of the system (taking p.e. $= 0$ for $\theta = 0°$).

(c) For what θ is the system in equilibrium?   (Express the answer in terms only of m, m', r, r'.)

(d) Carry out the test for stability of equilibrium.

131. A hoop of mass m and radius r is supported in a vertical plane by two light frictionless pulleys as shown in Fig. 16.65.   A load of mass $2m$ is attached at a point on the circumference.   When displaced in its own plane by an angle θ, the system oscillates.

(a) Write an expression for the potential energy relative to the equilibrium position in terms of θ, r, and m.

(b) Write an expression for the kinetic energy when

$$\frac{d\theta}{dt} = \omega$$

(c) Use the results of (a) and (b) to evaluate the period.

(d) Show that $\theta = 0°$ is a position of stable equilibrium.   Analyze, likewise, $\theta = 180°$.

132. A perfectly smooth hemispherical igloo has radius r.   A flexible light string passes through a small smooth hole in the top of the dome.   To the outside end is attached an object of weight w_1; on the inside end hangs an object of weight w_2.   When the system is in equilibrium, the radius toward the outside object makes an angle θ with the horizontal.   Evaluate θ and determine whether the equilibrium is stable.

133. A bar of weight 2 lb and length 3 ft is hinged at the lower end H as in Fig. 16.66.   A string from the other end B of the bar passes over a pulley P 3 ft above the hinge and by other pulleys to a hanging 1 lb weight w.   For what angles θ with the upward vertical is the bar in equilibrium?   Test for stability.

134. A smooth hemispherical bowl spins about its axis (vertical) at ω rad/sec.   A button rests inside the bowl at equilibrium.   The radius from the center of curvature of the bowl to the button makes an angle θ with the vertical.

(a) Find θ.

(b) Check for equilibrium.

135. A V-shaped trough is made of two boards fastened at right angles.   The trough is

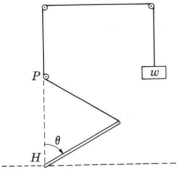

Figure
16.66

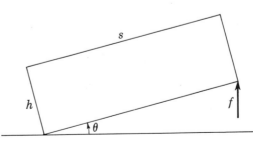

Figure
16.67

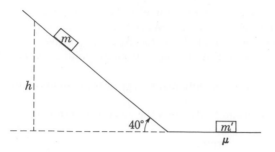

Figure
16.68

inclined at a small angle β with the horizontal.   A uniform solid sphere of radius r rolls without slipping down the trough.

(*a*) Show in detail that the total kinetic energy of the rolling sphere (translational plus rotational) is given by the formula

$$\text{k.e.} = \tfrac{9}{10}m\bar{v}^2$$

where $\bar{v}$ is the speed of the center of mass.

(*b*) Express the linear acceleration of the sphere in terms of g and β.

136. A uniform rectangular granite slab of weight w with dimensions of cross section h by s (as in Fig. 16.67) is slowly tipped by applying a varying vertical force of magnitude f at one lower edge as shown.

(*a*) Express f as a function of θ in terms of h, s, w.

(*b*) Compute the work done by f in getting the slab up to the unstable balance point.

137. A smooth block of mass m slides down a 40° incline (see Fig. 16.68) through a vertical distance h onto a horizontal surface to strike squarely a block of mass m' and coefficient of friction with the horizontal surface equal to μ.   How soon after the first impact do the blocks collide again?   Express your answer in terms of h, g, m, m', μ, and e (the coefficient of restitution for the two blocks), as necessary.

138. A smooth axle is set rigidly in horizontal position.   Two wheels of moment of inertia i_1 and i_2, respectively, turn freely about this axle as shown in Fig 16.69.   They are connected by a spring which provides a torque γ proportional and opposite to the angle θ through which one disk is rotated relative to the other.   Initially, the relative displacement is θ_m and the torque γ_m with both wheels at rest.   Then they

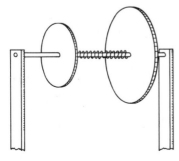

Figure
16.69

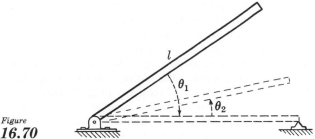

Figure
16.70

are released.   Show that when the spring reaches its unstrained position, the angular
velocity of the first wheel is

$$\omega_1 = \sqrt{\frac{i_2 \gamma_m \theta_m}{i_1(i_1 + i_2)}}$$

139.   A uniform rod of length l and mass m is pivoted at one end as in Fig. 16.70.   When
released from rest at an angle θ_1 with the horizontal, it falls from rest.   The other
end strikes a fixed object when the rod is horizontal and rebounds to an angle θ_2.
Show that the impulse **P** has magnitude

$$p = m\sqrt{\frac{gl}{3}}(\sqrt{\sin \theta_1} + \sqrt{\sin \theta_2})$$

140.   A plane rigid body of mass m free to move in the xy plane is set initially with its
center of mass $\bar{\mathbf{R}}$ at the origin as in Fig. 16.71.   At the point corresponding to
$(0, -d)$, a sudden blow of impulse $p\mathbf{I}$ is delivered.   Show that the instantaneous
speed of the point $\mathbf{Y}:(0,y)$ is given by

$$v = \frac{p}{m}\left[\frac{i - m\,d\,y}{i}\right]$$

i being the moment of inertia about the normal axis through the center of mass.

141.   A wheel lies flat on a horizontal table.   When a spoke receives a sharp normal

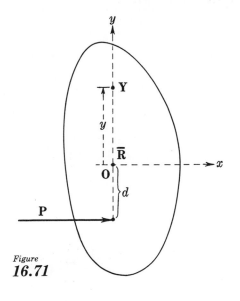

Figure
16.71

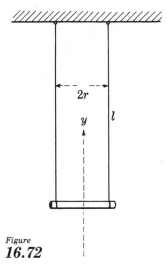

Figure
16.72

horizontal blow at a distance 24 in. from the center of the wheel, the wheel makes a small angular displacement, having apparently as center of rotation a point 20 in. beyond the center of the wheel. What is the approximate radius of gyration (about a normal axis through the center of the wheel)?

142. An airplane about to land at 90 mph loses a wheel (initially unspinning) which rolls along the ground. The rolling radius is 18 in. By the time the wheel stops slipping, its angular speed is 55 rad/sec. Find the radius of gyration.

143. A rigid body is in motion parallel to the xy plane. Show that the moment of momentum about the z axis can always be expressed as the sum of the angular momentum about a parallel axis through the center of mass plus the moment about the z axis of the momentum $m\bar{V}$ of the center of mass.

144. A plank of length l and thickness h balances in equilibrium across a horizontal cylinder of radius r. Under what conditions is equilibrium stable?

145. A smooth hemispherical cup has radius r. A needle of length $2l(l < r)$ is placed in the cup. Show that its only equilibrium positions are horizontal.

146. A *bifilar suspension* is shown in Fig. 16.72. It consists of two strings of length l supporting a bar of weight w horizontally. In equilibrium position the strings are separated by a distance $2r$. When a small vertical torque Γ is applied, the bar rotates through an angle θ about a vertical axis of symmetry to a new equilibrium position. If l is much larger than r and if θ is small, show that,

$$\gamma = \frac{wr^2 \sin \theta}{l}$$

147. A ball bearing of radius 0.500 in. rolls without slipping down a curved chute through a vertical drop of 20 ft. What angular speed does it attain?

148. A uniform disk of diameter 68 cm and weight 7.2 newtons is free to oscillate as a physical pendulum about a horizontal axis normal to the disk through a point 34 cm from the center. What angular speed must the disk receive at its equilibrium position if it is to make a complete revolution?

149. A spool consists of two 1-lb disks of radius 9 in. joined at the center by a short light axle of radius $\frac{1}{4}$ in. A string is wound many times around the axle, its free end being tied to a hook on the ceiling. The spool is allowed to fall, the string unwinding as it falls. What angular speed is acquired after a fall of 8 ft?

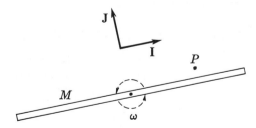

Figure
16.73

150. A uniform bar of length $2l$ and mass m is free to swing in a vertical plane about a pivot at one end.

(*a*) How great an instantaneous impulse is required to make this bar swing through an angle of $90°$?

(*b*) How great an instantaneous reaction impulse is produced at the pivot as a result of the impulse described in (*a*)?

151. A square board of length s and mass m lies on flat ice. A hockey puck of mass m' and velocity v_0 strikes the board at a corner in a direction parallel to an edge. The velocity of the puck at once becomes v', while the center of the board acquires a speed $\bar{v}$. The board also acquires an angular speed ω. The magnitude of the impulse of collision is p. The coefficient of restitution is e. In terms of s, m, m', v_0, v', $\bar{v}$, ω, p, and e, write the following:

(*a*) An equation applying the impulse-momentum principle to the puck.

(*b*) An equation applying the impulse-momentum principle to the board.

(*c*) An equation applying the principle of conservation of momentum.

(*d*) An equation applying conservation of angular momentum.

(*e*) An equation applying the restitution coefficient to velocities.

152. A meter stick M is spinning around its center on perfectly smooth ice at 10 rad/sec. It will spin forever unless something is done. A bystander drives an ice pick P solidly into the ice so that the meter stick strikes it at the 80 cm mark (see Fig. 16.73). The coefficient of restitution is 0.6. For the instant after the completion of the collision find:

(*a*) The velocity of the center of mass of the stick.

(*b*) The new angular speed (taking counterclockwise as positive).

(*c*) The energy loss in joules if the mass of the meter stick is 200 g. Set up your equations carefully, including full details.

153. A rigid uniform bar of mass m and length $4s$ is mounted with a smooth bearing B at a distance s from its center and also at a distance s from the point of attachment of two stretched springs each of compliance c, as shown in Fig. 16.74.

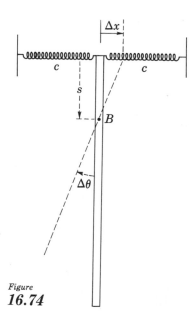

Figure
16.74

If the bar is displaced by a small angle $\Delta\theta$, the springs are, respectively, compressed and stretched an amount Δx. The bar is then released and allowed to oscillate.

(a) Express in terms of c, s, and $\Delta\theta$ the work required to displace the bar from equilibrium position to the position given by $\Delta\theta$. Neglect gravity.

(b) Compute the period of oscillation in terms of m, s, and c. Neglect gravity.

154. Two beads of masses $4m$ and $3m$ are on a smooth circular wire of radius r which is standing in a vertical plane. The beads are joined by a light cord of length $\sqrt{2}r$.

(a) Find an equilibrium position for the beads, assuming the cord to be taut.

(b) Test for stability.

155. A hula hoop (mass m, radius r') released from rest at the top of a spherical dome (radius r) rolls without slipping. Where do the hoop and dome part company?

156. A smooth circular hoop of radius r is fixed in a plane inclined at an angle of 30° with the horizontal plane. By judicious use of smooth screw eyes, a uniform rod of mass m and length $1.414r$ is constrained to move so that its ends lie on the circle. Use potential energy explicitly to investigate:

(a) Positions of equilibrium of the rod.

(b) Stability of equilibrium.

(c) Period of small oscillations about stable equilibrium, assuming $1.414r = 2$ ft.

157. A 5- by 8-ft sliding door weighing 322 lb is supported by two small wheels that run on a horizontal track as suggested by Fig. 16.75. These supports are 6 in. from

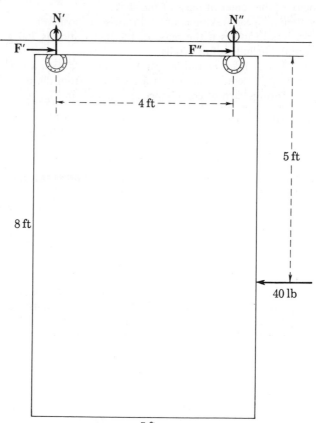

N'   N"

F'→   F"→

|←– – – – – – 4 ft – – – – – –→|

5 ft

8 ft

40 lb

5 ft

Figure
16.75

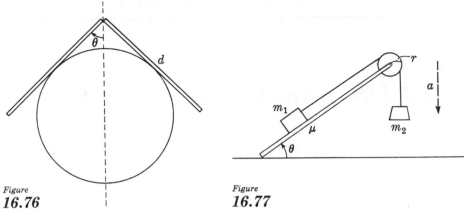

Figure
16.76

Figure
16.77

either side.   The forces which these supports exert on the door are resolved into horizontal and vertical components $\mathbf{F}'$, $\mathbf{N}'$ and $\mathbf{F}''$, $\mathbf{N}''$ as shown.   When a 40-lb horizontal force $\mathbf{F}$ is applied 5 ft from the top at the edge of the door, an acceleration of 3.0 ft/sec² results.   Find $\mathbf{N}'$ and $\mathbf{N}''$ in magnitude.

158.   A smooth cylinder of diameter d has its axis horizontal.   Two boards of width d are hinged together at one edge lengthwise.   This book-shaped combination is placed over the cylinder as shown in Fig. 16.76.   Write an equation which the angle θ between a board and the vertical must satisfy for equilibrium.   Show that the equilibrium is stable.

159.   Derive a formula for the moment of inertia of the pulley in Fig. 16.77 in terms of m_1, m_2, μ, r, θ, and the acceleration a.

160.   A uniform sphere of radius r and mass m has speed u as it approaches a wall at angle θ with the normal.   At what angle does it rebound?   If the coefficient of friction is μ and negligible slip occurs during the collision, what is the angular speed after the rebound?

161.   A hoop of mass m and radius r spinning in a vertical plane is projected horizontally in that plane with a speed v_0 and a back spin at angular speed ω_0.   It hits the horizontal rough floor, bounces, skids, etc., until finally it either rolls forward or backward without slipping.   Find the values for ω_0 in terms of r and v_0 to produce each of these cases.

CHAPTER SEVENTEEN

FIELDS and GRADIENTS

In many parts of physics variable quantities, both scalar and vector, are assigned to space. We have encountered some examples of such space functions. In Chap. 12 we were concerned with force functions varying according to an inverse-square law and with corresponding potential-energy functions. In Chap. 13 the velocity patterns possible for a rigid body provided another example of a vector function of position for limited regions. This chapter will make the idea of a function of position more precise and will introduce the calculus of such functions.

17.1. THE NATURE OF A FIELD

By now we are quite in the habit of describing the position of a point by coordinates: (x,y,z), $\mathbf{R}$, or (r,θ,z). Each point in a region of space may have characteristics of various sorts. For instance, height above the floor is a scalar characteristic of every point in a room. Since to each point in the room is assigned a number (say, the number of inches above the floor), we refer to height as a *scalar function of position*. It is a function having a scalar value for every point in a region. The region and function together are sometimes called a *scalar field*. Other examples of scalar point functions are temperature, $\mathbf{A} \cdot \mathbf{R}$ for a constant vector $\mathbf{A}$, and potential energy of a given particle. The functions with which we shall deal in this context are usually continuous, varying smoothly from point to point in the regions where they are used.

In an entirely similar manner a function which assigns a unique vector to each point of a region is called a *vector function of position* and the function and region together constitute a *vector field*. Examples of vector point functions have been encountered several times. Gravitational fields of force are clearly vector fields. The position vector $\mathbf{R}$ with respect to a specific origin is a simple vector function of position. Our discussion of velocity patterns for a rigid body (cf. Chap. 13) could have been phrased in terms of instantaneous vector fields.

Example

The unit radial vector $\mathbf{L}$ may be thought of as a vector function of position assigning to each point a vector drawn away from the origin. This is sketched for a few points in the xy plane in Fig. 17.1. Note that this function is not defined at the origin.

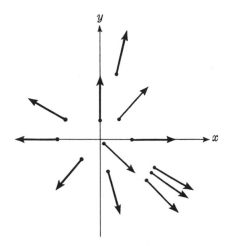

Figure
17.1

EXERCISES

1. For several points in the xy plane draw to scale vectors illustrating each of the following functions of position:
    (*a*) **L** + **I**.   (*b*) 0.5**R**.   (*c*) **K** × **R**.   (*d*) $-(1/r^2)$**L**.
2. For several points in the xy plane draw to scale vectors to illustrate the field given by:
    (*a*) $|y|^{\frac{1}{2}}$**I**.   (*b*) ω**M** for constant ω.

17.2. DIRECTIONAL DERIVATIVES FOR SCALAR FIELDS

Let us suppose that we are concerned with a scalar function of position $\varphi(\mathbf{R})$. Then we may often need to know how decidedly the function varies in the vicinity of any interesting point. This involves the simple but important concept of directional derivative.

Imagine that you pick a direction determined by a unit vector

$$\mathbf{T} = l\mathbf{I} + m\mathbf{J} + n\mathbf{K}$$

Call a line in that direction the s axis and move in that direction, noting variations in φ. The values encountered might be plotted as a graph to show φ as a function of s as in Fig. 17.2. The derivative of φ with respect to s at a given point as usual is equal to the slope of the tangent to the curve at the corresponding point. This derivative is the *directional derivative* for the **T** direction. Directional derivatives for the x, y, and z directions are customarily denoted by

$$\frac{\partial \varphi}{\partial x} \quad \frac{\partial \varphi}{\partial y} \quad \frac{\partial \varphi}{\partial z}$$

and are called *partial derivatives*, the implication being that y and z do not vary when $\partial \varphi / \partial x$ is being evaluated, etc. It should be observed that no mention has been made of the *existence* of these derivatives. In the cases we consider, differentiability may be assumed.

Directional derivatives offer a convenient language for dealing with small changes in a scalar function φ. For instance, if φ is known at (x,y,z), then at $(x + \Delta x, y, z)$ the value $\varphi + \Delta \varphi$ can be estimated (see Fig. 17.3) to be *approximately*

(17.1) $$\varphi + \Delta \varphi = \varphi + \frac{\partial \varphi}{\partial x} \Delta x$$

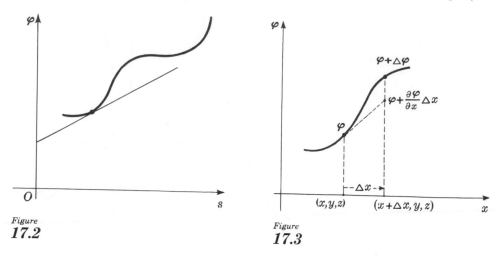

Figure
17.2

Figure
17.3

Similar approximate expressions for small changes in φ for y or z displacements will be used. The estimate of (17.1) is absolutely correct when φ varies uniformly with x. When this is not the case, we can take comfort in the fact that conclusions based on such an approximation usually become more reliable as one takes the limit as Δx becomes small. In this treatment the emphasis will be on ideas rather than rigor: we wish to use mathematical language without undertaking lengthy justifications. Additional details will be presented in Sec. 17.3, Example 3. Naturally the student will wish to reinforce his confidence and comprehension by detailed study of these methods in mathematical courses.[1]

It is easily possible to express directional derivatives for the s direction in terms of those for the x, y, and z directions. Regard a small displacement in the s direction as a vector

$$\Delta \mathbf{R} = \Delta x\, \mathbf{I} + \Delta y\, \mathbf{J} + \Delta z\, \mathbf{K} = \Delta s(l\mathbf{I} + m\mathbf{J} + n\mathbf{K})$$

The net displacement $\Delta \mathbf{R}$ could just as well have been carried out in three steps: $\Delta x\, \mathbf{I}$ followed by $\Delta y\, \mathbf{J}$ followed by $\Delta z\, \mathbf{K}$. Then the corresponding change in φ too may be calculated approximately in steps: the x step increases φ by $(\partial\varphi/\partial x)\, \Delta x$, the y step increases φ by $(\partial\varphi/\partial y)\, \Delta y$, and the z step increases φ by $(\partial\varphi/\partial z)\, \Delta z$. We have, then, approximately

$$(17.2) \qquad \Delta\varphi = \frac{\partial\varphi}{\partial x}\, \Delta x + \frac{\partial\varphi}{\partial y}\, \Delta y + \frac{\partial\varphi}{\partial z}\, \Delta z$$

If we divide through by Δs and take the limit as Δs becomes small, we arrive at

$$(17.3) \qquad \frac{d\varphi}{ds} = \frac{\partial\varphi}{\partial x}\, l + \frac{\partial\varphi}{\partial y}\, m + \frac{\partial\varphi}{\partial z}\, n$$

It is useful to interpret the right side of (17.3) as the scalar product of two vectors: the unit vector $\mathbf{T}$ in the s direction and the following vector $\boldsymbol{\nabla}\varphi$ ($\boldsymbol{\nabla}$ is read as "del" or "nabla").

$$(17.4) \qquad \boldsymbol{\nabla}\varphi = \frac{\partial\varphi}{\partial x}\, \mathbf{I} + \frac{\partial\varphi}{\partial y}\, \mathbf{J} + \frac{\partial\varphi}{\partial z}\, \mathbf{K}$$

[1] See for instance, Wilfred Kaplan, "Advanced Calculus," Addison-Wesley Publishing Company, Inc., Cambridge, Mass., 1952, and H. K. Nickerson, D. C. Spencer, and N. E. Steenrod, "Advanced Calculus," D. Van Nostrand Company, Inc., Princeton, N.J., 1959.

This allows us to write, instead of (17.3),

(17.5) $$\frac{d\varphi}{ds} = \mathbf{T} \cdot \nabla\varphi$$

Directional derivatives for vector fields are discussed later in this chapter. No new complications are involved since any vector can be expressed in terms of three scalars.

Example

If $\varphi(x,y,z) = 3xy + x^2z + yz$, find the directional derivative at the point $(2,0,-2)$ in the direction $\mathbf{T} = 0.8\mathbf{I} - 0.6\mathbf{K}$.

Solution

We shall use (17.3). This requires us to find $\partial\varphi/\partial x$, $\partial\varphi/\partial y$, $\partial\varphi/\partial z$. Now $\partial\varphi/\partial x$ is a directional derivative for displacements along a line parallel to the x axis, i.e., along a line for which y and z do not vary. So, in finding $\partial\varphi/\partial x$, we treat y and z as constants. Similarly, for the other coordinates,

$$\frac{\partial\varphi}{\partial x} = 3y + 2xz = -8$$

$$\frac{\partial\varphi}{\partial y} = 3x + z = 4$$

$$\frac{\partial\varphi}{\partial z} = x^2 + y = 4$$

Now using (17.3),

$$\frac{d\varphi}{ds} = (0.8)(-8) + (0.0)(4) - (0.6)(4) = -8.8$$

This same calculation can be regarded as the computation of a scalar product, using (17.5). For, at $(2,0,-2)$,

$$\nabla\varphi = -8\mathbf{I} + 4\mathbf{J} + 4\mathbf{K}$$

so that

$$\frac{d\varphi}{ds} = \mathbf{T} \cdot \nabla\varphi = -0.64 + 0 - 0.24 = -0.88$$

EXERCISES

3. Find the directional derivative at (x,y,z) parallel to $\mathbf{I} - \mathbf{J} - \mathbf{K}$ of the scalar point function $x + xy + xyz$.

4. If $\varphi(\mathbf{R}) = \mathbf{R} \cdot \mathbf{R}$, evaluate the directional derivative parallel to $\mathbf{R}$ at a point where $|\mathbf{R}| = r$.

5. If $\varphi(\mathbf{R}) = \mathbf{A} \cdot \mathbf{R}$, where $\mathbf{A}$ is a constant vector, show that the directional derivative for displacements parallel to the unit vector $\mathbf{T}$ is always equal to $\mathbf{A} \cdot \mathbf{T}$.

6. The scalar function $\varphi(x,y,z) = x^2y + y^2z + z^2x$ obviously has the value 3 at $(1,1,1)$. Use the methods of this section to evaluate it approximately at $(1.02, 1.00, 0.99)$.

17.3. THE NOTION OF GRADIENT

In the preceding section we started with a differentiable scalar function of position $\varphi(\mathbf{R})$, and we were led to a related vector function of position $\nabla\varphi$. From (17.5) we can deduce important properties of this function. Using the definition of scalar product, we have (see Fig. 17.4)

(17.6)
$$\frac{d\varphi}{ds} = \mathbf{T} \cdot \nabla\varphi = |\nabla\varphi| \cos\theta$$

If, for a particular point $\mathbf{R}$, we pick $\mathbf{T}$ in the direction of $\nabla\varphi$, we get the largest possible value of $d\varphi/ds$. We can then describe the vector $\nabla\varphi$ as follows:

(17.7) $\nabla\varphi$ has the direction *for which the directional derivative is maximum. It has the* magnitude *of this maximum directional derivative.*

Thus $\nabla\varphi$ is a function of position which at each point indicates in direction and magnitude the way in which φ varies with position. This function is called the *gradient of* φ, denoted by **grad** φ.

(17.8)
$$\mathbf{grad}\ \varphi = \nabla\varphi = \frac{\partial\varphi}{\partial x}\mathbf{I} + \frac{\partial\varphi}{\partial y}\mathbf{J} + \frac{\partial\varphi}{\partial z}\mathbf{K}$$

We may now restate (17.5) in words:

(17.9) *The directional derivative in a given direction of a scalar point function is merely the component in that direction of the gradient.*

(17.10)
$$\frac{d\varphi}{ds} = \mathbf{T} \cdot \nabla\varphi = \mathbf{T} \cdot (\mathbf{grad}\ \varphi)$$

For brevity, we shall use the symbol ∇ for gradient.

If the set of points for which a scalar point function $\varphi(\mathbf{R})$ has a constant value is a surface, it is called a *level surface*. In Fig. 17.5, a plane cross-sectional picture is given. The curved lines are the intersections of the plane with typical level surfaces whose equations are $\varphi = \varphi_1$, $\varphi = \varphi_2$, etc., where φ_1 and φ_2 are constants. At a typical point $\mathbf{R}$ on the particular level surface whose equation is $\varphi = \varphi_2$, the corresponding vector $\nabla\varphi$ is shown. For any direction tangent to a level surface the directional derivative $d\varphi/ds$ vanishes, since φ is constant on such a surface. Hence, by Eq. (17.10), for every $\mathbf{T}$ tangent to the level surface, $\mathbf{T} \cdot \nabla\varphi = 0$, so that $\nabla\varphi$ is normal to the surface.

A familiar two-dimensional example of these ideas is found in contour maps. Here the scalar function is height above sea level. The level surfaces are the lines

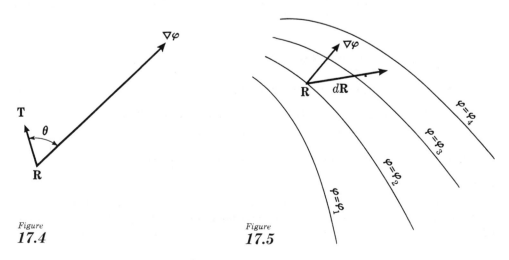

Figure
17.4

Figure
17.5

of constant altitude.   The gradient is steepest where the lines are closest together.
Weather maps show level lines of a different sort, representing constant-pressure
loci.

A simple three-dimensional example can be based on the instantaneous isothermal surfaces in a room.   The scalar point function is the temperature.   This function
has larger values for points near hot boundary surfaces such as radiators, lower
values for points near cool boundary surfaces such as windows in winter.   At
ordinary points the maximum directional derivative is nonzero and the temperature
gradient determines a unique direction.   There can be exceptions.   For example,
around a single point source of heat in an isotropic medium the isothermal surfaces
would be spherical.   For such an ideal case the temperature gradient would be
defined at every point except the source itself.   If the point source is replaced by
an isothermal spherical source, however small, the example looks more sensible
physically and the exceptional point is avoided.   If there are three-dimensional
regions within which the temperature is constant, then the gradient is a null vector.
In that case we lose both level surfaces and unique direction for the gradient.

The conclusion of (17.9) enables us easily to compute components of a gradient
relative to noncartesian orthogonal coordinates.   All that is necessary is to get an
expression for length of displacement Δs for each coordinate when the other coordinates are held constant.   Then one computes the limit $\Delta\varphi/\Delta s$ as Δs vanishes because
of the vanishing of the appropriate coordinate increment.   For spherical coordi-
nates, for example, the arc-length increments corresponding to the coordinates r, θ,
and γ are Δr, $r \sin \gamma \, \Delta\theta$, and $r \, \Delta\gamma$, so the components of grad φ are $\partial\varphi/\partial r$,
$(1/r \sin \gamma) (\partial\varphi/\partial\theta)$, and $(1/r)(\partial\varphi/\partial\gamma)$.   For cylindrical coordinates r', θ, z, the arc-
length increments are $\Delta r'$, $r' \, \Delta\theta$, and Δz, so that $\nabla\varphi$ has coordinates $\partial\varphi/\partial r'$,
$(1/r')(\partial\varphi/\partial\theta)$, $\partial\varphi/\partial z$.

Example 1

Let $\varphi = \log xy^2z^3$.   Find grad φ at $(1,2,3)$.

Solution

$$\nabla\varphi = \mathbf{I} \frac{\partial}{\partial x} (\log x + 2 \log y + 3 \log z) + \mathbf{J} \frac{\partial}{\partial y} (\cdots) + \mathbf{K} \frac{\partial}{\partial z} (\cdots)$$

$$= \frac{1}{x}\mathbf{I} + \frac{2}{y}\mathbf{J} + \frac{3}{z}\mathbf{K}$$

At $(1,2,3)$, $\nabla\varphi = \mathbf{I} + \mathbf{J} + \mathbf{K}$.

Example 2

Find a unit vector normal at the point $(12,-6,23)$ to the paraboloid with equation

$$\left(\frac{x}{4}\right)^2 + \left(\frac{y}{3}\right)^2 - z = -10$$

Solution

We can regard the given surface as a level surface for the scalar point function

$$\varphi(x,y,z) = \left(\frac{x}{4}\right)^2 + \left(\frac{y}{3}\right)^2 - z$$

We are interested in the particular surface where φ has the value -10. At the required point the gradient of φ is a normal vector, so we compute $\nabla\varphi$:

$$\nabla\varphi = \frac{x}{2}\mathbf{I} + \frac{2y}{3}\mathbf{J} - \mathbf{K}$$

$$= 6\mathbf{I} - 4\mathbf{J} - \mathbf{K} \quad \text{at} \quad (12, -6, 23)$$

A parallel unit vector is approximately $\mathbf{N} = 0.82\mathbf{I} - 0.55\mathbf{J} - 0.14\mathbf{K}$.

Example 3

It is shown in calculus courses[1] that if φ and its first partial derivatives are continuous at and near a point (x_0, y_0, z_0), then corresponding to increments Δx, Δy, Δz, one has a change in φ given by

$$(17.11) \qquad \Delta\varphi = \frac{\partial\varphi}{\partial x}\Delta x + \frac{\partial\varphi}{\partial y}\Delta y + \frac{\partial\varphi}{\partial z}\Delta z + \epsilon_x \Delta x + \epsilon_y \Delta y + \epsilon_z \Delta z$$

where the partial derivatives are evaluated at (x_0, y_0, z_0) and the ϵ's approach zero as Δx, Δy, and Δz approach zero. This result is equivalent to an evaluation in terms of a displacement $\Delta\mathbf{R}$:

$$(17.12) \qquad \Delta\varphi = \nabla\varphi \cdot \Delta\mathbf{R} + \boldsymbol{\epsilon} \cdot \Delta\mathbf{R}$$

where $|\boldsymbol{\epsilon}|$ approaches zero as $|\Delta\mathbf{R}|$ approaches zero. If we divide by Δs and take limits as Δs approaches zero, we can rederive (17.5). If we divide by Δt and let Δt approach zero, we get

$$(17.13) \qquad \dot{\varphi} = \mathbf{V} \cdot \nabla\varphi$$

This remarkable and useful formula indicates that if φ is a fixed or steady (relative to t) scalar field and if a point or particle moves through the field at velocity $\mathbf{V}$, then the instantaneous time rate of change of φ as experienced by the moving point is equal to the instantaneous inner product of the particle's velocity by the field's gradient.

Example 4

The relationship between directional derivative and gradient is illustrated by the slopes of a simple roof. The roof surface itself may be thought of as a graph of the scalar function altitude. This function is defined for points in the horizontal plane under the roof. Figure 17.6 shows two level lines: one for height zero, the other for height dh. A displacement ds' normal to these gives the direction of the

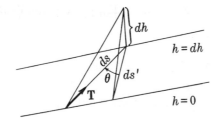

Figure
17.6

---

[1] See, for instance, C. T. Holmes, "Calculus and Analytic Geometry," p. 341, corollary, McGraw-Hill Book Company, Inc., New York, 1950.

gradient. A displacement ds in a direction $\mathbf{T}$ at an angle θ with the normal is obviously related to ds' by the equation

$$\frac{ds'}{ds} = \cos \theta$$

We have, then, for our directional derivative in the $\mathbf{T}$ direction,

$$\frac{dh}{ds} = \frac{dh}{ds'}\frac{ds'}{ds} = \frac{dh}{ds'}\cos \theta = |\nabla h| \cos \theta = \mathbf{T} \cdot \nabla h$$

EXERCISES

7. Plot level lines in the xy plane for $\varphi(x,y) = 2x + y$. Compute and draw vectors equal to the gradient at $(0,0)$, $(0,1)$, $(0,-1)$.
8. Draw several level curves for $\varphi(x,y) = 100/(x^2 + y^2)$. Compute and draw vectors equal to the gradient at $(5,0)$, $(0,10)$.
9. Compute $\nabla\varphi$, where (a) $\varphi = \gamma m'm/r$; (b) $\varphi = r$; (c) $\varphi = \sqrt{x^2 + y^2 + z^2}$.
10. The scalar point function

$$\varphi(x,y,z) = xy^2z^3$$

has the value 1 at the point $(1,1,1)$. Consider the surface of all points in space having $\varphi = 1$. What are the direction cosines of the normal to that surface at the point $(1,1,1)$?

11. At the point $\mathbf{R} = \mathbf{J} + 2\mathbf{K}$, what is the maximum rate of change with displacement of

$$\varphi(\mathbf{R}) = xy^2z^3$$

12. Elevation is a scalar function of position. Figure 17.7 is a topographic map; level lines are drawn. From the figure, find ∇h at the points A and B.

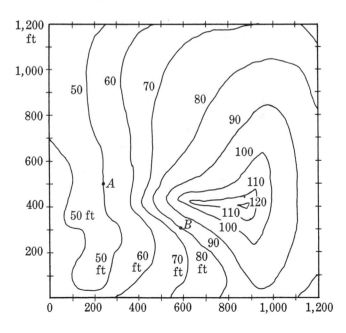

Figure
17.7

17.4. CONSERVATIVE FORCE FIELDS

As an example of a *vector* field we shall in this chapter consider cases where the function of position is a force. We have already seen that, with a *conservative* force $\mathbf{F}(\mathbf{R})$, there is associated a scalar function of position, the potential energy. Applying (7.52) to a small displacement $\Delta\mathbf{R}$, we get

$$\Delta(\text{p.e.}) = -\Delta(\text{work}) = -\mathbf{F} \cdot \Delta\mathbf{R}$$

Now if $\Delta\mathbf{R}$ is a displacement in the $\mathbf{T}$ direction, we may write

$$\Delta\mathbf{R} = \Delta s\, \mathbf{T}$$

Hence

$$\Delta(\text{p.e.}) = -\mathbf{F} \cdot \mathbf{T}\, \Delta s$$

Dividing by Δs and taking the limit as Δs becomes small, we have a directional derivative of this scalar function of position

$$(17.14) \qquad \frac{d(\text{p.e.})}{ds} = -\mathbf{F} \cdot \mathbf{T}$$

From (17.10) we have, then,

$$(17.15) \qquad -\mathbf{F} \cdot \mathbf{T} = \mathbf{T} \cdot \mathbf{\nabla}(\text{p.e.})$$

Since this is true for any choice of $\mathbf{T}$, we arrive at the very important equation

$$(17.16) \qquad \mathbf{F}(\mathbf{R}) = -\mathbf{\nabla}(\text{p.e.})$$

It should be recalled that these relationships have been met before in Sec. 7.13.

There is an interesting converse to the result just derived. Suppose that we have a force varying with position with which some scalar function φ is associated in such a way that

$$\mathbf{F}(\mathbf{R}) = \mathbf{\nabla}\varphi$$

Is this fact enough to ensure that $\mathbf{F}$ is conservative? We shall make a formal check on this point. The work done by $\mathbf{F}$ for a displacement from $\mathbf{R}_1$ to $\mathbf{R}_2$ is equal to

$$\int_{\mathbf{R}_1}^{\mathbf{R}_2} \mathbf{F} \cdot d\mathbf{R} = \int_{\mathbf{R}_1}^{\mathbf{R}_2} \mathbf{\nabla}\varphi \cdot \frac{d\mathbf{R}}{ds}\, ds = \int_{\mathbf{R}=\mathbf{R}_1}^{\mathbf{R}=\mathbf{R}_2} \mathbf{T} \cdot \mathbf{\nabla}\varphi\, ds$$

$$= \int_{\mathbf{R}=\mathbf{R}_1}^{\mathbf{R}=\mathbf{R}_2} \frac{d\varphi}{ds}\, ds = \int_{\mathbf{R}=\mathbf{R}_1}^{\mathbf{R}=\mathbf{R}_2} d\varphi = \varphi(\mathbf{R}_2) - \varphi(\mathbf{R}_1)$$

Thus the work done is merely equal to the net change in φ for the two positions. Consequently, it is independent of the path; therefore $\mathbf{F}$ is conservative. These important conclusions are recapitulated thus:

(17.17) *A force field is conservative if and only if it is expressible as the gradient of a scalar field.*

A second criterion for conservative fields is too important to be omitted, although a full treatment will not be given until later [see (18.35)]. If $\mathbf{F}$ is conservative, we have, by (17.17),

$$f_x = \frac{\partial\varphi}{\partial x}$$

$$f_y = \frac{\partial\varphi}{\partial y}$$

$$f_z = \frac{\partial\varphi}{\partial z}$$

It follows that (since order of partial differentiations is unimportant for decent functions whose derivatives are continuous—this is shown in calculus courses)

$$\text{(17.18)} \qquad \frac{\partial f_x}{\partial y} = \frac{\partial^2 \varphi}{\partial y \, \partial x} = \frac{\partial^2 \varphi}{\partial x \, \partial y} = \frac{\partial f_y}{\partial x}$$

Thus

$$\frac{\partial f_x}{\partial y} = \frac{\partial f_y}{\partial x}$$

and similarly,

$$\frac{\partial f_y}{\partial z} = \frac{\partial f_z}{\partial y}$$

$$\frac{\partial f_z}{\partial x} = \frac{\partial f_x}{\partial z}$$

A converse theorem can be shown to hold. Thus we may say:

(17.19) **F** *is a conservative force if and only if Eqs.* (17.18) *are valid.*

The qualitative role of conservative forces in physics is interesting. On the one hand, we regard conservative devices as idealizations because of the omnipresence of friction. Even the earth's orbital motion is slowed by tidal friction. Suppose, on the other hand, that we have a steady resultant force field which is not conservative. Then for some closed path the work done on a particle is not zero. Suppose this work is positive (if not, we cause the particle to retrace the path in the reverse direction). Each time the particle goes around this circuit its energy increases but the field is unchanged. The commercial potentialities of such a situation are breathtaking.

EXERCISES

13. Show that
$$\mathbf{F} = u(x)\mathbf{I} + v(y)\mathbf{J} + w(z)\mathbf{K}$$
is a conservative force.

14. Which of the following forces are conservative?
    (a) $x^2y\mathbf{I} + y^2x\mathbf{J}$. (b) $y^2x\mathbf{I} + x^2y\mathbf{J}$.
    (c) $\mathbf{F(R)} = k\mathbf{R}/(\mathbf{R} \cdot \mathbf{R})$, where k is a constant.

15. Show that $\mathbf{F(R)} = -k\mathbf{L}/(\mathbf{R} \cdot \mathbf{R})$ is conservative (k is a constant, **L** the unit radial vector).

16. In the xy plane a force field is defined by
$$\mathbf{F}(x,y) = x^2\mathbf{J} \qquad \text{newtons, m}$$
    (a) What total work is done by the field during displacement along straight lines around the square described by $(0,0)$ to $(0,1)$ to $(1,1)$ to $(1,0)$ to $(0,0)$?
    (b) If a 2-kg particle subject to this variable force is released at $(0,-2)$ m with a velocity of $4\mathbf{I}$ m/sec, with what speed will it reach the x axis?

17.5. FIELD STRENGTH AND POTENTIAL

The actual force experienced by a particle in a gravitational field depends on the mass of the particle. Thus the force itself is not really a property just of the field. It is perhaps more appropriate to talk about the *field strength* of a field. *Gravitational field strength*, denoted here by $\mathscr{F}$, is defined as the ratio of force to mass. It is a vector which has the direction of the force

$$\text{(17.20)} \qquad \mathscr{F}(\mathbf{R}) = \frac{\mathbf{F(R)}}{m}$$

This is a satisfactory concept since, for different small particles, the ratio has the same value at the same point:

$$(17.21) \qquad \mathscr{F}(\mathbf{R}) = \mathbf{A} = \frac{\mathbf{F}(\mathbf{R})}{m} = \frac{\mathbf{F}'(\mathbf{R})}{m'} = \mathbf{A}'$$

Gravitational potential is similarly defined as the ratio of potential energy to mass:

$$(17.22) \qquad \text{pot} = \frac{\text{p.e.}}{m}$$

From (17.16) we deduce at once for a conservative field

$$(17.23) \qquad \mathscr{F}(\mathbf{R}) = -\nabla(\text{pot})$$

The law of conservation of mechanical energy immediately yields this result:

$$(17.24) \qquad \text{pot} + \frac{v^2}{2} = \text{const}$$

In case of superimposed fields, field strengths are added vectorially while potentials are added as ordinary numbers. For complicated cases, the use of potentials is thus especially advantageous. In this course it will for the most part be convenient to work with particular force fields and potential energies rather than with field strength and potential. In electrical and magnetic work, the other choice is usually made.

In Sec. 17.3 we saw that $\nabla\varphi$ is normal to level surfaces of the scalar point function $\varphi(\mathbf{R})$. From (17.23) we can conclude that at any point in a gravitational field, the field strength is normal to the equipotential surface on which the point lies. For instance, around an isolated homogeneous spherical planet, the surfaces of constant gravitational potential are concentric spheres and the lines of force determined by the field strength are radial.

EXERCISES

17. What, in newtons per kilogram, is the gravitational field strength at the earth's surface?
18. How fast must a 9-oz baseball be thrown to attain a height of 150 ft (assume that the ball is released at a height of 6 ft): (*a*) Thrown vertically? (*b*) At an angle of 45°?
19. In a constant force field where

$$\mathbf{F}(\mathbf{R}) = 3\mathbf{I} - 7\mathbf{K} \qquad \text{lb}$$

a 6-lb object is projected from the origin with a speed of 6 ft/sec. A little later the particle passes through the point (2,0,0) ft. (*a*) Find a formula for potential relative to the origin. (State units.) (*b*) What is the speed of the particle at (2,0,0)?
20. A 5-kg particle is subject to a force

$$\mathbf{F}(\mathbf{R}) = -k\mathbf{R} \qquad \text{newtons} \qquad \text{for } \mathbf{R} \text{ in meters}$$

where k is a constant. Find a formula for potential relative to the origin.
21. Relative to the earth's surface, what is the gravitational potential at an elevation of 1,000 m?

17.6. THE INVERSE-SQUARE GRAVITATIONAL FIELD

In Sec. 12.4 we considered gravitational forces obeying an inverse-square law: The force on an object of mass m' due to another object of mass m was given by (12.12),

$$\mathbf{F}' = -\frac{\gamma m m'}{r^2}\mathbf{L}$$

Now let us concentrate on the one object, of mass m. The gravitational field strength at a distance r from this object is given as

(17.25)
$$\mathscr{F} = \frac{\mathbf{F}'}{m'} = -\frac{\gamma m}{r^2} \mathbf{L}$$

Relative to a point far away from the object ($r = \infty$), the potential is easily computed:

$$\text{pot} = -\int_\infty^R \mathscr{F} \cdot d\mathbf{R} = \gamma m \int_\infty^R \frac{\mathbf{L} \cdot d\mathbf{R}}{r^2} = \gamma m \int_\infty^r \frac{dr}{r^2} = -\gamma m \left[\frac{1}{r}\right]_\infty^r$$

or

(17.26)
$$\text{pot} = -\frac{\gamma m}{r}$$

The attraction between extended bodies may be computed by means of integral calculus. A body is thought of as an aggregate of elements of mass dm. The corresponding field strength at $\mathbf{P}$ has an x component equal to (referring to Fig. 17.8)

$$d\mathscr{F} \cdot \mathbf{I} = -\frac{\gamma \cos \theta \, dm}{r^2}$$

When the integrations are carried out, one for each component, the magnitude and direction are determined. The integrations are often tedious, and only a few of them will be examined in this course. They are standard exercises in courses in the calculus. Instead of the three integrations just suggested, one may integrate once to find the potential and then use (17.23) for computing field strength.

Example I

A uniform ring has radius a and mass m (see Fig. 17.9). Find the field strength at a point on its axis at a distance x from its plane.

Solution

From the symmetry it is clear that the y and z components are zero; therefore only one integration is necessary to find the field strength. An element of mass

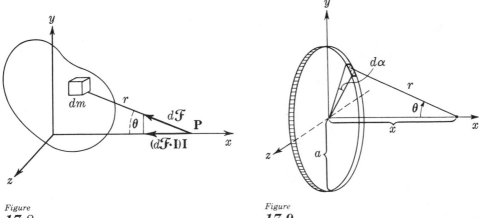

Figure
17.8

Figure
17.9

determined by the angle $d\alpha$ is

$$dm = \frac{m}{2\pi a} a \, d\alpha$$

Its contribution to the x component of field strength is

$$d\mathscr{F} \cdot \mathbf{I} = -\frac{\gamma m \cos \theta}{2\pi r^2} \, d\alpha$$

The integration is trivial, since r and θ are the same for each value of α.

$$\mathscr{F} \cdot \mathbf{I} = -\frac{\gamma m \cos \theta}{2\pi r^2} \int_0^{2\pi} d\alpha = -\frac{\gamma m \cos \theta}{r^2}$$

So

$$\mathscr{F} = -\frac{\gamma m \cos \theta}{r^2} \mathbf{I} = -\frac{\gamma m x}{r^3} \mathbf{I} = -\frac{\gamma m x}{(x^2 + a^2)^{\frac{3}{2}}} \mathbf{I}$$

Alternative Solution

The potential may be written down by inspection, using (17.26),

$$\text{pot} = -\frac{\gamma m}{r} = -\frac{\gamma m}{\sqrt{x^2 + a^2}}$$

We may now use (17.23):

$$\mathscr{F} = \nabla \left(\frac{\gamma m}{\sqrt{x^2 + a^2}} \right) = -\frac{\gamma m x}{(x^2 + a^2)^{\frac{3}{2}}} \mathbf{I}$$

as before.

Example 2

A uniform spherical shell has mass m and radius a. What is the gravitational situation at a point whose distance from the center is $x(>a)$?

Solution

Referring to Fig. 17.10, our element of mass dm will be a ring like that considered in Example 1:

$$dm = \frac{m}{4\pi a^2} (2\pi a \sin \alpha)(a \, d\alpha)$$

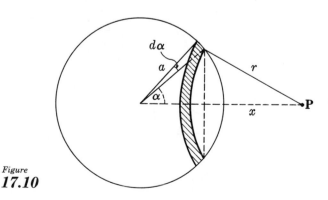

Figure
17.10

Its potential is

$$d(\text{pot}) = -\frac{\gamma\, dm}{r}$$

Now

$$a^2 + x^2 - 2ax \cos \alpha = r^2$$

Differentiating and dividing by 2,

$$ax \sin \alpha\, d\alpha = r\, dr$$

Therefore

$$\text{pot} = \frac{-\gamma m}{2ax} \int_{x-a}^{x+a} dr = \frac{-\gamma m}{2ax}(2a) = \frac{-\gamma m}{x}$$

This shows that *the gravitational attraction exerted at an external point by a uniform spherical shell would be unchanged if the body were compressed to a point at the center.*

Since a uniform solid sphere can be regarded as an aggregate of concentric uniform shells, the same result is valid:

(17.27) *A uniform solid sphere exerts gravitational attraction at external points just as if it were a particle at its own center.*

Example 3

A uniform spherical shell has mass m and radius a. What is the gravitational situation at a point whose distance from the center is $x(\leqq a)$?

Solution

Proceeding as before, we get

$$\text{pot} = \frac{-\gamma m}{2ax} \int_{a-x}^{a+x} dr = \frac{-\gamma m}{2ax}(2x) = -\frac{\gamma m}{a}$$

This shows that *within a uniform spherical shell the gravitational potential is constant.* This means that the gradient is zero; therefore the *field strength is zero.* Now imagine a point within a uniform *solid* sphere at some distance x from the center. It is then attracted toward the center by a sphere of radius x and is uninfluenced by the outer shell of inner radius x.

EXERCISES

22. Obtain a formula for gravitational field strength exerted by a uniform disk of mass m and radius a at a point at a distance x from its center on a normal axis through the center. (Do not hesitate to use tables of integrals.)
23. Show that the gravitational field strength within a solid uniform sphere varies directly as the distance from the center.
24. The diameter of the moon is 2,163 miles. Its mass is 0.0123 times that of the earth. What is the acceleration of gravity on the moon?
25. What is the ratio of the sun's pull on the moon to that of the earth? (Take the distances from the earth as 92.3 million and 239,000 miles. The mass of the sun is about 332,000 times that of the earth.)
26. Between two identical lead spheres (sp. gr. $= 11.3$) in contact, the gravitational force is 1 newton. Find the diameter.

17.7. THE EARTH'S GRAVITATIONAL FIELD

Let us now apply the ideas of the preceding section to motion of a particle in the neighborhood of the earth. Much of our work on this topic in Chap. 12 can be

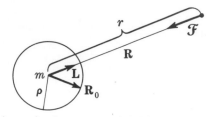

Figure
17.11

translated into the language of fields.   Let m denote the mass of the earth and ρ the radius (see Fig. 17.11).   Then a particle at a point with position vector $\mathbf{R}$ (relative to the center of the earth) experiences a force toward the center.   The equation

$$\mathscr{F} = -\frac{\gamma m}{r^2}\,\mathbf{L}$$

applies.   The mass of the earth is not a convenient constant to keep in mind; therefore let us use the fact that at the surface of the earth $\mathscr{F}$ has magnitude g:

$$\frac{\gamma m}{\rho^2} = g$$

Hence

(17.28)
$$\mathscr{F} = -\frac{g\rho^2}{r^2}\,\mathbf{L}$$

It is convenient in many cases to consider the earth's surface as a reference level for potential and potential energy.   Following the pattern of integration used previously,

$$\text{pot} = -\int_{\mathbf{R_0}}^{\mathbf{R}} \mathscr{F} \cdot d\mathbf{R} = g\rho^2 \int_{\rho}^{r} \frac{dr}{r^2} = -g\rho^2 \left[\frac{1}{r}\right]_{\rho}^{r}$$

or

(17.29)
$$\text{pot} = g\rho^2 \left(\frac{1}{\rho} - \frac{1}{r}\right) = \frac{g\rho}{r}(r - \rho)$$

Example

With what speed must a projectile be launched vertically from the surface of the earth to attain a height of 1,000 miles?   (Neglect air friction.)

Solution

Using the law of conservation of energy (17.24),

$$\text{pot} + \frac{v^2}{2} = \text{const}$$

we have at the earth's surface, pot $= 0$, and at the peak of the trajectory, $v = 0$; thus

$$0 + \frac{v^2}{2} = \frac{g\rho}{r}(r - \rho) + 0$$

or

$$v^2 = \frac{2g\rho(r - \rho)}{r} = \frac{(2)(32.2)\,(3,960)}{(5,280)\,(4,960)}\,1,000$$

Hence

$$v^2 = 9.73 \qquad \text{and} \qquad v = 3.1 \text{ mps}$$

EXERCISES

27. At what distance from the surface of the earth would one's "weight" be one-half its usual value?
28. How much work would be required to take a 1-lb object at the surface of the earth and remove it from the earth's gravitational field?
29. With what speed must a projectile be fired vertically from the earth in order that it never return? Neglect friction. ($\rho = 3{,}958.8$ miles.)
30. A projectile is fired vertically with a speed of 1 mps. How high will it rise: (*a*) Assuming gravity to be constant? (*b*) Allowing for the decrease of gravitational attraction away from the earth?
31. Using the formula for potential with respect to the earth's surface, derive the usual p.e. = *wh* by making suitable approximations. For how large values of *h* is this formula correct within 1 per cent?
32. What would be the diameter of a planet having the same average density as the earth but on whose surface the acceleration due to gravity is 4.9 m/sec^2?
33. (*a*) Compute the mass of the earth in kilograms. (*b*) What is the specific gravity of the earth?

17.8. DIRECTIONAL DERIVATIVE FOR VECTOR FIELDS

Let **V** be a vector function of position so that for every point **P** a corresponding value **V** = **V**(**P**) is determined. In Fig. 17.12 **V** is the value at **P**, **V** + Δ**V** is the value at **P** + Δ*s***T**. At any point **P** and for any direction given by the unit vector **T**, we may consider the directional derivative of **V**. It is easily defined (see Fig. 17.12) as

$$\frac{d\mathbf{V}}{ds} = \lim_{\Delta s \to 0} \frac{\Delta \mathbf{V}}{\Delta s}$$

To suggest how it may be evaluated let us express **V** in terms of its components and then differentiate term by term:

$$\mathbf{V} = v_x\mathbf{I} + v_y\mathbf{J} + v_z\mathbf{K}$$

$$\frac{d\mathbf{V}}{ds} = \frac{dv_x}{ds}\mathbf{I} + \frac{dv_y}{ds}\mathbf{J} + \frac{dv_z}{ds}\mathbf{K}$$

This effectively reduces the problem to one of computing three directional derivatives for the scalars v_x, v_y, v_z. Using (17.5),

(17.30)
$$\frac{d\mathbf{V}}{ds} = (\mathbf{T} \cdot \nabla v_x)\mathbf{I} + (\mathbf{T} \cdot \nabla v_y)\mathbf{J} + (\mathbf{T} \cdot \nabla v_z)\mathbf{K}$$

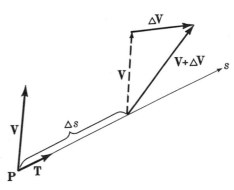

Figure
17.12

This equation shows how the derivative often may be computed, component by component. Abbreviating the right member, the following expression is commonly used:

$$(17.31) \qquad \frac{d\mathbf{V}}{ds} = (\mathbf{T} \cdot \nabla)\mathbf{V}$$

It should be clearly understood that the right member of (17.31) is merely an abbreviation for the right member of (17.30). The same sort of abbreviation is used even when $\mathbf{T}$ is replaced by a vector whose magnitude is not 1.

Example I

Find the directional derivative at $\mathbf{R} = 3\mathbf{I} - 2\mathbf{K}$ in the direction of $\mathbf{A} = 4\mathbf{J} + 3\mathbf{K}$ of the variable vector

$$\mathbf{V} = 3xz\mathbf{I} + 2xy\mathbf{J} + y^2\mathbf{K}$$

Solution

Here $\mathbf{T} = \mathbf{A}/a = 0.8\mathbf{J} + 0.6\mathbf{K}$.
The computation proceeds thus:

$$\nabla(3xz) = 3z\mathbf{I} + 3x\mathbf{K} \qquad \mathbf{T} \cdot \nabla(3xz) = 1.8x = 5.4$$
$$\nabla(2xy) = 2y\mathbf{I} + 2x\mathbf{J} \qquad \mathbf{T} \cdot \nabla(2xy) = 1.6x = 4.8$$
$$\nabla(y^2) = 2y\mathbf{J} \qquad \mathbf{T} \cdot \nabla(y^2) = 1.6y = 0$$

(The values for x and y are those given in the specification of $\mathbf{R}$: $x = 3$, $y = 0$, $z = -2$.) Thus

$$\frac{d\mathbf{V}}{ds} = (\mathbf{T} \cdot \nabla)\mathbf{V} = 5.4\mathbf{I} + 4.8\mathbf{J}$$

Example 2

As a special case consider the directional derivative parallel to the x axis of a vector function of position $\mathbf{V}$. Applying (17.31), but now using $\mathbf{I}$ in place of $\mathbf{T}$, we get

$$\frac{\partial \mathbf{V}}{\partial x} = (\mathbf{I} \cdot \nabla)\mathbf{V} = (\mathbf{I} \cdot \nabla v_x)\mathbf{I} + (\mathbf{I} \cdot \nabla v_y)\mathbf{J} + (\mathbf{I} \cdot \nabla v_z)\mathbf{K}$$
$$= \frac{\partial v_x}{\partial x}\mathbf{I} + \frac{\partial v_y}{\partial x}\mathbf{J} + \frac{\partial v_z}{\partial x}\mathbf{K}$$

But this last expression is merely the result of a term-by-term differentiation with respect to x:

$$\frac{\partial \mathbf{V}}{\partial x} = \frac{\partial}{\partial x}(v_x\mathbf{I} + v_y\mathbf{J} + v_z\mathbf{K})$$

Similarly for $\partial \mathbf{V}/\partial y$ and $\partial \mathbf{V}/\partial z$.

The symbol $\mathbf{T} \cdot \nabla$ can be regarded as a formal operator just as ∇ was treated as an operator. If $\mathbf{T} = l\mathbf{I} + m\mathbf{J} + n\mathbf{K}$, the operator may be expanded thus:

$$\mathbf{T} \cdot \nabla = l\frac{\partial}{\partial x} + m\frac{\partial}{\partial y} + n\frac{\partial}{\partial z}$$

When this operator is applied to a vector $\mathbf{V}$, we get

$$(\mathbf{T} \cdot \nabla)\mathbf{V} = l\frac{\partial \mathbf{V}}{\partial x} + m\frac{\partial \mathbf{V}}{\partial y} + n\frac{\partial \mathbf{V}}{\partial z}$$

Each of the terms in the right member may be expanded using the results of Example 2.

$$(\mathbf{T} \cdot \nabla)\mathbf{V} = l\left(\frac{\partial v_x}{\partial x}\mathbf{I} + \frac{\partial v_y}{\partial x}\mathbf{J} + \frac{\partial v_z}{\partial x}\mathbf{K}\right) + m\left(\frac{\partial v_x}{\partial y}\mathbf{I} + \frac{\partial v_y}{\partial y}\mathbf{J} + \frac{\partial v_z}{\partial y}\mathbf{K}\right)$$

$$+ n\left(\frac{\partial v_x}{\partial z}\mathbf{I} + \frac{\partial v_y}{\partial z}\mathbf{J} + \frac{\partial v_z}{\partial z}\mathbf{K}\right)$$

If the terms are rearranged and grouped, we again have the right member of (17.30). The same conclusion also is reached by multiplying out the right member of

$$(\mathbf{T} \cdot \nabla)\mathbf{V} = \left(l\frac{\partial}{\partial x} + m\frac{\partial}{\partial y} + n\frac{\partial}{\partial z}\right)(v_x\mathbf{I} + v_y\mathbf{J} + v_z\mathbf{K})$$

Example 3

Repeat Example 1 using the formal method just described.

Solution

$$\mathbf{T} \cdot \nabla = (0.8\mathbf{J} + 0.6\mathbf{K}) \cdot \left(\mathbf{I}\frac{\partial}{\partial x} + \mathbf{J}\frac{\partial}{\partial y} + \mathbf{K}\frac{\partial}{\partial z}\right)$$

$$= 0.8\frac{\partial}{\partial y} + 0.6\frac{\partial}{\partial z}$$

$$\frac{d\mathbf{V}}{ds} = (\mathbf{T} \cdot \nabla)\mathbf{V} = \left(0.8\frac{\partial}{\partial y} + 0.6\frac{\partial}{\partial z}\right)(3xz\mathbf{I} + 2xy\mathbf{J} + y^2\mathbf{K})$$

$$= 0.8\frac{\partial}{\partial y}(3xz)\mathbf{I} + 0.8\frac{\partial}{\partial y}(2xy)\mathbf{J} + 0.8\frac{\partial}{\partial y}(y^2)\mathbf{K}$$

$$+ 0.6\frac{\partial}{\partial z}(3xz)\mathbf{I} + 0.6\frac{\partial}{\partial z}(2xy)\mathbf{J} + 0.6\frac{\partial}{\partial z}(y^2)\mathbf{K}$$

$$= 0\mathbf{I} + 1.6x\mathbf{J} + 1.6y\mathbf{K} + 1.8x\mathbf{I} + 0\mathbf{J} + 0\mathbf{K}$$

$$= 1.8x\mathbf{I} + 1.6x\mathbf{J} + 1.6y\mathbf{K} \qquad \text{as before}$$

Example 4

Let us apply to a vector field $\mathbf{U}$ the results of Example 3 in Sec. 17.3. A change in $\mathbf{U}$ corresponding to a displacement $\Delta\mathbf{R} = \Delta x\mathbf{I} + \Delta y\mathbf{J} + \Delta z\mathbf{K}$ can be written

$$\Delta\mathbf{U} = \Delta u_x\mathbf{I} + \Delta u_y\mathbf{J} + \Delta u_z\mathbf{K}$$

Using (17.12), we have

(17.32) $$\Delta\mathbf{U} = \{(\nabla u_x + \boldsymbol{\epsilon}_x) \cdot \Delta\mathbf{R}\}\mathbf{I} + \{(\nabla u_y + \boldsymbol{\epsilon}_y) \cdot \Delta\mathbf{R}\}\mathbf{J}$$

$$+ \{(\nabla u_z + \boldsymbol{\epsilon}_z) \cdot \Delta\mathbf{R}\}\mathbf{K}$$

where the vectors $\boldsymbol{\epsilon}_x$, $\boldsymbol{\epsilon}_y$, $\boldsymbol{\epsilon}_z$ have magnitudes which approach zero as Δs approaches zero. If we divide both sides by $|\Delta\mathbf{R}| = \Delta s$ and take the limit as Δs approaches zero, we have, since $\lim_{\Delta s \to 0} \dfrac{\Delta\mathbf{R}}{\Delta s} = \mathbf{T}$,

$$\frac{d\mathbf{U}}{ds} = (\mathbf{T} \cdot \nabla u_x)\mathbf{I} + (\mathbf{T} \cdot \nabla u_y)\mathbf{J} + (\mathbf{T} \cdot \nabla u_z)\mathbf{K}$$

$$= (\mathbf{T} \cdot \nabla)\mathbf{U}$$

This, of course, is not unexpected. If we divide by Δt rather than Δs, we can use the fact that $\lim\limits_{\Delta t \to 0} \dfrac{\Delta \mathbf{R}}{\Delta t}$ is the velocity $\mathbf{V}$. This time the result is

$$(17.33) \qquad\qquad \dot{\mathbf{U}} = (\mathbf{V} \cdot \mathbf{\nabla})\mathbf{U}$$

which is analogous to (17.13) and is similarly interpreted.

EXERCISES

34. Find the directional derivative of

$$\mathbf{B} = xy\mathbf{I} + y^2\mathbf{J} + xz^3\mathbf{K}$$

at the point

$$\mathbf{R} = \mathbf{I} + 2\mathbf{J} + 3\mathbf{K}$$

in the direction of

$$\mathbf{A} = 2\mathbf{I} - \mathbf{J} + 2\mathbf{K}$$

35. If $\mathbf{A} = a_x\mathbf{I} + a_y\mathbf{J} + a_z\mathbf{K}$ and similarly $\mathbf{B} = b_x\mathbf{I} + b_y\mathbf{J} + b_z\mathbf{K}$, where b_x, b_y, b_z are scalar functions of x, y, and z, express completely in scalar symbols the x component of the vector $(\mathbf{A} \cdot \mathbf{\nabla})\mathbf{B}$.

36. Write out the x, y, and z components of the vector $(\mathbf{V} \cdot \mathbf{\nabla})\mathbf{V}$, where

$$\mathbf{V} = v_x\mathbf{I} + v_y\mathbf{J} + v_z\mathbf{K}$$

37. For a constant vector $\mathbf{A}$, compute a formula for $(\mathbf{A} \cdot \mathbf{\nabla})\mathbf{R}$, where, as usual, $\mathbf{R}$ is a position vector.

REVIEW EXERCISES

38. Derive formulas for $\mathbf{\nabla}(cf)$, $\mathbf{\nabla}(f+g)$, and $\mathbf{\nabla}(fg)$, where c is a constant scalar and f and g are scalar functions of position.

39. If $\varphi(x,y,z) = xy + y^2 + xz^2$, what is the directional derivative of φ at $(1,0,-2)$ for a displacement:
(a) Parallel to the vector $3\mathbf{I} + 3\mathbf{K}$?
(b) Parallel to the vector $2\mathbf{I} + 0.5\mathbf{J} - 2\mathbf{K}$?
(c) Parallel to the vector $6\mathbf{I} - 8\mathbf{J}$?

40. $\varphi(\mathbf{R}) = \mathbf{R} \cdot (\mathbf{R} + y\mathbf{I})$, where $\mathbf{R}$ is the variable position vector $\mathbf{R} = x\mathbf{I} + y\mathbf{J} + z\mathbf{K}$, is a scalar function of position.
(a) Derive a formula for the gradient of φ, in terms of coordinates (x,y,z).
(b) At the point $(1,-1,1)$, evaluate the directional derivative of φ parallel to the vector $3\mathbf{I} - 3\mathbf{J} - 3\mathbf{K}$.

41. If $\varphi(\mathbf{R})$ is a radial function [i.e., if $\varphi(\mathbf{R}) = \varphi(r)$, so that, over each sphere, $r = a$, φ has a constant value $\varphi(a)$], show that

$$\mathbf{grad}\ \varphi = \frac{d\varphi}{dr}\,\mathbf{L}$$

42. In the force field $\mathbf{F}(\mathbf{R}) = y\mathbf{I} + k\mathbf{K}$, where k is a scalar constant, show that it is possible to go from any point $\mathbf{R} = \mathbf{R}_1$ to any other point $\mathbf{R} = \mathbf{R}_2$ *doing zero work*.

43. Show that a directional derivative for direction $-\mathbf{T}$ is equal to minus the directional derivative for direction $\mathbf{T}$.

44. A particle of mass m is attracted toward a fixed point $\mathbf{O}$ by a force inversely proportional to the cube of its distance from $\mathbf{O}$. From an initial distance r_1 it is launched with an initial velocity $\mathbf{V}_0$ directly away from $\mathbf{O}$. Derive a formula for the maximum distance r_2 away from $\mathbf{O}$ attained by the particle.

45. Suppose that a rocket 100,000 miles from the center of the earth has exhausted its fuel. If it is heading outward radially, what minimum speed would prevent its falling back toward the earth?

46. If the sun's mass and diameter exceed those of the earth by factors 3.3×10^5 and 1.1×10^2, respectively, what speeds must particles have initially to attain heights of 10,000 miles in solar prominences? What speed would be required for escape from the sun?

47. Assuming that the earth is a homogeneous sphere, discuss the motion of a particle in a frictionless straight subway tube between two localities on the earth's surface.

48. Consider the function of position

$$f(x,y,z) = x^2y^2 + y^2z^2$$

(a) Write in **IJK** form the gradient of f at the point $(0,-1,2)$.
(b) At the point $(0,-1,2)$ what is the directional derivative of f in the direction parallel to the vector $4\mathbf{J} - 3\mathbf{K}$?
(c) Write in **IJK** form a unit vector normal to the surface

$$f(x,y,z) = 2$$

at the point $(1,1,1)$.

49. For constant $\mathbf{A}$, is $\mathbf{A} \cdot \nabla$ a linear operator? Justify your answer.

50. For the field strength $\mathscr{F}$ given in (17.25) evaluate the gradient of the x component of $\mathscr{F}$.

51. For the field strength $\mathscr{F}$ given in (17.25), evaluate $(\mathbf{L} \cdot \nabla)\mathscr{F}$.

52. If φ is a homogeneous quadratic polynomial function of $\mathbf{R}$, that is, if φ can be written

$$\varphi(\mathbf{R}) = a_{11}x^2 + a_{22}y^2 + a_{33}z^2 + a_{12}xy + a_{23}yz + a_{31}zx$$

show that

$$\mathbf{R} \cdot \nabla\varphi = 2\varphi \qquad \text{(Euler's theorem)}$$

CHAPTER EIGHTEEN

VECTOR PROPERTIES of FLUIDS and FLOW

In the preceding chapter we made a first approach to the calculus of both scalar and vector fields. The concept of directional derivative provided a tool for expressing local variations in a field of either type. Both scalar and vector fields proved to be useful in working with gravitational phenomena. In this chapter we use an ideal fluid as a means of introducing further properties of vector fields. This physical approach to vector analysis lacks the rigor of an abstract mathematical approach. The aim here is to develop a comprehension of the concepts and an ability to interpret the symbols. Our study of a fluid will start with the idea of pressure, which will be treated as a scalar function of position. We shall also deal with limited dynamical situations. In the flow patterns which result, we shall find further examples of vector fields. A fluid in motion will be treated as a continuous medium. Instead of studying individual objects, we shall be concerned with typical elements (in the sense of the calculus) to which elementary mechanical principles may be applied.

18.1. PRESSURE

Suppose we consider at a point within a fluid a plane element of area Δa of normal $\mathbf{N}$ across which a force $\Delta \mathbf{F}$ acts as in Fig. 18.1. This means that if we isolate the fluid on the $-\mathbf{N}$ side of Δa, it experiences a force $\Delta \mathbf{F}$, because of its interaction with fluid on the $+\mathbf{N}$ side of Δa. The *average pressure* for the orientation determined by $\mathbf{N}$ at the position of the area element is defined to be equal to the normal component of $\Delta \mathbf{F}$ divided by Δa:

$$(18.1) \qquad \bar{p}(\mathbf{N}) = -\frac{\Delta \mathbf{F}}{\Delta a} \cdot \mathbf{N}$$

Taking the limit as Δa becomes small, we get the *pressure*, still dependent on $\mathbf{N}$, as

$$(18.2) \qquad p(\mathbf{N}) = -\frac{d\mathbf{F}}{da} \cdot \mathbf{N}$$

For an *ideal fluid*, the angle θ between force and normal is $180°$:

$$(18.3) \qquad p(\mathbf{N}) = \left| \frac{d\mathbf{F}}{da} \right|$$

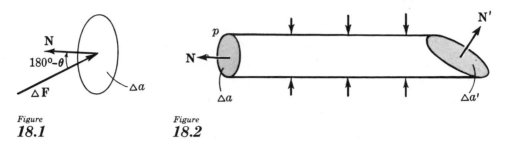

Figure
18.1

Figure
18.2

In this case the force across an area element can be written

(18.4) $$\Delta \mathbf{F} = -\bar{p}(\mathbf{N}) \, \Delta a \mathbf{N}$$

Now let us verify the fact that, for an ideal fluid, $p(\mathbf{N})$ is the same for every $\mathbf{N}$. We isolate a small cylindrical portion of the fluid as shown in Fig. 18.2. Let one end be terminated by a normal section of normal $\mathbf{N}$ and the other by a skew section of normal $\mathbf{N}'$. The area of the first end is Δa, of the second, $\Delta a'$. The density is δ. The mean length is Δl; therefore the mass is $\delta \, \Delta l \, \Delta a$. Taking components parallel to the axis of the cylinder, i.e., in the $-\mathbf{N}$ direction, we have

$$\bar{p}(\mathbf{N}) \, \Delta a + \bar{p}(\mathbf{N}') \, \Delta a'(\mathbf{N}' \cdot \mathbf{N}) - \delta \, \Delta l \, \Delta a \mathbf{G} \cdot \mathbf{N} = -\delta \, \Delta l \, \Delta a \, \mathbf{A} \cdot \mathbf{N}$$

Here $\mathbf{G}$ is the acceleration of gravity vector and $\mathbf{A}$ is the acceleration vector. Pressure forces on the lateral surface of the cylinder do not appear in this equation, since they must be normal (in as much as the fluid is ideal). Now divide by Δa, and take the limit as both Δa and Δl approach zero. We get

$$\bar{p}(\mathbf{N}) + \bar{p}(\mathbf{N}') \frac{\Delta a'}{\Delta a} \, (\mathbf{N}' \cdot \mathbf{N}) = 0$$

Since

$$-(\mathbf{N}' \cdot \mathbf{N}) \, \Delta a' = \Delta a$$

we have

(18.5) $$p(\mathbf{N}) = p(\mathbf{N}')$$

Since $\mathbf{N}$ and $\mathbf{N}'$ are arbitrary, we conclude that *pressure in an ideal fluid is a function of position, independent of orientation.* Thus we shall write p instead of $p(\mathbf{N})$. We assume that this scalar function of position has continuous first partial derivatives.

18.2. EQUILIBRIUM

It is well known that pressure differences can cause a fluid to flow, as, for instance, in a fire hose. Let us see how a fluid in equilibrium can be characterized. Select a point $\mathbf{O}$ in a fluid, and consider a small rectangular element of volume $\Delta x \, \Delta y \, \Delta z$ and center $\mathbf{O}$ as shown in Fig. 18.3. We shall let this volume approach zero; thus we shall assume that the gravitational field strength (or other field strength) $\mathscr{F}$ and the density δ are constant over the isolated region. If p is the pressure at $\mathbf{O}$, then the average pressure on the faces having normals $\mathbf{I}$ and $-\mathbf{I}$, are, respectively [approximately, compare (17.1)],

$$\left(p + \frac{\partial p}{\partial x} \frac{\Delta x}{2}\right)$$

and

$$\left(p - \frac{\partial p}{\partial x} \frac{\Delta x}{2}\right)$$

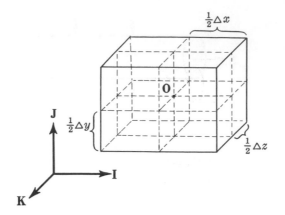

Figure
18.3

Similar expressions may be written for the other four faces. Now the condition for equilibrium $\Sigma \mathbf{F} = \mathbf{O}$ becomes

$$\mathscr{F}\,\delta\,\Delta x\,\Delta y\,\Delta z - \mathbf{I}\left(p + \frac{\partial p}{\partial x}\frac{\Delta x}{2}\right)\Delta y\,\Delta z + \mathbf{I}\left(p - \frac{\partial p}{\partial x}\frac{\Delta x}{2}\right)\Delta y\,\Delta z$$

$$-\mathbf{J}\left(p + \frac{\partial p}{\partial y}\frac{\Delta y}{2}\right)\Delta z\,\Delta x + \mathbf{J}\left(p - \frac{\partial p}{\partial y}\frac{\Delta y}{2}\right)\Delta z\,\Delta x$$

$$-\mathbf{K}\left(p + \frac{\partial p}{\partial z}\frac{\Delta z}{2}\right)\Delta x\,\Delta y + \mathbf{K}\left(p - \frac{\partial p}{\partial z}\frac{\Delta z}{2}\right)\Delta x\,\Delta y = \mathbf{O}.$$

or, dividing by $\Delta x\,\Delta y\,\Delta z$ and taking the limit as Δx, Δy, and Δz approach zero (so that our approximations become better), we get at $\mathbf{O}$

$$\mathscr{F}\,\delta - \frac{\partial p}{\partial x}\mathbf{I} - \frac{\partial p}{\partial y}\mathbf{J} - \frac{\partial p}{\partial z}\mathbf{K} = \mathbf{O}$$

or

(18.6) $$\mathscr{F}\,\delta - \nabla p = \mathbf{O}$$

This equation must be valid at each point within a fluid at equilibrium. This result means essentially that a fluid is at equilibrium when forces associated with pressure differences are exactly equal to and opposite to the forces of other origin. The force associated with pressure differences (usually called *buoyant force*) is opposite to the gradient: the trend is toward the lower pressure.

Now this derivation leaves much to be desired in the way of rigor. Calling $p + \dfrac{\partial p}{\partial x}\dfrac{\Delta x}{2}$ an average value over a whole face when we have reason to expect it to be only approximate at the center of the face may seem too sanguine. Of course, our aim is to give intuitive derivations rather than rigorous proofs. It is not assumed that the student has either background or, at the moment, the time for a sounder treatment. As soon as he is able, mathematically, to handle a more thorough presentation, he is encouraged to seek it out and to ponder it. It is hoped that the present approach will both make available important results and methods at an early stage and also provide practical motivation for further study of a more demanding sort.

Some of the objections to the preceding derivation may be avoided by using a different-shaped figure. Suppose we isolate a cylindrical element with center $\mathbf{O}$

and with an arbitrarily small cross-sectional area Δa. Let this cylinder at first be parallel to the x axis as in Fig. 18.4. Now the problem appears one-dimensional rather than three-dimensional, and Eq. (17.1) is a one-dimensional tool. The x equation of equilibrium gives us

$$(\mathscr{F} \cdot \mathbf{I})\, \delta\, \Delta x\, \Delta a - \left(p + \frac{\partial p}{\partial x} \frac{\Delta x}{2} \right) \Delta a + \left(p - \frac{\partial p}{\partial x} \frac{\Delta x}{2} \right) \Delta a = 0$$

or, dividing by $\Delta a\, \Delta x$ and taking the limit as Δx and Δa approach zero [the ratio between Δa and $(\Delta x)^2$ being constant, if you wish], we get

$$\frac{\partial p}{\partial x} = (\mathscr{F} \cdot \mathbf{I})\, \delta$$

Similarly, if we take cylinders in the y and z directions, we have

$$\frac{\partial p}{\partial y} = (\mathscr{F} \cdot \mathbf{J})\, \delta \qquad \frac{\partial p}{\partial z} = (\mathscr{F} \cdot \mathbf{K})\, \delta$$

Now multiplying the first equation by $\mathbf{I}$, the second by $\mathbf{J}$, the third by $\mathbf{K}$ and adding corresponding members, we get

$$\frac{\partial p}{\partial x} \mathbf{I} + \frac{\partial p}{\partial y} \mathbf{J} + \frac{\partial p}{\partial z} \mathbf{K} = \delta(\mathscr{F} \cdot \mathbf{I})\mathbf{I} + \delta(\mathscr{F} \cdot \mathbf{J})\mathbf{J} + \delta(\mathscr{F} \cdot \mathbf{K})\mathbf{K}$$

or, as before,

$$\mathbf{\nabla} p = \delta \mathscr{F}$$

This time the averaging difficulty may seem to have been dodged by making the faces so very small. But, if for a given pressure field it is possible to pick Δa small enough to make our approximations satisfactory, then clearly the cube of Fig. 18.3 can be picked with all its faces more than adequately small. We may conclude, then, that while demonstrations of this sort are not thorough proofs, they are instructive derivations of valid relationships.

Example I

The field strength of terrestrial gravitation may be expressed for $\mathbf{J}$ vertical downward:

$$\mathscr{F} = g\mathbf{J}$$

We may at once conclude:

$$\frac{\partial p}{\partial x} = \frac{\partial p}{\partial z} = 0$$

(for equilibrium), while

$$\frac{\partial p}{\partial y} = \delta g$$

In the case of a liquid where the density is constant, this last equation may be integrated to give

(18.7) $$p = p_0 + \delta g y$$

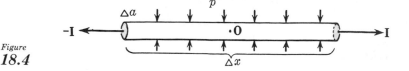

Figure
18.4

Ordinarily, the origin is taken at a free surface of the fluid so that the constant of integration p_0 is barometric pressure.

Example 2

If the body forces are negligible, the pressure is constant; for its maximum directional derivative is zero.

Center of Pressure.   The total force exerted across a plane boundary by a fluid is given by

$$(18.8) \qquad\qquad \mathbf{F} = \mathbf{N} \int_a p \, da$$

where $\mathbf{N}$ is the unit outward normal vector for the plane.   If we take two axes in this plane, the resultant force is located by moment equations.   If $(\bar{x}, \bar{y})$ is the point where the resultant acts in this plane,

$$(18.9) \qquad\qquad \begin{aligned} \bar{x}f &= \int_a xp \, da \\[2mm] \bar{y}f &= \int_a yp \, da \end{aligned}$$

$(\bar{x}, \bar{y})$ is called the *center of pressure*.   In practice, one side of the boundary is often exposed to the atmosphere; therefore the net pressure $p' = p - p_0$ is used instead of p.

Suppose that the y axis is vertical downward as in Fig. 18.5 and that the pressure varies only with the depth as in Eq. (18.7).   Then if the breadth b also can be expressed in terms of y, $da = b(y)\,dy$; thus we have

$$(18.10) \qquad\qquad \begin{aligned} f &= \int_0^h p'(y)b(y) \, dy \\[2mm] \bar{y}f &= \int_0^h yp'(y)b(y) \, dy \end{aligned}$$

The x coordinate of the center of pressure may be found similarly.

Example 3

A dam has the shape of a trapezoid (as in Fig. 18.5).   It is 40 ft deep, 70 ft wide at the top, and 50 ft wide at the bottom.   How far from the top is the center of net pressure if the water just reaches the top of the dam?

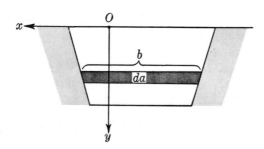

Figure
18.5

Solution

Since the sides are straight, we can express b in terms of y without taking account of the slopes of the sides.

$$b = 70 - 0.5y$$

Using Eq. (18.7) and the fact that

$$\delta g = 62.4 \ \text{lb/ft}^3$$

we have

$$p' = p - p_0 = 62.4y$$

These expressions may be substituted in (18.10) to determine $\bar{y}$. We get

$$f = \tfrac{1}{2}(62.4) \int_0^{40} (140y - y^2)\, dy = \tfrac{1}{2}(62.4)(1,600)(70 - \tfrac{40}{3})$$

$$\bar{y}f = \tfrac{1}{2}(62.4) \int_0^{40} (140y^2 - y^3)\, dy = \tfrac{1}{2}(62.4)(1,600)(40)(\tfrac{140}{3} - \tfrac{40}{4})$$

so

$$\bar{y} = \frac{(40)(36.7)}{56.7} = 25.9 \ \text{ft}$$

Equipotential Surfaces. If $\mathscr{F}$ is a conservative field strength, we know by Sec. 17.5 that there is a scalar point function pot $(\mathbf{R})$ whose gradient, with sign reversed, is equal to $\mathscr{F}$:

$$\mathscr{F} = -\nabla \ \text{pot}$$

The basic equation of the present section can be rewritten

$$\mathscr{F} = \frac{1}{\delta} \nabla p$$

Equating these two expressions for $\mathscr{F}$ and rearranging terms, we get

$$\frac{1}{\delta} \nabla p + \nabla \ \text{pot} = \mathbf{0}$$

Now if δ is constant throughout the fluid, the first term may be rewritten $\nabla(p/\delta)$. Then we may use the fact that ∇ is a linear operator (verified for scalar functions of position in Exercise 38 of the preceding chapter). The conclusion is

$$\nabla \left(\frac{p}{\delta} + \text{pot} \right) = \mathbf{0}$$

This may be integrated at once to yield

$$\frac{p}{\delta} + \text{pot} = \text{const}$$

The interpretation is immediate:

(18.11) *Free surfaces (p constant) are equipotential surfaces.* For an incompressible fluid at rest on the earth, then, a free surface is approximately spherical.

An accelerated fluid may be treated by these hydrostatics methods, provided that suitable fictitious forces are introduced.

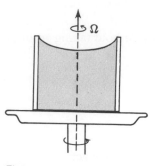

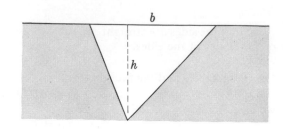

Figure
18.6

Figure
18.7

Example 4

Consider as in Fig. 18.6 a fluid rotating in a cylinder after steady state has been reached.   There are now two body forces (per unit mass):

Gravitational: $-\nabla gy$

Centrifugal: $\nabla \dfrac{\omega^2 r^2}{2}$

The field strength $\mathscr{F}$ is now

$$\mathscr{F} = \nabla\left(-gy + \frac{\omega^2 r^2}{2}\right)$$

By the preceding result, the free surface is one for which the potential is constant; so its equation is

$$+gy - \frac{\omega^2 r^2}{2} = \text{const} \qquad \text{parabolic}$$

EXERCISES

1. Assuming air of constant temperature (so that Boyle's law is valid), use the equation for hydrostatic equilibrium to derive the law of Halley for the variation of atmospheric pressure with height y:

$$p = p_0 e^{-(\delta_0/p_0)gy}$$

2. Use the result of Exercise 1 to predict air pressure at a height of 4,000 m when the barometer on the ground reads 76.   (Specific gravity of air is 0.0012.)
3. Find the force exerted against a vertical rectangular dam 60 ft long, when the water is 60 ft deep.
4. A trapezoidal dam similar to the one in Fig. 18.5 has upper length b_1, lower length b_2, and depth h.   Find the *net* force due to pressure against it in terms of the density δ of the fluid.
5. A dam is shaped like an inverted triangle (as in Fig. 18.7) of base b and depth h.   Find the depth of the center of *net* pressure.

18.3. THE GRADIENT THEOREM

The condition of equilibrium for an isolated particle is $\Sigma\,\mathbf{F} = \mathbf{O}$.   In the preceding section we saw that treating a small element of fluid as a particle led to the equilibrium equation $\mathscr{F}\delta - \nabla p = \mathbf{O}$. The first term has dimensions force per mass times mass per volume or force per volume. It represents the force per volume of gravitational origin. The second term represents, correspondingly, the net force per volume associated with pressure variations. We can conclude that *the net compressive force per volume is equal to minus the pressure gradient.* This interpretation of ∇p will enable us to derive intuitively a very important mathematical conclusion of considerable generality and usefulness.

Suppose that we are interested in a region of a fluid having a well-defined boundary. Let the region be divided up into small cubical elements as is suggested by Fig. 18.8. A typical element of volume Δv is subject to a net compressive force

$$-\nabla p\ \Delta v$$

If we isolate two adjoining elements such as those of volumes Δv and $\Delta v'$ in the figure, the net compressive force is

$$-\nabla p\ \Delta v - \nabla p'\ \Delta v'$$

because the forces across their common boundaries just cancel. Adding such terms for *all* the elements, we get

$$-\Sigma\ \nabla p\ \Delta v$$

as the net compressive force for the whole isolated region. Taking the limit of such sums as the elements are made arbitrarily small, we get as the net compressive force

$$-\int_v \nabla p\ dv$$

Isolating the whole region, we can also express the net compressive force in terms of the forces across the boundary of the region. For each surface element of area Δa, the net compressive force is

$$-\mathbf{N}p\ \Delta a$$

Adding up over the whole boundary, we get

$$-\Sigma\ \mathbf{N}p\ \Delta a$$

and taking the limit of such sums as the Δa's become arbitrarily small, we have as the net compressive force for the whole region

$$-\int_a \mathbf{N}p\ da$$

We have found two ways of expressing mathematically the net compressive force for a region. Equating them, we arrive at a formula which may be used for any

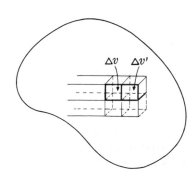

Figure
18.8

suitable scalar function of position p:

(18.12)
$$\int_v \mathbf{\nabla} p \, dv = \int_a \mathbf{N} p \, da$$

For any such scalar φ, the integral over the boundary of a solid region of the vector $\mathbf{N}\varphi$, where $\mathbf{N}$ is the unit normal vector (outward), is equal to the integral over the region of the gradient of the scalar function. This is the *gradient theorem*.

Archimedes' Principle. As an application of the gradient theorem let us consider the celebrated principle of Archimedes. Consider a random object submerged in a nonviscous fluid. The *buoyant force* is the net force due to pressure, that is, the net compressive force exerted across the boundary of the submerged object:

$$\int_a \mathbf{N} p - \, da$$

By the gradient theorem, this is equal to

$$-\int_v \mathbf{\nabla} p \, dv$$

where now we imagine that the object is removed and the integration is over the space previously occupied by the object. The *weight of the fluid displaced* is

$$\int_v \mathscr{F} \delta \, dv$$

But by the basic equation of hydrostatics,

$$\mathscr{F} \delta = \mathbf{\nabla} p$$

Hence the weight of the displaced fluid is

$$\int_v \mathbf{\nabla} p \, dv$$

Thus *buoyant force and weight of displaced fluid are equal and opposite.*

Alternative Characterization of Gradient. Our original definition of gradient was based on directional derivatives. The gradient theorem suggests an approach based on integration. Suppose that $\varphi(\mathbf{R})$ is a scalar function of position with continuous first partial derivatives. Imagine the gradient theorem to be applied to a small element of volume Δv. Then a mean value of $\mathbf{\nabla}\varphi$ for this volume element can be defined as

$$\overline{\mathbf{\nabla}\varphi} = \frac{1}{\Delta v} \int_{\Delta v} \mathbf{\nabla}\varphi \, dv$$

But by the gradient theorem the volume integral of $\mathbf{\nabla}\varphi$ is equal to an area integral of $\mathbf{N}\varphi$; so, letting Δa denote the area of the element having volume Δv, the mean value of $\mathbf{\nabla}\varphi$ can be expressed

$$\overline{\mathbf{\nabla}\varphi} = \frac{1}{\Delta v} \int_{\Delta a} \mathbf{N}\varphi \, da$$

If now we take a sequence of elements, all containing a particular point $\mathbf{R}$ but approaching zero in volume, the corresponding value of $\overline{\mathbf{\nabla}\varphi}$ will approach the value of $\mathbf{\nabla}\varphi$ at $\mathbf{R}$. A careful proof of this observation can be based on the mean-value

Figure
18.9

theorem of integral calculus.   Hence we may write

(18.13) $$\nabla\varphi = \lim_{\Delta v \to 0} \frac{1}{\Delta v} \int_{\Delta a} \mathbf{N}\varphi \, da$$

EXERCISES

6. A cylinder of length l and specific gravity σ oscillates vertically in water about its equilibrium position. (*a*) Is the oscillation simple harmonic motion? (*b*) What is the period? (*c*) What fraction of the length is above water at the equilibrium position?

7. Consider an enclosed liquid in equilibrium having a pressure function $p(\mathbf{R})$.   Now let the pressure at a part of the boundary be increased by a distinct small amount q_0 (as by driving in the plunger in Fig. 18.9). The pressure function throughout the fluid changes.   Show that, when equilibrium is restored, the new pressure function $p'(\mathbf{R})$ is given by

$$p'(\mathbf{R}) = p(\mathbf{R}) + q_0$$

This means that the impressed pressure has been transmitted equally throughout the volume (*Pascal's law*).

18.4. VELOCITY FIELDS

When a fluid is in motion, a velocity vector may be associated with each point in the region.   This vector may be constant (this is known as *steady flow*), but often it will vary.   In this sense, velocity is a vector function of position *and* time:

$$\mathbf{V} = \mathbf{V}(\mathbf{R},t)$$

At any given moment, velocity constitutes a specific *vector field*.   It is often convenient to express $\mathbf{V}$ in terms of components in fixed directions.

$$\mathbf{V} = v_x\mathbf{I} + v_y\mathbf{J} + v_z\mathbf{K}$$

For each choice of axes, v_x, v_y, and v_z are scalar functions of position and determine *three scalar fields*.

With t still held constant, we can consider the *directional derivative* of the vector $\mathbf{V}$.   This concept was presented in Sec. 17.8.   The directional derivative of $\mathbf{V}$ in the direction of the unit vector $\mathbf{T}$ is given by

(18.14) $$\frac{d\mathbf{V}}{ds} = (\mathbf{T} \cdot \nabla)\mathbf{V}$$

When we were discussing force fields, we were concerned especially with the conservative case for which the *work around a closed path* vanished:

$$\text{Work} = \oint \mathbf{F} \cdot d\mathbf{R} = 0$$

The analogous concept with a velocity field is the *circulation around a closed path*.

(18.15) $$\text{Circulation} = \oint \mathbf{V} \cdot d\mathbf{R}$$

If for *every* closed path in the fluid the circulation is zero, the motion is *irrotational*. The value of the circulation generally depends on the path taken. In Fig. 18.10, for instance, several vectors are drawn to illustrate the field

$$\mathbf{V} = |y|\mathbf{I}$$

The circulation is zero for circuit *a*, but not zero for circuit *b*. This can be seen mathematically, and it also may be visualized intuitively. Suppose that the circles *a* and *b* represented inflated rafts floating on water whose current pattern is indicated by the arrows. It is clear that raft *a* would not tend to rotate but that raft *b* would rotate in a clockwise fashion.

In the case of *motion in a plane* it is easy to see that, for any closed path in the plane and around the center of a whirlpool, the circulation is not zero. As a measure of the vorticity at a point **P**, one may divide the circulation by the area of a surface bounded by the closed path. In the limit the concept so defined is sometimes called the *rotation* at **P** about an axis normal to the surface. This clearly depends on the choice of path and surface, but in the limit, as smaller and smaller curves are used, the limit will be unique if the function **V** and its derivatives are continuous. For example, if the motion is like a rigid body in rotation at angular speed ω and if we take a circle with the center of rotation as its center, we get

$$c = \text{circulation} = \omega r(2\pi r)$$

and for our measure of the vorticity at the center about a normal axis

$$(18.16) \qquad \text{rot} = \text{rotation} = \lim_{r \to 0}\left(\frac{2\pi\omega r^2}{\pi r^2}\right) = 2\omega$$

This shows how in this special case the result is independent of the radius of the circle even before the limit is taken. A better measure of vorticity might be defined as one-half the rotation, so that for our special case it would be equal to ω. If a small raft were floated on the liquid, its angular velocity would tend to equal one-half the rotation at the point it occupied.

If the motion is not necessarily plane, another complication arises. Through a point **P** we may draw various planes for which the rotation might be computed. These planes are designated by the unit normal vector **N** directed so that **N** is parallel to the corresponding angular velocity vector.

In general, the circulation around the boundary of an element of area Δa and

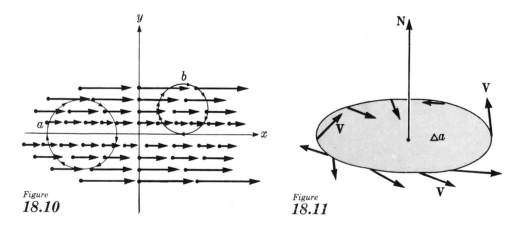

Figure
18.10

Figure
18.11

normal $\mathbf{N}$ as in Fig. 18.11 is given by

$$(18.17) \qquad \Delta c_N = \oint_{\Delta a} \mathbf{V} \cdot d\mathbf{R}$$

and correspondingly, we may define the $\mathbf{N}$ rotation or rotation about an axis in the $\mathbf{N}$ direction thus:

$$(18.18) \qquad \operatorname{rot}_N \mathbf{V} = \lim_{\Delta a \to 0} \frac{\Delta c_N}{\Delta a}$$

where Δc_N is the circulation about the curve bounding Δa.

It is a remarkable fact, reminiscent of a similar situation met in our study of directional derivatives, that $\operatorname{rot}_N \mathbf{V}$ can be expressed simply in terms of $\operatorname{rot}_I \mathbf{V}$, $\operatorname{rot}_J \mathbf{V}$, $\operatorname{rot}_K \mathbf{V}$. Consider the possible circulations about boundaries of triangles in Fig. 18.12 where a plane of normal $\mathbf{N} = l\mathbf{I} + m\mathbf{J} + n\mathbf{K}$ cuts axes parallel to the coordinate axes to form a tetrahedron. If each triangle is circulated in the direction shown, each edge is traversed twice, in opposite directions, so that the sum is zero. Let us use at once the obvious fact that

$$(18.19) \qquad \begin{aligned} \Delta c_I &= -\Delta c_{(-I)} \\ \Delta c_J &= -\Delta c_{(-J)} \\ \Delta c_K &= -\Delta c_{(-K)} \end{aligned}$$

so that

$$(18.20) \qquad \Delta c_N = \Delta c_I + \Delta c_J + \Delta c_K$$

If we denote the areas of the triangles by Δa, Δa_x, etc., we have

$$\begin{aligned} \Delta a_x &= l\,\Delta a \\ \Delta a_y &= m\,\Delta a \\ \Delta a_z &= n\,\Delta a \end{aligned}$$

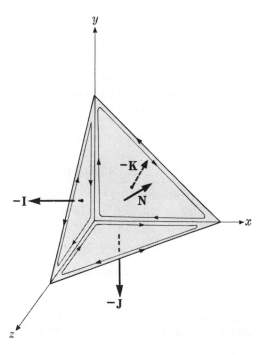

Figure
18.12

so that

(18.21) $$\frac{1}{\Delta a} = \frac{l}{\Delta a_x} = \frac{m}{\Delta a_y} = \frac{n}{\Delta a_z}$$

Multiplying successive entries in (18.20) by the equal quantities of (18.21) we get

(18.22) $$\frac{\Delta c_N}{\Delta a} = l\frac{\Delta c_I}{\Delta a_x} + m\frac{\Delta c_J}{\Delta a_y} + n\frac{\Delta c_K}{\Delta a_z}$$

Now let us take limits as Δa approaches zero. We clearly get

(18.23) $$\text{rot}_N \mathbf{V} = l\,\text{rot}_I \mathbf{V} + m\,\text{rot}_J \mathbf{V} + n\,\text{rot}_K \mathbf{V}$$

This expression bears a distinct resemblance to (17.3).

EXERCISES

8. A cylinder of fluid is in uniform rotation about the y axis, so

$$\mathbf{V} = \omega\mathbf{J} \times \mathbf{R}$$

Show that $(\mathbf{V} \cdot \nabla)\mathbf{V} = -\omega^2(x\mathbf{I} + z\mathbf{K})$.

9. A velocity field parallel to the xy plane is given by

$$\mathbf{V} = 2x\mathbf{J}$$

Compute the circulation for a clockwise trip around the square whose corners have coordinates (0,0), (0,1), (1,1), (1,0).

10. Suppose that a fluid travels in a horizontal circular ring-shaped conduit in such a way that the linear speed is a constant; the fluid traveling along a circle of large radius moves no faster than fluid traversing a smaller circle. Find how the circulation about these circles varies with the radius. For what kind of circular velocity pattern would these circulations be equal?

11. If the flow described in the first part of Exercise 10 were imagined to continue right up to the center of the circle, what would be the rotation at that point about a normal axis?

12. For rotation in a plane like a rigid body about a fixed axis, consider the circulation around the closed path bounded by concentric circles and radii whose corners are given in polar coordinates (origin on axis in plane) as (r,θ), $(r + \Delta r, \theta)$, $(r + \Delta r, \theta + \Delta\theta)$, $(r, \theta + \Delta\theta)$. From this find the rotation about a normal axis at (r, θ).

13. Compute in detail the rotation about an arbitrary axis for a constant vector field.

18.5. THE NOTION OF CURL

As in our treatment of (17.3), we note how convenient it would be to regard (18.23) as the scalar product of $\mathbf{N}$ with a new vector usually called the *curl* of $\mathbf{V}$ and here defined by

(18.24) $$\mathbf{curl}\ \mathbf{V} = (\text{rot}_I \mathbf{V})\mathbf{I} + (\text{rot}_J \mathbf{V})\mathbf{J} + (\text{rot}_K \mathbf{V})\mathbf{K}$$

In terms of this we can rewrite (18.23) as

(18.25) $$\text{rot}_N \mathbf{V} = \mathbf{N} \cdot \mathbf{curl}\ \mathbf{V}$$

This is analogous to Eq. (17.5). We note that, when $\mathbf{N}$ is chosen parallel to the vector **curl V**, we get a maximum rotation and that the magnitude of the vector is equal to this maximum rotation.   Thus curl plays the same role for rotation and vorticity that gradient does for directional derivative.   Paraphrasing (17.7), we have

(18.26) **Curl V** *has the direction for which the rotation of* **V** *is maximum.   It has the magnitude of this maximum rotation.*

Next let us seek analytical expressions for the components of **curl V**.   Consider a rectangle of normal **K** and edges Δx and Δy about a point **P** as center as shown in Fig. 18.13.   Average velocity components parallel to the respective edges are, approximately,

$$v_x - \frac{\partial v_x}{\partial y}\frac{\Delta y}{2} \qquad v_y + \frac{\partial v_y}{\partial x}\frac{\Delta x}{2}$$

$$-\left(v_x + \frac{\partial v_x}{\partial y}\frac{\Delta y}{2}\right) \qquad -\left(v_y - \frac{\partial v_y}{\partial x}\frac{\Delta x}{2}\right)$$

The circulation is, then, since several terms of opposite sign cancel each other,

$$\Delta c_K = -\frac{\partial v_x}{\partial y}\Delta y\,\Delta x + \frac{\partial v_y}{\partial x}\Delta x\,\Delta y$$

and we get

$$\operatorname{rot}_K \mathbf{V} = \lim_{\substack{\Delta x \to 0 \\ \Delta y \to 0}} \frac{\Delta c_K}{\Delta x\,\Delta y} = \frac{\partial v_y}{\partial x} - \frac{\partial v_x}{\partial y}$$

Similar evaluations may be carried out for $\operatorname{rot}_I \mathbf{V}$ and $\operatorname{rot}_J \mathbf{V}$, yielding the formula

(18.27) $$\mathbf{curl\ V} = \left(\frac{\partial v_z}{\partial y} - \frac{\partial v_y}{\partial z}\right)\mathbf{I} + \left(\frac{\partial v_x}{\partial z} - \frac{\partial v_z}{\partial x}\right)\mathbf{J} + \left(\frac{\partial v_y}{\partial x} - \frac{\partial v_x}{\partial y}\right)\mathbf{K}$$

We used the symbol ∇ in dealing with gradients.   If we regard it as a symbolic vectorial operator, it will have further use for us.   The use of operator equations has been met earlier, for example,

$$\frac{d}{dt} = \Omega \times \qquad \frac{d}{dt} = \frac{d'}{d't} + \Omega \times$$

Here we write

(18.28) $$\nabla = \mathbf{I}\frac{\partial}{\partial x} + \mathbf{J}\frac{\partial}{\partial y} + \mathbf{K}\frac{\partial}{\partial z}$$

When this "operates" on a scalar, we merely use symbolic multiplication by a scalar φ to get a formula for an actual operation; thus

$$\nabla\varphi = \mathbf{I}\frac{\partial \varphi}{\partial x} + \mathbf{J}\frac{\partial \varphi}{\partial y} + \mathbf{K}\frac{\partial \varphi}{\partial z} = \mathbf{grad}\ \varphi$$

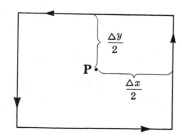

Figure
18.13

In this sense we may write

(18.29) $$\text{curl } \mathbf{V} = \nabla \times \mathbf{V}$$

for symbolically,

(18.30) $$\text{curl } \mathbf{V} = \begin{vmatrix} \dfrac{\partial}{\partial x} & \dfrac{\partial}{\partial y} & \dfrac{\partial}{\partial z} \\ v_x & v_y & v_z \\ \mathbf{I} & \mathbf{J} & \mathbf{K} \end{vmatrix}$$

$$= \mathbf{I} \begin{vmatrix} \dfrac{\partial}{\partial y} & \dfrac{\partial}{\partial z} \\ v_y & v_z \end{vmatrix} + \mathbf{J} \begin{vmatrix} \dfrac{\partial}{\partial z} & \dfrac{\partial}{\partial x} \\ v_z & v_x \end{vmatrix} + \mathbf{K} \begin{vmatrix} \dfrac{\partial}{\partial x} & \dfrac{\partial}{\partial y} \\ v_x & v_y \end{vmatrix}$$

This last expression expands to give (18.27). Since the determinant (18.30) is easily written down from (18.29), the symbolic approach is a real crutch for flagging memories when computations of curls are desired.

Example 1

$$\mathbf{V} = x\mathbf{I} + xy\mathbf{K}$$

Find **curl V**.

Solution

$$\text{curl } \mathbf{V} = \begin{vmatrix} \dfrac{\partial}{\partial x} & \dfrac{\partial}{\partial y} & \dfrac{\partial}{\partial z} \\ x & 0 & xy \\ \mathbf{I} & \mathbf{J} & \mathbf{K} \end{vmatrix} = \mathbf{I}(x - 0) + \mathbf{J}(0 - y) + \mathbf{K}(0 - 0)$$

$$= x\mathbf{I} - y\mathbf{J}$$

Example 2

Let us consider the field of Fig. 18.10 for points above the x axis. Then $\mathbf{V} = y\mathbf{I}$. It follows easily that

$$\text{curl } \mathbf{V} = -\mathbf{K}$$

EXERCISES

14. Show that for rigid-body motion the following equation holds for any point of the body:

$$\text{curl } \mathbf{V} = 2\mathbf{\Omega}$$

15. Evaluate **curl V** for:

   (a) $\mathbf{V} = x^2 y\mathbf{I} + (x - y)\mathbf{K}$.   (b) $\mathbf{V} = \mathbf{R}/(\mathbf{R} \cdot \mathbf{R})$.

16. Rephrase (17.19) in terms of the ideas of this section.
17. Evaluate **curl V** for $\mathbf{V} = \mathbf{L}$ (**L** being the unit radial vector, as usual).
18. Investigate the curl of $\nabla \varphi$ for a suitable scalar function of position φ.
19. Get a formula for **curl V** for a fluid rotating in circles in the xy plane about the z axis at an angular speed $\omega = k/r^2$, where k is a constant.

18.6. STOKES' THEOREM

For a very small element of area Δa and of normal **N** one may write approximately, according to (18.25) and (18.18),

(18.31) $$\Delta c_N = \mathbf{N} \cdot (\text{curl } \mathbf{V})\, \Delta a$$

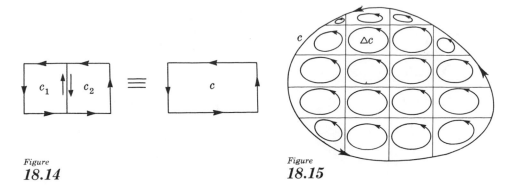

Figure
18.14

Figure
18.15

When two such small elements are adjacent, as in Fig. 18.14, it is apparent that the sum of the two circulations c_1 and c_2 is equal to the circulation c about the periphery of the combined area, since a cancellation occurs on the common boundary: $c = c_1 + c_2$. For any larger area, as in Fig. 18.15, the circulation around the boundary is equal to the sum of the circulations around all the elements, however small, into which the area may be divided,

$$c = \Sigma \, \Delta c$$

Let any simply connected (i.e., no holes) surface bounded by the simple curve in Fig. 18.16 be divided into very small elements Δa. Thus (18.31) applies for each such element. Adding these equations, we get

(18.32) $$c = \Sigma \, \mathbf{N} \cdot (\mathbf{curl} \ \mathbf{V}) \, \Delta a$$

Taking the limit as Δa gets smaller and smaller, the left member remains constant but the right member normally approaches a limit. Writing c in the form of (18.15), we have

(18.33) $$\oint \mathbf{V} \cdot d\mathbf{R} = \int_a \mathbf{N} \cdot \nabla \times \mathbf{V} \ da$$

In words:

(18.34) *The circulation around a simple curve is equal to the area integral over any simply connected surface bounded by the curve of the normal component of the curl of the velocity.* This is a form of Stokes' theorem.

Example

Let us use Stokes' theorem to determine how a fluid in a circular conveyor must travel to have a zero curl. Assume that the velocity is always transverse (normal to radius) and constant for a given radius. Suppose that the speed is v_1 for $r = r_1$ and v_2 for $r = r_2$. Then the circulation around the closed path shown in Fig. 18.17 is

$$c = -v_1 r_1 \theta + 0 + v_2 r_2 \theta + 0 = (v_2 r_2 - v_1 r_1)\theta$$

If **curl V** is zero throughout, the condition on the speeds is

$$v_2 r_2 = v_1 r_1 \quad \text{or} \quad v_2 = v_1 \left(\frac{r_1}{r_2}\right)$$

i.e., the speed varies inversely as the radius. This conclusion may be compared with the result of Exercise 19 of the preceding section.

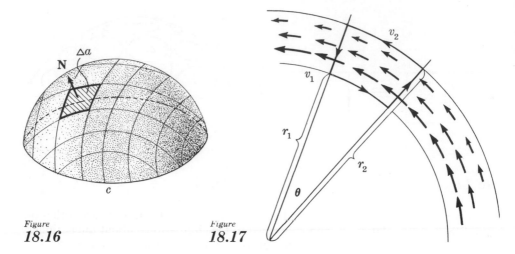

Figure
18.16

Figure
18.17

This important theorem assists us in arriving at a very useful conclusion.   We have seen that a force field **F(R)** is conservative if and only if it is possible to express **F** as equal to the gradient of a scalar function φ.   Similarly, a velocity field **V(R)** is irrotational if a corresponding function may be found.   But can one tell by looking at an analytic expression of **F(R)** or **V(R)** whether there is such a φ?   Clearly, a more direct test is desirable.   We shall demonstrate that (for a simply connected region and suitably smooth functions):

(18.35) *A vector function of position* **F(R)** *can be expressed as the gradient of a scalar function* $\varphi(\mathbf{R})$ *if and only if* **curl F = O** *at every point.*

First suppose that **F(R)** can be written as $\nabla\varphi$.   Then

$$\mathbf{curl\ F} = \begin{vmatrix} \dfrac{\partial}{\partial x} & \dfrac{\partial}{\partial y} & \dfrac{\partial}{\partial z} \\[2mm] \dfrac{\partial\varphi}{\partial x} & \dfrac{\partial\varphi}{\partial y} & \dfrac{\partial\varphi}{\partial z} \\[2mm] \mathbf{I} & \mathbf{J} & \mathbf{K} \end{vmatrix}$$

$$= \mathbf{I}\left(\frac{\partial^2\varphi}{\partial y\,\partial z} - \frac{\partial^2\varphi}{\partial z\,\partial y}\right) + \mathbf{J}\left(\frac{\partial^2\varphi}{\partial z\,\partial x} - \frac{\partial^2\varphi}{\partial x\,\partial z}\right) + \mathbf{K}\left(\frac{\partial^2\varphi}{\partial x\,\partial y} - \frac{\partial^2\varphi}{\partial y\,\partial x}\right)$$

If these second-order partial derivatives are continuous, as we assume, each expression in parentheses vanishes; thus

$$\mathbf{curl\ F} = \mathbf{O}$$

Suppose, on the other hand, that **curl F = O** everywhere.   Then let us take a closed path and evaluate the circulation of **F** around this path.   By Stokes' theorem

$$\oint \mathbf{F}\cdot d\mathbf{R} = \int_a \mathbf{N}\cdot \mathbf{curl\ F}\ da$$

for some surface bounded by the closed path.   But if **curl F** is zero everywhere, we get

$$\oint \mathbf{F}\cdot d\mathbf{R} = 0$$

We have considered simple curves only. For a simply connected region, the same ideas are easily applied to less simple curves, although the details are omitted here. We shall conclude, then, that $\mathbf{F}$ is conservative, and hence

$$\mathbf{F} = \boldsymbol{\nabla}\varphi$$

In the remaining sections we shall be concerned only with irrotational flow. Thus vortices will not be considered.

EXERCISES

20. Show that **curl V** = **O** if and only if **V** is irrotational.
21. Determine which of the following velocity fields are irrotational:
  (a) $\mathbf{V} = (2 - 2y - z)\mathbf{I} + (2 + 2x - z)\mathbf{J} + (x + y)\mathbf{K}.$
  (b) $\mathbf{V} = (x^2 - 4)\mathbf{I} + 4y\mathbf{J} - (z^2 + z)\mathbf{K}.$
  (c) $\mathbf{V} = (yz^2 + 2yzx + zy^2)\mathbf{I} + (zx^2 + 2zxy + xz^2)\mathbf{J} + (xy^2 + 2xyz + yx^2)\mathbf{K}.$

18.7. FLUX AND DIVERGENCE

The word "flux" is very frequently used in physics in connection with flow patterns. For a velocity field, the volume of fluid crossing a boundary area per second is called the *volume flux*. For an element of area Δa of normal $\mathbf{N}$, the flux is (see Fig. 18.18)

$$(18.36) \qquad\qquad \Delta(\text{flux}) = \mathbf{N} \cdot \mathbf{V}\,\Delta a$$

and for an extended area it is given by

$$(18.37) \qquad\qquad \text{Flux} = \int_a \mathbf{N} \cdot \mathbf{V}\,da$$

The vector $\mathbf{N}\,\Delta a$ is often written $\Delta\mathbf{A}$, treating area as a vector. Then Eq. (18.36) would be rewritten

$$\Delta(\text{flux}) = \mathbf{V} \cdot \mathbf{N}\,\Delta a = \mathbf{V} \cdot \Delta\mathbf{A}$$

In the special case of a plane boundary of normal $\mathbf{I}$, the flux is

$$\text{Flux} = (\mathbf{I} \cdot \bar{\mathbf{V}})a = \bar{v}_x a$$

where $\bar{\mathbf{V}}$ and $\bar{v}_x$ indicate average values for the surface. If the velocity is uniform across this surface, no averaging is necessary.

Now consider a small boxlike element of volume $\Delta x\,\Delta y\,\Delta z$. Let $\mathbf{V}$ be the velocity at the center of the box. As usual, we estimate the average velocity across the various faces by using formula (17.1). The net outward flux across faces perpendicular to $\mathbf{I}$ is then

$$\left(v_x + \frac{\partial v_x}{\partial x}\frac{\Delta x}{2}\right)\Delta y\,\Delta z - \left(v_x - \frac{\partial v_x}{\partial x}\frac{\Delta x}{2}\right)\Delta y\,\Delta z$$

or

$$\frac{\partial v_x}{\partial x}\Delta x\,\Delta y\,\Delta z$$

Similar terms describe the net efflux in the y and z directions. Adding these three, dividing by the volume of the box, and taking the limit as the size of the box shrinks, we get an expression for the *net outward flux per volume* which is given the name *divergence of the velocity*. It is written div $\mathbf{V}$:

$$(18.38) \qquad\qquad \text{div } \mathbf{V} = \frac{\partial v_x}{\partial x} + \frac{\partial v_y}{\partial y} + \frac{\partial v_z}{\partial z}$$

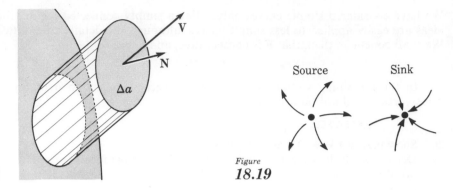

Figure
18.18

Figure
18.19

It is interesting that this formula can be given a symbolic representation in terms of the operator ∇:

$$\nabla \cdot \mathbf{V} = \left(\mathbf{I}\frac{\partial}{\partial x} + \mathbf{J}\frac{\partial}{\partial y} + \mathbf{K}\frac{\partial}{\partial z}\right) \cdot (v_x\mathbf{I} + v_y\mathbf{J} + v_z\mathbf{K})$$

or

(18.39) $\nabla \cdot \mathbf{V} = \operatorname{div} \mathbf{V}$

For an incompressible fluid, a point of positive divergence is a *source* (such as the end of a nozzle).   Correspondingly (see Fig. 18.19), a point of negative divergence is a *sink* or negative source.   For steady flow, similar conclusions can be drawn about any reasonable fluid.

Example

Find $\operatorname{div} \dfrac{\mathbf{R}}{\mathbf{R} \cdot \mathbf{R}}$.

Solution

$$\frac{\mathbf{R}}{\mathbf{R} \cdot \mathbf{R}} = \frac{x}{r^2}\mathbf{I} + \frac{y}{r^2}\mathbf{J} + \frac{z}{r^2}\mathbf{K}$$

where

$$r^2 = x^2 + y^2 + z^2$$

$$\operatorname{div}\frac{\mathbf{R}}{\mathbf{R} \cdot \mathbf{R}} = \frac{x^2 + y^2 + z^2 - 2x^2}{r^4} + \frac{x^2 + y^2 + z^2 - 2y^2}{r^4}$$

$$+ \frac{x^2 + y^2 + z^2 - 2z^2}{r^4} = \frac{1}{r^2} = \frac{1}{\mathbf{R} \cdot \mathbf{R}}$$

It is interesting that the words used to define divergence, net outward flux per volume, can be expressed mathematically in a manner analogous to the alternative characterization of gradient given in Sec. 18.3:

(18.40) $\operatorname{div} \mathbf{V} = \lim\limits_{\Delta v \to 0} \dfrac{1}{\Delta v} \displaystyle\int_{\Delta a} \mathbf{N} \cdot \mathbf{V} \, da$

The Equation of Continuity.   The rate at which *mass* streams across an element of area da in a moving fluid is

(18.41) $d(\text{mass flux}) = \mathbf{N} \cdot \delta\mathbf{V} \, da$

This equation for a flux involving a density factor is a prototype for many situations in theoretical physics. In Eq. (18.36) the density factor, being merely volume per volume, was omitted since its value obviously is unity. Whenever quantities are transported across a frontier, real or imagined, such a flux formula is likely to be useful. For instance, in the kinetic theory of gases, δ may be replaced by the number of particles per volume. In other applications one might be concerned with energy per volume, electric charge per volume, etc. Applications appear in the examples of the following section. Mathematically speaking, the vector $\mathbf{V}$ in Eq. (18.36) has been replaced by the vector $\delta\mathbf{V}$. Hence the net outward flux of mass per volume at a point is

$$\mathbf{V} \cdot \delta\mathbf{V}$$

But this is precisely the rate at which the density is decreasing (*if there are no sources or sinks*), so

$$\mathbf{V} \cdot \delta\mathbf{V} = -\frac{\partial\delta}{\partial t}$$

or

$$(18.42) \qquad \frac{\partial\delta}{\partial t} + \mathbf{V} \cdot \delta\mathbf{V} = 0$$

This is one of the fundamental results of hydrodynamics. It is known as the *equation of continuity*. For an incompressible fluid (δ constant) this gives

$$(18.43) \qquad \mathbf{V} \cdot \mathbf{V} = 0$$

That is, for any fluid where there are no sources or sinks, mass is conserved, while for an incompressible fluid, volume also is conserved. To get a mental picture of the two equations of continuity, visualize a football being inflated (*a*) with air and (*b*) with water. In the first case (see Fig. 18.20), the air slows up as it passes through a tube to the ball: more enters the tube than leaves it since the pressure, and hence the density, increases. Here the divergence of the velocity pattern is negative. In the second case, the density cannot change appreciably: as much water leaves the tube as enters it. Here the divergence is zero.

EXERCISES

22. Find the divergence of the following vector point functions:
  (a) $x\mathbf{I}$.   (b) $\mathbf{R}$.   (c) $\mathbf{L}$.
  (d) **grad** xy^2z^3.   (e) $(1/r^2)\mathbf{L}$.
23. Evaluate (a) $\mathbf{V} \cdot r^n\mathbf{R}$, where $r = |\mathbf{R}|$; (b) $\mathbf{V} \cdot \mathbf{A} \times \mathbf{R}$ for a constant $\mathbf{A}$.

18.8. SOLID ANGLE

In this section the geometry of flux is explored further and illustrated by physical applications. When we speak precisely of the position of a particle on a line, we give

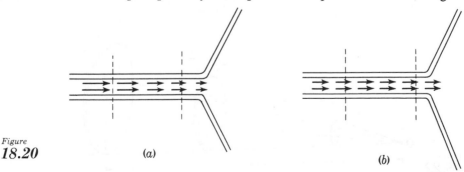

Figure
18.20   (a)   (b)

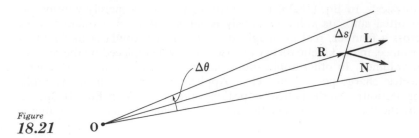

Figure
18.21   O

its coordinate, say, *x*.   If we wish to state its position less exactly, we might say that
it lies in a range Δx, including *x*.   Similarly, to specify a position in space, we might
say that a particle is at **R** or that it lies in an element of volume Δb which includes
R.   The same sort of nomenclature may be used for another purpose.   If all points
in a fixed volume *b* are equally probable for a particle, a natural evaluation of the
probability that the particle is in a volume element of size Δb is the ratio $\Delta b/b$.   For
example, if a cottage consists of exactly four rooms of equal volume and a bathroom
half as large, and if a wasp is known to be in the cottage, then the probability that
it is in the bathroom is one-ninth, again assuming that all equal elements of space
are equally likely.

In naming a direction in the plane, as in Sec. 2.7, we state an angle θ.   For
specifying a range of directions, we might name an increment of angle $\Delta\theta$, including
θ.   The angle subtended at **O** by an element of arc Δs along a circle with center at **O**
and radius *r* is by definition equal to $\Delta\theta = \Delta s/r$.   In Fig. 18.21 the range of directions
subtended at **O** by the arc Δs having unit normal **N** is given for small $\Delta\theta$ by

$$(18.44) \qquad\qquad \Delta\theta = \frac{\mathbf{L}\cdot\mathbf{N}}{r}\,\Delta s$$

The scalar *r* is the length of the position vector **R** of a point on the subtending arc.
If all directions of travel are equally likely, the probability that a direction taken in
the plane will lie in an angular range $\Delta\theta$ is the fraction $\Delta\theta/2\pi$, for the total range of
directions is 2π rad.

Solid angle is defined in a manner entirely analogous to the definition of radian
measure for ordinary plane angles.   The *solid angle* $\Delta\omega$ at **O** subtended by an
element of area Δa on a sphere of radius *r* with center at **O** is

$$(18.45) \qquad\qquad \Delta\omega = \frac{\Delta a}{r^2}$$

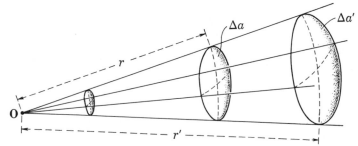

Figure
18.22

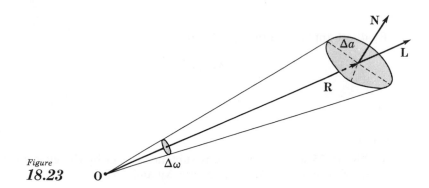

Figure
18.23

It is easy to show that the definition does not depend on the particular sphere chosen: in Fig. 18.22

$$\frac{\Delta a}{r^2} = \frac{\Delta a'}{r'^2}$$

Note that the total solid angle about a point is 4π solid radians or steradians.

To name a direction in space we state a unit vector $\mathbf{L}$ and to specify a range of directions we record an increment of solid angle $\Delta\omega$. Let Δa denote a small area element with unit normal $\mathbf{N}$, including the point with position vector $\mathbf{R}$. In Fig. 18.23, the solid angle subtended at $\mathbf{O}$ by the area Δa is

$$(18.46) \qquad\qquad\qquad \Delta\omega = \frac{\mathbf{L}\cdot\mathbf{N}}{r^2}\,\Delta a$$

If particles are traveling in random directions, then the expected fraction traveling with a velocity vector parallel to a direction in the cone of directions having solid angle $\Delta\omega$ is $\Delta\omega/4\pi$, the space analogue of $\Delta\theta/2\pi$.

Example 1a. Solid Angle in Terms of Coordinates

In Fig. 18.24 at $\mathbf{R}$, what solid angle is subtended at $\mathbf{O}$ by the area element of dimensions Δy by Δz?

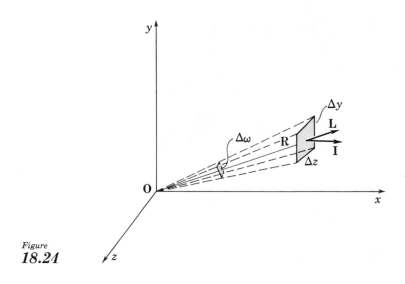

Figure
18.24

Solution

By direct application of Eq. (18.46),

$$\Delta\omega = \frac{\mathbf{L}\cdot\mathbf{I}}{r^2}\,\Delta y\,\Delta z$$

or

$$\Delta\omega = \frac{x}{r^3}\,\Delta y\,\Delta z$$

Example 1b

In Fig. 18.25 what solid angle is subtended at **O** by the element on the sphere of radius r determined by the increments $\Delta\gamma$ and $\Delta\theta$?

Solution

By (18.45), for small $\Delta\gamma$ and $\Delta\theta$, we have

$$\Delta\omega = \frac{(r\sin\gamma\,\Delta\theta)(r\,\Delta\gamma)}{r^2} = \sin\gamma\,\Delta\gamma\,\Delta\theta$$

Example 2. Escape Flux of a Gas

Suppose that a container of gas has a small hole of area Δa and outward unit normal **N**. Assume that all molecules are traveling at speed $\bar{v}$ and that all directions of travel are equally likely. What is the expected rate of efflux?

Solution

Consider first only those molecules whose velocity vectors point in the cone of directions determined by the solid angle $d\omega$ around the unit vector **E**. If there are in all n molecules per volume, then the number per volume of molecules having directions in the desired range is $(d\omega/4\pi)n$. Using this expression as the density factor in our flux formula, we have for the flux in the specified range of directions

$$\Delta(\text{flux})_E = \mathbf{N}\cdot\left(\frac{d\omega}{4\pi}\right)n\mathbf{V}\,\Delta a$$

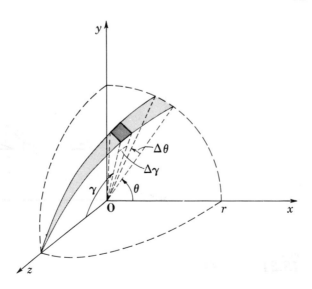

Figure
18.25

Now $\mathbf{V} \cdot \mathbf{N} = \bar{v} \cos \gamma$ (see cross-sectional view in Fig. 18.26) and in spherical coordinates, using Example 1b,

$$d\omega = \sin \gamma \, d\gamma \, d\theta$$

so we have

$$\Delta(\text{flux})_E = \frac{n\bar{v}}{4\pi} \cos \gamma \sin \gamma \, d\gamma \, d\theta \, \Delta a$$

To get the total flux through Δa, we must sum for all directions having positive z components:

(18.47)
$$\frac{\Delta(\text{flux})}{\Delta a} = \frac{n\bar{v}}{4\pi} \int_0^{2\pi} \int_{\gamma=0}^{\gamma=\pi/2} \sin \gamma \, d(\sin \gamma) \, d\theta$$

$$= \frac{n\bar{v}}{4\pi} \cdot 2\pi \cdot \frac{\sin^2 \gamma}{2} \Big|_0^{\pi/2} = \tfrac{1}{4} n\bar{v}$$

Example 3. Radiation Pressure

In Sec. 7.14, Example 2, we treated a photon as a particle subject to the momentum laws of classical mechanics. Suppose that a cavity or hole in a suitable material has reflecting surfaces and is filled with homogeneous isotropic electromagnetic radiation, all at frequency v. As in the preceding example, let n be the number of photons per volume. The radiant energy per volume is then $nh v$, where h is Planck's constant. Denoting this energy per volume by the symbol u, we can write in place of n in the flux formulas the expression $u/h v$.

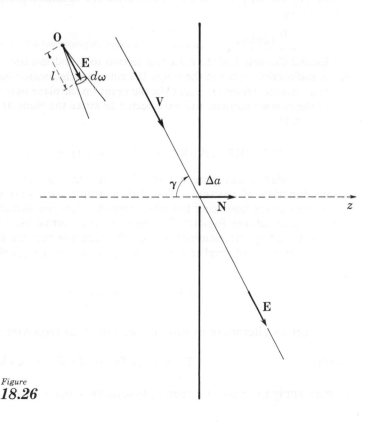

Figure
18.26

Isolate a small area element Δa of the interior surface of the cavity. For radiation traveling in directions determined by a solid angle $d\omega$ containing a particular unit vector $\mathbf{E}$, the flux incident on the isolated area is

$$\Delta(\text{flux})_E = \frac{nc}{4\pi} \cos\gamma \, d\omega \, \Delta a$$

as in the preceding example. Now the change in momentum for each photon, assuming regular reflection, is $-2(h/\lambda)\cos\gamma$, that is, twice the normal component of momentum. The number of photons per time (flux) times the momentum change per photon is equal to the momentum change per time for those particles in the specified sample:

$$\frac{d}{dt}(\text{momentum at } \Delta a)_E = \left(-2\frac{h}{\lambda}\cos\gamma\right)\left(\frac{u}{h\nu}\right) c \cos\gamma \left(\sin\gamma \, \frac{d\gamma \, d\theta}{4\pi}\right) \Delta a$$

The left member is the magnitude of a force normal to the surface. The total force Δf is found by integrating over the range of directions. Recall that $\lambda\nu = c$.

$$\Delta f = \frac{u}{2\pi}\int_0^{2\pi}\int_0^{\pi/2}\cos^2\gamma \sin\gamma \, d\gamma \, d\theta \, \Delta a = \tfrac{1}{3}u \, \Delta a$$

Dividing by Δa, we get an important formula for radiation pressure in terms of energy density: $p = \tfrac{1}{3}u$.

EXERCISES

24. Extend Example 1 of the preceding section to cylindrical coordinates.

25. A radioactive source at the origin $\mathbf{O}$ emits particles isotropically. A plane surface is at a distance d from $\mathbf{O}$. Let $\mathbf{Q}$ be the point on the plane nearest to $\mathbf{P}$. What fraction of the emitted particles will be expected to strike the plane at points not farther than d from $\mathbf{Q}$?

18.9. THE DIVERGENCE THEOREM

Consider within a fluid a region in which the divergence of the velocity is a continuous function of position. We shall examine two ways of expressing the flux across the surface bounding the given region. Let the surface be divided into elements of area da (see Fig. 18.27) with outward normal $\mathbf{N}$. Then the net outward flux is the sum of the elements of flux through the various area elements. In the limit, for smaller and smaller area elements, this sum approaches a definite integral:

$$\text{Net outward flux} = \int_a \mathbf{N} \cdot \mathbf{V} \, da$$

To get an alternative expression, we note that (compare Exercise 26)

(18.48) $$\mathbf{\nabla} \cdot \mathbf{V} = \mathbf{I} \cdot \mathbf{\nabla}v_x + \mathbf{J} \cdot \mathbf{\nabla}v_y + \mathbf{K} \cdot \mathbf{\nabla}v_z$$

We may apply the gradient theorem as follows (b denotes volume to avoid confusion with the use of v for speed):

$$\int_b \nabla \cdot \mathbf{V} \, db = \mathbf{I} \cdot \int_b \nabla v_x \, db + \mathbf{J} \cdot \int_b \nabla v_y \, db + \mathbf{K} \cdot \int_b \nabla v_z \, db$$

$$= \mathbf{I} \cdot \int_a \mathbf{N} v_x \, da + \mathbf{J} \cdot \int_a \mathbf{N} v_y \, da + \mathbf{K} \cdot \int_a \mathbf{N} v_z \, da$$

or finally,

(18.49)
$$\int_b \nabla \cdot \mathbf{V} \, db = \int_a \mathbf{N} \cdot \mathbf{V} \, da$$

This is the *divergence theorem*. Like the gradient theorem, it enables us to go from local information to surface information, and vice versa.

Example

Electric flux density $\mathbf{D}$ associated with an isolated charge q at the origin is given by

$$\mathbf{D} = \frac{q\mathbf{L}}{4\pi r^2}$$

Compute the net outward electric flux across a closed surface σ: (*a*) with $\mathbf{O}$ outside of the surface, (*b*) with $\mathbf{O}$ enclosed by the surface.

Solution

The net outward flux is given by the area integral over the surface of the outward normal component of $\mathbf{D}$:

$$\text{Flux} = \int_\sigma \mathbf{D} \cdot \mathbf{N} \, da = \frac{q}{4\pi} \int_\sigma \frac{\mathbf{N} \cdot \mathbf{L}}{r^2} \, da$$

a. The divergence of $\mathbf{D}$ away from the origin has a continuous derivative (see Exercise 22e), so we may apply the divergence theorem:

$$\text{Flux} = \frac{q}{4\pi} \int_b \nabla \cdot \frac{\mathbf{L}}{r^2} \, db = 0$$

Thus the net outward flux is zero.

b. If $\mathbf{O}$ is in the interior of the region bounded by the surface, one can construct inside the surface a sphere σ' with $\mathbf{O}$ as center as suggested by Fig. 18.28. The

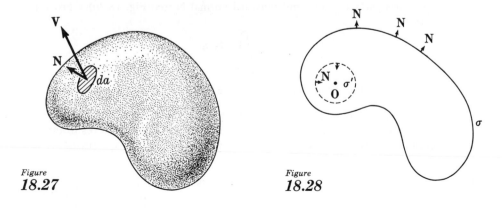

Figure
18.27

Figure
18.28

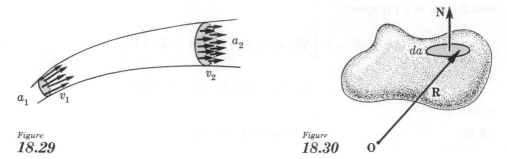

Figure
18.29

Figure
18.30   O

region between surface and sphere has **O** outside, so the result of (*a*) may be used:

$$\int_\sigma \frac{\mathbf{N}\cdot\mathbf{L}}{r^2}\, da \; | \; \int_{\sigma'} \frac{\mathbf{N}\cdot\mathbf{L}}{r^2}\, da = 0$$

But for the sphere $\mathbf{N} = -\mathbf{L}$ and r is constant:

$$\int_\sigma \frac{\mathbf{N}\cdot\mathbf{L}}{r^2}\, da = \frac{1}{r^2}\int_{\sigma'} da = \frac{4\pi r^2}{r^2} = 4\pi$$

Hence

$$\text{Flux} = \frac{q}{4\pi}(4\pi) = q$$

Thus in this case the net outward flux is equal to the isolated charge.

EXERCISES

26. Derive (18.48).

27. Consider an incompressible nonviscous fluid flowing steadily in a pipe of variable cross section as in Fig. 18.29. There are no sinks or sources. For two normal cross sections of areas a_1 and a_2, prove that

$$\frac{v_1}{v_2} = \frac{a_2}{a_1}$$

using the equation of continuity and the divergence theorem. This result is often called the *equation of continuity* in elementary courses. State any additional assumptions which you make.

28. A region has surface a and unit outward normal **N** (see Fig. 18.30). Prove that its volume is

$$\tfrac{1}{3}\int_a \mathbf{R}\cdot\mathbf{N}\, da$$

18.10. THE EQUATIONS OF EULER

In our discussion of hydrostatics, we had the resultant of forces per mass set equal to zero as a condition for equilibrium. In the more general case, this resultant is equal to the acceleration experienced by a particle at the position in question.

(18.50) $$\mathfrak{F} - \frac{1}{\delta}\nabla p = \mathbf{A}$$

The particle whose motion is examined traces out a path

$$\mathbf{R} = \mathbf{R}(t)$$

Its velocity is

$$\mathbf{V} = \mathbf{V}(\mathbf{R},t)$$

where $\mathbf{R}$ satisfies the preceding equation.   The acceleration is

$$\mathbf{A} = \frac{d\mathbf{V}}{dt} = \frac{\partial \mathbf{V}}{\partial s}\frac{ds}{dt} + \frac{\partial \mathbf{V}}{\partial t} = v\frac{\partial \mathbf{V}}{\partial s} + \frac{\partial \mathbf{V}}{\partial t}$$

Note that two types of velocity change are involved:
   1. The change due to variations in the field at each fixed point $\partial \mathbf{V}/\partial t$
   2. The change due to variations in the field along the path, i.e., the directional derivative

$$\frac{\partial \mathbf{V}}{\partial s} = (\mathbf{T} \cdot \nabla)\mathbf{V}$$

Changes of this type were discussed in Sec. 17.8, Example 4.
   Since $v\mathbf{T} = \mathbf{V}$, we have, finally,

(18.51) $$\mathfrak{F} - \frac{1}{\delta}\nabla p = \mathbf{A} = \frac{\partial \mathbf{V}}{\partial t} + (\mathbf{V} \cdot \nabla)\mathbf{V}$$

This is *Euler's equation of motion*.   This is equivalent to the following three scalar equations:

(18.52)
$$f_x - \frac{1}{\delta}\frac{\partial p}{\partial x} = \frac{\partial v_x}{\partial t} + v_x\frac{\partial v_x}{\partial x} + v_y\frac{\partial v_x}{\partial y} + v_z\frac{\partial v_x}{\partial z}$$

$$f_y - \frac{1}{\delta}\frac{\partial p}{\partial y} = \frac{\partial v_y}{\partial t} + v_x\frac{\partial v_y}{\partial x} + v_y\frac{\partial v_y}{\partial y} + v_z\frac{\partial v_y}{\partial z}$$

$$f_z - \frac{1}{\delta}\frac{\partial p}{\partial z} = \frac{\partial v_z}{\partial t} + v_x\frac{\partial v_z}{\partial x} + v_y\frac{\partial v_z}{\partial y} + v_z\frac{\partial v_z}{\partial z}$$

   Bernoulli's Theorem.   We shall consider steady flow of an incompressible fluid subject to gravity.   Several of these limitations have a precise bearing on the use of Euler's equation.

Steady: $$\frac{\partial \mathbf{V}}{\partial t} = \mathbf{O}$$

Incompressible: δ is a constant so that $\dfrac{1}{\delta}\nabla p = \nabla\dfrac{p}{\delta}$

Gravity: $$\mathfrak{F} = -g\mathbf{J} = -\nabla gy$$

Euler's equation now may be written

$$(\mathbf{V} \cdot \nabla)\mathbf{V} + \nabla gy + \nabla\frac{p}{\delta} = \mathbf{O}$$

Recall now that

$$(\mathbf{V} \cdot \nabla)\mathbf{V} = v\frac{d\mathbf{V}}{ds}$$

where ds is in the direction of $\mathbf{V}$; consequently,

$$\mathbf{T} \cdot (\mathbf{V} \cdot \nabla)\mathbf{V} = \mathbf{T} \cdot \left(v\frac{d\mathbf{V}}{ds}\right) = \mathbf{V} \cdot \frac{d\mathbf{V}}{ds} = \frac{1}{2}\frac{d}{ds}(\mathbf{V} \cdot \mathbf{V})$$

Recall also that for a scalar point function φ (such as gy or p/δ),

$$\mathbf{T} \cdot \boldsymbol{\nabla}\varphi = \frac{d\varphi}{ds}$$

(i.e., the directional derivative of φ).

Let us now multiply our modified form of Euler's equation by $\mathbf{T}$. The result

$$\mathbf{T} \cdot (\mathbf{V} \cdot \boldsymbol{\nabla})\mathbf{V} + \mathbf{T} \cdot \boldsymbol{\nabla}gy + \mathbf{T} \cdot \boldsymbol{\nabla}\frac{p}{\delta} = 0$$

means

(18.53) $$\frac{d}{ds}\left(\frac{1}{2}v^2 + gy + \frac{p}{\delta}\right) = 0$$

Therefore

$$\tfrac{1}{2}v^2 + gy + \frac{p}{\delta}$$

is a constant along the curve determined by $\mathbf{T}$, that is, *along a streamline*. For irrotational fields, this constant is independent of the particular streamline.

EXERCISES

29. Gas under pressure (p_1) escapes from a container (see Fig. 18.31) through a small aperture in a steady stream of speed v. At atmospheric pressure (p_0) the density of the gas is δ_0. Assume that temperature is constant throughout, that the weight of the gas is negligible, and that the motion of flow is essentially all in one direction. Find v.

30. What is the velocity of efflux (see Fig. 18.32) of an incompressible ideal fluid from a small opening at the bottom of a very large tank of depth h (*Torricelli's theorem*)?

31. In the *Venturi flowmeter* (see Fig. 18.33) the pressure variation in a constricted pipe is used to measure flux of a liquid. Show that the flux is given by

$$\text{Flux} = a_1\sqrt{\frac{2(p_1 - p_2)}{[(a_1/a_2)^2 - 1]\delta}}.$$

REVIEW EXERCISES

32. An object of mass 0.02 kg and volume 2.0×10^{-6} m³ is submerged at a point having coordinates $(2.00, 0.00, -0.50)$ m. The z axis is vertical upward. The pressure at a

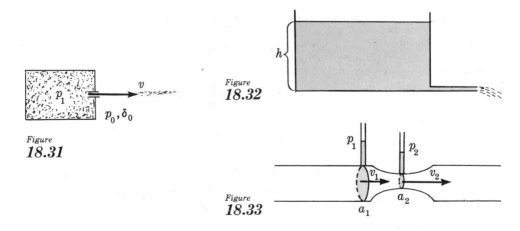

Figure 18.31

Figure 18.32

Figure 18.33

point (x,y,z) is given by

$$p = 10^5(0.5x^2 + 0.5y^2 + 1.00 - 0.11z) \qquad \text{newtons/m}^2$$

Find the x, y, and z components of the acceleration of the particle.

33.   V is a vector function of position given by

$$\mathbf{V} = y\mathbf{I} + (x + z^2)\mathbf{J} + 2yz\mathbf{K}$$

(a) Evaluate the divergence of V at the point $(1, -1, 2)$.
(b) Evaluate the curl of V at the point $(1, -1, 2)$.
(c) Evaluate the directional derivative of V parallel to $0.8\mathbf{I} - 0.6\mathbf{J}$ at $(1, -1, 2)$.
(d) Calculate the circulation of V around the square path $(0,0,0)$ to $(1,0,0)$ to $(1,1,0)$ to $(0,1,0)$ to $(0,0,0)$.

34.   Given the vector function of position $\mathbf{V} = xyz\mathbf{I} + xy\mathbf{J} + z\mathbf{K}$ and the scalar function of position $\varphi = xyz + xy + z$, compute the following:
(a) curl V.   (b) div V.   (c) grad φ.
(d) The directional derivative at $(1,0,-1)$ parallel to $0.33\mathbf{I} - 0.55\mathbf{J} - 0.77\mathbf{K}$ of V.
(e) The directional derivative at $(1,0,-1)$ parallel to $0.33\mathbf{I} - 0.55\mathbf{J} - 0.77\mathbf{K}$ of φ.

35.   The pressure in a rotating liquid is given by the equation

$$p = p_0 + ax^2 - by + cz^2$$

where p_0 is the barometer reading in the laboratory and a, b, c are positive constants.
(a) Derive in IJK form a formula for the gradient of the pressure at a representative point within the fluid.
(b) Show how the preceding result may be used to compute a unit normal vector at a specified point on the free surface of the liquid.

36.   Show that for a constant vector field the rotation vanishes for all axes.   (Use direct approach involving circulation rather than formal approach involving curl.)

37.   Show briefly that any irrotational velocity field can be expressed as the gradient of a scalar *velocity potential*.

38.   Demonstrate that
(a) $\nabla \times (c_1\mathbf{U}_1 + c_2\mathbf{U}_2) = c_1\nabla \times \mathbf{U}_1 + c_2\nabla \times \mathbf{U}_2$
(b) $\nabla \cdot (c_1\mathbf{U}_1 + c_2\mathbf{U}_2) = c_1\nabla \cdot \mathbf{U}_1 + c_2\nabla \cdot \mathbf{U}_2$
where c_1, c_2 are scalar constants and $\mathbf{U}_1$, $\mathbf{U}_2$ vector functions of position.

39. $\mathbf{V}(x,y,z)$ is a vector point function. $f(x,y,z)$ is a scalar point function.   Show that

$$\nabla \cdot (f\mathbf{V}) = f\nabla \cdot \mathbf{V} + \mathbf{V} \cdot \nabla f$$

40.   Show that the velocity potential ψ of an irrotational velocity field V, where $\nabla \cdot \mathbf{V}$ is zero, satisfies the equation

$$\frac{\partial^2 \psi}{\partial x^2} + \frac{\partial^2 \psi}{\partial y^2} + \frac{\partial^2 \psi}{\partial z^2} = 0$$

(This is *Laplace's equation*.)

41.   Show that div curl $\mathbf{V} = 0$ for any V.

42.   Show how $\nabla \cdot$ can be treated as an operator equal to

$$\mathbf{I} \cdot \frac{\partial}{\partial x} + \mathbf{J} \cdot \frac{\partial}{\partial y} + \mathbf{K} \cdot \frac{\partial}{\partial z}$$

43.   Devise and test a formula for the operator $\nabla \times$ analogous to the result of the preceding problem.

44. A vector field $V(R)$ is *solenoidal* if its divergence vanishes. Show that $V = \text{curl } W$ is a solenoidal field for a vector field $W(R)$. In this case W is called a *vector potential* of V. It can be shown that, in general, solenoidal fields have vector potentials.[1]

45. Suppose that $F(R)$ is not conservative but that a new force field $\lambda(R)F(R)$, obtained by multiplying the first force function by a scalar function of position, is conservative. Then show that F must be perpendicular to its curl except at points where $\lambda(R)$ vanishes.

46. Repeat Example 2 of Sec. 18.8, assuming that all molecules move parallel to the xy plane: derive a formula for rate of escape through a slit of width ds parallel to the z axis.

47. Can you give a geometric argument, with figures, to make the result of Exercise 28 appear obvious?

48. Show that for a scalar function of position $\phi(R)$ and a vector function of position $V(R)$ one has the identity

$$(\phi V) \cdot \text{curl } \phi V = \phi^2 V \cdot \text{curl } V$$

49. If $V = qL/4\pi\epsilon_0 r$, where q and ϵ_0 are constants, compute

$$\nabla^2 V = \nabla(\nabla \cdot V)$$

50. Write an expression for $\nabla \times V$ analogous to (18.48). Use this to construct a proof of the *curl theorem*:

$$\int_b \nabla \times V \, db = \int_a N \times V \, da$$

51. Use the curl theorem to determine an alternative characterization of curl analogous to that for gradient in Eq. (18.13).

52. Consider, as in Fig. 18.6, a cylindrical volume of liquid rotating in steady state about a vertical axis.

(a) Use Euler's equation (see Sec. 18.4, Exercise 8) to show that

$$\nabla p = \delta\omega^2 x I - \delta g J + \delta\omega^2 z K$$

(b) Compute $\nabla p \cdot dR = dp$, and integrate, evaluating the constant of integration for the center point on the free surface of the fluid.

(c) What is an equation for the free surface?

[1] See, for instance, C. J. Coe, "Theoretical Mechanics," sec. 106, The Macmillan Company, New York, 1938, or L. Brand, "Vector Analysis," sec. 54, John Wiley & Sons, Inc., New York, 1957.

CHAPTER NINETEEN

ELEMENTARY PROPERTIES
of ELASTICITY

If an ideal rigid body is subjected to forces, its shape and size necessarily remain unchanged. Any actual body behaves differently. A loaded beam bends, and a body under pressure shrinks. When forces are applied, both the size and shape may be altered. The changes bear a direct relation to the forces involved. When the forces are removed, the distortion often disappears. This is called *elastic* behavior. Many materials exhibit this behavior within limits. When the *elastic limit* is reached, shape and size are not restored after the removal of the forces. For elastic behavior a very simple sort of relationship is found experimentally to hold. This important phenomenon was announced in 1676 by Robert Hooke. His conclusion was that *the force is proportional to the stretch*. In this chapter we shall make a preliminary study of elastic behavior. A central feature will be *Hooke's law*: *The stress is proportional to the strain*. The terms *stress* and *strain* will be defined in the following sections. In this very short introduction only the elementary ideas about stress, strain, and moduli are reviewed, and a few applications are developed. In the succeeding chapter a more systematic mathematical treatment of stress and strain is given.

19.1. SIMPLE STRAINS

Strain may be defined as relative distortion. In this section we shall introduce a few simple special cases.

   Stretched Rod. Consider a homogeneous solid cylindrical rod as is shown in Fig. 19.1. Let its original length be l and its original radius be r. When the rod is stretched, l increases by an amount Δl. The *longitudinal strain* in this case is

(19.1)
$$e_l = \frac{\Delta l}{l}$$

The radius is likely to change also. For a stretch Δr is negative; therefore the corresponding *radial strain* e_r is negative.

(19.2)
$$e_r = \frac{\Delta r}{r}$$

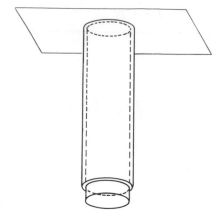

Figure
19.1

The positive ratio of lateral to longitudinal strain (when no external lateral forces are applied), here given by $-e_r/e_l$, is known as *Poisson's ratio*:

(19.3) $$\sigma = -\frac{e_r}{e_l}$$

The value of σ is usually between 0.30 and 0.40. (When lateral forces are applied to keep $e_r = 0$, the strain is called a *simple* extension.)

Let us now see how the volume v of the rod has changed. Assuming, as must be true for elastic behavior of most solids, that the strains are small, we have,

$$v = \pi r^2 l$$
$$\Delta v = 2\pi r l \, \Delta r + \pi r^2 \, \Delta l$$

and hence that the *volume strain* or *cubical dilatation*, as it is called, is

(19.4) $$e_v = \frac{\Delta v}{v} = 2e_r + e_l$$

Using (19.3), this may be written

(19.5) $$e_v = e_l(1 - 2\sigma)$$

Simple Shear. Suppose that a homogeneous cubical block has one pair of opposite faces pushed out of line without changing the planes or areas of another pair of opposite faces. One of these faces is shown in Fig. 19.2. It is distorted into a rhombus. The angle ϕ by which the third pair of opposite faces is tipped is a measure of the *shearing strain*

(19.6) $$e_s = \phi$$

EXERCISES

1. An isotropic rectangular beam has length l, breadth b, and depth h. It is stretched a little longitudinally until the new length is $l + \Delta l$. Poisson's ratio is σ. Find an expression for the fractional decrease in area of cross section.

2. A rod of Poisson's ratio 0.3 is stretched until its length is increased by 0.5 per cent. What is the percentage decrease in density?

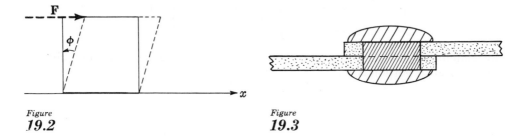

Figure
19.2

Figure
19.3

3. A $\frac{1}{4}$-in. section of a $\frac{1}{2}$-in. rivet (shaded) in Fig. 19.3 is distorted in a shear so that the top face is 0.001 in. out of line with the bottom face.   What is its shearing strain?

4. A thin cylindrical pipe of radius r and length l has one end firmly fastened.   The other end is twisted through an angle θ.   What is the shearing strain?   (HINT: To get a rectangle to work with, imagine the cylinder slit and unrolled.)

19.2. SIMPLE STRESSES

When a body is in a state of strain due to external forces, a pattern of internal forces will result.   The body is thus said to be in a state of stress.   Stress is measured as force per area.   In Fig. 19.4 is shown an element of area Δa with unit normal $\mathbf{N}$. Let the force acting across the area be $\Delta\mathbf{F}$.   That is, if we isolate the part of the body on the $-\mathbf{N}$ side of Δa, we consider the force exerted across Δa by the part of the body on the $+\mathbf{N}$ side of Δa.   The *mean stress* $\bar{\mathbf{S}}$ [or $\bar{\mathbf{S}}(\mathbf{N})$ if we wish to emphasize its dependence on the orientation of the area] across Δa is defined by

$$(19.7) \qquad \bar{\mathbf{S}}(\mathbf{N}) = \bar{\mathbf{S}} = \frac{\Delta\mathbf{F}}{\Delta a}$$

If the angle θ between $\mathbf{N}$ and $\Delta\mathbf{F}$ is zero, the stress is called a *traction*.   If θ is 180°, the stress is called a *pressure*.   If $\theta = 90°$, the stress is called a *shearing stress*.   *Stress at a point in a given direction* may be defined as the limit, as Δa becomes small, of the stress across Δa.

$$(19.8) \qquad \mathbf{S}(\mathbf{N}) = \mathbf{S} = \frac{d\mathbf{F}}{da}$$

One of the simplest kinds of stress is hydrostatic pressure.   The stress at a point in an ideal fluid is always a *uniform pressure*.   This topic was studied in the preceding chapter.   Other simple cases will be considered now.

Simple Traction.   Consider a narrow cylindrical rod being stretched by a force F.   Let us consider the stress across a plane section.   Assuming uniformity, we shall assign a single stress $\mathbf{S}$ to the whole area a.   Neglecting other forces, it is apparent

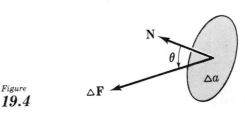

Figure
19.4

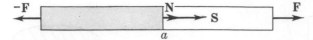

Figure
19.5

for equilibrium that S is parallel to N (in Fig. 19.5). The equation of equilibrium for the shaded portion is

$$Sa - F = O$$

Thus

$$S = \frac{F}{a}$$

To emphasize that stress at a point varies with direction, let us consider the same rod but a different plane of section, tilted at an angle θ, as in Fig. 19.6. The area is now $a \sec \theta$. So the net stress is

$$S_\theta = \frac{F}{a} \cos \theta$$

It is interesting to resolve this stress into tangential (shearing) and normal (tractive) components.

$$s_t = |S_\theta| \sin \theta = \frac{|F|}{a} \sin \theta \cos \theta$$

$$s_n = |S_\theta| \cos \theta = \frac{|F|}{a} \cos^2 \theta$$

Both are zero for $\theta = 90°$. s_t is maximum for $\theta = 45°$; s_n is maximum for $\theta = 0°$.

Simple Shearing Stress. To produce a simple shear (Fig. 19.7), a couple $\{F, -F\}$ is needed. Then to restore equilibrium a countercouple $\{G, -G\}$ is required. If the dimensions of the square block shown in Fig. 19.7 are b, b, h, then for equilibrium

$$f = g$$

This means that the tangential stresses have the same magnitude f/bh. Now let us find the stress across the diagonal plane of dimensions c, h. Isolating the shaded half of the cube, we see that for equilibrium the tangential components of the forces across this plane must add up to

$$f\left(\frac{b}{c}\right) - g\left(\frac{b}{c}\right) = 0$$

The normal components add up to

$$f\left(\frac{b}{c}\right) + g\left(\frac{b}{c}\right) = 2f\left(\frac{b}{c}\right)$$

The corresponding normal stress has magnitude

$$\frac{2f(b/c)}{ch} = 2\frac{f}{bh}\left(\frac{b^2}{c^2}\right)$$

Since $c = \sqrt{2}b$, we have again a stress of magnitude f/bh. Thus *equal tangential stresses on perpendicular surfaces indicate a normal traction of the same magnitude across a set of planes at 45°.*

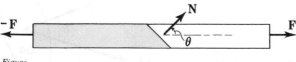

Figure
19.6

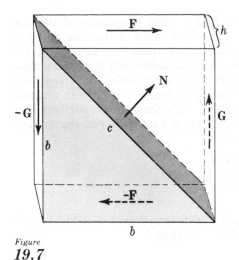

Figure
19.7

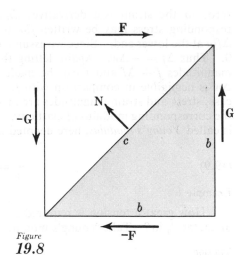

Figure
19.8

Similarly, let us compute the stress across the other diagonal plane, diagramed in cross section in Fig. 19.8. Isolating the shaded half, the tangential force across the plane is clearly zero. The normal force is equal to $-2f(b/c)$, and the stress again has the same magnitude. This shows that *the simple shearing stress with which we started might equally well have been described as the result of a compression of one diagonal and an equal traction along the other.*

EXERCISES

5. A disk of radius r and thickness h centered in the xy plane is subjected to compression forces $-G$ and G at the ends of the x diameter and tensile forces F and $-F$ at the ends of the y diameter. Compute in terms of f, g, r, h, and θ the normal and tangential components of stress for a plane section through the origin making an angle θ with the x axis.

6. A wire 1 mm in diameter holds a load of 150 lb. Find the magnitude and direction of the total stress for a cross section whose normal makes an angle of 30° with the wire. What are the normal and tangential components of this stress?

7. Compute the normal and tangential stress components across the diagonal planes in a rectangular block like that of Fig. 19.7, except that the dimensions are b, d, h ($b \neq d$). Assume that the two couples are in equilibrium.

19.3. THE ELASTIC MODULI

For the primitive situations described in the preceding sections, we can now formulate Hooke's law: Stress is proportional to strain. These simple formulations are sufficient for many important applications.

Young's Modulus. Consider a rod of cross-sectional area a as in Fig. 19.1, and designate points along the unstretched rod by the coordinate y, the origin being taken at the fixed upper end. In particular, let us isolate the slice from y to $y + \Delta y$. After the rod is stretched (or compressed) longitudinally, the bounding planes of the isolated slice have larger or smaller coordinates: $y + \eta(y)$, $y + \Delta y + \eta(y + \Delta y)$. The strain for this slice is $e_t = \eta(y + \Delta y) - \eta(y)/\Delta y$, or more concisely, $\Delta\eta/\Delta y$. To get the longitudinal strain at a point, we can take the limit as Δy approaches zero, so the strain is a derivative: $d\eta/dy$ or $\partial\eta/\partial y$. The magnitude of the corresponding stress may be written f/a at the upper boundary of the slice and $f + \Delta f/a$ at the lower end. Since we assume the rod in equilibrium, $f - \Delta w - f - \Delta f = 0$. Thus $\Delta f = -\Delta w$. Again, letting the slice become sufficiently thin, the tension magnitudes $f + \Delta f$ and f can be made to differ arbitrarily little. In many cases Δw is negligible in comparison with f. According to Hooke's law for this special case, stress and strain magnitudes are proportional. The factor of proportionality is the corresponding modulus of elasticity. For the case of a stretched rod, the modulus is called *Young's modulus*, here denoted by ψ:

$$(19.9) \qquad \frac{f}{a} = \psi\frac{d\eta}{dy}$$

Example I

How great a tension is required to stretch a 10-ft-long round steel rod $\frac{1}{2}$ in. in diameter $\frac{1}{16}$ in? Take Young's modulus as 3.0×10^7 lb/in.²

Solution

In this case the strain, $d\eta/dy$, is merely $\Delta l/l$ as in Sec. 19.1: $\Delta l/l = 1/16 \times 120 = 5.2 \times 10^{-4}$. The area $a = 0.197$ in.² Thus

$$f = 0.197 \times 3.0 \times 10^7 \times 5.2 \times 10^{-4} = 3.1 \times 10^3 \text{ lb}$$

Bulk Modulus. Suppose that a cubical sample of material (solid, liquid, or gas) is subjected to a uniform increment of pressure Δp over its whole boundary. The change in volume is negative, so the volume strain also is negative. The bulk modulus β is defined by the following stress-strain proportionality:

$$(19.10) \qquad \Delta p = -\beta\frac{\Delta v}{v}$$

Taking a limit as Δv approaches zero, we get as a defining equation

$$(19.11) \qquad \beta = -v\frac{dp}{dv}$$

In some instances the thermal conditions under which the compression is carried out become important. Unless otherwise stated, temperature will be assumed constant.

Example 2

For an ideal gas at constant temperature Boyle's law is applicable: $pv = $ const. Differentiating relative to v,

$$p + v\frac{dp}{dv} = 0$$

Hence one has the usual but startling result

$$\beta = p$$

Modulus of Shear. For the simple shear illustrated in Fig. 19.2 the stress-strain proportionality may be written

$$(19.12) \qquad s = \frac{f}{a} = \mu\phi$$

This equation serves to define the modulus of shear μ.   The stress magnitude is the quotient of the shearing-force magnitude $f = |\mathbf{F}|$ divided by the area of the upper face of the cubical block.   If the altitude of the block is h, we may write

$$\frac{f}{a} = \frac{fh}{ah}$$

so the shearing stress is a torque divided by volume: γ/v.   An important illustration of the shear modulus appears in the next section.

19.4. TWISTED RODS

The modulus of shear was defined in terms of a cubical element.   The same formula, Eq. (19.12), can be used for any rectangular sample undergoing a simple shear as in Fig. 19.9, since it could be cut up into a large number of small cubical elements undergoing the same strain and stress.   In spite of this possibility, the range of usefulness of this particular modulus may still seem limited.   It can be used effectively, however, in dealing with a most important example of a deformed body, the twisted rod.   The theory of this example will be outlined briefly.

Suppose that a uniform cylindrical body of length l and radius a, as is shown in Fig. 19.10, has one end anchored and that a torque γ is applied at the other end. An angular displacement θ at that end will result.   From the dimensions of the rod, together with γ and θ, the modulus of shear may be determined.   Let us conceive of the cylinder as being made up of numerous coaxial cylindrical shells, a typical one having radius r and thickness dr.   If such a shell were slit down one side and unrolled, a rectangular sheet would result.   When twisted, assuming that a simple shear takes place, it would be deformed into a parallelogram similar to Fig. 19.9.   From the geometry of this shell it is apparent that

$$\phi = \frac{\theta r}{l}$$

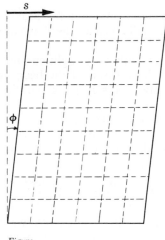

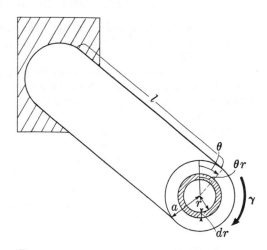

Figure
19.9

Figure
19.10

From (19.12) the corresponding shearing stress is

$$s = \frac{\mu\theta r}{l}$$

Since the rod and the deformation are uniform, this stress consists of tangential forces adding up to df distributed over the area $2\pi r\,dr$ of the end of the shell.

$$s = \frac{df}{2\pi r\,dr}$$

The torque associated with this df is

$$d\gamma = r\,df = 2\pi s r^2\,dr = \frac{2\pi\mu\theta}{l} r^3\,dr$$

Thus we have, adding the necessary torques over all the shells from $r = 0$ to $r = a$,

$$\gamma = \int_0^a d\gamma = \frac{2\pi\mu\theta}{l}\int_0^a r^3\,dr$$

or

(19.13)
$$\gamma = \frac{\pi\mu\theta a^4}{2l}$$

EXERCISES

8. Derive a formula for the ratio γ/θ for a hollow cylindrical rod having inner and outer radii a' and a. Let the length and shear modulus be l and μ.
9. A uniform rod 1 m long has one end fixed. A torque of 0.01 newton-m suffices to turn the other end through 60°. If the radius is 0.2 cm, what is the modulus of shear?
10. A uniform disk of radius r and mass m fastened at the end of a uniform wire of radius a and length l operates as a torsion pendulum of period τ. Find a formula for the modulus of shear.
11. A hollow steel rod has an outer diameter of 2 in. and an inner diameter of $1\frac{7}{8}$ in. What would be the diameter of a solid steel rod having the same torsional stiffness? Compute the ratio γ/θ for such a rod 8 ft long if the modulus of shear for the steel is 11.5×10^6 lb/in.^{2}

19.5. DEFLECTIONS OF BEAMS

In Sec. 11.4 we evaluated shearing force and bending moment for beams having various loads. As a final exercise in elasticity, we shall consider the shape of a beam under such loads.

We assume that the beam, initially straight, has only very slight curvature even when deflected by a load. And we assume that the stiffness of the beam is solely dependent on stretching and compressing of elastic fibers running parallel to the beam itself.

If Fig. 19.11 represents a beam bent under its own weight, then a plane intermediate layer called the *neutral layer* (shown in cross section by the dotted line) is assumed to retain its initial length. Layers above this are compressed; those below are stretched. The stresses associated with these strains are the source of bending moments. To see this quantitatively, let us look at a segment of length Δx in the unstrained beam. It is bounded by planes normal to the beam, both before and after we assume the distortion. Initially, then, it is a rectangular box, but after strain it becomes slightly wedge-shaped. The nature of this distortion is shown in Fig. 19.12, where the neutral layer and the original size of the section are shown by the dotted lines. Since we are isolating the segment of length Δx, let us consider the

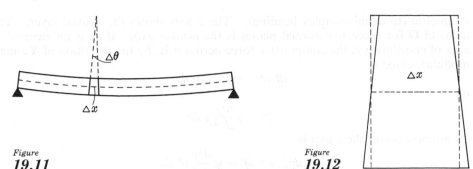

Figure
19.11

Figure
19.12

distortion relative to its left plane of section as in Fig. 19.13. Originally, the other plane was parallel. Now it is tilted by an angle $\Delta\theta$. Calling $-\Delta\xi$ the contraction of fibers in the layer of coordinate y, we can express $\Delta\theta$ as

$$\Delta\theta = \frac{-\Delta\xi}{y}$$

or since the neutral layer is normal to the plane of section, its change in slope (and hence in angle for such small angles) is

$$\Delta\left(\frac{dy}{dx}\right) = \Delta\theta = \frac{-\Delta\xi}{y}$$

But $\Delta\xi/\Delta x$ represents the longitudinal strain for fibers at a distance y from the neutral layer; therefore

$$\text{Strain} = \frac{-y\Delta(dy/dx)}{\Delta x}$$

In the limit, for smaller and smaller Δx,

$$\text{Strain} = -y\frac{d^2y}{dx^2}$$

Now let us consider a cross section of the beam (see Fig. 19.14). It is assumed

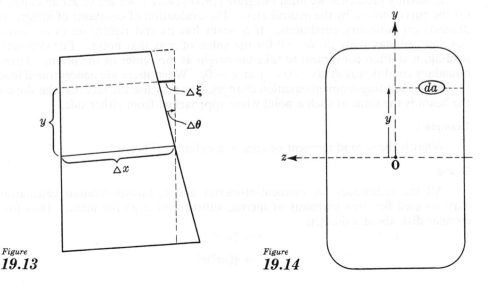

Figure
19.13

Figure
19.14

symmetric (to avoid complex bending).   The z axis shows the neutral layer.   The locus of **O** for successive normal planes is the *neutral axis*.   If da is an element of area of coordinate y, the compressive force across it is, by the definition of Young's modulus, equal to

$$df = -\psi(\text{strain}) \, da$$

or

$$df = \psi \frac{d^2y}{dx^2} y \, da$$

Its moment about the z axis is

$$d\gamma_b = y \, df = \psi \frac{d^2y}{dx^2} y^2 \, da$$

The total moment may be found by summing over the whole area:

(19.14)
$$\gamma_b = \int_a y \, df = \psi \frac{d^2y}{dx^2} \int_a y^2 \, da$$

Since the quantity $\int_a y^2 \, da$ bears much resemblance to the defining expression for *moment of inertia*, the same term is often used in this context, especially by engineers. Here we shall call it *second moment of area*, but to emphasize the similarity we shall denote it by i'.

(19.15)
$$i' = \int_a y^2 \, da$$

We shall deal with symmetric beams under no tension or compression, for which it is safe to take the neutral layer as a central one.   Equation (19.14) may now be written

(19.16)
$$\gamma_b = \psi i' \frac{d^2y}{dx^2}$$

This is an equation that must be obeyed by the neutral axis of a symmetric beam, if our assumptions about its elastic behavior are justified.   It is called the *differential equation for the bending of beams*.

In solving problems, we must integrate (19.16) twice if we are to get an equation for the curve formed by the neutral axis.   The evaluation of constants of integration depends on boundary conditions.   If a beam has its end rigidly set in horizontal position, we may write $dy/dx = 0$ for the value of x at that point.   For symmetric loading, it is often convenient to take the origin at the center of the beam.   Then a boundary condition is $dy/dx = 0 = y$ at $x = 0$.   When there are concentrated loads so that the bending-moment equation changes, one may use the fact that the slope of the beam is the same at such a point when approached from either side.

Example I

What is the second moment of area of a cylindrical beam?

Solution

All the techniques for moment-of-inertia and radius-of-gyration calculations may be used for area moments of inertia, substituting area for mass.   Thus for a circular disk about a diameter,

$$i = \tfrac{1}{4}mr^2$$

$$i' = \tfrac{1}{4}(\pi r^2)r^2$$

Example 2

Find an equation for a uniform beam of weight w and length l supported at its ends.

Solution

Since symmetry is assured, let us take origin at the center. Then isolating the beam at the left of x (see Fig. 19.15), we have for a moment equation of equilibrium

$$-\frac{w}{2}\left(x+\frac{l}{2}\right)+\left[\frac{x+(l/2)}{l}\right]w\left[\frac{x+(l/2)}{2}\right]+\gamma_b=0$$

or

$$\gamma_b=\frac{wl}{8}-\frac{wx^2}{2l}$$

Now using (19.16),

$$\frac{wl}{8}-\frac{wx^2}{2l}=\psi i'\frac{d^2y}{dx^2}$$

Integrating,

$$\frac{wlx}{8}-\frac{wx^3}{6l}+c=\psi i'\frac{dy}{dx}$$

Since the slope is zero at the center, $c=0$. Integrating again,

$$\frac{wlx^2}{16}-\frac{wx^4}{24l}+c'=\psi i'y$$

Since the origin is at the center, $c'=0$. To find the deflection at the center due to the bending, we merely evaluate y for $x=l/2$:

$$\psi i'y=\frac{wl(l/2)^2}{16}-\frac{w(l/2)^4}{24l}=\frac{5wl^3}{384}$$

EXERCISES

12. A uniform rectangular beam of length l, breadth b, and depth d rests horizontally on simple supports at its ends. A load w, large in comparison with the weight of the beam, is placed at its center. Find a formula for the deflection at the center.
13. A wood cylinder 20 ft long and 4 in. in diameter rests horizontally on supports at its ends. If the specific gravity is 0.6 and Young's modulus (longitudinally) is 1.5×10^6 lb/in.[2], find how much it will sag under its own weight.
14. A uniform beam is free at one end, but the other is set horizontally in concrete. Find an equation for its shape as it bends under its own weight.
15. A beam of length l is free at one end, but the other is set horizontally in concrete. Find an equation for its shape as it bends under a concentrated heavy load w at its free end.
16. Rewrite Eq. (19.13) in terms of the second moment of area i'. Do the same for your result for Sec. 19.4, Exercise 8.

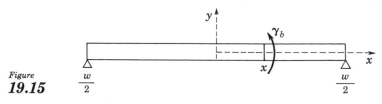

Figure
19.15

REVIEW EXERCISES

17. A copper wire has diameter 2 mm, length 1 m, Young's modulus 1.2×10^{11} newtons/m², and Poisson's ratio 0.4. If it holds a load of 80 newtons, how much is its length increased? How much is its diameter diminished? (State answer as percentages.)

18. A uniform rod hangs vertically from one end. Show that under its own weight it stretches an amount equal to $\delta g l^2 / 2\psi$. δ is density, g acceleration of gravity, l the length, and ψ Young's modulus.

19. A uniform metal rod of length l, area of cross section a, and Young's modulus ψ is rigidly clamped at both ends. The center of the rod is forcibly moved a distance ϵ toward one end, compressing one half and stretching the other. Find a formula for the work done.

20. Change in length due to temperature change is studied by means of a coefficient of linear expansion defined as the ratio of extension to increase in temperature.

    A weight of 40 lb is hung on a wire 0.040 in. in diameter, 20 ft long, with Young's modulus 2.8×10^7 lb/in.² and linear coefficient of 6.2×10^{-6} per degree Fahrenheit. If the temperature falls 100°F after the weight is hung, what is the net change in length?

21. A cylinder of diameter 2 in. and length 10 in. is held rigidly in place so that its length is constant. There is no stress at 80°F. What pull is exerted at 40°F? Use the constants of the preceding exercise.

22. A cylindrical wooden rod 1 cm in radius and 1 m long rests in horizontal position on supports at its ends. A 2-kg object is suspended from the beam's center. Neglecting the weight of the beam itself, compute the amount by which the center of the beam is deflected by this load. Young's modulus for the wood is 1.40×10^{10} newtons/m².

23. A 5-m vertical pole in the form of a cylindrical shell of diameter 10 cm has its base set in concrete, so that it may be regarded as fixed in a vertical direction. How large a horizontal force at the top of the pole will cause a displacement of 5.0 cm? Take Young's modulus as 1.9×10^{11} newtons/m².

24. Derive a formula for the derivative relative to length of the density of a stretched rod.

CHAPTER TWENTY

VECTOR TREATMENT of STRESS and STRAIN

In the preceding chapter we saw that small distortions of deformable bodies are, at least in special cases, closely related to the forces which produce the distortions. We now proceed to use our knowledge of vector fields to describe more general small distortions. In a number of situations the main relationships will be summarized in terms of matrices. This does not mean that a prior knowledge of matrix theory is needed for the reading of this chapter. If you do know something about matrices, you will presumably appreciate the concise formulation which results from their use. If you previously have encountered tensors, dyadics, or linear vector functions, you will easily translate the matrix equations into a more adequate language. If you have no knowledge of these mathematical topics, you may either ignore the matrix summaries or else study Appendix 4, which provides a brief introduction to the language of matrices.

20.1. SMALL DISTORTIONS OF A DEFORMABLE BODY

If a body is subject to forces in equilibrium, the distortion which ensues can usually be described in terms of a small displacement for each point. In the distortions which we shall ordinarily consider (linear or homogeneous strains), straight-line segments will be straight-line segments after distortion. Thus we shall be interested in the way in which a line segment alters its direction or length. We shall assume, in any case, that the distortions are smooth, so that derivatives will exist and be continuous.

As usual, let $\mathbf{R}$ denote the position vector of an arbitrary point, and let $\mathbf{H}$ be its displacement under the distortion. Then $\mathbf{H} = \mathbf{H}(\mathbf{R})$ is a vector function of position and $\mathbf{R}' = \mathbf{R} + \mathbf{H}$ is a related vector function of position. Let us concentrate for the moment on the directed segment from $\mathbf{R}$ to $\mathbf{R} + \Delta\mathbf{R}$. In Fig. 20.1, $\Delta\mathbf{R}$ is the original directed segment. The displacement of the initial end is $\mathbf{H}$, and that of the terminal end is $\mathbf{H} + \Delta\mathbf{H}$. The altered directed segment is $\Delta\mathbf{R}'$. From the diagram we may write

$$\Delta\mathbf{R}' = -\mathbf{H} + \Delta\mathbf{R} + \mathbf{H} + \Delta\mathbf{H} = \Delta\mathbf{R} + \Delta\mathbf{H}$$

Since the distortion is small, $|\Delta\mathbf{H}|$ is much smaller than Δs, Δs being the length of $\Delta\mathbf{R}$. We shall write $\Delta\mathbf{R} = \Delta s\mathbf{T}$, where $\mathbf{T}$ is a unit vector.

Starting with the defining equation for $\mathbf{R}'$,

(20.1)
$$\mathbf{R}' = \mathbf{R} + \mathbf{H}$$

for any direction $\mathbf{T}$ and corresponding coordinate s, we have for directional derivatives in the $\mathbf{T}$ direction

$$\frac{d\mathbf{R}'}{ds} = \frac{d\mathbf{R}}{ds} + \frac{d\mathbf{H}}{ds}$$

or since $d\mathbf{R}/ds = \mathbf{T}$, let us write $\mathbf{T}'$ for $d\mathbf{R}'/ds$,

(20.2)
$$\mathbf{T}' = \mathbf{T} + \frac{d\mathbf{H}}{ds}$$

where, in general, $\mathbf{T}'$ is not exactly a unit vector.

Now by analogy with the elementary definition of longitudinal strain,

$$e_l = \frac{\Delta l}{l} = \frac{1}{2}\frac{\Delta(l^2)}{l^2}$$

let us define for any pair of directions given by unit vectors $\mathbf{T}_1$ and $\mathbf{T}_2$ a bidirectional strain by the following equation:

(20.3)
$$e_{T_1 T_2} = \tfrac{1}{2}\Delta(\mathbf{T}_1 \cdot \mathbf{T}_2) = \tfrac{1}{2}(\mathbf{T}_1' \cdot \mathbf{T}_2' - \mathbf{T}_1 \cdot \mathbf{T}_2)$$

A formal development will be followed by interpretations. Recall that for a rigid body we used the fact that scalar products of relative position vectors were invariant under possible motions. Hence it is particularly interesting that a change in scalar product should be a useful measure of distortion. Note that

(20.4)
$$e_{T_2 T_1} = e_{T_1 T_2}$$

Substituting in Eq. (20.3) the expressions for $\mathbf{T}_1'$ and $\mathbf{T}_2'$ given by Eq. (20.2), if we neglect higher powers of $d\mathbf{H}/ds$ (in accordance with our assumption that $|\Delta\mathbf{H}|$ is much smaller than Δs), we get

(20.5)
$$e_{T_1 T_2} = \frac{1}{2}\left(\mathbf{T}_1 \cdot \frac{d\mathbf{H}}{ds_2} + \mathbf{T}_2 \cdot \frac{d\mathbf{H}}{ds_1}\right) = e_{T_2 T_1}$$

In the next section we shall consider useful special cases of Eq. (20.5). First note that for $\mathbf{T}_1 = \mathbf{T}_2 = \mathbf{T}$, one has, writing e_T for e_{TT},

(20.6)
$$e_T = \mathbf{T} \cdot \frac{d\mathbf{H}}{ds}$$

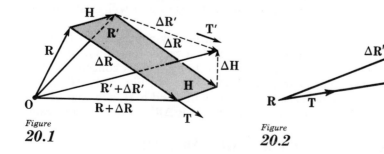

Figure
20.1

Figure
20.2

To see the nature of e_T, let us use the substitution $\Delta H/\Delta s = dH/ds$. This substitution is valid as an approximation even if the distortion is not linear (sending straight lines into straight lines). Then we may write

$$e_T = \frac{\mathbf{T} \cdot \Delta \mathbf{H}}{\Delta s} = \frac{\Delta l}{l}$$

The numerator is the component of the displacement $\Delta \mathbf{H}$ in the $\mathbf{T}$ direction (cf. Fig. 20.2), so e_T is the longitudinal strain in the $\mathbf{T}$ direction.

EXERCISES

1. Suppose that we consider, instead of a deformation, a rigid rotation through a *small* angle θ about the z axis.
   (a) Evaluate in IJK form the directional derivative dH/ds in the direction of a unit vector $\mathbf{T}_1 = l_1\mathbf{I} + m_1\mathbf{J} + n_1\mathbf{K}$.
   (b) Use the result of part (a) to evaluate e_T.
   (c) Similarly, evaluate $e_{T_1 T_2}$, where $\mathbf{T}_2 = l_2\mathbf{I} + m_2\mathbf{J} + n_2\mathbf{K}$.
2. Evaluate e_T and $e_{T_1 T_2}$ (cf. Exercise 1) for a small transformation given by $\mathbf{H} = \epsilon x\mathbf{I} + \epsilon' y\mathbf{J}$ for small scalar constants ϵ and ϵ'.
3. If the unit vectors $\mathbf{T}_1$ and $\mathbf{T}_2$ are initially at right angles, show that after distortion the cosine of their angle $(\mathbf{T}_1', \mathbf{T}_2')$ is given by

$$\cos (\mathbf{T}_1', \mathbf{T}_2') = \frac{2e_{T_1 T_2}}{(1 + e_{T_1})(1 + e_{T_2})}$$

20.2. COEFFICIENTS OF EXTENSION AND SHEAR

For a particular choice of coordinate axes, the values of e_T and $e_{T_1 T_2}$ associated with the unit vectors $\mathbf{I}, \mathbf{J}, \mathbf{K}$ are given special symbols: $e_I = e_{xx}$, $e_{IJ} = e_{xy}$, etc. These special quantities may be evaluated by suitable application of Eq. (20.5) or Eq. (20.6). The quantities e_{xx}, e_{yy}, e_{zz} are called *coefficients of extension*, while e_{xy}, e_{yz}, and e_{zx} are *coefficients of shear*. If we write $\mathbf{H}$ in IJK form as $\xi\mathbf{I} + \eta\mathbf{J} + \zeta\mathbf{K}$, we get, using for each directional derivative dH/ds the proper formula $(\mathbf{T} \cdot \nabla)\mathbf{H}$,

(20.7)
$$e_{xx} = e_{II} = \mathbf{I} \cdot \frac{\partial \mathbf{H}}{\partial x} = \mathbf{I} \cdot (\mathbf{I} \cdot \nabla)\mathbf{H} = \frac{\partial \xi}{\partial x}$$

and similarly,

$$e_{yy} = \frac{\partial \eta}{\partial y} \qquad e_{zz} = \frac{\partial \zeta}{\partial z}$$

Also

(20.8)
$$e_{xy} = e_{IJ} = \frac{1}{2}\left(\mathbf{I} \cdot \frac{\partial \mathbf{H}}{\partial y} + \mathbf{J} \cdot \frac{\partial \mathbf{H}}{\partial x}\right) = e_{JI} = e_{yx}$$

$$= \frac{1}{2}[\mathbf{I} \cdot (\mathbf{J} \cdot \nabla)\mathbf{H} + \mathbf{J} \cdot (\mathbf{I} \cdot \nabla)\mathbf{H}]$$

$$= \frac{1}{2}\left(\frac{\partial \xi}{\partial y} + \frac{\partial \eta}{\partial x}\right)$$

and similarly,

$$e_{yz} = \frac{1}{2}\left(\frac{\partial \eta}{\partial z} + \frac{\partial \zeta}{\partial y}\right) \qquad e_{zx} = \frac{1}{2}\left(\frac{\partial \zeta}{\partial x} + \frac{\partial \xi}{\partial z}\right)$$

The general bidirectional strain of Eq. (20.3) can, for any particular choice of coordinate axes, be expressed in an orderly fashion in terms of the coefficients of extension and shear.   If we write $T_1 = l_1 I + m_1 J + n_1 K$ and $T_2 = l_2 I + m_2 J + n_2 K$, then Eq. (20.3) may be expanded to yield

(20.9) $e_{T_1 T_2} = l_1 l_2 e_{xx} + m_1 m_2 e_{yy} + n_1 n_2 e_{zz} + (l_1 m_2 + l_2 m_1) e_{xy}$
$$+ (m_1 n_2 + m_2 n_1) e_{yz} + (n_1 l_2 + n_2 l_1) e_{zx}$$

If, for a given choice of axes, we let E stand for the strain matrix,

(20.10)
$$E = \begin{bmatrix} e_{xx} & e_{xy} & e_{zx} \\ e_{xy} & e_{yy} & e_{yz} \\ e_{zx} & e_{yz} & e_{zz} \end{bmatrix}$$

then Eq. (20.9) may be expressed succinctly:

$$e_{T_1 T_2} = [l_1 m_1 n_1] \begin{bmatrix} e_{xx} & e_{xy} & e_{zx} \\ e_{xy} & e_{yy} & e_{yz} \\ e_{zx} & e_{yz} & e_{zz} \end{bmatrix} \begin{bmatrix} l_2 \\ m_2 \\ n_2 \end{bmatrix}$$

or

(20.11)
$$e_{T_1 T_2} = T_1^t E T_2$$

(See Appendix 4, Sec. A4.4, for matrix nomenclature.)   Similarly, the expanded form of e_T is

(20.12) $e_T = l^2 e_{xx} + m^2 e_{yy} + n^2 e_{zz} + 2lm e_{xy} + 2mn e_{yz} + 2nl e_{zx}$

or in matrix form,

(20.13)
$$e_T = T^t E T$$

Equations (20.12) and (20.13) are analogous to (15.18) for moments of inertia and lead to the theory of a strain ellipsoid analogous to the ellipsoid of inertia.

Applications.   We have seen how the coefficients of extension and of shear may be used in calculations of an extension in any direction.   If we combine (20.9) and (20.12) with the result of Exercise 3, we can calculate angular distortions.   In particular, the coefficients of shear may, for a given set of coordinate axes, be interpreted approximately by the following equations:

(20.14)
$$e_{xy} = 0.5 \cos (I', J')$$
$$e_{yz} = 0.5 \cos (J', K')$$
$$e_{zx} = 0.5 \cos (K', I')$$

Finally, let us see what happens to the volume of a small cubical figure when it experiences a small strain.   Let the cube be aligned with the axes, its dimensions being Δx, Δy, Δz.   Then the volume $v = \Delta x\, \Delta y\, \Delta z$.   After deformation, the edges are

$$\Delta x (1 + e_{xx}) \qquad \Delta y (1 + e_{yy}) \qquad \Delta z (1 + e_{zz})$$

and the volume is approximately

$$v' = \Delta x\, \Delta y\, \Delta z (1 + e_{xx})(1 + e_{yy})(1 + e_{zz})$$

Multiplying out and discarding higher powers in the e's, we have for the cubical dilatation

(20.15)
$$e_v = \frac{v' - v}{v} = e_{xx} + e_{yy} + e_{zz}$$

We have seen, then, how three main aspects of strain (changes in length, angle, and volume) are expressible in terms of the six elementary coefficients of extension and shear.

Significance of the Coefficients. Since e_{xx}, e_{yy}, e_{zz} were defined as extensions in the coordinate directions, their significance in terms of simple strains is obvious. Each is a measure of stretch (either positive or negative) in these directions. The relationship of coefficients of shear to simple shear may be less apparent. Consider a linear strain in which all displacement is parallel to the xy plane, the origin being kept fixed. Suppose that the square **OABC** (see Fig. 20.3) is deformed into the rhombus **OA'B'C'**. This is an example of what is called a *pure shear*. In terms of our previous terminology, referring to Fig. 20.3 (somewhat idealized to clarify the example),

$$|\mathbf{OA}| = \Delta x \qquad |\mathbf{AA'}| = \Delta \eta \qquad |\mathbf{OC}| = \Delta y \qquad |\mathbf{CC'}| = \Delta \xi$$

Hence, for small strains, we have

$$\alpha = \tan \alpha = \frac{\Delta \eta}{\Delta x} = \frac{\partial \eta}{\partial x}$$

$$\alpha' = \tan \alpha' = \frac{\Delta \xi}{\Delta y} = \frac{\partial \xi}{\partial y}$$

(The last equality in each case follows since straight lines are deformed into straight lines.) Now how are α and α' related to ϕ of Fig. 19.2? Since the whole body may be rotated through an angle $-\alpha$ without further distortion, it is apparent that

$$(20.16) \qquad e_s = \phi = \alpha + \alpha' = \frac{\partial \eta}{\partial x} + \frac{\partial \xi}{\partial y} = 2e_{xy}$$

Thus we see that the three coefficients of shear are measures of shearing strains associated with the three coordinate planes.

Pure Shear and Coefficients of Extension. If an x extension and a y compression are combined, a square figure with the x and y axes as diagonals is distorted into a rhombus as shown in Fig. 20.4. This, too, will be a *pure shear*, provided that the

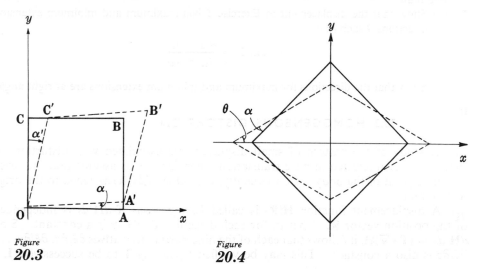

Figure
20.3

Figure
20.4

area does not change.   This requires

$$(1 + e_{xx})(1 + e_{yy}) = 1$$

or

$$e_{xx} = -e_{yy}$$

The angle α is determined by

$$\tan \alpha = \tan (45° - \theta)$$

Thus

$$\tan \alpha = \tan (45° - \theta) = \frac{1 - \tan \theta}{1 + \tan \theta}$$

or

$$\alpha = \frac{1 - (1 - e_{xx})/(1 + e_{xx})}{1 + (1 - e_{xx})/(1 + e_{xx})} = e_{xx}$$

Thus

(20.17) $$\alpha = e_{xx} = -e_{yy}$$

EXERCISES

4. Compute the six coefficients of extension and shear for **H** as given in Exercise 1.
5. A small displacement parallel to the xy plane carries each point (x,y) into a point (x',y') given by

$$x' = a_{11}x + a_{12}y$$

$$y' = a_{21}x + a_{22}y$$

Evaluate the six coefficients of extension and shear for this displacement in terms of the four coefficients a_{ij}.
6. A small displacement parallel to the xy plane carries each point (x,y) into a point (x',y') given by

$$x' = 1.005x - 0.002y$$

$$y' = 0.006x + 0.995y$$

For what directions $\mathbf{T} = 1/\theta$ is the extension maximum?   For what directions is it minimum?
7. (*a*) Show that the displacement in Exercise 5 has maximum and minimum extensions for directions θ such that

$$\tan 2\theta = \frac{a_{12} + a_{21}}{a_{11} - a_{22}}$$

(*b*) Show that the directions for maximum and minimum extensions are at right angles.

20.3. HOMOGENEOUS DISTORTION

In our study of the pattern of small displacements associated with distortion, we surely are not interested in pure translation; therefore let us assume that the origin is a fixed point of the body.   Consequently, the value of $\mathbf{H}(\mathbf{R})$ assigned to the origin will be null.

A displacement function $\mathbf{H}(\mathbf{R})$ is called *homogeneous* if $d\mathbf{H}/ds$ is independent of the position vector $\mathbf{R}$.   That is, for each direction $\mathbf{T}$, $d\mathbf{H}/ds$ is a constant.   Since $d\mathbf{H}/ds = (\mathbf{T} \cdot \nabla)\mathbf{H}$, it follows that each of the nine partial derivatives $\partial \xi/\partial x, \partial \xi/\partial y, \ldots,$ $\partial \zeta/\partial z$ is also a constant.   This may be verified by taking $\mathbf{T}$ to be successively $\mathbf{I}$, $\mathbf{J}$, and **K**. The implication of all this is that **H** is a *linear* function of **R**.

(20.18)
$$\xi = a_{11}x + a_{12}y + a_{13}z$$
$$\eta = a_{21}x + a_{22}y + a_{23}z$$
$$\zeta = a_{31}x + a_{32}y + a_{33}z$$

where the a_{ij}'s are scalar constants. In matrix form this would be written more conveniently as

$$\begin{bmatrix} \xi \\ \eta \\ \zeta \end{bmatrix} = \begin{bmatrix} a_{11} & a_{12} & a_{13} \\ a_{21} & a_{22} & a_{23} \\ a_{31} & a_{32} & a_{33} \end{bmatrix} \begin{bmatrix} x \\ y \\ z \end{bmatrix}$$

or

$$H = AR$$

The corresponding statement about **R′** is given by

(20.19)
$$x' = x + \xi = (1 + a_{11})x + a_{12}y + a_{13}z$$
$$y' = y + \eta = a_{21}x + (1 + a_{22})y + a_{23}z$$
$$z' = z + \zeta = a_{31}x + a_{32}y + (1 + a_{33})z$$

In matrix form this becomes

$$\begin{bmatrix} x' \\ y' \\ z' \end{bmatrix} = \begin{bmatrix} x \\ y \\ z \end{bmatrix} + \begin{bmatrix} \xi \\ \eta \\ \zeta \end{bmatrix} = \begin{bmatrix} 1 & 0 & 0 \\ 0 & 1 & 0 \\ 0 & 0 & 1 \end{bmatrix} \begin{bmatrix} x \\ y \\ z \end{bmatrix} + \begin{bmatrix} a_{11} & a_{12} & a_{13} \\ a_{21} & a_{22} & a_{23} \\ a_{31} & a_{32} & a_{33} \end{bmatrix} \begin{bmatrix} x \\ y \\ z \end{bmatrix}$$

or

(20.20)
$$R' = R + H = (I + A)R$$

Note that any plane of equation $a'x' + b'y' + c'z' + d' = 0$ in the deformed space is the image of

$$a'[(1 + a_{11})x + a_{12}y + a_{13}z] + b'[a_{21}x + (1 + a_{22})y + a_{23}z]$$
$$+ c'[a_{31}x + a_{32}y + (1 + a_{33})z] + d' = 0$$

i.e., of the plane

$$(a' + a'a_{11} + b'a_{21} + c'a_{31})x + (a'a_{12} + b' + b'a_{22} + c'a_{32})y$$
$$+ (a'a_{13} + b'a_{23} + c' + c'a_{33})z + d' = 0$$

Consequently, homogeneous (i.e., linear) displacements send planes into planes and straight lines into straight lines.

If we deal with a small distortion which is not strictly homogeneous, we still may use the same linear machinery for points sufficiently near any reference point. Using the approximation

(20.21)
$$\mathbf{H} = \left(\frac{d\mathbf{H}}{dr}\right) r = (\mathbf{R} \cdot \nabla)\mathbf{H}$$

we may replace the constants a_{ij} thus: $a_{11} = \partial\xi/\partial x$, $a_{12} = \partial\xi/\partial y$, ..., $a_{33} = \partial\zeta/\partial z$. Then

(20.22)
$$A = \begin{bmatrix} \dfrac{\partial\xi}{\partial x} & \dfrac{\partial\xi}{\partial y} & \dfrac{\partial\xi}{\partial z} \\[2mm] \dfrac{\partial\eta}{\partial x} & \dfrac{\partial\eta}{\partial y} & \dfrac{\partial\eta}{\partial z} \\[2mm] \dfrac{\partial\zeta}{\partial x} & \dfrac{\partial\zeta}{\partial y} & \dfrac{\partial\zeta}{\partial z} \end{bmatrix}$$

Note that for the displacement described in (20.19), we have

$$(20.23) \qquad e_{xx} = \frac{\partial \xi}{\partial x} = a_{11} \qquad e_{xy} = \frac{1}{2}\left(\frac{\partial \xi}{\partial y} + \frac{\partial \eta}{\partial x}\right) = \tfrac{1}{2}(a_{12} + a_{21}), \dots$$

The matrix in (20.22) is the *Jacobian matrix* of the displacement function $\mathbf{H}(\mathbf{R})$.

EXERCISES

8. Show that deformation equations for a *simple homogeneous extension* in the x direction may be written

$$x' = x(1 + e)$$
$$y' = y$$
$$z' = z$$

where e is the longitudinal strain. Write corresponding equations for ξ, η, ζ.

9. Show that deformation equations for a *uniform dilation* may be written

$$x' = x(1 + e)$$
$$y' = y(1 + e)$$
$$z' = z(1 + e)$$

where e is the longitudinal strain in each of the coordinate directions. Write corresponding equations for ξ, η, ζ.

10. Show that deformation equations for a *simple shear* such as is shown in Fig. 19.2 may be written

$$x' = x + ey$$
$$y' = y$$
$$z' = z$$

where e is equal to the angle ϕ which measures the strain. Write corresponding equations for ξ, η, ζ.

11. Show that deformation equations for a *pure shear* in terms of axes as in Fig. 20.3 may be written

$$x' = x + ey$$
$$y' = ex + y$$
$$z' = z$$

where $e = \alpha = a'$.

20.4. SUPERPOSITION OF SMALL HOMOGENEOUS DISPLACEMENTS

If a displacement described by equations of the form (20.19) is followed by a second displacement with a similar set of equations

$$(20.24) \qquad \begin{aligned} x'' &= (1 + a_{11}')x' + a_{12}'y' + a_{13}'z' \\ y'' &= a_{21}'x' + (1 + a_{22}')y' + a_{23}'z' \\ z'' &= a_{31}'x' + a_{32}'y' + (1 + a_{33}')z' \end{aligned}$$

then by substituting (20.19) into (20.24) we get, discarding products $a_{ij}a_{kl}'$ as negligibly small,

$$(20.25) \qquad \begin{aligned} x'' &= (1 + a_{11}' + a_{11})x + (a_{12}' + a_{12})y + (a_{13}' + a_{13})z \\ y'' &= (a_{21}' + a_{21})x + (1 + a_{22}' + a_{22})y + (a_{23}' + a_{23})z \\ z'' &= (a_{31}' + a_{31})x + (a_{32}' + a_{32})y + (1 + a_{33}' + a_{33})z \end{aligned}$$

Thus *a displacement resulting from two successive small homogeneous displacements is characterized by constants which are the sums of those for the two original displacements taken separately.* In particular, note that, using (20.23),

(20.26a) $e''_{xx} = e'_{xx} + e_{xx}$

(20.26b) $e''_{xy} = e'_{xy} + e_{xy}$

This result is particularly useful in reverse: a complex displacement may often be analyzed as compounded of simpler ones. In matrix form the main conclusion of this section is deduced almost trivially. From

$$R'' = (I + A')R' \quad \text{and} \quad R' = (I + A)R$$

we conclude that

$$R'' = (I + A')(I + A)R$$

or

$$R'' = (I + A' + A)R$$

if we neglect $A'A$.

EXERCISES

12. Show that deformation equations for a *pure shear* in terms of axes as in Fig. 20.4 may be written
$$x' = x(1 + e)$$
$$y' = y(1 - e)$$
$$z' = z$$
where the measure ϕ of the corresponding simple strain is $\phi = 2e$. Write corresponding equations for ξ, η, ζ.

13. Show by rotating axes through 45° that the strains of Exercises 11 and 12 are equivalent.

14. A plane square figure has its diagonals stretched with extensions e_{xx} and e_{yy} (the coordinate axes are taken as the diagonals). Use the main result of this section to show that this distortion may be regarded as a uniform dilatation (in x and y directions only) with
$$e_v = e_{xx} + e_{yy}$$
superimposed on a pure shear corresponding to a simple shear of amount
$$\phi = e_{xx} - e_{yy}$$

15. Use the main result of this section to show that a simple shear like that of Fig. 19.2 may be regarded as a pure shear (see Exercise 11) and a rotation through an angle $-e$. (Exercise 1 was concerned with such a rotation.)

20.5. ROTATION AND PURE STRAIN

In discussing homogeneous strains, we were careful to eliminate translations by choosing a fixed origin. We have not yet eliminated the possibility of small rotations. A small rigid rotation would be just such a small displacement as we have discussed, and yet it would involve no distortion. Let us see what equations for such a displacement would look like. Any instantaneous rotation during a time Δt can be described by

$$\mathbf{V} = \mathbf{\Omega} \times \mathbf{R} \quad \text{where } \mathbf{\Omega} = \omega \mathbf{E}$$

or

$$\frac{\Delta \mathbf{R}}{\Delta t} = \frac{\Delta \theta}{\Delta t} (\mathbf{E} \times \mathbf{R})$$

Let us write $\Delta\theta\mathbf{E} = \theta_1\mathbf{I} + \theta_2\mathbf{J} + \theta_3\mathbf{K}$. We get

(20.27)
$$\Delta\mathbf{R} = \begin{vmatrix} \theta_1 & \theta_2 & \theta_3 \\ x & y & z \\ \mathbf{I} & \mathbf{J} & \mathbf{K} \end{vmatrix}$$

Multiplying out and equating x, y, and z components, we have

(20.28)
$$\begin{aligned} x' - x = \xi = \Delta x = &\quad -\theta_3 y + \theta_2 z \\ y' - y = \eta = \Delta y = \theta_3 x &\quad -\theta_1 z \\ z' - z = \zeta = \Delta z = -\theta_2 x &+ \theta_1 y \end{aligned}$$

We shall now be able to recognize a *small rotation* by the skew-symmetric array of coefficients. (Taking main diagonal, the broken line above, as axis of symmetry, symmetrically situated coefficients are equal but opposite in sign.)

It is now instructive to rearrange terms in the displacement equations (20.19) thus:

$$x' - x = \xi = a_{11}x + \tfrac{1}{2}(a_{12} + a_{21})y + \tfrac{1}{2}(a_{13} + a_{31})z + \tfrac{1}{2}(a_{12} - a_{21})y + \tfrac{1}{2}(a_{13} - a_{31})z$$

Similarly,

$$\eta = \tfrac{1}{2}(a_{21} + a_{12})x + a_{22}y + \tfrac{1}{2}(a_{23} + a_{32})z + \tfrac{1}{2}(a_{21} - a_{12})x + \tfrac{1}{2}(a_{23} - a_{32})z$$
$$\zeta = \tfrac{1}{2}(a_{31} + a_{13})x + \tfrac{1}{2}(a_{32} + a_{23})y + a_{33}z + \tfrac{1}{2}(a_{31} - a_{13})x + \tfrac{1}{2}(a_{32} - a_{23})y$$

If we let

(20.29)
$$\begin{aligned} \theta_1 &= \tfrac{1}{2}(a_{32} - a_{23}) \\ \theta_2 &= \tfrac{1}{2}(a_{13} - a_{31}) \\ \theta_3 &= \tfrac{1}{2}(a_{21} - a_{12}) \end{aligned}$$

it is apparent, by use of the superposition property of Sec. 20.4, that the displacement equation may be analyzed into a rotation with Eqs. (20.28), together with a symmetrical transformation (taking what is left of the rearranged equations) as follows:

(20.30)
$$\begin{aligned} \xi &= e_{xx}x + e_{xy}y + e_{zx}z \\ \eta &= e_{xy}x + e_{yy}y + e_{yz}z \\ \zeta &= e_{zx}x + e_{yz}y + e_{zz}z \end{aligned}$$

Equations (20.30) represent a small homogeneous displacement free from both rotation and translation. It is a *pure strain*.

The general conclusions achieved thus far are then:

(20.31) *Any small homogeneous displacement of a body may be analyzed into a rigid-body displacement plus a pure strain.*

(20.32) *Any pure homogeneous strain is determined uniquely by the six coefficients of shear and extension.*

This last statement, in view of the superposition possibility, is equivalent to resolving any such strain into three simple extensions plus three simple shears.

Note that, for a *pure strain*,

(20.33)
$$\frac{\partial\xi}{\partial y} = \frac{\partial\eta}{\partial x} = e_{xy} \qquad \frac{\partial\eta}{\partial z} = \frac{\partial\zeta}{\partial y} = e_{yz} \qquad \frac{\partial\zeta}{\partial x} = \frac{\partial\xi}{\partial z} = e_{zx}$$

The matrix equivalent of this section is very simple. Suppose that a small homogeneous displacement is described by a matrix equation

$$H = AR$$

The matrix A is equal to a sum

$$A = \tfrac{1}{2}(A + A^t) + \tfrac{1}{2}(A - A^t)$$

The first matrix in this decomposition is symmetric: it is the pure-strain matrix

$$A = E = \tfrac{1}{2}(A + A^t)$$

The skew-symmetric matrix $\tfrac{1}{2}(A - A^t)$ represents the rigid-body motion. If A is symmetric so that $A^t = A$, then the strain is pure and the equations of symmetry given in (20.33) are valid.

EXERCISES

16. In a pure strain a typical point (x,y,z) is distorted to (x',y',z') given by

$$x' = 1.052x - 0.008y + 0.004z$$
$$y' = -0.008x + 0.967y$$
$$z' = 0.004x \qquad\qquad + 1.009z$$

Evaluate the six coefficients of extension and shear.

17. Evaluate the six coefficients of extension and shear for the displacement described by

$$x' = 1.032x - 0.012y - 0.008z$$
$$y' = 0.042x + 1.026y + 0.044z$$
$$z' = \qquad\qquad 0.036y + 0.988z$$

20.6. PRINCIPAL STRAINS

We have considered in some detail the nature of strain and the way in which complex situations may be analyzed in terms of simple ones. Much of this development could have been abbreviated and generalized if tensor analysis were used. In a number of situations we have at least indicated matrix summaries for sets of equations meaningful for a particular reference frame. In this section we make use of the fact that great simplification is possible if principal axes are used. This topic has occurred before in our discussion of moments of inertia. In Appendix 4 some attention is given to the problem of finding characteristic vectors associated with a transformation or a matrix. In the present section a brief intuitive description is combined with an elementary mathematical treatment for the plane case.

Consider a solid sphere within the body with center at the origin. Let this be subject to a small homogeneous pure strain. Since parallel lines in the body before deformations are parallel afterwards it is not surprising that the sphere is deformed into an ellipsoid. Its axes are the *principal axes of strain*. If they are taken as co-ordinate axes, the coefficients of shear are zero.

(20.34) *Relative to principal axes a pure strain may be analyzed as three simple extensions superimposed.*

The equations (20.30) now take the form

$$(20.35) \qquad \begin{aligned} \xi &= e'_{xx}x \\ \eta &= e'_{yy}y \\ \zeta &= e'_{zz}z \end{aligned}$$

For these axes, e'_{xx}, e'_{yy}, and e'_{zz} are called principal strains.

Since volume dilatation is manifestly independent of axes, we have it as an invariant

$$e_{xx} + e_{yy} + e_{zz} = e'_{xx} + e'_{yy} + e'_{zz}$$

A pure strain is sometimes defined as a deformation for which there are three mutually perpendicular directions such that a position vector in each one of these directions is deformed into a vector in the same direction. Such vectors are called characteristic or proper vectors (eigenvectors) of the deformation. The corresponding factors of multiplication $1 + e'_{xx}$, $1 + e'_{yy}$, and $1 + e'_{zz}$ are called characteristic or proper values (eigenvalues).

Principal Axes in the Plane. To make these concepts seem more concrete, let us consider briefly the plane case. Suppose that a figure confined to the xy plane is given a pure strain described by the equations

(20.36)
$$x' = a_{11}x + a_{12}y = (1 + e_{xx})x + e_{xy}y$$
$$y' = a_{12}x + a_{22}y = e_{xy}x + (1 + e_{yy})y$$

Let us explore this question: For what angles θ (given by)

(20.37)
$$\tan \theta = \frac{y}{x}$$

is a position vector $\mathbf{R} = r/\underline{\theta}$ transformed into a vector $\mathbf{R}' = r'/\underline{\theta}$ in the same direction? Algebraically the condition may be stated thus:

$$\frac{y}{x} = \tan \theta = \frac{a_{12}x + a_{22}y}{a_{11}x + a_{12}y} = \frac{y'}{x'}$$

or equivalently,

$$\tan \theta = \frac{a_{12} + a_{22} \tan \theta}{a_{11} + a_{12} \tan \theta}$$

This gives us a quadratic equation in $\tan \theta$:

$$a_{11} \tan \theta + a_{12} \tan^2 \theta = a_{12} + a_{22} \tan \theta$$

(20.38)
$$\tan^2 \theta - \left(\frac{a_{22} - a_{11}}{a_{12}}\right) \tan \theta - 1 = 0$$

This quadratic equation always has two real roots which determine directions. Suppose that $\tan \theta_1$ and $\tan \theta_2$ are such roots. Then

$$(\tan \theta - \tan \theta_1)(\tan \theta - \tan \theta_2) = 0$$

must be a factored form of our quadratic. Let us multiply out and compare coefficients:

$$\tan^2 \theta - (\tan \theta_1 + \tan \theta_2) \tan \theta + \tan \theta_1 \tan \theta_2 = 0$$

Comparing, we get for the sum of the roots

(20.39)
$$\tan \theta_1 + \tan \theta_2 = \frac{a_{22} - a_{11}}{a_{12}}$$

and for their product

(20.40)
$$\tan \theta_1 \tan \theta_2 = -1$$

The last equation tells us that the two directions are perpendicular. It is equivalent to $\mathbf{E}_1 \cdot \mathbf{E}_2 = 0$, where

$$\mathbf{E}_1 = \cos \theta_1 \mathbf{I} + \sin \theta_1 \mathbf{J}$$
$$\mathbf{E}_2 = \cos \theta_2 \mathbf{I} + \sin \theta_2 \mathbf{J}$$

This shows us that in the plane case at least the *principal axes* are suitable coordinate axes. The roots of (20.38) tell us how to find these axes. A slightly different approach may be found at once. Since our directions are perpendicular,

$$\tan (\theta_1 + \theta_2) = \tan (90° + 2\theta) = - \cot 2\theta$$

(where θ is the more suitable choice of the two angles selected). Using simple trigonometric identities,

$$-\cot 2\theta = \tan (\theta_1 + \theta_2) = \frac{\tan \theta_1 + \tan \theta_2}{1 - \tan \theta_1 \tan \theta_2}$$

Now substituting (20.39) and (20.40),

$$(20.41) \qquad\qquad \cot 2\theta = \frac{a_{11} - a_{22}}{2a_{12}}$$

or

$$(20.42) \qquad\qquad \tan 2\theta = \frac{2a_{12}}{a_{11} - a_{22}} = \frac{2e_{xy}}{e_{xx} - e_{yy}}$$

This last equation is particularly useful since it gives us *both* axes, for 2θ and $2\theta + 180°$ have the same tangent. Hence θ and $\theta + 90°$ are both roots.

If you are an avid student of analytical geometry, you will wish to pursue the matter further, showing that the principal axes discovered here by proper vectors are in fact the axes of symmetry of an ellipse into which the circle $x^2 + y^2 = r^2$ is deformed. Equation (20.42) should also be compared with Exercise 7.

EXERCISES

18. In a plane strain the principal axes bisect the angles formed by the coordinate axes. Show that the strain is a uniform plane dilatation.

19. For a plane strain characterized by $e_{xx} = 0.0050$, $e_{yy} = 0.0020$, $e_{xy} = 0.0015$, find the principal axes of strain.

20.7. PURE PLANE HOMOGENEOUS STRAIN

Let us collect for special attention the plane form of some of our conclusions. Suppose that the z component of displacement, ζ, is zero everywhere. Hence $e_{zx} = e_{yz} = e_{zz} = 0$ everywhere. The extension or longitudinal strain e_T in the direction of a unit vector $\mathbf{T}$ was given by (20.12). The plane version (with $\mathbf{T} = l\mathbf{I} + m\mathbf{J}$) is

$$(20.43) \qquad\qquad e_T = l^2 e_{xx} + m^2 e_{yy} + 2lm e_{xy}$$

To get a formula for the shear or angular distortion suffered by a vector in the $\mathbf{T}$ direction, we evaluate the angle α_T in Fig. 20.5. Using again the substitution (20.21), $\mathbf{H} = (d\mathbf{H}/dr)r$, we have

$$(20.44) \qquad \frac{\mathbf{H}}{r} = \left(l\frac{\partial \xi}{\partial x} + m\frac{\partial \xi}{\partial y} \right) \mathbf{I} + \left(l\frac{\partial \eta}{\partial x} + m\frac{\partial \eta}{\partial y} \right) \mathbf{J}$$

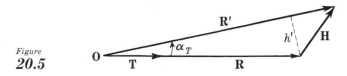

Figure
20.5

Now the angle α_T is approximately h'/r rad, where h' is the component of $\mathbf{H}$ perpendicular to $\mathbf{T}$, or

$$\alpha_T \mathbf{K} = \mathbf{T} \times \frac{\mathbf{H}}{r} = \left[l^2 \frac{\partial \eta}{\partial x} - m^2 \frac{\partial \xi}{\partial y} + ml \left(\frac{\partial \eta}{\partial y} - \frac{\partial \xi}{\partial x} \right) \right] \mathbf{K}$$

But, substituting the coefficients of extension and shear, we may write

(20.45) $$\alpha_T = (l^2 - m^2)e_{xy} + lm(e_{yy} - e_{xx})$$

Note that this result is exactly what is given by Eq. (20.9) when $\mathbf{T}_1 = \mathbf{T} = l\mathbf{I} + m\mathbf{J}$ and $\mathbf{T}_2 = \mathbf{T}' = -m\mathbf{I} + l\mathbf{J}$, so that $\mathbf{T}_1 \cdot \mathbf{T}_2 = 0$:

(20.46) $$\alpha_T = e_{TT'}$$

In the special case where $\mathbf{T} = \mathbf{I}$, $\mathbf{T}' = \mathbf{J}$, this result checks our conclusion in (20.16) when the symmetry condition (20.33) for pure strain holds. Finally, if we use $\mathbf{T}$ in terms of polar coordinates, $\mathbf{T} = 1/\theta$, the relation becomes

(20.47) $$\alpha_T = \tfrac{1}{2}[2 \cos 2\theta e_{xy} + \sin 2\theta(e_{yy} - e_{xx})]$$

Relative to principal axes, these general strain equations are simply

(20.48) $$e_T = l^2 e'_{xx} + m^2 e'_{yy}$$
(20.49) $$\alpha_T = lm(e'_{yy} - e'_{xx})$$

The matrix formulation for the pure-plane case is especially simple:

(20.50) $$e_T = [lm] \begin{bmatrix} e_{xx} & e_{xy} \\ e_{xy} & e_{yy} \end{bmatrix} \begin{bmatrix} l \\ m \end{bmatrix}$$

(20.51) $$\alpha_T = e_{TT'} = [lm] \begin{bmatrix} e_{xx} & e_{xy} \\ e_{xy} & e_{yy} \end{bmatrix} \begin{bmatrix} -m \\ l \end{bmatrix}$$

These equations could, of course, have been recorded at once as a consequence of (20.13) and (20.11).

Example I

Suppose that a homogeneous pure plane strain is characterized by

$$e_{xx} = 0.0020 \qquad e_{yy} = -0.0010 \qquad e_{xy} = 0.0010$$

Find the principal axes and the principal strains.

Solution

To find the principal axes, we use (20.42), which gives

$$\tan 2\theta = \tfrac{2}{3} \qquad 2\theta = 33.7° \qquad \text{or} \qquad 213.7°$$
$$\theta = 16.8° \qquad \text{or} \qquad 106.8°$$

To find the principal strains, we first need some sines and cosines, which, with slide-rule accuracy, are

$$\cos 16.8° = 0.96 = \sin 106.8°$$
$$\sin 16.8° = 0.29 = -\cos 106.8°$$

Substituting in (20.43),

$$e'_{xx} = (0.96)^2(0.002) + (0.29)^2(-0.001) + (0.96)(0.29)(0.002) = 0.0022$$
$$e'_{yy} = (-0.29)^2(0.002) + (0.96)^2(-0.001) + (-0.29)(0.96)(0.002) = -0.0013$$

Example 2

Work backward to get original data from principal strains of Example 1.

Solution
$$l = \cos \theta = 0.96 \qquad m = \sin \theta = -0.29$$
Thus, using (20.48),
$$e_T = (0.96)^2(0.0022) + (0.29)^2(-0.0013) = 0.0021 - 0.0001 = 0.0020$$
Now taking
$$\theta = 90° - 16.8° = 73.2°$$
$$l = \cos 73.2° = 0.29$$
$$m = \sin 73.2° = 0.96$$
$$e_{T'} = (0.29)^2(0.0022) + (0.96)^2(-0.0013) = 0.0002 - 0.0012 = -0.0010$$
Both of these results check with the original data.   Finally, using (20.49),
$$e_s = lm(e'_{yy} - e'_{xx}) = (0.96)(-0.29)(-0.0035) = 0.0010$$
which is the correct value for e_{xy}.

EXERCISES

These exercises all have to do with pure plane homogeneous strain.
20. Use (20.48) to verify that maximum and minimum extensions occur in the directions of the principal axes.
21. In what directions relative to the principal axes are vectors subject to the greatest or least shearing strains?
22. In what directions relative to the principal axes is the extension equal to one-half the volume dilatation?
23. If $e_{xx} = -0.0020$, $e_{yy} = 0.0060$, $e_{xy} = -0.0035$, what is the maximum (or minimum) shearing strain?
24. If principal strains are $e'_{xx} = 0.004$, $e'_{yy} = -0.002$, what are the extension and shearing strains for a vector $\mathbf{T} = 1/20°$?

20.8. COMPONENTS OF STRESS

At any point in a strained solid let us denote by $\mathbf{X}$, $\mathbf{Y}$, and $\mathbf{Z}$ the stresses across areas whose normals are, respectively, $\mathbf{I}$, $\mathbf{J}$, and $\mathbf{K}$.   Now for a random direction given by
$$\mathbf{N} = l\mathbf{I} + m\mathbf{J} + n\mathbf{K}$$
what is the stress $\mathbf{S}$ across an area having $\mathbf{N}$ as normal?   It is the aim of this section to show how the components of $\mathbf{S}$ may be expressed in terms of those of $\mathbf{X}$, $\mathbf{Y}$, and $\mathbf{Z}$.   At the point in question, draw coordinate axes and consider the small tetrahedron cut off by a plane of normal $\mathbf{N}$ at a small distance h from the origin.   The outward unit normals for the four faces are (see Fig. 20.6), respectively, $-\mathbf{I}$, $-\mathbf{J}$, $-\mathbf{K}$, and $\mathbf{N}$. The corresponding areas are, respectively, a_x, a_y, a_z, and a.   Let us isolate this part of the body.   For equilibrium the vector sum of the forces must be zero.   Neglecting the weight (depends on volume, which may be neglected, since limit vol/a as $h \to 0$ is 0),

(20.52) $-\mathbf{X}a_x - \mathbf{Y}a_y - \mathbf{Z}a_z + \mathbf{S}a = \mathbf{O}$

The minus signs go back to the definition of stress, from which it is apparent that

(20.53) $\mathbf{S}(-\mathbf{N}) = -\mathbf{S}(\mathbf{N})$

Now a_x, a_y, a_z are the projections of a onto the coordinate planes; thus

$$a_x = al \qquad a_y = am \qquad a_z = an$$

Hence

(20.54) $$\mathbf{S} = l\mathbf{X} + m\mathbf{Y} + n\mathbf{Z}$$

In order for $\mathbf{S}$ to represent the stress at the given point, we must take the limit as the plane approaches the origin. The equations are unchanged thereby. The corresponding three scalar equations are

(20.55)
$$S_x = lx_x + my_x + nz_x$$
$$S_y = lx_y + my_y + nz_y$$
$$S_z = lx_z + my_z + nz_z$$

Thus at any point the stress is determined uniquely (relative to a particular reference frame) by the *nine components of stress*

$$x_x,\; x_y,\; x_z,\; y_x,\; y_y,\; y_z,\; z_x,\; z_y,\; z_z$$

We shall soon see that the coefficients of (20.55) are symmetrical in the same sense that those for a pure strain are. Consider a small box within the body, the edges being aligned with the axes and the dimensions Δx, Δy, Δz (see Fig. 20.7). Take the center of the box as temporary origin. We shall treat the force across each face as if it acted at the mean position, i.e., the center of that face. The box is subject to forces as follows:

$$\mathbf{X}\,\Delta y\,\Delta z \qquad \text{at}\ \left(\frac{\Delta x}{2}, 0, 0\right)$$

$$-\mathbf{X}\,\Delta y\,\Delta z \qquad \text{at}\ \left(-\frac{\Delta x}{2}, 0, 0\right)$$

$$\mathbf{Y}\,\Delta z\,\Delta x \qquad \text{at}\ \left(0, \frac{\Delta y}{2}, 0\right)$$

$$-\mathbf{Y}\,\Delta z\,\Delta x \qquad \text{at}\ \left(0, -\frac{\Delta y}{2}, 0\right)$$

$$\mathbf{Z}\,\Delta x\,\Delta y \qquad \text{at}\ \left(0, 0, \frac{\Delta z}{2}\right)$$

$$-\mathbf{Z}\,\Delta x\,\Delta y \qquad \text{at}\ \left(0, 0, -\frac{\Delta z}{2}\right)$$

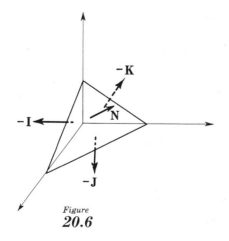

Figure
20.6

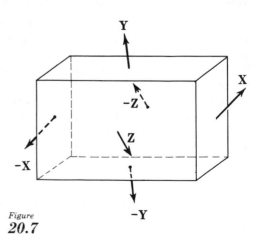

Figure
20.7

The vector sum of these forces is zero. For equilibrium the moments about the origin must add up to zero. For the first force, the moment is

$$\Delta y\, \Delta z \begin{vmatrix} \dfrac{\Delta x}{2} & 0 & 0 \\ x_x & x_y & x_z \\ \mathbf{I} & \mathbf{J} & \mathbf{K} \end{vmatrix} = (x_y\mathbf{K} - x_z\mathbf{J})\left(\frac{\Delta x}{2}\,\Delta y\, \Delta z\right)$$

For the second force,

$$\Delta y\, \Delta z \begin{vmatrix} -\dfrac{\Delta x}{2} & 0 & 0 \\ -x_x & -x_y & -x_z \\ \mathbf{I} & \mathbf{J} & \mathbf{K} \end{vmatrix} = (x_y\mathbf{K} - x_z\mathbf{J})\left(\frac{\Delta x}{2}\,\Delta y\, \Delta z\right)$$

Treating the other forces similarly, adding, setting the sum equal to zero, dividing by Δx, Δy, Δz, and taking the limit as the sides of the box approach zero in length,

$$\mathbf{I}(y_z - z_y) + \mathbf{J}(z_x - x_z) + \mathbf{K}(x_y - y_x) = \mathbf{O}$$

Or

(20.56) $$y_z = z_y \qquad z_x = x_z \qquad x_y = y_x$$

Thus only six quantities are required to specify the stress in any direction at a point.

Let us use this result to derive a stress analogue of a strain equation which proved to be very useful. Equation (20.12) gave us the extension e_T associated with any direction $\mathbf{T}$. The corresponding stress concept would be the component s_N of stress normal to a plane having unit normal $\mathbf{N}$. This is a simple vector problem

$$s_N = \mathbf{S} \cdot \mathbf{N} = s_x l + s_y m + s_z n$$

Using (20.55) and (20.56), we get for *normal stress*

(20.57) $$s_N = l^2 x_x + m^2 y_y + n^2 z_z + 2lm x_y + 2mn y_z + 2nl z_x$$

The *tangential stress* is easily computed from

(20.58) $$s_t = |\mathbf{N} \times \mathbf{S}|$$

For a given choice of axes, the stress components are conveniently represented by a *symmetric matrix*

(20.59) $$S = \begin{bmatrix} x_x & x_y & x_z \\ y_x & y_y & y_z \\ z_x & z_y & z_z \end{bmatrix}$$

In terms of S we may simplify Eq. (20.57):

(20.60) $$s_N = N^t S N$$

analogous to (20.13). The interpretation of the stress equation analogous to (20.11) is left for Exercise 42.

EXERCISES

25. Write for a *plane stress* ($z_z = y_z = z_x = 0$) in terms of x_x, y_y, x_y, and θ formulas for normal and tangential stresses s_N and s_t across a plane whose normal $\mathbf{N}$ is in the xy plane: $\mathbf{N} = 1\underline{/\theta}$.

26. At a given point, the three stresses **X**, **Y**, and **Z** are given by

$$\mathbf{X} = 40,000(2\mathbf{I} - \mathbf{J} + \mathbf{K})$$
$$\mathbf{Y} = 30,000(\mathbf{I} + 2\mathbf{J} - \mathbf{K})$$
$$\mathbf{Z} = 50,000(-\mathbf{I} - \mathbf{J} + 2\mathbf{K})$$

(units are pounds per square inch).   What normal stress is experienced across an area normal to the vector $3\mathbf{I} - 4\mathbf{K}$?

20.9. PRINCIPAL STRESSES

Just as with strains, it is possible to pick three mutually perpendicular directions for which the stress is parallel to the direction.   These are called *principal axes of stress*.   We shall prove neither this result nor the following:

(20.61)   *Any state of stress may be analyzed as three tractions (or pressures) along the principal axes of stress.*

Relative to principal axes, the stress is specified by only three quantities called *principal stresses*: x'_x, y'_y, z'_z.

The discussion has considered stresses at a point.   When the same state of stress exists throughout a body, the stress is called *homogeneous*.

Application to Plane Stresses.   In the case of plane stress in the xy plane, (20.55) may be written

(20.62)
$$s_x = lx_x + mx_y$$
$$s_y = lx_y + my_y$$

The question may be asked, For what unit normal vector $\mathbf{N} = l\mathbf{I} + m\mathbf{J}$ is the corresponding stress vector $\mathbf{S} = s_x\mathbf{I} + s_y\mathbf{J}$ parallel to $\mathbf{N}$.   Such directions are principal directions, and the stresses are *principal stresses*.   Following the same algebra used for (20.36), we conclude that principal directions are given for $\mathbf{N} = 1/\theta$ such that

(20.63)
$$\tan 2\theta = \frac{2x_y}{x_x - y_y}$$

The same argument shows that two mutually perpendicular directions are obtained.

The plane form of (20.57) is

(20.64)
$$s_N = l^2 x_x + m^2 y_y + 2lm x_y$$

The plane form of (20.58) is

(20.65)
$$s_t = (l^2 - m^2)x_y + lm(y_y - x_x)$$

These results should be compared with the corresponding strain equations (20.43) and (20.45).

Relative to principal axes, the equations are

(20.66)
$$s_N = l^2 x'_x + m^2 y'_y$$

(20.67)
$$s_t = lm(y'_y - x'_x)$$

Note that for the plane case the equation

$$s_N = [lm] \begin{bmatrix} x_x & x_y \\ x_y & y_y \end{bmatrix} \begin{bmatrix} l \\ m \end{bmatrix}$$

becomes

$$s_N = [lm] \begin{bmatrix} x'_x & 0 \\ 0 & y'_y \end{bmatrix} \begin{bmatrix} l \\ m \end{bmatrix}$$

and that

$$s_t = [lm] \begin{bmatrix} x_x & x_y \\ x_y & y_y \end{bmatrix} \begin{bmatrix} -m \\ l \end{bmatrix}$$

becomes

$$s_t = [lm] \begin{bmatrix} x'_x & 0 \\ 0 & y'_y \end{bmatrix} \begin{bmatrix} -m \\ l \end{bmatrix}$$

EXERCISES

27. A plane sample is subjected to two normal stresses as follows: in the x direction a compression of 4,000 lb/in.^{2} and in the y direction a traction of 2,000 lb/in.^{2} Find the normal and tangential stresses for sections bisecting the angles between axes.

28. A plane stress is characterized by $x_x = -3,000$ lb/in.^{2}, $y_y = 6,000$ lb/in.^{2}, $x_y = -2,000$ lb/in.^{2} Find the maximum and minimum values of normal stress and tangential stress.

29. Principal stresses are given as $x_x = 4,000$ lb/in.^{2}, $y_y = 3,000$ lb/in.^{2}, $z_z = -4,000$ lb/in.^{2} Find the normal stress across an area whose unit normal vector is $0.8\mathbf{I} + 0.6\mathbf{J}$.

20.10. GENERALIZED HOOKE'S LAW

The basic experimental fact relating stress and strain was stated, though not precisely, in Chap. 19. For any choice of axes, we have seen that strain can be expressed in terms of six coefficients and that the stress also can be expressed in terms of six components. A generalized form of Hooke's law says that the six stresses depend linearly on the six strains. The mathematical expression of this assertion involves 36 constants of the body, the c_{ij} of the following:

(20.68)
$$
\begin{aligned}
x_x &= c_{11}e_{xx} + c_{12}e_{yy} + c_{13}e_{zz} + c_{14}e_{yz} + c_{15}e_{zx} + c_{16}e_{xy} \\
y_y &= c_{21}e_{xx} + c_{22}e_{yy} + c_{23}e_{zz} + c_{24}e_{yz} + c_{25}e_{zx} + c_{26}e_{xy} \\
z_z &= c_{31}e_{xx} + c_{32}e_{yy} + c_{33}e_{zz} + c_{34}e_{yz} + c_{35}e_{zx} + c_{36}e_{xy} \\
y_z &= c_{41}e_{xx} + c_{42}e_{yy} + c_{43}e_{zz} + c_{44}e_{yz} + c_{45}e_{zx} + c_{46}e_{xy} \\
z_x &= c_{51}e_{xx} + c_{52}e_{yy} + c_{53}e_{zz} + c_{54}e_{yz} + c_{55}e_{zx} + c_{56}e_{xy} \\
x_y &= c_{61}e_{xx} + c_{62}e_{yy} + c_{63}e_{zz} + c_{64}e_{yz} + c_{65}e_{zx} + c_{66}e_{xy}
\end{aligned}
$$

It does not, however, take a table of 36 constants to predict the elastic behavior of a material. An analysis of work-energy relations into which we shall not go shows that the coefficient array is symmetrical (that is, $c_{ij} = c_{ji}$). So, in any case, not more than $18 + 3$, or 21, constants are needed.

We shall agree to deal with *isotropic bodies*, i.e., bodies in which elastic behavior is the same for all directions. This choice rules out considerations of problems involving anisotropic crystals, although the crystalline aspects of most metal samples are lost because of the random arrangement. For isotropic bodies, principal axes of stress and principal axes of strain coincide, as one would expect. Using principal axes as coordinate axes, the equations (20.68) are replaced by

(20.69)
$$
\begin{aligned}
x_x &= c_{11}e_{xx} + c_{12}e_{yy} + c_{12}e_{zz} \\
y_y &= c_{12}e_{xx} + c_{11}e_{yy} + c_{12}e_{zz} \\
z_z &= c_{12}e_{xx} + c_{12}e_{yy} + c_{11}e_{zz}
\end{aligned}
$$

The *two constants* c_{11} and c_{12} suffice to describe the elastic properties of a homogeneous isotropic material. The details for other axes will not be given here.

20.11. RELATIONS BETWEEN ELASTIC MODULI

We shall apply the simplified stress-strain equations (20.69) to some special cases. First, the stretched rod. Here, taking the x axis along the rod, x_x is the only nonzero stress component and $e_{yy} = e_{zz} = -\sigma e_{xx}$. Thus, if the stretching force is f and the area of cross section a, the first two of these equations become, respectively,

$$\frac{f}{a} = c_{11}e_{xx} - 2c_{12}\sigma e_{xx}$$

$$0 = c_{12}e_{xx} - c_{11}\sigma e_{xx} - c_{12}\sigma e_{xx}$$

We conclude from the second equation that *Poisson's ratio* σ is expressible as

(20.70)
$$\sigma = \frac{c_{12}}{c_{11} + c_{12}}$$

Writing *Young's modulus* ψ as

(20.71)
$$\psi = \frac{f/a}{e_{xx}}$$

the first equation yields

(20.72)
$$\psi = c_{11} - 2\sigma c_{12}$$

and substituting (20.70),

(20.73)
$$\psi = \frac{(c_{11} - c_{12})(c_{11} + 2c_{12})}{(c_{11} + c_{12})}$$

If now we solve (20.70) and (20.73) for c_{11} and c_{12}, we can replace the constants of (20.69) by expressions in ψ and σ which have more familiar physical significance. The results are

(20.74)
$$c_{11} = \frac{(1 - \sigma)\psi}{(1 + \sigma)(1 - 2\sigma)}$$

$$c_{12} = \frac{\sigma\psi}{(1 + \sigma)(1 - 2\sigma)}$$

Next let us consider a uniform compression:

$$x_x = y_y = z_z = -p$$

$$e_{xx} = e_{yy} = e_{zz}$$

Equation (20.69) gives us

$$-p = (c_{11} + 2c_{12})e_{xx}$$

Now the *bulk modulus* β is given by [cf. (19.11)]

(20.75)
$$\beta = \frac{p}{-(\Delta v/v)}$$

By (20.15),

$$\frac{\Delta v}{v} = 3e_{xx}$$

Thus we get

(20.76)
$$\beta = \frac{c_{11} + 2c_{12}}{3}$$

From this, using (20.74), we can at once express β in terms of ψ and σ:

(20.77)
$$\beta = \frac{\psi}{3(1 - 2\sigma)}$$

This last relationship may be interpreted less formally. A uniform dilatation (negative compression) may be considered as three equal simple extensions superimposed. Suppose that each face of a cube is pulled normally, as in Fig. 20.8, the stress being of magnitude s. Such a pull in, say, the x direction causes a stretch in the x direction, but at the same time it causes contractions in the y and z directions. When three such pulls are superimposed, the y and z pulls reduce the effectiveness of the x pull. For the x direction, the modified equation is

$$s - 2\sigma s = \psi e_{xx}$$

Replacing $s/3e_{xx}$ by β, we have

$$3\beta(1 - 2\sigma) = \psi$$

as before.

It remains to consider the *modulus of shear* μ. It was defined in terms of a simple shear as the ratio of shearing stress s to the angle ϕ of the shear.

(20.78)
$$\mu = \frac{s}{\phi}$$

To bring this within the scope of Eqs. (20.69), where principal axes are used, we shall regard the distortion as due to numerically equal traction and pressure along the diagonals (as was exhibited in Sec. 19.2). We shall also use (20.16) and (20.17). The stresses are (see Fig. 20.9)

$$X_x = s \qquad Y_y = -s$$

and the strains are

$$e_{xx} = \frac{\phi}{2} \qquad e_{yy} = -\frac{\phi}{2}$$

Substituting in (20.69), we have

$$s = c_{11}\frac{\phi}{2} - c_{12}\frac{\phi}{2}$$

$$-s = c_{12}\frac{\phi}{2} - c_{11}\frac{\phi}{2}$$

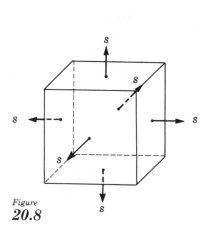

Figure **20.8**

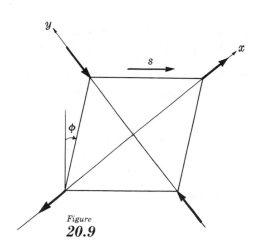

Figure **20.9**

Consequently,

(20.79)
$$\mu = \frac{c_{11} - c_{12}}{2}$$

In terms of ψ and σ,

(20.80)
$$\mu = \frac{\psi}{2(1 + \sigma)}$$

The constants ψ and μ are easily measured for many materials. Formulas for β and σ in terms of ψ and μ are thus clearly desirable. These are left for Exercise 31.

$$\beta = \frac{\psi\mu}{3(3\mu - \psi)}$$

$$\sigma = \frac{\psi - 2\mu}{2\mu}$$

EXERCISES

30. From the data of Exercise 17 of Chap. 19, what would you expect for values of the modulus of shear? Of the bulk modulus?
31. Derive formulas for β and σ in terms of ψ and μ.
32. Derive formulas for ψ and σ in terms of β and μ.
33. A rod is found to have Young's modulus 1.8×10^{11} newtons/m² and modulus of shear 0.7×10^{11} newtons/m². Find Poisson's ratio and the bulk modulus for this material.

REVIEW EXERCISES

34. A solid homogeneous rectangular sample is stretched parallel to one set of edges until the extension is e. What is the extension of a line segment on one face of the sample if its direction makes an angle of 45° with the direction of stretch? The answer will be in terms of Poisson's ratio σ.
35. A plane square figure has one diagonal compressed with a strain $-e$ and the other stretched by a strain $+e'$. By what angles are the sides of the square distorted?
36. What is the percentage change in density associated with the displacement described in Exercise 6?
37. Verify or disprove the formula
$$e_{zx} = 0.5\mathbf{J} \cdot \left(\mathbf{K} \times \frac{\partial \mathbf{H}}{\partial z} - \mathbf{I} \times \frac{\partial \mathbf{H}}{\partial x} \right)$$
38. Can you interpret $\mathbf{I}' \cdot \mathbf{J}' \times \mathbf{K}' - \mathbf{I} \cdot \mathbf{J} \times \mathbf{K}$ as a strain? Give details.
39. In a pure plane shear characterized by $\alpha = \alpha'$ (see Fig. 20.3) show that (a) $e_{xy} = \alpha$; (b) $e_{xx} = e_{yy} = 0$.
40. In the strain shown in Fig. 20.4, what is e_T for $\mathbf{T} = 1\underline{/45°}$?
41. A rod is stretched so that the longitudinal strain is equal to e. Poisson's ratio for the material is 0.3.
   (a) Evaluate $e_{xx}, e_{yy}, e_{zz}, e_{xy}, e_{yz}, e_{xz}$ for axes chosen as follows: origin at center and x axis along axis of rod.
   (b) Evaluate e_T at the origin for the direction $\mathbf{T} = 0.8\mathbf{I} + 0.6\mathbf{J}$.
   (c) Evaluate e_{TJ} for $\mathbf{T}$ as given in (b).
42. Can you give a physical interpretation of the quantity [note analogy with (20.11)] $N_1{}^t S N_2$?

CHAPTER TWENTY-ONE

WAVE MOTION in ONE DIMENSION

Chapter 18 gave an introduction to one important branch of the dynamics of deformable bodies. The emphasis was on actual flow of material from one position to another. In this chapter another important branch will be introduced. The motions investigated will involve the flow of energy from one place to another. The energy will be transmitted mechanically, but no material will move from the source to the destination. These two phases of deformation dynamics have an analogy in the field of electricity. When there is electric current in a wire, we say that electric charge actually flows along it. But when a radio signal is picked up with an antenna, we do not pretend that a charge carried the signal from the transmitter. The analogy must not be carried too far, for in the electrical case no mechanism for energy transmission is apparent: a vacuum will do. In our present study the elastic mechanism is to be very much in evidence; therefore a medium is necessary.

21.1. THE NATURE OF WAVE MOTION

The transmission of energy without an actual transfer of material is accomplished in a way that is easily visualized. Imagine a hundred people lined up in single file with Mr. A at one end and Mr. B at the other. If Mr. A has a note for Mr. B, he may get out of line and carry it to him. That epitomizes the subject matter of Chap. 18. Or the note may be passed from person to person down the line until B receives it. The note has been delivered, but the carriers are still in their original positions. This epitomizes the sort of transmission to be studied in the present chapter. Suppose, for example, that one part of an elastic body is subjected to a deforming force and is hen released. The deforming force creates strains with their corresponding stresses. Upon removal of this applied force, the stresses institute a motion. Each moving portion acquires momentum and in being halted imparts a shove to its neighbor, setting it in motion. In this way motion is transmitted elastically throughout the body. This is an example of *wave motion*. Mechanical wave motion may be characterized as a traveling disturbance in a medium without any net displacement of the medium. The word "disturbance" is used in a very broad sense: it might, for example, be a displacement, a change in pressure, a change in tension, a change in angular orientation.

We have seen in our discussions of springs and pendulums that when restoring forces are proportional to displacements, they tend to cause simple harmonic oscillations. It is not surprising, then, that in studying elastic transmission of energy subject to Hooke's law we shall give particular attention to periodic or repetitive disturbances. When a note is sounded on a whistle, a periodic compressional pattern travels out in all directions. This is a periodic sound wave. If the end of a steel rail is struck by a hammer, a longitudinal elastic wave travels along it. This too is a sound wave, although not periodic. If a long taut string is struck normally near the middle, transverse kinks may be seen traveling in both directions. This too is wave motion. Classical physics abounds in such examples, and in modern physics wavelike aspects of observable phenomena motivate the use of a mathematical model closely akin to the mathematics of wave motion as we shall study it in this chapter.

21.2. SIMPLE HARMONIC WAVES

Among mechanical periodic waves the most important are the ones for which the disturbance at any one point is a simple harmonic oscillation. Such a wave is a *simple harmonic wave*. There are other instances. In fact, any disturbance which can be described as sinusoidal and which is propagated as a wave may be regarded as a simple harmonic wave. By means of Fourier analysis, any periodic wave may be regarded as an aggregate of simple harmonic waves superimposed. These ideas may even be extended to a harmonic analysis of nonperiodic waves.

In this section we shall review some of the properties of periodic waves by looking closely at equations for simple harmonic waves. Suppose that the disturbance at the source is measured by y_0. y_0 might be a transverse or a longitudinal displacement, an increment in pressure or tension, or any other such disturbance. We assume that y_0 is simple harmonic and can be represented thus:

$$(21.1) \qquad\qquad y_0 = y_m \sin \omega t$$

Let us assume that this disturbance travels parallel to the x axis at speed c. Then, if the source is at the origin, the disturbance y at a point with coordinate x is at a given moment exactly the same as the disturbance at the origin x/c sec earlier.

$$(21.2) \qquad\qquad y = y_m \sin \omega \left(t - \frac{x}{c} \right)$$

Equation (21.1) is then the special case of (21.2) for $x = 0$.

For a random position x and time t, y is determined by (21.2). y is thus a function of the two variables x and t. Suppose we select a particular instant, say, $t = 7.8$ sec. Then the equation is

$$(21.3) \qquad\qquad y = y_m \sin \omega \left(7.8 - \frac{x}{c} \right)$$

which is merely a sine curve showing the *wave profile* in the position corresponding to that particular moment. Figure 21.1 is a graph of this wave profile. There are regularly spaced points such as a and a' on the x axis for which the disturbance is maximum. Their separation λ is called the *wavelength* of the wave. Actually, *any two points separated by a distance λ have at any one moment equal disturbances*. As we have seen in setting up Eq. (21.2), the wave profile moves in the positive x direction at speed c. Since c is the rate at which a peak or a zero or any other particular phase of the oscillation appears to move, it is called the *phase velocity*.

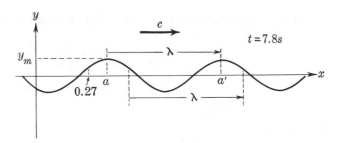

Figure
21.1

By analyzing (21.3) it is easy to show that

(21.4)
$$\frac{\lambda}{c} = \frac{2\pi}{\omega} = \tau$$

As in Sec. 5.9, τ is called the *period* of the oscillation given by (21.1). The reciprocal of τ is the *frequency* ν; thus we may write

(21.5)
$$\lambda\nu = c$$

This is one of the most important equations of wave physics. The reciprocal of λ is the *wave number* k, so

(21.6)
$$\nu = ck$$

Now let us select a point, say, $x = 0.27$ m, on the x axis. The wave equation becomes

(21.7)
$$y = y_m \sin \omega \left(t - \frac{0.27}{c} \right)$$

This is merely the equation of an oscillation like that of the source having period $2\pi/\omega$. It is out of phase with the source unless $0.27/c$ happens to be an integral number of periods. A graph of the oscillation at $x = 0.27$ would be like Fig. 21.2.

We have seen, then, that a uniform simple harmonic wave has a dual aspect. At *each point* the disturbance is simple harmonic, the period being the same for all points. Neighboring points have oscillations out of phase. Points a wavelength apart have oscillations in phase. At *each moment* the sinusoidal pattern of disturbance or wave profile may be observed. This pattern moves at a certain phase velocity, but the net displacement of the oscillating substance is zero.

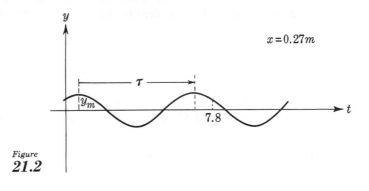

Figure
21.2

Two more symmetric forms of (21.2) are often used. The first is obtained by substituting $2\pi/\tau$ for ω.

$$(21.8) \qquad y = y_m \sin 2\pi\left(\frac{t}{\tau} - \frac{x}{\lambda}\right)$$

$$(21.9) \qquad y = y_m \sin 2\pi(\nu t - kx)$$

EXERCISES

1. Derive (21.4) from (21.3).
2. Derive (21.9) from (21.2).
3. Rewrite (21.2) in terms of ν and c.
4. Plot $y = 10 \sin 2\pi(4{,}000t - 4x)$ as a function of x for $t = 12.5, 25.0, 37.5, 50.0, 62.5$ μsec. Use a single set of axes so that the progressive nature of the wave will be evident. (The prefix *micro-* is equivalent to a factor of 10^{-6}.)
5. Plot $y = 10 \sin 2\pi(4{,}000t - 4x)$ as a function of t for $x = 0.00, 0.05, 0.10$ ft.

21.3. DOPPLER EFFECT

One interesting property of mechanical periodic waves may be studied as an application of Eq. (21.5) and of the kinematics of relative motion. It is well known that the observed pitch of a whistle varies with the relative velocity of the source and the observer. Here we shall consider motion along the x axis. Let us assume that the x axis is fixed in the medium and that the source and observer have velocities along the x axis denoted by v_s and v_o. These may be either positive or negative or zero. The frequency of the signal emitted by the source is ν, and the observer experiences a frequency ν'.

There are two quite distinct aspects of this problem. The source causes waves of length λ to be set up in the medium. If v_s is positive, the wave leaves the source at a slower relative speed and the wavelength, according to (21.5), is shorter. When v_s is negative, the relative speed is greater, and the wave is stretched out. In either case

$$\lambda \nu = c - v_s$$

or

$$(21.10) \qquad \lambda = \frac{c - v_s}{\nu}$$

This part of the deduction concerns only the source. Nothing has been said about the observer.

Now let us consider the frequency ν' experienced by the observer. ν' is merely the rate at which peaks in the waves already set up are encountered by the observer. If v_o is positive, the waves overtake the observer with a smaller relative speed. If v_o is negative, he is rushing to meet the oncoming waves. In either case (21.5) applies:

$$(21.11) \qquad \nu' = \frac{c - v_o}{\lambda}$$

This part of the argument has nothing to do with the source: given the wave train of wavelength λ moving at speed c in the medium, then the observed frequency ν' depends only on the speed of the observer relative to the medium.

Equations (21.10) and (21.11) may be combined to get a formula relating ν' and ν:

$$(21.12) \qquad \nu' = \nu\left(\frac{c - v_o}{c - v_s}\right)$$

6. A train going north at 60 mph whistles at a southbound train approaching at 90 mph. If the true frequency of the whistle is 350 per sec, what is the observed frequency on the second train? (Take c as 1,100 ft/sec.)

7. If c is much larger than both v_o and v_s and if the medium is stationary, show that the Doppler formula may be written

$$\nu' = \nu\left(1 - \frac{v'}{c}\right)$$

where v' is the velocity of the observer relative to the source.

8. A steamship heads south at 10 mph. The wind from the south is 30 mph. A motorboat sails north toward the steamer at 20 mph. The steamer blows a whistle of frequency 150 cycles/sec. What frequency is observed at the motorboat? (Take c as 1,100 ft/sec.)

21.4. VIBRATION OF A TENSE STRING

Suppose that a long light flexible string is held taut with a tension f. If a portion of the string is suddenly deflected slightly and released, a wave travels along the string. This phenomenon is very familiar, although of course a string used in an experiment would not be ideally light or perfectly flexible. Let us isolate a portion of the string at a given moment and see what dynamical conclusions may be reached. Let q denote the linear density m/l of the string. Refer now to Fig. 21.3. The angle between the deflected string and its equilibrium direction is θ. This is assumed to be small. We shall isolate the portion of the string between x and $x + \Delta x$. Since the string is flexible, no torque is transmitted to the isolated portion. Since the string is light, the tensions f of the two ends are the only forces. We shall apply the dynamics equation for y components:

$$\Sigma f_y = m \frac{d^2 y}{dt^2}$$

The derivative will be a partial derivative here, since y varies with x as well as t. We shall call the mass $q \, \Delta x$, but it should be realized that some small approximation is involved: once the string is deflected, the distribution of mass along the x axis is no longer uniform. We get

$$- f \sin \theta + f \sin (\theta + \Delta\theta) = (q \, \Delta x) \frac{\partial^2 y}{\partial t^2}$$

or

$$\frac{f \, \Delta(\sin \theta)}{\Delta x} = q \frac{\partial^2 y}{\partial t^2}$$

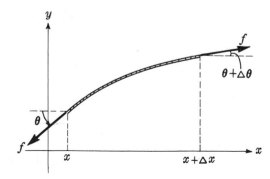

Figure
21.3

Since θ is small, we shall make the approximation

$$\sin \theta = \theta = \tan \theta = \frac{\partial y}{\partial x}$$

Then taking the limit as Δx approaches zero, we get this condition for wave motion along such a string

(21.13)
$$f \frac{\partial^2 y}{\partial x^2} = q \frac{\partial^2 y}{\partial t^2}$$

Equation (21.13) is an example of an extremely important differential equation. It can be satisfied only by equations of wave profiles traveling in either direction along the x axis. From what we know of kinks on taut strings, this assertion is hardly surprising. In courses on differential equations a demonstration is usually given. Most students using this book will not have had such a course; therefore we shall give a brief statement of results here. The general solution of the *differential equation of wave motion parallel to the x axis*

(21.14)
$$\frac{\partial^2 y}{\partial x^2} = \frac{1}{c^2} \frac{\partial^2 y}{\partial t^2}$$

has the form

(21.15)
$$y = y_1(x - ct) + y_2(x + ct)$$

where y_1 is any wave profile traveling in the positive x direction and y_2 is any wave profile traveling in the negative x direction, the speed of propagation being c. Our simple harmonic wave of Sec. 21.2 can be written in this form:

$$y = -y_m \sin \frac{\omega}{c} (x - ct)$$

A comparison of the general equation (21.14) with the special result for a string (21.13) gives us an important formula for the speed of a transverse wave along a string:

(21.16)
$$c = \sqrt{\frac{f}{q}}$$

In the introductory paragraphs on waves the concept of energy played a conspicuous role. Now that we have the theory of one type of wave to scrutinize, let us evaluate the energy. First, let us see what change in potential energy is involved in taking the string, under tension, from the equilibrium position to a displaced position. The only forces which can do work are tensions (assumed uniform) along the string. The potential energy, then, is equal to this tension times the increase in length of the string. In computing, we shall avoid the complication of lateral displacements during stretching (that is, the problem of nonuniform x density already mentioned) by isolating either a long piece of the string or, to include a fair sample of all aspects of the phenomenon, for simple harmonic waves an integral number of quarter wavelengths. Let x range from 0 to l for the portion isolated. Then

$$\text{p.e.} = f \int_0^l (ds - dx)$$

where ds is the arc length corresponding to dx. Now

$$ds = \sqrt{1 + \left(\frac{dy}{dx}\right)^2} \, dx$$

But for sufficiently small smooth displacements, the square of the derivative is very small; therefore we shall substitute an *approximate* value based on the binomial theorem.

$$\sqrt{1 + \left(\frac{dy}{dx}\right)^2} = 1 + \frac{1}{2}\left(\frac{dy}{dx}\right)^2$$

Our conclusion is, using partial derivatives since here y is a function of both t and x,

(21.17) $$\text{p.e.} = \tfrac{1}{2}f\int_0^l \left(\frac{\partial y}{\partial x}\right)^2 dx$$

A similar sample of the string has kinetic energy which can readily be expressed. For an element corresponding to dx, the mass is approximately $q\,dx$ and the kinetic energy $\tfrac{1}{2}q\,dx(\partial y/\partial t)^2$. This ignores the slight energy of lateral displacement. Integrating,

(21.18) $$\text{k.e.} = \tfrac{1}{2}q\int_0^l \left(\frac{\partial y}{\partial t}\right)^2 dx$$

It is left as an exercise to use (21.16) in proving that, for a wave going in one direction on a string, these two expressions for energies are equal.

EXERCISES

9.   Show by direct substitution that Eq. (21.9) satisfies the wave equation (21.14).
10. How long will it take a transverse wave to travel the length of a string 3 m long, of radius 2 mm, weighing 300 g, and subjected to a tension of 10 newtons?
11. If $y_1 = y_1(x,t)$ and $y_2 = y_2(x,t)$ are solutions of (21.14) and if a_1 and a_2 are constants, show that the following also is a solution:

$$y = a_1 y_1 + a_2 y_2$$

12. Check Eq. (21.16) dimensionally.
13. Use Eq. (21.9) to verify that for a simple harmonic wave on a string the potential energy and kinetic energy are equal.

21.5. SUPERPOSITION THEOREM. BEATS

The differential equation of wave motion is linear; therefore any linear combination

$$y = a_1 y_1 + a_2 y_2$$

of solutions y_1 and y_2 (a_1 and a_2 are constants) is also a solution. This is called a *superposition theorem*. The proof is omitted in this section since it was the content of Sec. 21.4, Exercise 11. As a first application, consider what happens when two waves of slightly different frequency but the same amplitude travel in the same medium in the same direction. Let their equations be

$$y_1 = y_m \sin 2\pi v_1\left(t - \frac{x}{c}\right)$$

$$y_2 = y_m \sin 2\pi v_2\left(t - \frac{x}{c}\right)$$

We shall use the trigonometric identity

$$\sin \alpha + \sin \beta = 2 \sin \frac{\alpha + \beta}{2} \cos \frac{\alpha - \beta}{2}$$

We get

$$y = y_1 + y_2$$
$$= 2y_m \sin 2\pi \left(\frac{v_1 + v_2}{2}\right)\left(t - \frac{x}{c}\right)\cos 2\pi \left(\frac{v_1 - v_2}{2}\right)\left(t - \frac{x}{c}\right)$$

This is the product of a wave of average frequency $(v_1 + v_2)/2$ times a wave of low frequency $(v_1 - v_2)/2$. The general effect is shown in Fig. 21.4. At any point along the x axis an oscillation of the average frequency takes place, but its amplitude varies between 0 and $2y_m$, achieving two moments of maximum amplitude (approximately) in each period of the slower oscillation. These pulses of maximum amplitude are called *beats*. They occur at a frequency twice that of the slow oscillation,

(21.19) $v_{\text{beat}} = v_1 - v_2 = \Delta v$

where v_1 is the faster of the two initial frequencies.

Whenever the phase velocity of waves depends on the frequency, the preceding deduction is incomplete, for we used c as the velocity in each case. Let us repeat, using the symmetric form (21.9) and writing $v_1 - v_2$ as Δv. The development is as follows:

$$y_1 = y_m \sin 2\pi[(v + \Delta v)t - (k + \Delta k)x]$$
$$y_2 = y_m \sin 2\pi(vt - kx)$$
$$y = y_1 + y_2$$
$$= 2y_m \sin 2\pi \left[\left(v + \frac{\Delta v}{2}\right)t - \left(k + \frac{\Delta k}{2}\right)x\right]\cos 2\pi \left(\frac{\Delta v}{2} t - \frac{\Delta k}{2} x\right)$$

The result as before is the product of a wave of average frequency by a wave of frequency $\frac{1}{2}\Delta v$. But this time it is easy to express the rate at which the grouping of waves into pulses progresses. The velocity with which such beat formations move is called the *group velocity u*. Just as $c = v/k$ as in (21.6), so here

(21.20) $u = \dfrac{\Delta v}{\Delta k}$

Since the frequencies are assumed to be close (and since in some cases a whole continuous range of frequencies might be involved), we write

(21.21) $u = \dfrac{dv}{dk}$

The concept of group velocity is especially important in electromagnetic theory.

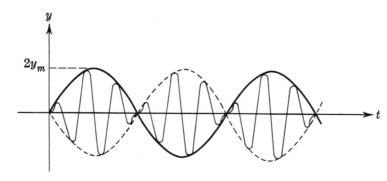

Figure
21.4

EXERCISES

14. A tone of frequency 300 per second is superimposed on a tone of unknown frequency. Beats of frequency 5 per second result. What can be said concerning the unknown frequency?
15. Express group velocity in terms of v and λ.
16. Verify the equation $u = c - \lambda(dc/d\lambda)$.

21.6. STANDING WAVES

As a second application of the superposition theorem, let us consider what happens when two simple harmonic waves differing only in direction are superimposed. To allow for various phase relationships, epoch angles ϵ_1 and ϵ_2 are added. The equations of the waves are written thus:

$$y_1 = y_m \sin\left[2\pi(vt + kx) + \epsilon_1\right]$$
$$y_2 = y_m \sin\left[2\pi(vt - kx) + \epsilon_2\right]$$

Then the net disturbance is given by

$$y = y_1 + y_2$$

(21.22) $$y = 2y_m \sin\left(2\pi vt + \frac{\epsilon_1 + \epsilon_2}{2}\right) \cos\left(2\pi kx + \frac{\epsilon_1 - \epsilon_2}{2}\right)$$

This pattern of disturbance is quite different from the ones looked at so far. It is not going anywhere. The first factor, depending only on t, shows that there is a simple harmonic oscillation of frequency v at each point. The amplitude of this oscillation varies from point to point. The second factor, depending only on x, allows us to evaluate this amplitude. This second factor describes the limits between which the oscillation can take place. In Fig. 21.5 the black curve is merely a graph of

$$y = 2y_m \cos\left(2\pi kx + \frac{\epsilon_1 - \epsilon_2}{2}\right)$$

The dotted lines show how the disturbance pattern oscillates when the remaining factor, $\sin\left[2\pi vt + (\epsilon_1 + \epsilon_2)/2\right]$, assumes values other than $+1$. It is clear that there are some points where the amplitude is always zero. These are called *nodes* and are indicated by N_1, N_2, N_3 in the figure. They are points where the two waves always cancel each other. The points of maximum amplitude halfway between the nodes are *antinodes* or *loops*. Since both nodes and antinodes are fixed in position and since each point partakes of an oscillation of constant amplitude, the phenomenon is called a *standing wave* or *stationary wave*.

The location of certain nodes and antinodes is usually fixed by the conditions of a specific problem. For instance, a string with both ends fixed must have nodes

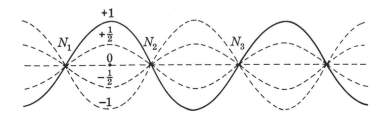

Figure
21.5

at these ends if stationary waves are set up. Other nodes may occur between, but the fixed ends are nodes anyway. A free end of a one-dimensional oscillating medium is normally a loop. Equation (21.22) may be adapted to such situations, with convenient coordinates, by taking suitable values for ϵ_1 and ϵ_2. First, let us take $\epsilon_1 = \epsilon_2 = 0$. We have

$$(21.23) \qquad\qquad y = 2y_m \sin 2\pi vt \cos 2\pi kx$$

This form will be convenient when a loop is at the origin. Now take $-\epsilon_1 = +\epsilon_2 = \pi/2$. We then have

$$(21.24) \qquad\qquad y = 2y_m \sin 2\pi vt \sin 2\pi kx$$

This indicates a node at the origin.

Let us see how stationary waves might be set up in a string of length l. Nodes must occur at $x = 0$ and $x = l$; therefore we shall use Eq. (21.24) and insist that

$$\sin 2\pi kl = 0$$

This is satisfied if $2\pi kl = n\pi$ for any integer $n = 0, 1, 2, 3, \ldots$, but the case $n = 0$ is not interesting here. An equivalent statement is

$$\lambda = \frac{2}{n} l = \frac{1}{k} \qquad n = 1, 2, 3, \ldots$$

Let us see what frequencies are possible, assuming that the phase velocity c is fixed:

$$v = ck = \frac{nc}{2l} \qquad n = 1, 2, 3, \ldots$$

These frequencies correspond to the various *normal modes of oscillation* given by the successive integers. The lowest frequency, for $n = 1$, is called *fundamental*.

These basic facts about stationary waves on a string enable us to check formula (21.16) for c. Suppose that transverse sinusoidal stationary waves are set up in a string of linear density q and tension f. Isolate the portion of the string between adjacent nodes as shown in Fig. 21.6. An equation of the curve at time t is

$$y = b \sin 2\pi kx$$

where b is, by (21.24), given by

$$b = 2y_m \sin 2\pi vt$$

The center of mass of the isolated segment is in simple harmonic motion, so

$$\bar{a} = -\omega^2 \bar{y}$$

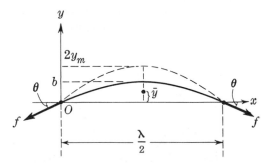

Figure
21.6

As usual,

(21.25) $$\Sigma f_y = m\bar{a}$$

First, let us compute the forces

$$\Sigma f_y = -2f \sin \theta$$

But for small displacements we have at the origin

$$\sin \theta = \frac{dy}{dx} = 2\pi kb \cos 2\pi kx = 2\pi kb$$

Thus

$$\Sigma f_y = -4\pi kbf$$

Next $\bar{y}$ is computed as

$$\bar{y} = \frac{1}{m} \int_0^{\lambda/2} y \, dm = \frac{2}{\lambda q} \int_0^{\lambda/2} qb \sin 2\pi kx \, dx$$

$$= \frac{b}{\pi} \left[- \cos 2\pi kx \right]_0^{\lambda/2} = \frac{2b}{\pi}$$

Substituting in (21.25)

$$-4\pi kbf = \frac{\lambda}{2} q \left(-\omega^2 \frac{2b}{\pi} \right)$$

Regrouping, and substituting $k = 1/\lambda$,

$$\frac{f}{q} = \frac{\lambda^2 \omega^2}{4\pi^2}$$

By (21.4) we recognize the right member of this equation as c^2, so

(21.26) $$c^2 = \frac{f}{q}$$

EXERCISES

17. A string 3 m long and weighing 50 g is subjected to a tension of 200 newtons. Both ends are fixed. Find the frequency and the location of the nodes for the first and third normal modes of oscillation.

18. Derive a formula for normal frequencies for a string of length l, mass m, and tension f.

21.7. LONGITUDINAL VIBRATIONS IN A NARROW UNIFORM BAR

As a second concrete illustration of wave motion, let us consider a straight narrow uniform bar of cross section a, density δ, and Young's modulus ψ. We shall suppose that a state of longitudinal strain is caused to exist in part of the rod and that this disturbance is allowed to be transmitted along the rod. Because of the narrowness of the bar, we shall neglect all transverse effects such as contractions given by Poisson's ratio. We shall assume that each plane normal to the rod acts as a unit. In other words, all points in a given plane section always have the same displacements. We shall find a basic equation, analogous to (21.13), which must be satisfied. We isolate the portion of the undisturbed rod determined by coordinates x and $x + \Delta x$ as shown in Fig. 21.7. When the rod is disturbed, to each point x is associated a displacement ξ. Thus ξ is a function of both position and time. It corresponds to the vector displacement **H** in Chap. 20. The isolated portion is then bounded by

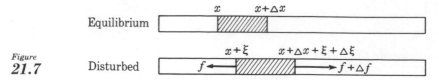

Figure
21.7   Disturbed

planes at $x + \xi$ and $x + \Delta x + \xi + \Delta \xi$. Let the corresponding tensions be f and $f + \Delta f$. By Hooke's law (see 19.9) we have at any point

$$(21.27) \qquad \frac{f}{a} = \psi \, \frac{\partial \xi}{\partial x}$$

Therefore Δf can be expressed

$$(21.28) \qquad \Delta f = a\psi \, \Delta \left(\frac{\partial \xi}{\partial x} \right)$$

But the equation of motion, $f - ma$, for the isolated portion is

$$(21.29) \qquad \Delta f = a\delta \, \Delta x \, \frac{\partial^2 \xi}{\partial t^2}$$

Equate the two expressions for Δf, divide by Δx, and take the limit as Δx is allowed to approach zero. We get

$$(21.30) \qquad \psi \, \frac{\partial^2 \xi}{\partial x^2} = \delta \, \frac{\partial^2 \xi}{\partial t^2}$$

Comparison with (21.14) shows this to be the condition for waves traveling at speed

$$(21.31) \qquad c = \sqrt{\frac{\psi}{\delta}}$$

Since each normal section acts as a unit, the resulting motion is an example of a *plane wave*.

Problems involving standing waves follow a pattern similar to those for transverse waves on a string. A fixed end of a bar is automatically a node. For it, $\xi = 0$. A free end, on the other hand, is characterized by $f = 0$ or, according to (21.27), by $\partial \xi / \partial x = 0$. Specific cases are left as exercises.

Let us now look at the energies carried by such a wave. When an arbitrarily small segment of length dx is stretched by an amount $d\xi$, the work done is $\frac{1}{2} f \, d\xi$, so, in the limit, the potential energy per length is $\frac{1}{2} f (\partial \xi / \partial x)$. Using (21.27), we get

$$(21.32) \qquad \text{p.e. per volume} = \tfrac{1}{2} \psi \left(\frac{\partial \xi}{\partial x} \right)^2$$

The kinetic energy per volume is at once seen to be

$$(21.33) \qquad \text{k.e. per volume} = \tfrac{1}{2} \delta \left(\frac{\partial \xi}{\partial t} \right)^2$$

In the case of a traveling wave given by

$$\xi = \xi(z) = \xi(x - ct)$$

the derivatives are

$$\frac{\partial \xi}{\partial x} = \frac{d\xi}{dz} \frac{\partial z}{\partial x} = \frac{d\xi}{dz} \quad (1)$$

$$\frac{\partial \xi}{\partial t} = \frac{d\xi}{dz} \frac{\partial z}{\partial t} = \frac{d\xi}{dz} (-c)$$

so that

(21.34)
$$\frac{\partial \xi}{\partial t} = -c \frac{\partial \xi}{\partial x}$$

Substituting in (21.33), we get

$$\text{k.e. per volume} = \tfrac{1}{2} c^2 \delta \left(\frac{\partial \xi}{\partial x} \right)^2$$

which, by (21.31), is equal to the expression in (21.32); thus for a progressive longitudinal wave along a bar at a given instant and at a given position

(21.35)   k.e. per volume = p.e. per volume

The preceding conclusion may seem startling. In simple oscillators such as pendulums the kinetic energy and potential energy are out of phase. For waves, we have just seen that they can rise and fall together. This solution may seem like a violation of conservation of energy. But we are discussing merely the energy *at a point*: the energy flows in pulses in the direction of the wave. Some of these points may be cleared up by Fig. 21.8. A section of the bar is shown in unstrained state. A number of equidistant plane normal sections are drawn. The graph of ξ represents a simple harmonic wave at a given moment t. The diagram of the strained bar shows the positions at time t of each plane section previously noted. Observe that the points of zero displacement are points of *rarefaction* and *condensation*. The graph of $\partial \xi / \partial x$ (showing the slope of the other graph) has peaks at

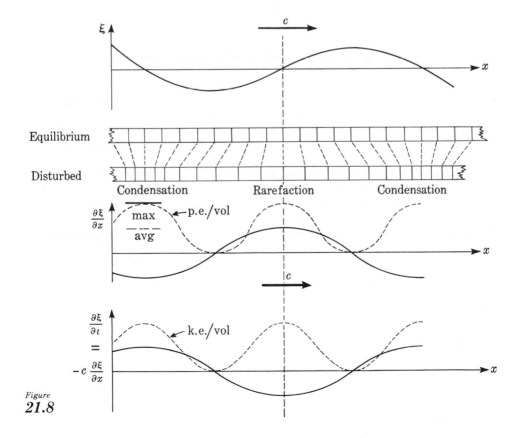

Figure
21.8

the rarefactions and valleys at the condensations. The graph of $\partial \xi/\partial t$, based on (21.34), shows that points in the section at the middle of the condensation are moving to the right at maximum speed, while those at the rarefactions are moving to the left with maximum speed. This clearly has the effect of moving the condensations and rarefactions to the right—and of course all the patterns shown must move to the right at speed c. The two dotted graphs, of the energies per volume, based on the squares of the other curves in accordance with (21.32) and (21.33), have peaks at the points of condensation (maximum compression) and points of rarefaction (maximum stretch). For the simple harmonic case, it is clear that the average total energy per volume is equal to the peak value of either the kinetic or the potential energy per volume. The following outlines the argument, using overlines for averages, on a per-volume basis:

$$\overline{\text{t.e.}} = \overline{\text{p.e.} + \text{k.e.}} = 2\,\overline{\text{k.e.}} = (\text{k.e.})_{max}$$

Assuming constant density, this gives us

$$\text{max k.e. per volume} = \tfrac{1}{2}\delta v_{max}^2$$

Now let us take an equation of the disturbance to be

(21.36)
$$\xi = \xi_m \sin \omega\left(t - \frac{x}{c}\right)$$

Then we get

$$v_{max} = \left(\frac{\partial \xi}{\partial t}\right)_{max} = \omega \xi_m$$

and so

(21.37)
$$\overline{\text{t.e. per volume}} = \tfrac{1}{2}\delta(\omega\xi_m)^2$$

EXERCISES

19. What is the speed of a longitudinal vibration along a steel wire for which the density is 7,900 kg/m³ and Young's modulus is 20×10^{10} newtons/m²?
20. A uniform bar is stretched with a force f. Its length, area, density, and Young's modulus are l, a, δ, and ψ. Find the speed with which longitudinal vibrations travel along the bar. Show all details of your deduction.
21. A uniform bar of length l has one end clamped and the other end free. Write a standing-wave equation for the nth normal mode in terms of n, c, l.
22. A steel bar 1 m long is clamped at its mid-point. What are its normal frequencies? Use the constants of Exercise 19.
23. A free uniform bar of length l carries standing waves. Write a standing-wave equation for the nth normal mode in terms of n, c, l.

21.8. PLANE SOUND WAVES IN A COLUMN OF FLUID

The analysis of the preceding section can easily be adapted to cover plane longitudinal waves in a fluid. We may apply the Euler equation from the chapter on hydromechanics:

(21.38)
$$\mathscr{F} - \frac{1}{\delta}\nabla p = \mathbf{A}$$

For this application we are concerned only with the wave motion; thus we ignore the $\mathscr{F}$. Since we shall consider only motion in the x direction where each plane normal to the x direction moves as a unit, the equation for us is

(21.39)
$$\frac{\partial p}{\partial x} = -\delta \frac{\partial^2 \xi}{\partial t^2}$$

(The partial derivative is still used for p, since p varies with t as well as with x.) Denoting the equilibrium pressure by p_0 and the instantaneous pressure by p, we may write

$$p = p_0 + p'$$

and

(21.40)
$$\frac{\partial p}{\partial x} = \frac{\partial p'}{\partial x}$$

The excess pressure p' (positive, zero, or negative) will interest us more than the absolute pressure p.

At any point in the fluid the excess pressure p' goes hand in hand with a strain $\Delta v/v$. This strain, assuming the column of fluid to be of uniform cross section, is given by

$$\frac{\Delta v}{v} = \frac{\partial \xi}{\partial x}$$

For, as in Fig. 21.9, if $v = a \, \Delta x$ and $\Delta v = a \, \Delta \xi$, then in the limit the preceding evaluation of $\Delta v/v$ must hold. Hence, using the bulk modulus equation (19.11),

$$p' = -\beta \frac{\partial \xi}{\partial x}$$

(The student should convince himself that it is valid to use this equation with only the excess pressure p' taken account of.) Differentiating the last equation with respect to x,

(21.41)
$$\frac{\partial p'}{\partial x} = -\beta \frac{\partial^2 \xi}{\partial x^2}$$

We may now eliminate p and p' from (21.39), (21.40), and (21.41) to get

(21.42)
$$\beta \frac{\partial^2 \xi}{\partial x^2} = \delta \frac{\partial^2 \xi}{\partial t^2}$$

This is satisfied by waves of velocity

(21.43)
$$c = \sqrt{\frac{\beta}{\delta}}$$

For gases, the bulk modulus β depends conspicuously on the way in which compressions take place. If the processes are *isothermal*, an ideal gas satisfies

$$\beta = p$$

	x		$x + \Delta x$	
Equilibrium	p_0	v	p_0	

	$x + \xi$		$x + \Delta x + \xi + \Delta \xi$	
Disturbed	$p_0 + p'$	$v + \Delta v$	$p_0 + p' + \Delta p'$	

Figure
21.9

as will be shown in the chapter on the kinetic theory of gases. If the process is *adiabatic*,

$$\beta = \gamma p$$

where γ is the ratio of two important specific heats of a gas. These matters also will be taken up in the next chapter. For air, this ratio has the value 1.4. Since the longitudinal motion in a sound wave is too rapid to allow temperature to remain constant, the hypothesis of adiabatic processes gives results more nearly in accord with experiment.

EXERCISES

24. Compute the speed of sound in air under standard conditions assuming (*a*) isothermal compressions and (*b*) adiabatic compressions. Take the density of air as 1.2 kg/m³.

25. What is the speed of sound in water? Take bulk modulus as 2.1×10^9 newtons/m².

REVIEW EXERCISES

26. What is the speed of a wave whose equation is

$$y = 0.10 \sin 2\pi(1{,}000t - 3x)$$

27. Verify that for a wave on a string given by $y = y(x - ct)$ the kinetic energy and potential energy are equal.

28. Show that the total energy (k.e. + p.e.) of a simple harmonic transverse wave on a string is proportional to the square of the amplitude.

29. Show that the total energy (p.e. + k.e.) of a string with its ends fixed and experiencing stationary waves in the *n*th normal mode is given by

$$\text{t.e.} = 4\pi^2 q l v^2 y_m^2$$

where the symbols have the same meaning as in Sec. 21.6.

30. Find algebraic expressions for the potential and kinetic energies per volume for a simple harmonic longitudinal traveling wave on a uniform bar. Express results in terms of ξ_m, ν, c, and δ as functions of t and x.

31. Show that the total energy in a long bar of length l and cross section a carrying a wave given by (21.36) is equal to $2\pi^2 k^2 \psi a l \xi_m^2$.

32. Show that the average rate at which energy is propagated by a longitudinal wave given by (21.36) along a narrow bar of cross section a is equal to $2\pi^2 \nu^2 \delta a c \xi_m^2$.

33. Derive formulas analogous to (21.32) and (21.33) for energies per volume for a plane sound wave. (Recall the work formula for ideal fluids: $\int p\, dv$.)

34. Show that, when simple harmonic plane sound waves are set up in a tube, the excess pressure always has its extreme values at displacement nodes.

35. The *intensity* of a sound wave is equal to the average power transmitted per area. Show that for a plane simple harmonic sound wave in a tube of fluid of uniform cross section the intensity is proportional to the square of the amplitude of the oscillation.

CHAPTER TWENTY-TWO

KINETIC THEORY

In the fitting of mathematical descriptions to physical phenomena, some conscious approximations are always made. Max Planck remarks, "Nature does not allow herself to be exhaustively expressed in human thought." No theory is the last word, but rather a partial description. A theory is good as long as it is useful. The model of a gas which we are about to study is based on admittedly inadmissible assumptions. It is not a modern theory; it was in its prime many years ago, and some of its ideas were advanced two thousand years ago. One justification for studying this doctrine is that it is still a useful one, for many verifiable conclusions can be easily deduced from the simple mechanical model postulated. Another justification is the fact that here we have a first significant application of mechanics using probability. Theoretical physics now abounds with fruitful combinations of mechanical ideas and statistical arguments. A brief but more sophisticated illustration will be presented in Sec. 23.6.

22.1. CLAUSIUS' POSTULATES FOR THE KINETIC THEORY OF GASES

The supposition that *temperature* is closely related to the *kinetic energy of molecules* in motion had antecedents in the meditations of Democritus (400 B.C.) and Lucretius (A.D. 55), in the deductions of Gassendi (1620) and Hooke (1650), and in the theorizing of Daniel Bernoulli (1730). In the middle of the last century the relationship between heat and mechanical energy was investigated experimentally by Joule and Rowland. Soon after this the kinetic theory was established as a sound mathematical theory by the efforts of Clausius and Maxwell. As a starting point, we shall accept Clausius' postulates for gases:

(22.1) *For a monatomic gas, molecules are identical solid spheres traveling in straight lines except for collisions.*

(22.2) *Collisions are instantaneous and perfectly elastic. No other forces are exerted between molecules.*

(22.3) *The size of molecules is negligible in comparison with the space in which they move.*

From these postulates one may deduce many of the classical properties of ideal gases. These results may then be modified when necessary in order that the behavior of real gases be understood.

22.2. AN ELEMENTARY APPROACH TO MOLECULAR VELOCITIES

As a first exercise in treating molecules as perfectly elastic spheres, let us consider a single sphere rattling around in an otherwise empty spherical room. This molecule will be subject only to forces of collisions when it strikes the wall. These forces are normal, since the wall is smooth, and radial, since it is spherical. This implies that the motion is plane, for each impulse is a vector in the plane determined by the path before collision and by the center of the sphere. In other terms one might note that the forces are central; so plane motion results. The great circle shown in Fig. 22.1 is in this plane of motion. $\mathbf{R}$ and $\mathbf{R}'$ are successive points of collision. Since the coefficient of restitution is 1, it follows that

$$v' \cos \theta' = v \cos \theta$$

Taking the tangential component of the impulse-momentum equation, we have

$$-mv \sin \theta + mv' \sin \theta' = 0$$

Hence

$$v' \sin \theta' = v \sin \theta$$

and dividing by the previous equation,

$$\tan \theta' = \tan \theta$$

Thus

$$\theta' = \theta \qquad v = v'$$

The impulse at such a collision has magnitude (see Fig. 22.1b)

$$\left| \int \mathbf{F} \, dt \right| = 2mv \sin (90° - \theta) = 2mv \cos \theta$$

The distance traveled between collisions is

$$d = 2r \cos \theta$$

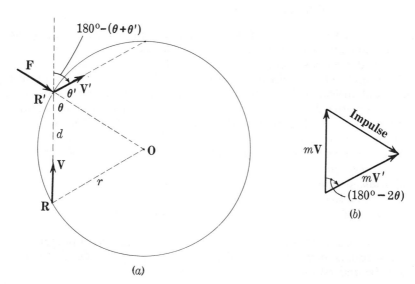

Figure
22.1

(a)

Hence the time between collisions is

$$t = \frac{d}{v} = \frac{2r \cos \theta}{v}$$

Now the force in the preceding discussion is intermittent. Its average magnitude, however, has some interest:

(22.4)
$$\bar{f} = \frac{1}{t} \left| \int \mathbf{F} \, dt \right| = \frac{2mv \cos \theta}{(2r \cos \theta)/v} = m \frac{v^2}{r}$$

Note that this value is independent of θ: it is the same for $\theta = 0°$ and $\theta = 90°$. The extreme case of $\theta = 90°$ we must interpret as uniform circular motion; therefore it is reassuring to observe that the value $\bar{f}$ is correct for the corresponding centripetal force.

Let us now consider what changes there would be if there were a large number, n, of molecules in the room. Collisions between molecules are perfectly elastic; therefore we shall assume that on the average the total force exerted by the room will be the same as if the molecules did not interfere with each other. If there are enough spheres as with a gas, the force magnitude may be described in terms of the pressure,

(22.5)
$$p = \frac{n\bar{f}}{4\pi r^2} = \frac{nm\bar{v}^2}{4\pi r^3}$$

where $\bar{v}^2$ is the result of averaging v^2 for the different molecules. Now the density of the gas in the room is evaluated as the mass of the gas divided by the volume of the room:

(22.6)
$$\delta = \frac{nm}{\frac{4}{3}\pi r^3}$$

We have, then,

(22.7)
$$p = \frac{\delta \bar{v}^2}{3}$$

or

(22.8)
$$\bar{v} = \sqrt{\frac{3p}{\delta}}$$

Since $\bar{v}$ was defined as the square root of the average of the squares of velocities, it is called the *root-mean-square speed* or *rms speed*.

For oxygen at standard temperature and pressure, this formula gives the value

$$\bar{v} = 460 \text{ m/sec}$$

EXERCISES

1. Find the rms molecular speed of hydrogen under standard conditions (density is 9.0×10^{-2} kg/m³).

2. Two molecules collide; the first having mass m has velocities $\mathbf{U}$ and $\mathbf{V}$ before and after impact. The second has mass m' and corresponding velocities $\mathbf{U}'$ and $\mathbf{V}'$. Take their line of centers at impact as the x axis. Show that the energy gained by the first molecule is

$$\frac{2mm'}{(m + m')^2} [(m'u_x'^2 - mu_x^2) + (m - m')u_x u_x']$$

Compare this result with that of Chap. 12, Exercise 40.

3. A rectangular box contains perfectly elastic spherical molecules. Assume that the molecules all travel at speed $\bar{v}$, one-third of them parallel to each edge. Show that Eq. (22.8) is satisfied.

22.3. THE VIRIAL THEOREM OF CLAUSIUS

The derivation of the preceding section gave us a formula which actually is valid for containers of other shapes. In this section a more general derivation is given. The method used makes it possible to deduce further results in later sections.

Consider a finite set of particles of masses m_i and position vectors $\mathbf{R}_i$ moving in a *confined space* with finite speeds. Let $\mathbf{F}_i$ be the resultant of all forces acting on the ith particle. For each particle we consider the quantity $-0.5\mathbf{R}_i \cdot \mathbf{F}_i$. The time average of the sum of these quantities is called the *virial* of the system of particles:

$$(22.9) \qquad \text{Virial} = \overline{-0.5 \sum_{i=1}^{n} \mathbf{R}_i \cdot \mathbf{F}_i} = \overline{-0.5 \sum_{i=1}^{n} m_i \mathbf{R}_i \cdot \mathbf{A}_i}$$

We shall compare the virial with the average translational kinetic energy of the system.

$$\overline{\text{k.e.}} - \text{virial} = \overline{0.5 \sum_{i=1}^{n} m_i (\mathbf{V}_i \cdot \mathbf{V}_i + \mathbf{R}_i \cdot \mathbf{A}_i)}$$

$$= \overline{0.5 \sum_{i=1}^{n} m_i \frac{d}{dt}(\mathbf{R}_i \cdot \mathbf{V}_i)}$$

$$= \overline{0.25 \sum_{i=1}^{n} m_i \frac{d^2}{dt^2}(\mathbf{R}_i \cdot \mathbf{R}_i)}$$

In random chaotic motion of gas molecules within a confined space the distribution of particles tends to become statistically steady even though the motion of any individual may be far from regular. For this reason, the sum of the quantities $\mathbf{R}_i \cdot \mathbf{R}_i$ is practically constant, and its derivatives are practically zero.

The average value of its second derivative is certainly indistinguishable from zero if the average is taken over a sufficiently long time (say, a thousandth of a second, during which time a typical molecule would have experienced a million collisions). With the right member of the last equation equal to zero, we have the conclusion

$$(22.10) \qquad \overline{\text{k.e.}} = \text{virial}$$

This is the *virial theorem of Clausius*. This theorem will be employed in computing the average kinetic energy of gas molecules under given conditions of pressure and density.

Consider now gas molecules in a closed container. By our postulates only forces of collision are exerted on the molecules. Since the forces of impact between particles occur in equal and opposite pairs, the only forces which contribute to the virial are the contact forces at the boundary. These contact forces are best described in terms of the average pressure. For an element of boundary having area da and outward normal $\mathbf{N}$ (see Fig. 22.2), the total average force on the gas is

$$(22.11) \qquad d\mathbf{F} = -p\mathbf{N}\,da$$

The virial is then given by

$$(22.12) \qquad \text{Virial} = -\tfrac{1}{2}\int_a \mathbf{R} \cdot (-p\mathbf{N})\,da$$

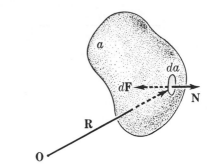

Figure
22.2   O

By the divergence theorem this may be rewritten as

$$(22.13) \qquad \text{Virial} = \tfrac{1}{2}p \int_b \boldsymbol{\nabla} \cdot \mathbf{R} \, db = \frac{3pb}{2}$$

where b denotes volume. By the virial theorem, then,

$$(22.14) \qquad \overline{\text{k.e.}} = \frac{1}{2} \overline{\sum_{i=1}^{n} m_i v_i^2} = \frac{3pb}{2}$$

This result has been derived for gases whose molecules are particles, i.e., for mon-atomic molecules. It may be used for other gases if it is understood that the virial theorem concerns only translational kinetic energy.

We shall denote by $\bar{v}$ the rms molecular speed defined for this more general situation by

$$(22.15) \qquad \bar{v}^2 = \frac{\Sigma \, m_i v_i^2}{\Sigma \, m_i}$$

The rms speed is then given by

$$\bar{v}^2 = \frac{3pb}{\Sigma \, m_i}$$

Since the average density δ of the gas is precisely mass divided by volume, we conclude as before

$$(22.16) \qquad \bar{v} = \sqrt{\frac{3p}{\delta}}$$

In Chap. 18 gas velocities were discussed, but in that treatment our gas model was quite different. We then treated gas as a continuous homogeneous fluid. The chaotic motion of individual molecules was ignored, and only motion of the fluid as a whole was investigated. It should be emphasized that the results just derived concern the individual motion of a fairly typical molecule. The statistical question about the range and distribution of molecular speeds will be considered later.

EXERCISES

4. A perfectly elastic spherical molecule of mass 4.0×10^{-26} kg travels in a repetitive path around a cubical box 5.0 cm wide as shown in Fig. 22.3. Its speed is 500 m/sec. (a) Taking the center O as origin, compute the contributions to the virial at **A, B, C,** and **D.** (b) Taking the corner **O'** as origin, compute the contributions to the virial at **A, B, C,** and **D.** (c) What is the kinetic energy?

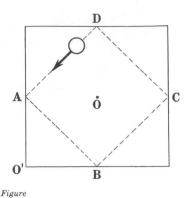

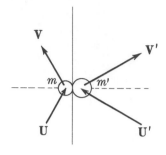

Figure
22.3

Figure
22.4

5. Use the virial theorem directly to compute the rms molecular velocity of a gas in a spherical vessel without appealing to the divergence theorem. (HINT: Use center of sphere as origin.)

22.4. EQUIPARTITION OF ENERGY

Consider a collision as in Fig. 22.4 between a gas molecule of mass m' and a vibrating wall molecule (in the boundary of the container) of mass m. If the line of centers at impact is taken as the x axis, the y and z components of velocity will be unchanged by the collision. Since such molecules are considered as perfectly elastic spheres, the coefficient of restitution is 1. A direct calculation (see Sec. 22.2, Exercise 2) shows that the energy gained at impact by the wall molecule is

$$\frac{2mm'}{(m + m')^2} [(m'u_x'^2 - mu_x^2) + (m - m')u_x u_x']$$

Assuming that the wall molecule is in harmonic oscillation, the average value of u_x is zero; thus *on the average* the gas molecules gain kinetic energy from such collisions only if their energy before collision is less than that of wall molecules. This average molecular kinetic energy may be taken as a measure of temperature. The temperatures of gas and container thus tend to become equal.

   If two gases are in the same container, their temperatures approach that of the container, and when equal temperatures exist, the average molecular kinetic energies are equal:

(22.17) $\frac{1}{2}m_1\bar{v}_1^2 = \frac{1}{2}m_2\bar{v}_2^2$

At a given temperature, then, big molecules move more slowly on the average than small ones.

   These examples show how energy tends to become uniformly distributed among molecules of gases. Thus far we have considered only monatomic molecules (spherical) having three degrees of freedom (three of translation; rotation is ignored because of the trivial moment of inertia). A diatomic molecule (dumbbell-shaped) has five degrees of freedom (two of rotation in addition to three of translation). At a given temperature such a molecule will have on the average 67 per cent more total kinetic energy than a monatomic molecule. Thus the principle of equipartition of energy extends to degrees of freedom: energy tends to become uniformly distributed among degrees of freedom of molecular motion.

22.5. THE LAWS OF DALTON, BOYLE, AND AVOGADRO

In Sec. 22.3 we concluded that

$$\overline{k.e.} = \text{virial} = \tfrac{3}{2}pb$$

for gas in a container. Let us now consider what happens when two distinct families of molecules are mixed together in the same container. As before,

$$\overline{k.e.} = (\overline{k.e.})_1 + (\overline{k.e.})_2 = \text{virial} = \tfrac{3}{2}pb$$

Also, considering each of the gases by itself,

$$(\overline{k.e.})_1 = (\text{virial})_1 \qquad (\overline{k.e.})_2 = (\text{virial})_2$$

Now, $(\text{virial})_1$ has two parts: that due to the boundary and that due to the other gas.

$$(\text{virial})_1 = (\text{virial})_{1b} + (\text{virial})_{1g}$$

Similarly,

$$(\text{virial})_2 = (\text{virial})_{2b} + (\text{virial})_{2g}$$

The contributions of the walls are already known:

$$(\text{virial})_{1b} = \tfrac{3}{2}p_1 b$$

$$(\text{virial})_{2b} = \tfrac{3}{2}p_2 b$$

where p_1 is the pressure that would be caused by the first gas if it alone occupied the container, and p_2 likewise is the pressure which would exist if only the second gas were present. The other terms will, of course, be equal and opposite:

$$(\text{virial})_{1g} = -(\text{virial})_{2g}$$

because whenever there are collisions between the two families of molecules, the forces are equal and opposite. Combining the equations, we have

$$\tfrac{3}{2}pb = \tfrac{3}{2}p_1 b + \tfrac{3}{2}p_2 b$$

or

(22.18)
$$p = p_1 + p_2$$

This is *Dalton's law of partial pressures*. The pressure of a mixture of gases is the sum of the pressures which would be caused by the constituent gases taken singly.

For constant temperature, the average molecular kinetic energy is, we shall assume, constant. Under this interpretation of constancy of temperature, the equation

(22.19)
$$pb = \tfrac{2}{3}(\overline{k.e.})$$

is merely a restatement of *Boyle's law* concerning isothermal behavior of an ideal gas. In the next section we shall discuss this equation for the general case where $\overline{k.e.}$ is not constant.

If we have two samples of gases occupying equal volumes at equal pressures and equal temperatures, the number of molecules is the same for both samples. This is *Avogadro's hypothesis*. It is easily deduced from the principles already examined. By Boyle's law,

$$pb = (\tfrac{2}{3}n_1)(\tfrac{1}{2}m_1\bar{v}_1^2) = (\tfrac{2}{3}n_2)(\tfrac{1}{2}m_2\bar{v}_2^2)$$

where n_1 and n_2 are the numbers of molecules and m_1 and m_2 are the masses of single molecules. Equality of temperature implies equality of average molecular kinetic energy; thus

$$\tfrac{1}{2}m_1\bar{v}_1^2 = \tfrac{1}{2}m_2\bar{v}_2^2$$

Consequently,

(22.20) $n_1 = n_2$

Under standard conditions (0°C, barometer 76 cm), one molecular weight (mole, gram molecule) of an ideal gas occupies 22.4 liters. The number of molecules is called Avogadro's number: 6.02×10^{23}.

EXERCISES

6. Oxygen has rms molecular speed of 460 m/sec under standard conditions. Oxygen has molecular weight 32. Helium has molecular weight 4.0. What is its rms speed under standard conditions?

7. The bulk modulus of a gas is defined as

$$\beta = -b\frac{dp}{db}$$

Evaluate it in terms of pressure for *isothermal* compressions.

8. What in joules is the total kinetic energy of a roomful of air under standard conditions, taking the volume as 30 m³? (Treat as monatomic and then correct to allow for rotation of diatomic molecules.)

9. Explain qualitatively in terms of the virial why *real* gases do not obey Boyle's law at (*a*) low temperatures and (*b*) high pressures.

22.6. TEMPERATURE AND MOLECULAR ENERGY

For a gas consisting of n molecules, Boyle's law (22.19) may be written

(22.21) $pb = \tfrac{2}{3}n(\tfrac{1}{2}m\bar{v}^2)$

This may be compared with the general ideal-gas law of elementary physics

(22.22) $pb = nm\bar{g}\theta$

where m is the mass of a single molecule, and hence nm is the total mass, $\bar{g}$ is a gas constant depending on the particular gas considered, and θ is the absolute temperature. From this comparison we get a precise statement as to how temperature and average molecular energy are related:

$$\tfrac{1}{2}m\bar{v}^2 = \tfrac{3}{2}(m\bar{g})\theta$$

Now the product $m\bar{g}$ turns out to be independent of the gas used. It is equal to the famous *Boltzmann gas constant per molecule*, k. Its value is 1.38×10^{-23} joule/°C.

(22.23) $m\bar{g} = k$

We have, then,

(22.24) $\tfrac{1}{2}m\bar{v}^2 = \tfrac{3}{2}k\theta$

and for the *general ideal-gas law*,

(22.25) $pb = nk\theta$

Now the mean molecular energy used in (22.24) is that of translation only; thus only three degrees of freedom are involved. By the principle of equipartition, the energy associated with each degree of freedom is one-third of this amount. In general, if f is the number of degrees of freedom of a molecule, the total kinetic energy of the gas is given by

(22.26)   k.e. $= \tfrac{1}{2}fnk\theta$

22.7. THE SPECIFIC HEATS OF A GAS

When a gas is heated, the heat or added energy e is equal to the gain in kinetic energy plus the work done by the gas in expansion:

$$(22.27) \qquad \Delta e = \Delta(\text{k.e.}) + \int p \, db$$

This is a statement of the *first law of thermodynamics* for this situation.   In differential form,

$$(22.28) \qquad de = d(\text{k.e.}) + p \, db$$

A *specific heat* c of a gas is defined as heat per temperature change per mass:

$$(22.29) \qquad c = \frac{1}{nm} \frac{de}{d\theta}$$

The specific heat *at constant pressure* c_p will first be evaluated.   From (22.25), we get

$$p \, db = nk \, d\theta$$

and from (22.26)

$$d(\text{k.e.}) = \tfrac{1}{2} fnk \, d\theta$$

Using (22.28), we have

$$c_p = \frac{1}{nm} (\tfrac{1}{2} fnk + nk)$$

or

$$(22.30) \qquad c_p = \frac{(f+2)k}{2m}$$

The specific heat *at constant volume* c_v is more easily computed since we assume that no work is done.

$$(22.31) \qquad c_v = \frac{fk}{2m}$$

The ratio γ of these two principal specific heats occurs often in physics.

$$(22.32) \qquad \gamma = \frac{c_p}{c_v} = \frac{f+2}{f}$$

It is interesting to compare the last result with experimental values for real gases.   A few selected ones are tabulated below.

Gas	Temperature, °C	γ
Argon	15	1.67
Helium	18	1.63
Mercury vapor	360	1.67
Carbon monoxide	15	1.40
Hydrogen	15	1.41
Nitrogen	15	1.40
Oxygen	15	1.40
Ammonia	15	1.31
Carbon dioxide	15	1.30
Water vapor	100	1.32

Less convincing examples are easy to find. For example, at $-181°$ hydrogen has the value 1.60.

EXERCISES

10. What value of γ would be predicted by elementary kinetic theory for the 10 gases listed previously?

11. Show that

$$c_p - c_v = \bar{g} = \frac{k}{m}$$

12. *Molecular heat* is defined as the product of molecular weight by specific heat at constant volume. Show that

$$\text{Molecular heat} = 0.99f \quad \text{cal/°C}$$

This is essentially the *law of Dulong and Petit* (1819). This result may be compared with the following laboratory results for selected temperatures:

Argon:	3.0	Helium:	3.0	Mercury vapor:	3.0
Oxygen:	5.0	Hydrogen:	4.8	Nitrogen:	5.0

This law may be extended to solids by recognizing that, in addition to the kinetic energy of three degrees of vibratory freedom, there is an equal potential energy, so that here $j = 6$.
Compare with laboratory results:

Aluminum:	5.8	Iron:	6.0	Copper:	5.9
Zinc:	6.0	Silver:	.0	Tin:	6.4
Gold:	6.2				

13. Find the rms molecular velocity of hydrogen (compare Sec. 22.2, Exercise 1) at a pressure of 0.2 atm and a temperature of 100°C.

22.8. ADIABATIC PROCESSES

We have noted that when heat is added to a gas, it may result in an expansion as well as in a change in the energy of the gas. It is possible for a gas to expand or contract without the addition or removal of heat. In a very quick expansion, for instance, there may not be time for the gradual transfer of energy from walls of a cylinder; therefore the decrease in the virial caused by the withdrawal of a piston must be matched by a decrease in the kinetic energy of the gas. A process involving no transfer of heat is called *adiabatic*. It is characterized by the equation

(22.33) $de = 0$

or, using (22.28),

(22.34) $d(\text{k.e.}) = -p \, db$

We shall now derive an equation relating the pressure and volume of a gas. Using (22.26) to express the general ideal-gas law (22.25) in terms of kinetic energy rather than temperature, we have

(22.35) $pb = \frac{2}{f}(\text{k.e.})$

Differentiating and substituting (22.34),

$$p \, db + b \, dp = \frac{2}{f}d(\text{k.e.}) = -\frac{2}{f} p \, db$$

Rearranging terms,

$$b\,dp = -\left(1 + \frac{2}{f}\right)p\,db$$

Using (22.32) and dividing by bp,

(22.36)
$$\frac{dp}{p} = -\gamma\frac{db}{b}$$

This may be integrated to give

(22.37)
$$pb^\gamma = \text{const}$$

which is a standard equation for adiabatic behavior of an ideal gas.

EXERCISES

14. Derive a formula in terms of pressure for the bulk modulus of a gas for *adiabatic* compressions. Compare with Sec. 22.5, Exercise 7.
15. Show that for an adiabatic process $\theta b^{\gamma-1}$ is a constant.
16. The volume of a sample of air is suddenly doubled. The original temperature was 27°C. What is the final temperature?
17. A flask of gas is allowed to expand adiabatically. The original temperature is θ_1; the final temperature is θ_2. Show that the work done by the gas in expanding is

$$mc_v(\theta_1 - \theta_2)$$

where m is the total mass of the gas.

22.9. AN ADIABATIC OSCILLATOR

In this section we shall look briefly at a dynamic method of determining the ratio of specific heats, γ, of a gas. A flask of volume b is fitted with a precision-bore glass tube as shown in Fig. 22.5. A pellet of mass m and radius r (very slightly less than that of the tube) is dropped down the tube. If b is of a suitable size and if the fit is sufficiently snug, there will be an equilibrium position (shown by the dotted axis in the figure) for which the weight of the pellet and the net force due to pressure of the air outside and gas inside will just balance:

(22.38)
$$mg = \pi r^2(p - p_0)$$

When the pellet is at some other position, the net force is a restoring force. For a displacement y, let the pressure increase be Δp; then the equation of motion is

$$\pi r^2(p + \Delta p - p_0) - mg = m\frac{d^2y}{dt^2}$$

or, using the equilibrium equation,

$$\pi r^2\,\Delta p = m\frac{d^2y}{dt^2}$$

To find how Δp and y are related, we assume that the process is adiabatic, and hence we use (22.36)

$$\Delta p = -\gamma p\frac{\Delta b}{b}$$

For a displacement y, the volume change is

$$\Delta b = \pi r^2 y$$

Thus we may substitute

$$\Delta p = -\gamma p\frac{\pi r^2}{b}y$$

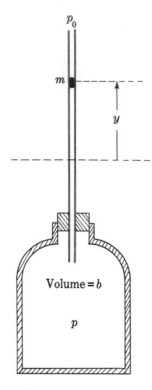

Figure
22.5

and find for an equation of motion

(22.39)
$$-\gamma p\,\frac{\pi^2 r^4}{bm}\,y = \frac{d^2y}{dt^2}$$

This represents a simple harmonic oscillation of period

(22.40)
$$\tau = \frac{2}{r^2}\sqrt{\frac{mb}{\gamma p}}$$

In this equation b is the volume up to the equilibrium position of the pellet and p is given by (22.38). If m, b, τ, r, and p are measured, γ may be computed. This method is due to Rüchhardt.

EXERCISE

18. An experiment of the type described in this section was carried out with a 5-liter jar and a tube of inner diameter $\frac{5}{8}$ in. The pellet had mass 33.2 g. Its equilibrium position was 44 cm above the top of the jar. The barometer reading was 76 cm. The period of oscillation was measured as 1.14 sec. On the basis of these data compute γ.

22.10. VELOCITY-SPACE REPRESENTATION OF A GAS

In Sec. 5.8 a brief introduction was given to the idea of a velocity space. In thinking about varying speeds for gas molecules, we shall find it very useful to represent in velocity space the motion of each molecule by a point called the *representative point* of the molecule. Consider, then, a three-dimensional space in which each point is designated by a triple of numbers (v_x, v_y, v_z). Just as the position vector of each molecule in configuration space (**R** space) is given by $\mathbf{R} = x\mathbf{I} + y\mathbf{J} + z\mathbf{K}$, where x, y, z are the coordinates of the particle, so in velocity space (**V** space), each representative point has position vector $\mathbf{V} = \dot{x}\mathbf{I} + \dot{y}\mathbf{J} + \dot{z}\mathbf{K} = v_x\mathbf{I} + v_y\mathbf{J} + v_z\mathbf{K}$, where the coordinates are the x, y, and z components of the velocity of the particle. Using the language of Chap. 12, Exercise 48, a path traced out in **V** space by the representative point of a molecule is the hodograph of the molecule.

It is interesting to reflect on the behavior in **V** space of the multitude of representative points for a sample of a Clausius gas. Since the only forces are those of instantaneous collision, the velocity of a particle is constant most of the time. An instantaneous shift from one state of motion to another state of motion occurs at each collision. Hence each hodograph consists of successive isolated points. Slow molecules are represented by points near the origin of **V** space, and fast ones by more remote points, for the length of the position vector of each representative point equals the speed of the corresponding molecule. If the Clausius model is modified slightly, the points representing each state of free motion are joined by curves representing the rapid transition from one state to another. Note that if several molecules instantaneously have equal velocities, then their representative points temporarily coincide but are counted separately.

Suppose we have a sample of a gas in thermal equilibrium. The statistically steady, although individually chaotic, motion of the n molecules is represented by n points in **V** space. The number of molecules per "volume" is given by a density function ρ. This means that in an element with dimensions dv_x, dv_y, dv_z, the population of representative points is equal to

$$\rho \, dv_x \, dv_y \, dv_z$$

ρ is a function of position in **V** space. Let us assume *isotropy*, that is, that there are no preferred directions in the gas, so that the distribution of representative points in **V** space is radial. This means that for a given speed one direction is as likely as another. Hence for any spherical shell of radius v, the population density is uniform. That is, ρ can be regarded as a function of v only, or for convenience, of v^2 only. While at a given temperature we may not expect many slow molecules, it is to be predicted that $\rho(v^2)$ has a fairly large value near the origin: there is much less space close to the origin than outside of a sphere of large radius. Since the energy is finite, $\rho(v^2)$ must approach zero for large v^2. We next inquire about the nature of this function $\rho(v^2)$.

EXERCISES

19. If the density function in **V** space is given for $v > v_0$ by $\rho(v) = 0$ and for $v \le v_0$ by

$$\rho(v) = \frac{k}{v_0^3}$$

where $v = |\mathbf{V}|$, k is a constant, and v_0 is a constant reference speed:
(a) Evaluate k so that the total number of molecules will be n.
(b) What is the number of molecules with speed greater than $0.75v_0$?
(c) What is the total translational kinetic energy of the gas if the mass of each molecule is m?

20. If the density function in **V** space is given for $v > 2v_0$ by $\rho(v) = 0$ and for $v \le 2v_0$ by

$$\rho(v) = \frac{3n}{20v_0^4} (2v_0 - v)$$

where $v = |\mathbf{V}|$, n is a constant, and v_0 is a constant reference speed:

(a) What is the total number of molecules?

(b) What is the number of molecules with speed greater than v_0?

(c) What is the total translational kinetic energy of the gas if the mass of each molecule is m?

22.11. THE DISTRIBUTION OF REPRESENTATIVE POINTS IN V SPACE

A dependable analysis of molecular velocities requires a careful study of collisions between molecules. Such treatments may be found in treatises on kinetic theory of gas or statistical mechanics. Here we merely observe that one further simple assumption happens to yield a rather good formula for $\rho(v)$. We assume that the statistical distribution of x components of velocity is independent of the corresponding y and z distributions. It is not hard to think of reasons (for instance, the speed limit of special relativity) for mistrusting this hypothesis. For simple situations it is a very good first approximation.

To save space, let us see what this assumption of *independence* would mean in the $v_x v_y$ plane, ignoring the third dimension, treating ρ as an area density rather than a volume density. It here implies that the fraction of all molecules with v_x in the range δv_x is the same as the fraction of those especially selected molecules whose v_y is limited to the range δv_y. Let $v_x = a$ and $v_y = b$ within the "area" element $\delta v_x \, \delta v_y$. In Fig. 22.6 the hypothesis requires that the ratio of the population of strip A to the total population is equal to the ratio of the population of the common intersection of strip A with strip B (that is, $A \cap B$) to the population of strip B. In symbols,

$$\frac{\left[\int_{-\infty}^{\infty} \rho(a^2 + v_y^2) \, dv_y \right] \delta v_x}{n} = \frac{\rho(a^2 + b^2) \, \delta v_x \, \delta v_y}{\left[\int_{-\infty}^{\infty} \rho(v_x^2 + b^2) \, dv_x \right] \delta v_y}$$

Simplifying,

$$(22.41) \qquad n\rho(a^2 + b^2) = \int_{-\infty}^{\infty} \rho(a^2 + v_y^2) \, dv_y \int_{-\infty}^{\infty} \rho(v_x^2 + b^2) \, dv_x$$

Now a is any particular value of v_x, and b is any particular value of v_y. In the right member of (22.41), the first factor is a function of a^2, say, $g(a^2)$. The second factor is an identical function of b^2. So our conclusion is

$$(22.42) \qquad n\rho(v_x^2 + v_y^2) = g(v_x^2)g(v_y^2)$$

The same sort of argument, carried out for three dimensions, gives the conclusion

$$(22.43) \qquad n\rho(v_x^2 + v_y^2 + v_z^2) = g(v_x^2)g(v_y^2)g(v_z^2)$$

This means that a density function ρ exhibiting both properties isotropy and independence is sharply limited in character. For if we differentiate (22.43) with respect to v_x, v_y, and v_z, respectively, and divide the results by the members of Eq. (22.43), we get, after simplification:

$$(22.44) \qquad \frac{\rho'(v_x^2 + v_y^2 + v_z^2)}{\rho(v_x^2 + v_y + v_z^2)} = \frac{g'(v_x^2)}{g(v_x^2)} = \frac{g'(v_y^2)}{g(v_y^2)} = \frac{g'(v_z^2)}{g(v_z^2)}$$

We can only conclude, since v_x, v_y, v_z may be chosen arbitrarily, that each member of (22.44) is equal to a constant:

$$(22.45) \qquad \frac{\rho'(v^2)}{\rho(v^2)} = c_1$$

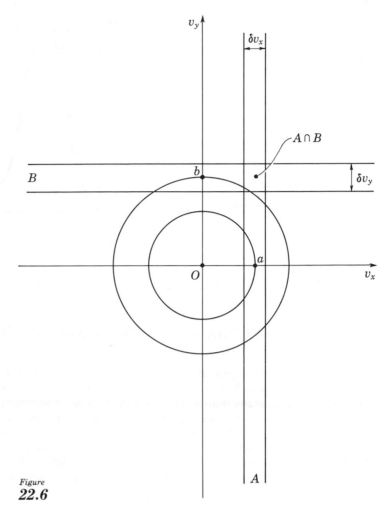

Figure
22.6

If this equation is integrated, we get

$$\log \rho(v^2) = c_1 v^2 + \log c_2$$

which is equivalent to

(22.46) $$\rho(v^2) = c_2 e^{c_1 v^2}$$

The constant c_1 is clearly negative: otherwise the total kinetic energy of the gas would be infinite. The constant c_2 is the density at the origin. Equation (22.46) merely gives the shape of the density curve. In **V** space the population density falls off radially like a standard-error curve (see Fig. 22.7).

EXERCISES

21. Discuss the density functions of Exercises 19 and 20 from the point of view of isotropy and independence.

22. The physical significance of the function $g(v_x^2)$ may be characterized as follows: The quantity $g(v_x^2)\, dv_x$ is equal to the fraction dn_{v_x}/n of the molecules whose velocities have x components between v_x and $v_x + dv_x$.

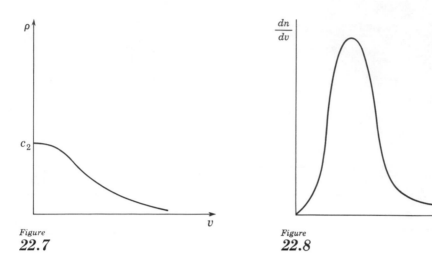

Figure
22.7

Figure
22.8

(a) Plot a graph of the function dn_{v_x}/dv_x.
(b) What is the most likely x component for molecular velocities? [HINT: Find the maximum of the graph in part (a).]

22.12. THE MAXWELL DISTRIBUTION OF MOLECULAR SPEEDS

We now interpret the result of the preceding section. We have learned that the representative points in **V** space are more crowded near the origin than elsewhere. But it does not take many individuals to create crowded conditions in a small enough space. To determine the number of molecules having speeds between v and $v + dv$, we merely count in **V** space the representative points whose distances from the origin lie between v and $v + dv$. This set of points lies in a spherical shell whose radius runs from v to $v + dv$. The volume of this shell is $4\pi v^2\, dv$. The number dn of representative points in this shell is, according to (22.46), given by

$$dn = c_2 e^{c_1 v^2} 4\pi v^2\, dv$$

The derivative dn/dv is a convenient quantity for describing the speed distribution:

(22.47)
$$\frac{dn}{dv} = 4\pi c_2 v^2 e^{c_1 v^2}$$

An approximate graph of this function is given in Fig. 22.8. Using (22.24) and the equation

(22.48)
$$n = \int dn = 4\pi c_2 \int_0^\infty v^2 e^{c_1 v^2}\, dv$$

one can evaluate the constants c_1 and c_2. Details of the integration are omitted, but the results are

(22.49)
$$c_1 = \frac{-m}{2k\theta}$$

and

(22.50)
$$c_2 = n\left(\frac{m}{2\pi k\theta}\right)^{\frac{3}{2}}$$

Once one has the speed-distribution equation (22.47), it is easy to compute averages. The average speed v_{av}, according to the Maxwell distribution, is given by

$$(22.51) \qquad\qquad v_{av} = \frac{1}{n} \int_0^\infty v \, dn$$

and the rms speed $\bar{v}$ is given by

$$(22.52) \qquad\qquad \bar{v}^2 = \frac{1}{n} \int_0^\infty v^2 \, dn$$

Of course, the result of the integration in (22.52) should yield the same result as (22.24):

$$(22.53) \qquad\qquad \bar{v} = \left(\frac{3k\theta}{m}\right)^{\frac{1}{2}}$$

Similarly, one gets for the average speed

$$v_{av} = \left(\frac{8k\theta}{\pi m}\right)^{\frac{1}{2}} = \left(\frac{8}{3\pi}\right)^{\frac{1}{2}} \bar{v}$$

These integrations are routine if one has at hand standard tables of definite integrals.

EXERCISES

23. Show that the graph of Fig. 22.8 has a maximum at $v = v_m = (2k\theta/m)^{\frac{1}{2}}$.
24. Use a differential approximation to estimate the fraction of the molecules in a box having speed between v_m and $1.05v_m$ (the speed v_m is defined in the preceding problem).
25. Evaluate the imi (inverse of the mean of the inverses) speed for molecules, using the Maxwell distribution.
26. Use the distribution function $g(v_x^2)$ as in Exercise 22 to show directly that the mean value of $\frac{1}{2}mv_x^2$ is $\frac{1}{2}k\theta$.

22.13. MEAN FREE PATH

The speed with which a typical gas molecule travels has been considered: in air at normal temperature it is roughly the speed of sound. In the section on the virial theorem it was mentioned that collisions occur with very great frequency. We shall now investigate this matter by seeking a rough answer to the question, On the average, how far is any given molecule likely to go before it has a collision? This distance is called the *mean free path*.

In the first place, we must now recognize that molecules have size. The effective or kinetic diameter of a molecule will be written as d. The problem of computing the mean free path is complex. In order to get an estimate without too much labor, we shall make some assumptions and guesses. First, let us temporarily assume that the mean free path of a given molecule will be unchanged if all the other molecules are made to stand still in typical positions. It will be convenient to replace our moving molecule by a sphere of radius d and the stationary ones by points as shown in Fig. 22.9. The occurrence of collisions will not be changed by this substitution. The moving molecule sweeps out each second a cylinder of volume

$$\pi d^2 v$$

v being the average molecular velocity. If n_0 is the number of molecules per cubic centimeter, there will be $\pi d^2 n_0 v$ collisions each second. The mean free path λ is then

$$(22.54) \qquad\qquad \lambda = \frac{v}{\pi n_0 d^2 v} = \frac{1}{\pi n_0 d^2}$$

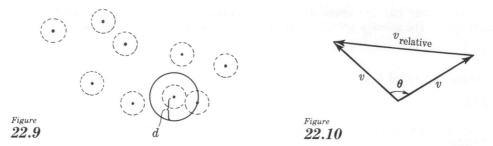

Figure
22.9   *d*

Figure
22.10

This result, based on untenable assumptions, turns out to be wrong only by a factor of about 1.4.

Now let us admit that all molecules are in motion but assume at least that each one is moving at the average speed v. We now use the average value of the *relative speed* of two molecules, i.e., the average value of the magnitude of the vector difference of two velocities. For the case where all actual speeds are v, the relative speed is (see Fig. 22.10)

$$v' = 2v \sin \frac{\theta}{2}$$

where θ is the angle between the velocity vector of the molecule we are studying and the velocity vector of a second molecule. Since all directions for this second vector are equally likely, we compute the space average of the relative speed; that is, we multiply each element of area on a unit sphere about our molecule by the relative speed for a second molecule moving in that direction, integrate, and then divide by the area of the sphere. The computation of the average relative speed $\bar{v}'$ follows. The coordinates are shown in Fig. 22.11 (compare Sec. 18.8, Example 1b).

$$\bar{v}' = \frac{1}{\text{area}} \int v' \, da = \frac{1}{4\pi} \int_0^{2\pi} \int_0^{\pi} 2v \sin \frac{\theta}{2} \sin \theta \, d\theta \, d\phi = \tfrac{4}{3}v$$

The number of collisions per second is now

$$\tfrac{4}{3}\pi n_0 d^2 v$$

and the mean free path is

(22.55) $$\lambda = \frac{3}{4\pi n_0 d^2}$$

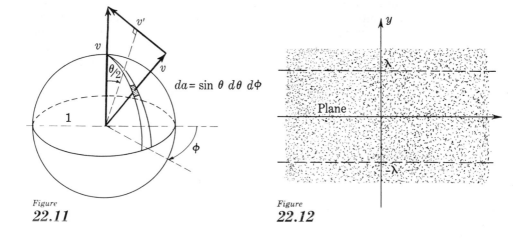

Figure
22.11

Figure
22.12

This formula is due to Clausius. If allowance is made for the fact that velocities are not uniform but follow a distribution curve such as indicated in Fig. 22.8, a slightly different value is obtained.

EXERCISES

27. Under standard conditions what would be the mean free path of a gas molecule having kinetic diameter 2.97×10^{-8} cm? What would the mean free path be at normal pressure but a temperature of $27,027°C$? What would the mean free path be at $0°C$ at a pressure of 0.1 mm of mercury?

28. Compute in miles, using the Clausius formula, the mean free path for hydrogen molecules in space, assuming an average of one per cubic centimeter. Take the effective diameter of a hydrogen molecule as 2.74×10^{-10} m.

22.14. TRANSPORT PHENOMENA

Let an imaginary plane divide a gas into two portions as shown in Fig. 22.12. The division is soon violated, for the molecules in their chaotic motion cross the "boundary" repeatedly. In crossing, they transport physical characteristics. For instance, if the lower region has a tendency to drift parallel to the plane, the tendency will soon appear above the plane also. This phenomenon is one of *viscosity*. Molecules acquiring momentum below the boundary *transport the momentum* to the upper region. Again, if the lower region is hotter than the upper, the molecules emigrating carry with them excessive kinetic energy. This is a case of *thermal conduction*, the *transport of energy*. As such interpenetrations take place, it is obvious that *mass* is transported across the boundary. This is called *diffusion*.

These three transport phenomena can be investigated quantitatively in terms of the kinetic theory. We shall formulate the viscosity problem in a somewhat naïve manner. To make the task simpler, we shall assume that the viscosity would be unchanged if all molecules had the same speed (i.e., we assign the average speed to each molecule). We shall assume, moreover, that the laminar (plane) drift of the gas as a whole can be thought of as a regular motion superimposed on the chaotic thermal agitation already discussed.

The drift of the gas will be parallel to the xz plane, as indicated in Fig. 22.13.

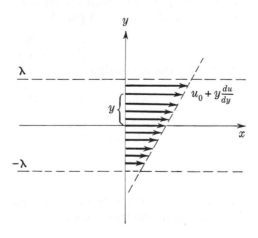

Figure
22.13

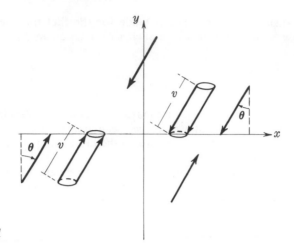

Figure
22.14

The speed u of the drift is

$$u = u_0 + y\frac{du}{dy}$$

Within the limits

$$-2\lambda \leq y \leq 2\lambda$$

at least, we shall treat du/dy as a constant.

Let dn_θ be the number of molecules per unit volume traveling toward the xz plane at an angle of between θ and $\theta + d\theta$ with the y axis. The average number of these crossing a unit area of the xz plane per second is then (see Fig. 22.14)

$$2\,dn_\theta v\cos\theta$$

where v is the average molecular speed (quite aside from the superimposed drift).

A typical molecule crossing the xz plane upward will travel one mean free path *after* crossing the plane (its expectation of unmolested progress does not depend on the distance previously traveled). Symmetrically, one may also say that a typical molecule crossing the plane upward will have traveled one mean free path since its last collision. A similar statement may be made for molecules traveling downward. Since as many molecules travel down as up, we may merely evaluate the transfer of momentum associated with the interchange of particles separated by a distance 2λ as in Fig. 22.15. For each pair this amounts to

$$m\left(u_0 + y_2\frac{du}{dy}\right) - m\left(u_0 + y_1\frac{du}{dy}\right)$$

or, ignoring the minus sign,

$$m(y_2 - y_1)\frac{du}{dy} = 2m\lambda\frac{du}{dy}\cos\theta$$

There are $dn_\theta/2$ such pairs per unit volume; thus the exchange per second of momentum for tracks with angles between θ and $\theta + d\theta$ is, per unit area,

$$2\,dn_\theta m\lambda v\cos^2\theta\frac{du}{dy}$$

All directions of travel from the original location of a molecule are equally likely. The fraction of the molecules taking courses in the $d\theta$ range toward the xz plane is proportional to the area which they would pierce on a sphere of unit radius about their origin. If n_0 is the total number per unit volume, this fraction is, referring to the shaded strip of width $d\theta$ in Fig. 22.16,

$$\frac{dn_\theta}{n_0} = \frac{\text{area of strip}}{\text{area of sphere}} = \frac{2\pi \sin \theta \, d\theta}{4\pi} = 0.5 \sin \theta \, d\theta$$

The total change of momentum per second per area (or in other words, the force per area) on one side of the plane is then

$$\frac{f}{a} = n_0 m \lambda v \frac{du}{dy} \int_0^{\pi/2} \cos^2 \theta \sin \theta \, d\theta$$

$$= \tfrac{1}{3} n_0 m \lambda v \frac{du}{dy}$$

As usual (see almost any elementary physics book) the *coefficient of viscosity* η is defined as the ratio of force per area to the speed-of-drift gradient; thus

(22.56)
$$\eta = \frac{f/a}{du/dy}$$

so

$$\eta = \tfrac{1}{3} n_0 m \lambda v$$

or

(22.57)
$$\eta = \tfrac{1}{3} \delta \lambda v$$

EXERCISES

29. Show that the coefficient of viscosity of a gas is given by

$$\eta = \frac{mv}{4\pi d^2}$$

and hence that it is independent of density and pressure.

30. The viscosity coefficient of helium under standard conditions is 1.891×10^{-5} mks units, while the density is 0.1785 kg/m³. The molecular weight is 4.0. (a) Compute the mean free path. (b) From part (a), compute the kinetic diameter of the helium atom.

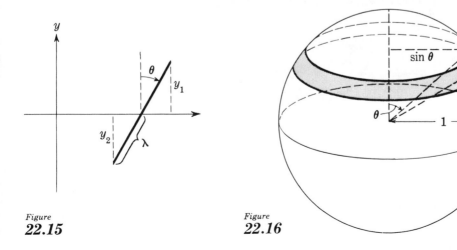

Figure
22.15

Figure
22.16

31. Using arguments similar to those of the preceding section, show that the thermal conductivity of a monatomic gas is equal to

$$\tfrac{1}{3}n_0 c_v m\lambda v = \eta c_v$$

    HINT: Show that the energy of each molecule is

$$e = \tfrac{3}{2}k\theta = c_v m\left(\theta_0 + y\frac{d\theta}{dy}\right)$$

32. Show that the thermal conductivity of a monatomic gas is equal to

$$\frac{c_v m v}{4\pi d^2}$$

    and hence is independent of pressure.

REVIEW EXERCISES

33. Using the density function of Exercise 19, compute (a) $\bar{v}$; (b) v_{av}; (c) v_{imi} (see Exercise 25).
34. Using the density function of Exercise 20, compute (a) $\bar{v}$; (b) v_{av}; (c) v_{imi}.
35. Show that the virial of a Clausius gas is approximately equal to $-(\tfrac{1}{2}t)\sum_{1}^{n} \mathbf{R}_i \cdot \mathbf{P}_i$,

    where $\mathbf{P}_i$ is an impulse exerted by the wall of the container on a molecule of position vector $\mathbf{R}_i$.   The summation is over the n collisions between wall and molecules which take place during the time t.
36. When electrons travel in an un-ionized gas whose molecules have diameter d, the free paths are longer than those of the molecules because:
    (a) The velocities are much larger (so the molecules may be considered at rest).
    (b) The diameters are much smaller (so the electrons may be treated as moving points).
    Under these assumptions derive a formula for λ_e, the electronic mean free path.
37. Let v_0 be the reference speed such that $n/8v_0^3$ equals the Maxwell density in $\mathbf{V}$ space at the origin.   Thus if all the representative points in $\mathbf{V}$ space were redistributed evenly over a cube with center at the origin, edges parallel to the axes, and density throughout equal to the Maxwell density at $\mathbf{V} = \mathbf{O}$, then the corners of the cube would be $(\pm v_0, \pm v_0, \pm v_0)$.
    (a) Evaluate v_0 in terms of k, m, θ.
    (b) Evaluate v_m, $\bar{v}$, v_{av}, and v_{imi} as multiples of v_0.

CHAPTER TWENTY-THREE

INTRODUCTION
to METHODS of LAGRANGE
and HAMILTON

Courses in elementary mechanics customarily lean most heavily, as we have done, on the equations of motion due to Newton. The vector concepts of force and acceleration are fairly easy to accept (unless one is particularly searching in one's questions) and fairly easy to apply to simple problems. The central scalar concept of mass usually seems somewhat more sophisticated to the beginner, but eventually familiarity begets confidence. In this chapter a brief and elementary introduction is given to a different formulation of mechanics. Here the key role will be played by energy, supported by a broader interpretation of kinematical ideas. The resulting equations of motion, due to Lagrange and to Hamilton, are concise, symmetric, and powerful. They provide a natural approach to quantum theories, as well as to the classical mechanics which is the subject of this course. It is possible, in fact usual, to begin the study of the mechanics of Lagrange and Hamilton from fresh and inclusive postulates quite different in appearance from those of Newtonian mechanics. In the present treatment it is more suitable to approach the newer theories from the old.

23.1. A NEW INTERPRETATION OF THE EQUATION $\mathbf{F} = m\mathbf{A}$

If a particle of mass m moves on the x axis, its equation of motion can be written $f = dp/dt$, where p stands for the momentum $m\dot{x}$ (it is assumed that m is constant). Note further that p can be derived from the kinetic energy $p = (d/d\dot{x})\frac{1}{2}m\dot{x}^2 = m\dot{x}$. Here we have taken the unusual step of regarding $\dot{x}$ as an independent variable. If the applied forces are conservative, then the resultant force may be derived from a potential energy $f = -d(\text{p.e.})/dx$. For this simple one-dimensional case, we can rewrite the equation of motion as follows:

$$(23.1) \qquad -\frac{d(\text{p.e.})}{dx} = \frac{d}{dt}\left[\frac{d}{d\dot{x}}(\text{k.e.})\right]$$

Now we define a new function of the state of the particle

$$L = \text{k.e.} - \text{p.e.}$$

Mathematically, L is a function of x and $\dot{x}$. In terms of L, Eq. (23.1) can be written compactly as

(23.2)
$$\frac{\partial L}{\partial x} = \frac{d}{dt}\left(\frac{\partial L}{\partial \dot{x}}\right)$$

Postponing further theoretical justification, let us apply this equation of motion to additional examples.

Example I

Suppose that a wheel of radius r rolls down the x axis (see Fig. 23.1). Its kinetic energy is given by

$$\text{k.e.} = \tfrac{1}{2}m\dot{x}^2 + \tfrac{1}{2}i\dot{\theta}^2$$

If no slipping takes place, we can dispense with the rotational variable, since $r\theta = x - x_0$ for a suitable constant x_0, and hence $r\dot{\theta} = \dot{x}$; so we can write

$$\text{k.e.} = \frac{1}{2}\left(m + \frac{i}{r^2}\right)\dot{x}^2$$

The gravitational potential energy can be expressed as

$$\text{p.e.} = -mgx \sin \alpha$$

Again we regard the difference, $L = \text{k.e.} - \text{p.e.}$, as a function of *both* of the variables x and $\dot{x}$:

$$L = \frac{1}{2}\left(m + \frac{i}{r^2}\right)\dot{x}^2 + mgx \sin \alpha$$

This function L is called the *Lagrangian* of the system. Next, form the two derivatives $\partial L/\partial x$ and $\partial L/\partial \dot{x}$:

$$\frac{\partial L}{\partial x} = mg \sin \alpha \qquad \frac{\partial L}{\partial \dot{x}} = \left(m + \frac{i}{r^2}\right)\dot{x}$$

Finally, note that the equation

$$\frac{\partial L}{\partial x} = \frac{d}{dt}\left(\frac{\partial L}{\partial \dot{x}}\right)$$

leads here, assuming that m, i, and r are constant, to

$$mg \sin \alpha = \left(m + \frac{i}{r^2}\right)\ddot{x}$$

which is exactly the equation of motion we should have gotten in solving for the acceleration $\ddot{x}$ by the methods of earlier chapters.

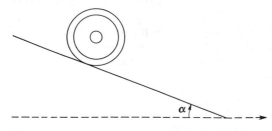

Figure
23.1

In the preceding example, as long as no slipping took place, *one* coordinate (either x or θ) sufficed to specify the position of the moving object. In such a case we say that the mechanical system uses *one degree of freedom*. If slipping takes place but if the motion is otherwise as described, the motion has two degrees of freedom.

Example 2

Consider a rod of mass m and length l free to rotate about a fixed horizontal axis at one end. This system has a single degree of freedom: its position can be specified by a single angle θ measured, say, from the equilibrium position. We then have

$$\text{k.e.} = \tfrac{1}{6}ml^2\dot{\theta}^2$$
$$\text{p.e.} = -\tfrac{1}{2}mgl\cos\theta$$
$$L = \tfrac{1}{6}ml(l\dot{\theta}^2 + 3g\cos\theta)$$

Applying a suitable modification of Eq. (23.2) to the derivatives

$$\frac{\partial L}{\partial \theta} = \tfrac{1}{6}ml(-3g\sin\theta)$$

$$\frac{\partial L}{\partial \dot{\theta}} = \tfrac{1}{6}ml(2l\dot{\theta})$$

we get

$$-3g\sin\theta = 2l\ddot{\theta}$$

This equation of motion agrees with the usual one.

Example 3

Let m be the mass of a free particle subject only to conservative forces, so that a potential energy $U(x,y,z)$ is defined. The particle has three degrees of freedom:

$$L = \tfrac{1}{2}m(\dot{x}^2 + \dot{y}^2 + \dot{z}^2) - U(x,y,z)$$
$$\frac{\partial L}{\partial x} = -\frac{\partial U}{\partial x} \qquad \frac{\partial L}{\partial \dot{x}} = m\dot{x} \qquad \frac{d}{dt}\left(\frac{\partial L}{\partial \dot{x}}\right) = m\ddot{x}$$

Similar expressions follow for derivatives with respect to y, z, $\dot{y}$, $\dot{z}$. Lagrange's equations clearly yield the equations of motion

$$-\frac{\partial U}{\partial x} = m\ddot{x} \qquad -\frac{\partial U}{\partial y} = m\ddot{y} \qquad -\frac{\partial U}{\partial z} = m\ddot{z}$$

This conclusion may be summarized as

$$-\nabla U = m\mathbf{A}$$

This equation is, of course, exactly what the Newtonian approach yields. The examples thus far merely suggest that this method of Lagrange is valid in uncomplicated cases involving conservative forces. The more serious treatment which follows is a sparse introduction, but it will illustrate the generality and some of the advantages of the method.

23.2. GENERALIZED COORDINATES

Probably the most conspicuous new feature of the method exhibited in the preceding section is the fact that angular and linear coordinates received precisely the same treatment. This is entirely in contrast with our earlier dynamical equations in which translational and rotational concepts appeared as subject to quite different, although analogous, equations of motion. We were continually conscious of the fact that θ and x, $\boldsymbol{\Gamma}$ and $\mathbf{F}$, $\boldsymbol{\Omega}$ and $\mathbf{V}$, and $\boldsymbol{\mathfrak{A}}$ and $\mathbf{A}$ are dimensionally distinct. In this chapter coordinates are chosen to fit each problem in a natural way. Consider, for example, a dumbbell-shaped object toppling through space. A conventional approach, treating the spheres as particles, might assign a total of six coordinates, (x_1,y_1,z_1) and (x_2,y_2,z_2), to the centers of mass P_1 and P_2 of the respective spheres. The rigidity of the system would provide an equation of constraint:

$$(x_2 - x_1)^2 + (y_2 - y_1)^2 + (z_2 - z_1)^2 = d^2$$

where d is constant. A natural choice of generalized coordinates would exploit the fact that a constraint removes a degree of freedom so that five, not six, coordinates are needed. Any five variables which adequately specify the instantaneous position of the system may be used. For example, one could give the coordinates $(\bar{x},\bar{y},\bar{z})$ of the center of mass, together with two direction angles, as in spherical coordinates, (γ,θ) of the segment P_1P_2. The five variables $(\bar{x},\bar{y},\bar{z},\gamma,\theta)$ then are coordinates for the whole system. If the spheres are not treated as particles, a sixth coordinate is necessary to specify rotation of the dumbbell about its own axis. In general, the positions of three points are enough to determine the position of a rigid body. Each point requires three coordinates, but three independent constraints are provided by rigidity: the distances between pairs of points are constant. Hence again we say that a rigid body has six degrees of freedom.

In general, a system of n particles has $3n$ scalar coordinates, which may be limited by constraints. We shall in the following discussion assume that only as many variables (angles, distances, arc lengths, etc.) are chosen as there are degrees of freedom. If the n particles are tied together pairwise as in the diatomic model (dumbbell) just considered, there are only $5n/2$ degrees of freedom—unless vibration as well as rotation is allowed. Let f denote the number of degrees of freedom of a system made up of n particles. Then the usual $3n$ cartesian coordinates $(x_1, x_2, \ldots, x_{3n})$ are to be expressed in terms of f properly chosen generalized scalar coordinates $q_1, \ldots, q_f$ by means of $3n$ equations of the form

(23.3) $$x_i = x_i(q_1, \ldots, q_f) \qquad i = 1, 2, \ldots, 3n$$

For example, consider a single particle free to move on the surface of a sphere of radius a. The usual equations relating cartesian to spherical coordinates are examples of equations like (23.3).

(23.4)
$$x = a \cos \theta \sin \phi$$
$$y = a \cos \theta \cos \phi$$
$$z = a \sin \theta$$

In this example x, y, z are the x_i's and θ, ϕ are the q_j's.

In applying equations such as (23.3), a number of related equations are helpful. Writing δq_j for differentials to be used as virtual displacements, in the sense of the Δx's of our early study of virtual work, we obtain by direct differentiation

(23.5)
$$\delta x_i = \sum_{j=1}^{f} \frac{\partial x_i}{\partial q_j} \delta q_j$$

and

(23.6)
$$\dot{x}_i = \sum_{j=1}^{f} \frac{\partial x_i}{\partial q_j} \dot{q}_j$$

Now, as a convenient formal manipulating procedure, we regard $\dot{x}_i$ as a function of the $2f$ variables $q_1, \ldots, q_f, \dot{q}_1, \ldots, \dot{q}_f$. This is consistent with the viewpoint of the preceding section in which $\dot{x}$ and $\dot{\theta}$ as well as x and θ were treated as independent variables. Differentiating (23.6) with respect to each variable $\dot{q}_j$, we get such pleasantly symmetrical equations as

$$(23.7) \qquad \frac{\partial \dot{x}_i}{\partial \dot{q}_j} = \frac{\partial x_i}{\partial q_j}$$

Note that Eq. (23.7) is in reality $3nf$ equations, for i stands successively for the integers $1, 2, \ldots, 3n$, while j stands for $1, 2, \ldots, f$. In many concrete cases, however, most of these numerous equations would convey only the information $0 = 0$. But each $\dot{x}_i$ has $3f$ additional partial derivatives which we proceed to compute:

$$\frac{\partial \dot{x}_i}{\partial q_k} = \frac{\partial}{\partial q_k}\left(\sum_{j=1}^{f} \frac{\partial x_i}{\partial q_j} \dot{q}_j \right) = \sum_{j=1}^{f} \frac{\partial^2 x_i}{\partial q_k \, \partial q_j} \dot{q}_j = \sum_{j=1}^{f} \frac{\partial^2 x_i}{\partial q_j \, \partial q_k} \dot{q}_j$$

where k, like j in the preceding discussion, stands, successively, for the integers $1, 2, \ldots, f$. Note that the last member is exactly what one would get by taking the time derivative of $\partial x_i / \partial q_k$. Thus we conclude:

$$(23.8) \qquad \frac{\partial \dot{x}_i}{\partial q_k} = \frac{d}{dt}\left(\frac{\partial x_i}{\partial q_k} \right)$$

The preceding paragraph consists not of physics primarily, but of useful conventions and formulas from the calculus of several variables. The use of summation symbols sometimes conceals what is going on. If you are at all inexperienced in such matters, you are urged (see Exercise 1) to derive formulas corresponding to (23.7) and (23.8) for the case where coordinates x, y, z are replaced by θ, φ. In this derivation you should refrain from using a single Σ or a single letter subscript!

EXERCISES

1. Assuming that the coordinates x, y, z for a coordinate system can be expressed in terms of variables θ, φ, by Eq. (23.4), derive in detail formulas such as

$$\frac{\partial \dot{x}}{\partial \dot{\theta}} = \frac{\partial x}{\partial \theta} \quad \text{and} \quad \frac{\partial \dot{x}}{\partial \theta} = \frac{d}{dt}\left(\frac{\partial x}{\partial \theta} \right)$$

2. How many degrees of freedom has: (a) An unconstrained rigid body? (b) A pair of rigid bars joined by a hinge?

23.3. DERIVATION OF LAGRANGE'S EQUATIONS

If usual cartesian coordinates $x_1, x_2, \ldots, x_{3n}$ are used to describe the instantaneous positions of a system of n particles, we can write Newtonian equations of motion in the form

$$(23.9) \qquad f_i + f_i'' = m_i \ddot{x}_i \qquad i = 1, \ldots, 3n$$

The symbolism of these $3n$ equations needs some explanation. Since there are only n particles, it is clear that in the list of masses $m_1, m_2, \ldots, m_{3n}$, each particle is represented three times. Thus the first particle has mass $m_1 = m_2 = m_3$, the seventh particle has mass $m_{19} = m_{20} = m_{21}$, etc. Each equation of motion deals with one direction for one particle at a time. Thus $m_{20}\ddot{x}_{20}$ is what normally would be written $m\ddot{y}$ for the seventh particle. Finally, the two force components in the left member of (23.9) are, respectively, resultants of applied forces and forces of constraint. Thus f_1 is the x component of the resultant of applied forces for the first particle and f_1'' is the x component of the resultant of forces of constraint for the first particle.

Using the approach of d'Alembert, we can rewrite equation (23.9) as

$$(23.10) \qquad f_i + f_i'' - m_i \ddot{x}_i = 0$$

so that we are effectively considering each particle as in *equilibrium* under the three forces of the left member of (23.10). If now we use the virtual work criterion for the equilibrium of this system, we get an immediate simplification. Let $\delta x_1, \delta x_2, \ldots, \delta x_{3n}$ be a set of components of virtual displacements for the particles of the system. The virtual works associated with force components f_i'' are individually zero because constraints do zero work (cf. Sec. 7.12). We can thus write, adding virtual works,

$$(23.11) \qquad \sum_{i=1}^{3n} (f_i - m_i \ddot{x}_i)\, \delta x_i = 0$$

The various formulas of the preceding section may now be used for replacing the x's by the q's. First we work on the acceleration terms:

$$m_i \ddot{x}_i \, \delta x_i = m_i \ddot{x}_i \sum_j \frac{\partial x_i}{\partial q_j} \delta q_j \qquad \text{for } i = 1, 2, \ldots, 3n$$

by substitution of Eq. (23.5). Using the usual distribution law for real numbers, we can multiply the summation through by the factor $\ddot{x}_i$, getting

$$m_i \ddot{x}_i \, \delta x_i = m_i \sum_j \left(\ddot{x}_i \frac{\partial x_i}{\partial q_j} \right) \delta q_j$$

In the right member each factor in parentheses may be rewritten thus, using the usual formula for derivative of a product:

$$\ddot{x}_i \frac{\partial x_i}{\partial q_j} = \frac{d}{dt} \left(\dot{x}_i \frac{\partial x_i}{\partial q_j} \right) - \dot{x}_i \frac{d}{dt} \left(\frac{\partial x_i}{\partial q_j} \right)$$

When these substitutions are made for $i = 1, 2, \ldots, 3n$, we have

$$m_i \ddot{x}_i \, \delta x_i = m_i \sum_j \left[\frac{d}{dt} \left(\dot{x}_i \frac{\partial x_i}{\partial q_j} \right) - \dot{x}_i \frac{d}{dt} \left(\frac{\partial x_i}{\partial q_j} \right) \right] \delta q_j$$

Now we can use the substitutions (23.8) and (23.7) to get

$$m_i \ddot{x}_i \, \delta x_i = m_i \sum_j \left[\frac{d}{dt} \left(\dot{x}_i \frac{\partial \dot{x}_i}{\partial \dot{q}_j} \right) - \dot{x}_i \frac{\partial \dot{x}_i}{\partial q_j} \right] \delta q_j$$

It is now apparent that the use of the $\dot{q}$'s as independent variables has resulted in advantageous simplifications, for both terms within the brackets can be rewritten, when multiplied by the coefficient m_i, in a form of recognizable physical significance.

$$(23.12) \qquad m_i \ddot{x}_i \, \delta x_i = \sum_j \left[\frac{d}{dt} \frac{\partial}{\partial \dot{q}_j} (\tfrac{1}{2} m_i \dot{x}_i^2) - \frac{\partial}{\partial q_j} (\tfrac{1}{2} m_i \dot{x}_i^2) \right] \delta q_j$$

Now we go back to the force terms of (23.11). Suppose that the applied forces are conservative and that the potential energies associated with these forces are indicated by functions of the q's:

$$U_i = U_i(q_1, q_2, \ldots, q_f)$$

Then

$$\sum_i f_i \, \delta x_i = -\sum_i \delta U_i = -\sum_i \sum_j \frac{\partial U_i}{\partial q_j} \delta q_j$$

Regrouping the terms, we have

(23.13)
$$\sum_i f_i \, \delta x_i = -\sum_j \left(\sum_i \frac{\partial U_i}{\partial q_j} \right) \delta q_j$$

Substituting these results, Eqs. (23.12) and (23.13), into (23.11) and rearranging terms, we get

(23.14)
$$\sum_j \left[\frac{d}{dt} \frac{\partial}{\partial \dot{q}_j} \sum_i (\tfrac{1}{2} m_i \dot{x}_i^2) - \frac{\partial}{\partial q_j} \sum_i (\tfrac{1}{2} m_i \dot{x}_i^2) + \sum_i \frac{\partial U_i}{\partial q_j} \right] \delta q_j = 0$$

Since the q's are associated with independent degrees of freedom, the coefficients of δq_j must vanish separately.   Writing

(23.15)
$$T = \sum_i \tfrac{1}{2} m_i \dot{x}_i^2 \qquad U = \sum_i U_i$$

We have, then, from (23.14)

(23.16)
$$\frac{d}{dt} \left(\frac{\partial T}{\partial \dot{q}_j} \right) - \frac{\partial}{\partial q_j} (T - U) = 0$$

Since U is a function of the q's only, the partial derivatives $\partial U / \partial \dot{q}_j$ vanish trivially. For the sake of symmetry, we define the Lagrangian L by

(23.17)
$$L = T - U$$

Since $\partial L / \partial \dot{q}_j = \partial T / \partial \dot{q}_j$, we rewrite (23.16) in the form which we first met in (23.2):

(23.18)
$$\frac{d}{dt} \left(\frac{\partial L}{\partial \dot{q}_j} \right) - \frac{\partial L}{\partial q_j} = 0 \qquad j = 1, 2, \ldots, f$$

These f equations are Lagrange's equations for the case where the forces are conservative.   We have seen how these equations are consequences of Newton's second law for special cases where the constraints are simple, where the relationship between the q's and x's do not involve time explicitly, and where the applied forces are conservative.   For a fuller development of the scope and applicability of Lagrange's equations, see any treatise on classical mechanics.   The extension to time-dependent constraints is not difficult, but will be omitted in this first introduction.

If the applied forces are not all conservative, the equations are slightly less compact.   Let f_i' denote force components not associated with a potential energy. Then the virtual work is augmented by

$$\delta W = \sum_i f_i' \, \delta x_i = \sum_i f_i' \left(\sum_j \frac{\partial x_i}{\partial q_j} \delta q_j \right)$$

$$= \sum_j \left(\sum_i f_i' \frac{\partial x_i}{\partial q_j} \right) \delta q_j$$

$$= \sum_j \bar{f}_j \, \delta q_j$$

In this final expression, $\bar{f}_j$ is the component of a *generalized force* associated with the coordinate q_j.   This component is defined by

(23.19)
$$\bar{f}_j = \sum_i f_i' \frac{\partial x_i}{\partial q_j}$$

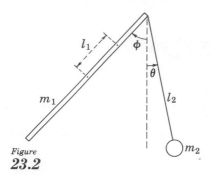

Figure
23.2

When such nonconservative forces are present, Lagrange's equations take the form

(23.20)
$$\frac{d}{dt}\left(\frac{\partial L}{\partial \dot{q}_j}\right) - \frac{\partial L}{\partial q_j} = \bar{f}_j$$

EXERCISES

3. A single particle of mass m has coordinates x, y. Its position can also be expressed by generalized coordinates q_1, q_2. It is subjected to a force $\mathbf{F} = f_1\mathbf{I} + f_2\mathbf{J}$ such that $f_1 = -\partial U_1/\partial x$, $f_2 = -\partial U_2/\partial y$. Derive, without using Σ's or literal subscripts, Eq. (23.18) for $j = 1, 2$.

4. How much is the preceding development modified by the assumption that the substitutions in Eq. (23.3) have the form

$$x_i = x_i(q_1, q_2, \ldots, q_f, t)$$

5. Carry through the development of the two preceding sections using vector equations $\mathbf{R}_i = \mathbf{R}_i(q_1, q_2, \ldots, q_f)$ for $i = 1, \ldots, n$ instead of Eq. (23.3).

6. A uniform bar of mass m_1 and length $4l_1$ is pivoted about a horizontal frictionless bearing at a distance l_1 from its center as shown in Fig. 23.2. At the upper end is attached a simple pendulum of length l_2 and mass m_2, which moves in the plane swept out by the bar when it rotates. Using the angles φ and θ as shown in the figure for generalized coordinates, write out the Lagrangian of the system.

7. What, in spherical coordinates, is the Lagrangian of a free particle?

23.4. APPLICATIONS OF LAGRANGE'S EQUATIONS

In Sec. 23.1 some applications of Lagrange's equations have already been given. Let us now apply this method to additional sample problems.

Example 1

Consider the frictionless system shown in Fig. 23.3 with generalized coordinates q_1 and q_2 as indicated. l is a constant. Assume that the pulleys have negligible mass. Then the kinetic energies of the three particles are, respectively, $\frac{1}{2}m_1\dot{y}_1^2$ $\frac{1}{2}m_2\dot{y}_2^2$, $\frac{1}{2}m_3\dot{y}_3^2$. Relative to the level of the table, the potential energies are, respectively, 0, $-m_2gy_2$, $-m_3gy_3$. The y's can be expressed in terms of the q's as follows:

$$y_1 = q_1 \qquad y_2 = l + q_1 - q_2 \qquad y_3 = q_1 + q_2$$

The Lagrangian is given by

$$L = \tfrac{1}{2}m_1\dot{q}_1^2 + \tfrac{1}{2}m_2(\dot{q}_1 - \dot{q}_2)^2 + \tfrac{1}{2}m_3(\dot{q}_1 + \dot{q}_2)^2 + m_2g(q_1 + l - q_2) + m_3g(q_1 + q_2)$$

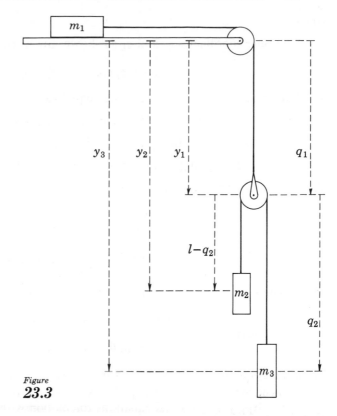

Figure
23.3

We may now compute the partial derivatives needed for Lagrange's equations:

$$\frac{\partial L}{\partial \dot{q}_1} = m_1\dot{q}_1 + m_2(\dot{q}_1 - \dot{q}_2) + m_3(\dot{q}_1 + \dot{q}_2)$$

$$\frac{\partial L}{\partial \dot{q}_2} = -m_2(\dot{q}_1 - \dot{q}_2) + m_3(\dot{q}_1 + \dot{q}_2)$$

$$\frac{\partial L}{\partial q_1} = m_2 g + m_3 g$$

$$\frac{\partial L}{\partial q_2} = -m_2 g + m_3 g$$

The corresponding equations of motion are then

$$(m_1 + m_2 + m_3)\ddot{q}_1 + (m_3 - m_2)\ddot{q}_2 = (m_2 + m_3)g$$

$$(m_3 - m_2)\ddot{q}_1 + (m_2 + m_3)\ddot{q}_2 = (m_3 - m_2)g$$

These equations are easily solved for $\ddot{q}_1$ and $\ddot{q}_2$ as constant multiples of g.

Example 2

A smooth right prism of mass m_2 and base angle θ rests on a horizontal plane as shown in Fig. 23.4. A particle of mass m_1 is placed on the prism. Find the Lagrange equations of motion.

Solution

Choosing coordinates q_2 and q_1 as shown, the usual coordinates of the particle are

$$x_1 = q_2 + q_1 \cos \theta \qquad y_1 = q_1 \sin \theta$$

The kinetic energy of the particle is then equal to

$$\tfrac{1}{2}m_1(\dot{x}_1^2 + \dot{y}_1^2) = \tfrac{1}{2}m_1(\dot{q}_2^2 + 2\dot{q}_2\dot{q}_1 \cos \theta + \dot{q}_1^2)$$

Hence the Lagrangian of the system may be written

$$L = \tfrac{1}{2}m_1(\dot{q}_2^2 + 2\dot{q}_2\dot{q}_1 \cos \theta + \dot{q}_1^2) + \tfrac{1}{2}m_2\dot{q}_2^2 - m_1 g q_1 \sin \theta$$

The four partial derivatives of L are

$$\frac{\partial L}{\partial q_2} = 0 \qquad \frac{\partial L}{\partial \dot{q}_2} = m_1\dot{q}_2 + m_1\dot{q}_1 \cos \theta + m_2\dot{q}_2$$

$$\frac{\partial L}{\partial q_1} = -m_1 g \sin \theta \qquad \frac{\partial L}{\partial \dot{q}_1} = m_1\dot{q}_2 \cos \theta + m_1\dot{q}_1$$

The equation of motion for the prism then is

$$m_1\ddot{q}_2 + m_1\ddot{q}_1 \cos \theta + m_2\ddot{q}_2 = 0$$

and for the particle

$$-g \sin \theta = \ddot{q}_2 \cos \theta + \ddot{q}_1$$

From these equations one may solve for $\ddot{q}_1$ and $\ddot{q}_2$ as constant multiples of g. If they are applied, for instance, to Chap. 7, Exercise 105, one finds $\ddot{q}_1 = -5\sqrt{2}g/9$ and $\ddot{q}_2 = g/9$. Applying the usual equations for motion with constant acceleration, one finds for the time of descent t that $t^2 = 18/5g$, and hence that the ultimate speed v of the prism is given by $v^2 = 2g/45$, yielding $v = 1.2$ ft/sec.

Example 3. Lagrange's Equations and Conservation of Energy

From Eq. (23.6) we can conclude that the kinetic energy T is a homogeneous quadratic polynomial function of the $\dot{q}$'s:

$$T = \tfrac{1}{2} \sum_{i,j} a_{ij}\dot{q}_i\dot{q}_j$$

where the coefficients a_{ij} are, at worst, functions of the q's. By Euler's theorem on homogeneous functions (compare Chap. 17, Exercise 52) it follows that

$$2T = \sum_i \dot{q}_i \frac{\partial T}{\partial \dot{q}_i} = \sum_i \dot{q}_i \frac{\partial L}{\partial \dot{q}_i}$$

Consequently,

$$2\frac{dT}{dt} = \sum_i \ddot{q}_i \frac{\partial L}{\partial \dot{q}_i} + \sum_i \dot{q}_i \frac{d}{dt}\left(\frac{\partial L}{\partial \dot{q}_i}\right)$$

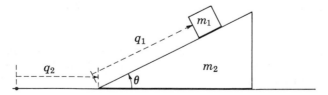

Figure
23.4

Substituting Lagrange's equation,

$$2\frac{dT}{dt} = \sum_i \ddot{q}_i \frac{\partial L}{\partial \dot{q}_i} + \sum_i \dot{q}_i \frac{\partial L}{\partial q_i}$$

But L is a function of the $2f$ variables $\dot{q}_i$, q_i, so the right member of the preceding equation is merely the total derivative dL/dt:

$$2\frac{dT}{dt} = \frac{d}{dt}L = \frac{d}{dt}(T - U)$$

Consequently, we conclude that $T + U$ is a constant, for

$$\frac{d}{dt}(T + U) = 0$$

EXERCISES

8. Find equations of motion for a rough sphere rolling down the smooth prism of Example 2.

9. Two uniform rods AB and BC as shown in Fig. 23.5 are jointed smoothly at B and supported at A so as to oscillate freely in a vertical plane. Find equations of motion for this system.

10. A uniform sphere of mass m_1 and radius r is initially at rest on a horizontal plane surface. A smooth particle of mass m_2 is placed on the top of the sphere and allowed to slide off, while the sphere, reacting to the particle, starts to roll without slipping. Set up equations of motion for the system before particle and sphere part company.

11. A uniform bar of length l and mass m_1 lies on a smooth horizontal surface. A sphere of radius r and mass m_2 is rolling without slipping along the upper surface of the bar. Use Lagrange's equations to show that neither object experiences an acceleration because of the interaction.

12. Let a simple pendulum of length l and mass m be described by spherical coordinates as in Fig. 2.34, with the positive z axis inverted. Set up the Lagrangian and examine the equations of motion for the two special cases $\dot{\theta} = 0$ and $\dot{\gamma} = 0$.

13. Derive the law of areas (compare Sec. 12.3) by Lagrange's equations. HINT: Express T in terms of plane polar coordinates and U in the form $f(r)$.

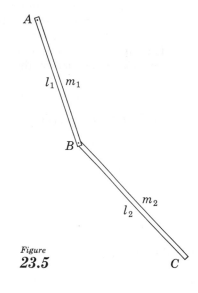

Figure
23.5

23.5. HAMILTON'S CANONICAL EQUATIONS

The key concepts of the Lagrange method were generalized coordinates, the Lagrangian, and generalized forces. In this section we associate with each generalized coordinate a corresponding generalized momentum and then develop simple and symmetric equations of motion. These new equations are particularly useful for statistical investigations in phase space and for problems in quantum theory. We shall not use them for solving specific problems, but shall regard them rather as an admirable culmination of the theoretical side of basic mechanics.

In Sec. 23.1 we noted that for one-dimensional motion of a particle the momentum p is equal to the derivative with respect to the velocity component of kinetic energy. We use this idea as the definition of a *generalized momentum* p_i conjugate to the generalized coordinate q_i:

$$(23.21) \qquad p_i = \frac{\partial T}{\partial \dot{q}_i}$$

As before, we formally regard T and L as functions of both the q's and the $\dot{q}$'s. To check on the appropriateness of this definition, consider the case of a rotating object. The kinetic energy $\frac{1}{2}i\dot{\theta}^2$ leads at once to the familiar angular momentum $i\dot{\theta}$. In the case of a sphere, rolling but not slipping, the kinetic energy $\frac{7}{10}m\dot{x}^2$ leads to a generalized momentum $\frac{7}{5}m\dot{x}$, which is an effective momentum, taking account of both translational and rotational aspects.

Let us again assume that the forces are conservative, so that each force component f_i is equal to a derivative of the potential energy of the system: $f_i = -\partial U/\partial q_i$. Since U does not depend on $\dot{q}_i$, we may write, instead of Eq. (23.21),

$$(23.22) \qquad p_i = \frac{\partial L}{\partial \dot{q}_i}$$

Lagrange's equations may now be written in the form

$$(23.23) \qquad \dot{p}_i = \frac{\partial L}{\partial q_i}$$

Note the remarkable symmetry of the pair of equations (23.22) and (23.23). The Lagrangian is a function whose velocity derivatives are momenta and whose space derivatives are forces. Observe that several of the words in the preceding sentence are used in a generalized sense.

The equations of motion may be expressed in a still simpler form by introducing the *Hamiltonian*, defined by the equation

$$(23.24) \qquad H = \sum_i p_i \dot{q}_i - L$$

First we identify the physical nature of H. Recall that

$$T = \frac{1}{2} \sum_i m_i \dot{x}_i^2$$

and that in terms of the q's and $\dot{q}$'s, $\dot{x}_i$ may be expressed

$$\dot{x}_i = \sum_k \frac{\partial x_i}{\partial q_k} \dot{q}_k$$

so that

$$(23.25) \qquad T = \frac{1}{2} \sum_{i,j,k} m_i \frac{\partial x_i}{\partial q_j} \frac{\partial x_i}{\partial q_k} \dot{q}_j \dot{q}_k$$

Now we apply (23.21) to get

$$(23.26) \qquad p_k = \frac{\partial T}{\partial \dot{q}_k} = \sum_{i,j} m_i \frac{\partial x_i}{\partial q_j} \frac{\partial x_i}{\partial q_k} \dot{q}_j$$

(the $\frac{1}{2}$ disappears because each term in the summation occurs twice after the differentiation). Therefore, if we multiply both sides of (23.26) by $\dot{q}_k$ separately for $k = 1, 2, \ldots, f$ and then sum, we merely reconstruct the right member of (23.25) with the $\frac{1}{2}$ omitted:

$$(23.27) \qquad \sum p_k \dot{q}_k = 2T$$

Consequently,

$$(23.28) \qquad H = 2T - L = 2T - (T - U) = T + U$$

This function of q's and $\dot{q}$'s defined by (23.24) has been identified as the total energy of the system.

Thus far the independent variables for T, U, L have been q_i, $\dot{q}_i$. Now we shall use p_i in place of $\dot{q}_i$. In the simplest case this is obviously feasible: we merely shift from $\dot{x}_i$ to $m_i \dot{x}_i$. It is, however, not obvious that for all generalized coordinates we may solve (23.22) for $\dot{q}_i$. The general feasibility of expressing H in terms of the p's and the q's appears from an analysis of the total differential of H:

$$dH = d(\Sigma\, p_i \dot{q}_i - L) = \Sigma\, p_i\, d\dot{q}_i + \Sigma\, \dot{q}_i\, dp_i - \Sigma \frac{\partial L}{\partial q_i} dq_i - \Sigma \frac{\partial L}{\partial \dot{q}_i} d\dot{q}_i$$

This first step involved only term-by-term differentiation. Using (23.22) and (23.23), we get a simplified formula

$$dH = \Sigma\, p_i\, d\dot{q}_i + \Sigma\, \dot{q}_i\, dp_i - \Sigma\, \dot{p}_i\, dq_i - \Sigma\, p_i\, d\dot{q}_i$$

The two sets of terms involving $d\dot{q}_i$ occur with opposite sign, so we have finally

$$(23.29) \qquad dH = \Sigma\, \dot{q}_i\, dp_i - \Sigma\, \dot{p}_i\, dq_i$$

In this equation $d\dot{q}_i$ does not appear: H will now be treated as a function of the p's and q's only. Hence we may write the total differential according to the usual formula:

$$(23.30) \qquad dH = \Sigma \frac{\partial H}{\partial p_i} dp_i + \Sigma \frac{\partial H}{\partial q_i} dq_i$$

Comparing coefficients in (23.29) and (23.30), we get

$$(23.31) \qquad \dot{q}_i = \frac{\partial H}{\partial p_i}$$

$$(23.32) \qquad -\dot{p}_i = \frac{\partial H}{\partial q_i}$$

These symmetric equations, involving only first derivatives, are *Hamilton's canonical equations*.

Example I

Suppose that a particle of mass m moves on the x axis subject to a conservative force whose potential energy is $U(x)$. The kinetic energy is now to be written in terms of p: $\frac{1}{2}m\dot{x}^2 = (1/2m)p^2$. The Hamiltonian is then, using x for q,

$$H = (1/2m)p^2 + U(x)$$

The canonical equations yield

$$\frac{\partial H}{\partial p} = \frac{p}{m} = \dot{x}$$

and

$$\frac{\partial H}{\partial x} = \frac{\partial U}{\partial x} = -\dot{p}$$

The first equation, $p = m\dot{x}$, may be differentiated to give

$$\dot{p} = m\ddot{x}$$

This may be combined with the second equation to yield

$$-\frac{\partial U}{\partial x} = m\ddot{x}$$

which is the usual equation of motion for a particle subject to a conservative force.

Example 2

Consider a particle of mass m moving in the coordinate plane subject to a conservative central force toward the origin such that U is a function of the distance. The kinetic energy, in terms of polar coordinates, is

$$T = \tfrac{1}{2}m\dot{r}^2 + \tfrac{1}{2}mr^2\dot{\theta}^2$$

The corresponding generalized momenta are

$$p_r = \frac{\partial T}{\partial \dot{r}} = m\dot{r}$$

$$p_\theta = \frac{\partial T}{\partial \dot{\theta}} = mr^2\dot{\theta}$$

The Hamiltonian may be written

$$H = (1/2m)p_r^2 + (1/2mr^2)p_\theta^2 + U(r)$$

Since this system has two degrees of freedom, there are four Hamilton equations:

$$\dot{r} = \frac{\partial H}{\partial p_r} = \frac{p_r}{m}$$

$$-\dot{p}_r = \frac{\partial H}{\partial r} = -\frac{1}{mr^3}p_\theta^2 + U'(r)$$

$$\dot{\theta} = \frac{\partial H}{\partial p_\theta} = \frac{1}{mr^2}p_\theta$$

$$-\dot{p}_\theta = \frac{\partial H}{\partial \theta} = 0$$

The first and third equations restate the formula for p_r and p_θ. The second equation, with proper substitutions made, is a differential equation for the orbit. The fourth equation asserts the constancy of angular momentum and, for a particle of constant mass, is equivalent to the law of areas.

14. A simple oscillator has mass m and compliance c. Oscillation takes place along a straight line, which should be taken as the q axis. What is the Hamiltonian of the system? From Hamilton's equations show that the motion is simple harmonic.
15. A charged particle moves, starting from rest, in an electric field of strength E. Taking the q axis parallel to the field, what is the Hamiltonian? Apply Hamilton's equations.
16. Repeat Example 1 using cylindrical coordinates.
17. Repeat Example 1 using spherical coordinates.

23.6. APPLICATIONS TO PHASE SPACE

In Secs. 5.8 and 22.10 we have considered the possibility of representing the state of a physical system by a point and the behavior of such a system by a trajectory in a phase space. Let us now take the $2f$ coordinates $(q_1, q_2, \ldots, q_f, p_1, p_2, \ldots, p_f)$ as the coordinates of a point in a $2f$-dimensional space. It represents the instantaneous mechanical state of the system. As time passes, the configuration of the system may change, so the q's may vary. Similarly, the state of motion, and hence the p's, are functions of the time t. It is sometimes convenient to think of each representative point as a vector:

$$(23.33) \qquad \mathbf{R} = \sum_1^f q_i \mathbf{I}_i + \sum_1^f p_i \mathbf{J}_i$$

If we take the time derivative, we get a *phase velocity*

$$(23.34) \qquad \mathbf{V} = \Sigma \dot{q}_i \mathbf{I}_i + \Sigma \dot{p}_i \mathbf{J}_i$$

Not all points of phase space may be possible representative points of a given system. For instance, suppose that we consider a box of n gas molecules as the system of interest with usual cartesian coordinates for the q's. Then, in the directions of the $3n$ different q axes, only a restricted range is accessible. Similarly, the momentum components are limited by energy considerations. Within that region of phase space where the points represent possible states of the system, to each state $\mathbf{R}$ is associated a velocity vector $\mathbf{V}$. Thus $\mathbf{V}$ is a vector function of position in our phase space. In phase space, then, there is defined a flow of possible representative points.

We can now derive an astoundingly simple property of a phase space for a mechanical system governed by the laws of classical mechanics. To investigate the nature of the intrinsic flow of points, we compute the divergence of the velocity vector $\mathbf{V}$, using the formula

$$(23.35) \qquad \mathbf{\nabla} \cdot \mathbf{V} = \Sigma \frac{\partial \dot{q}_i}{\partial q_i} + \Sigma \frac{\partial \dot{p}_i}{\partial p_i}$$

which is merely the $2f$-dimensional analogue of the 3-dimensional formula which we used earlier, (18.38). First we evaluate $\dot{q}_i$ and $\dot{p}_i$ in (23.34), using Hamilton's equations. We get

$$(23.36) \qquad \mathbf{V} = \sum_1^f \frac{\partial H}{\partial p_i} \mathbf{I}_i - \sum_1^f \frac{\partial H}{\partial q_i} \mathbf{J}_i$$

Now apply (23.35):

$$(23.37) \qquad \mathbf{\nabla} \cdot \mathbf{V} = \Sigma \frac{\partial^2 H}{\partial q_i\, \partial p_i} - \Sigma \frac{\partial^2 H}{\partial p_i\, \partial q_i} = 0$$

This shows that in our phase space the flow is that of an *incompressible 2f-dimensional fluid*. Incidentally, the physical dimensions of phase space (as contrasted with the mathematical enumeration of independent variables just alluded to) are equal to $[qp]^f = [q]^f[U/\dot{q}]^f = [Ut]^f = [\text{action}]^f$. In statistical mechanics it is thus natural to divide phase space into cells of measure h^f, where h is Planck's constant. Because of the principle of indeterminacy, the classical trajectories described in this section are often replaced by tubes.

In our discussion of V space in Chap. 22, we considered the density of representative points. Let us use the same notion in a qp space. In statistical mechanics one often considers an ensemble of copies of a system of interest in random states so as to introduce in phase space a multiplicity of representative points. Here we merely assume that a large number of representative points are selected and that the density function is $\rho(\mathbf{R})$. The points participate in the flow already described. As in hydrodynamics, the rate of density change experienced at a moving point is given by

(23.38)
$$\dot{\rho} = \frac{\partial \rho}{\partial t} + \mathbf{V} \cdot \boldsymbol{\nabla}\rho$$

where the first term is the local rate of change and the second term is the rate due to change of position [cf. Eq. (17.13)]. The use of $2f$ instead of 3 dimensions changes nothing. Since, however, we have, also as in hydromechanics,

(23.39)
$$\frac{\partial \rho}{\partial t} = -\boldsymbol{\nabla} \cdot \rho\mathbf{V} = -\rho\boldsymbol{\nabla} \cdot \mathbf{V} - \mathbf{V} \cdot \boldsymbol{\nabla}\rho$$

we can substitute (23.39) into (23.38) and use (23.37) to get

(23.40)
$$\dot{\rho} = 0$$

This result, *Liouville's theorem*, is a notable consequence of Hamilton's equations. It is an important tool in the foundations of statistical mechanics.

EXERCISES

18. Describe the motion in phase space of a representative point for a simple oscillator (described in Exercise 14). Show that the trajectory of this point in qp space is periodic. Express the "area" of the region enclosed by the trajectory in terms of the period τ and total energy E of the oscillator.

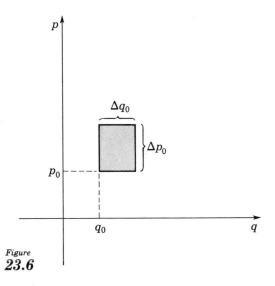

Figure
23.6

19. Show that $|\nabla H| = |\mathbf{V}|$ at any given point in phase space but that $\mathbf{V} \cdot \nabla H = 0$.

20. Each phase point in the rectangle shown in Fig. 23.6 represents a particle of mass m subject to a constant acceleration $\ddot{q} = a$.

(a) Plot the phase points approximately after a time t.

(b) Determine analytically whether the "area" occupied by the swarm of phase points has changed.

21. If f and g are functions of $q_1, \ldots, q_f, p_1, \ldots, p_f, t$, then the "Poisson bracket" of f and g is defined by

$$[f,g] = \sum_i \left(\frac{\partial f}{\partial q_i} \frac{\partial g}{\partial p_i} - \frac{\partial f}{\partial p_i} \frac{\partial g}{\partial q_i} \right)$$

Verify:

(a) $\dot{f} = \partial f / \partial t + [f,H]$.

(b) If f does not involve t explicitly, $\dot{f} = [f,H]$.

22. In Exercise 21b substitute (a) $f = p_i$; (b) $f = q_i$.

23. Show that $[q_j, p_k] = \delta_{jk}$, where $\delta_{jk} = 0$ for $j \neq k$ and $\delta_{jk} = 1$ for $j = k$.

24. Show that Liouville's theorem can be written $\partial \rho / \partial t = -[\rho, H]$.

Appendix 1 AXIOMS FOR VECTOR SPACES

In Chap. 2 elementary parts of vector algebra are developed from an intuitive geometric point of view which is close to the physicist's view of local space. The mathematical system so constructed has a standard structure which is best appreciated by listing axioms for a vector space and comparing these axioms with the properties already developed.

AI.I. AXIOMS FOR ADDITION

We shall list properties which a set of objects **A, B,** . . . , called *vectors*, must enjoy in order that they and their operations qualify as a *vector space*. In the background, there must be a suitable set of *scalars* (for us the real numbers). First we consider the addition properties.

1. *For every pair of vectors* **A** *and* **B** *there is in the given set of vectors a unique vector called the sum of* **A** *and* **B**:

$$\mathbf{A} + \mathbf{B} = \mathbf{B} + \mathbf{A}$$

The vectors we have studied satisfy this requirement: addition is defined for any two vectors, and the operation was shown to be commutative.

2. *For any three vectors* **A, B, C,**

$$\mathbf{A} + (\mathbf{B} + \mathbf{C}) = (\mathbf{A} + \mathbf{B}) + \mathbf{C}$$

This associative property was demonstrated for addition of vectors in Sec. 2.6.

3. *There is a null vector* **O** *such that*

$$\mathbf{A} + \mathbf{O} = \mathbf{A}$$

for every vector **A**.

We invented a symbol **O** to represent any arrow of zero length. This vector has the property claimed in axiom 3 according to Sec. 2.6, Exercise 15.

4. *Corresponding to every vector* **A** *there is an opposite vector* $-\mathbf{A}$ *such that*

$$\mathbf{A} + (-\mathbf{A}) = \mathbf{O}$$

The special character of $-\mathbf{A}$ was pointed out in Sec. 2.6, where **O** was defined. Thus far we have made no use of scalars. Any system satisfying axioms 1 to 4 constitutes a commutative group under addition. If this were a course in algebra, we should proceed to derive numerous results from these axioms.

AI.2. AXIOMS FOR MULTIPLICATION BY SCALARS

The operation of multiplication by scalars must, for a vector space, have certain limiting properties.

5. *For every scalar c and vector* **A**, *there is in the given set of vectors a unique vector called the product of c and* **A**:

$$c\mathbf{A} = \mathbf{A}c$$

These requirements of closure and commutativity surely were satisfied by our definition in Sec. 2.8.

6. *For every scalar c and every pair of vectors* **A** *and* **B**,

$$c(\mathbf{A} + \mathbf{B}) = c\mathbf{A} + c\mathbf{B}$$

7. *For every pair of scalars c and c' and every vector* **A**,

$$c(c'\mathbf{A}) = (cc')\mathbf{A}$$

and

$$(c + c')\mathbf{A} = c\mathbf{A} + c'\mathbf{A}$$

8. *For every vector* **A**, *the product by the scalar* 1 *yields the same vector*

$$1\mathbf{A} = \mathbf{A}$$

Axioms 6 to 8 were verified in Sec. 2.8, Exercise 22.   Any system satisfying axioms 1 to 8 is a *vector space over the stated scalars*.   Thus the system built up geometrically in Chap. 2 is a *vector space over the real numbers*.

In order that this perusal of axioms may be profitable, it is important that they be interpreted thoughtfully relative to the model we have set up in Chap. 2.   For example, in axiom 7 it should be observed, in the second equation, that the two plus signs have entirely different significance: one is an addition of numbers, the other is a composition of vectors according to the parallelogram rule.   It should be emphasized that the abstract formulation of a vector space in the eight axioms is exemplified by examples quite different from the geometric vectors which we met in Chap. 2. For instance, the set of polynomials in x with real coefficients is a vector space for the usual operations of addition and multiplication by constants.

AI.3. AXIOMS FOR INNER PRODUCT

The particular vector space of Chap. 2 has the additional property of possessing an inner product.   Now an inner product is a function assigning to each pair of vectors **A** and **B** a scalar $\mathbf{A} \cdot \mathbf{B}$.   When the scalars are real numbers, for such a function to qualify as an inner product, all that is required is that it satisfy the following axioms.

9. *For every pair of vectors* **A** *and* **B** *there is a unique real number called the inner product of* **A** *and* **B**:

$$\mathbf{A} \cdot \mathbf{B} = \mathbf{B} \cdot \mathbf{A}$$

10. *For every three vectors* **A**, **B**, *and* **C**,

$$\mathbf{A} \cdot (\mathbf{B} + \mathbf{C}) = \mathbf{A} \cdot \mathbf{B} + \mathbf{A} \cdot \mathbf{C}$$

11. *For every real number c and every pair of vectors* **A** *and* **B**,

$$c(\mathbf{A} \cdot \mathbf{B}) = c\mathbf{A} \cdot \mathbf{B}$$

12. *For every vector* **A**,

$$\mathbf{A} \cdot \mathbf{A} \geq 0 \qquad \mathbf{A} \cdot \mathbf{A} = 0 \text{ only if } \mathbf{A} = \mathbf{O}$$

The symmetric or commutative property axiom 9 was shown to be immediate from the definition in our geometric model in Chap. 2.   The linear property of the inner-product function asserted in axiom 10 is merely a statement of the distributive law. Axiom 11 is contained in Eq. (2.43).   Axiom 12 is particularly interesting as an abstract statement, but for our model (see Sec. 2.12, special conclusion 1) it devolves into an analysis of the quantity $a^2 \cos 0°$, where a is a real number.

A vector space with an inner product is called a *euclidean vector space*.   It appears then that the vectors of Chap. 2 form such a space.   Proceeding from the 12 axioms, one can define the length of a vector **A** as $(\mathbf{A} \cdot \mathbf{A})^{\frac{1}{2}}$.   In Chap. 2, length was a primitive idea, but it is not mentioned in the above axioms. Next one can proceed to define distance and angle. In Chap. 2, of course, the inner product was defined in terms of angle and length. The abstract approach is clearly more orderly and more general than the geometric one. But for elementary mechanics our need for vectors is specific rather than general. Hence the main advantage to us of a glance at the axioms is that they give us a systematic and economical summary of basic formal properties.

For a more detailed study of vector spaces, see, for example, one of the following references:

Birkhoff, G., and S. MacLane: "A Survey of Modern Algebra," rev. ed., chap. 7, The Macmillan Company, New York, 1953.
Finkbeiner, D. T., II: "Introduction to Matrices and Linear Transformations," W. H. Freeman and Company, San Francisco, 1960.
Halmos, P. R.: "Finite Dimensional Vector Spaces," 2d ed., D. Van Nostrand Company, Inc., Princeton, N.J., 1958.
Paige, L. J., and J. D. Swift: "Elements of Linear Algebra," Ginn and Company, Boston, 1961.

Appendix 2 FURTHER GEOMETRIC APPLICATIONS OF VECTOR ALGEBRA

In Chaps. 2 and 9 a few applications of vectors to geometry have been given. Such applications would in fact be hard to avoid in a treatment based on geometrical ideas as ours has been. In this Appendix, a few more specific applications to geometry are given. Exercises are given at the end of this Appendix.

A2.I. EQUATIONS OF A STRAIGHT LINE

As a first example, let us write a vector equation for a line through the point $\mathbf{P}'$ and parallel to the unit vector $\mathbf{E}$. Let $\mathbf{P}$ be any point on this line (see Fig. A2.1). Then, treating this line as an axis, with $\mathbf{P}'$ as origin, denote by s the scalar coordinate of $\mathbf{P}$. Then

$$\mathbf{P}'\mathbf{P} = s\mathbf{E}$$

so that

$$\mathbf{P} = \mathbf{P}' + s\mathbf{E}$$

This is an equation, in parametric form, of the line. Assuming that $\mathbf{P}$ has coordinates (x,y,z), that $\mathbf{P}'$ has coordinates (x',y',z'), and that the components of $\mathbf{E}$ are the direction cosines l, m, n, this simple equation can be expanded thus:

$$(x\mathbf{I} + y\mathbf{J} + z\mathbf{K}) = (x'\mathbf{I} + y'\mathbf{J} + z'\mathbf{K}) + s(l\mathbf{I} + m\mathbf{J} + n\mathbf{K})$$

which yields, using previous results on equality of vectors and multiplication by scalars, three scalar equations of the same form:

$$x = x' + sl \qquad y = y' + sm \qquad z = z' + sn$$

Note that the scalar parametric equations can be combined by eliminating the parameter. Solving each for s and equating the results, we obtain

$$\frac{x - x'}{l} = \frac{y - y'}{m} = \frac{z - z'}{n}$$

This symmetric form is a standard result of solid analytic geometry.

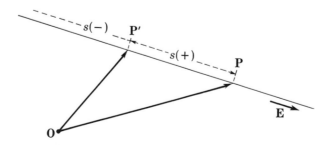

Figure
A2.1

Often, of course, a line is described by stating *two* points on it. Suppose that **P″** is a distinct second point on the line. It must satisfy our first equation:

$$\mathbf{P}'' = \mathbf{P}' + r\mathbf{E} \qquad \text{where } r \neq 0$$

Solving for **E** we get

$$\mathbf{E} = \frac{\mathbf{P}'' - \mathbf{P}'}{r}$$

and the equation can be written

$$\mathbf{P} = \mathbf{P}' + \frac{s}{r}(\mathbf{P}'' - \mathbf{P}')$$

or

$$\mathbf{P} = \left(1 - \frac{s}{r}\right)\mathbf{P}' + \frac{s}{r}\mathbf{P}''$$

In general, then, the equation of a line through **P′** and **P″** has the form

$$\mathbf{P} = a'\mathbf{P}' + a''\mathbf{P}'' \qquad \text{where } a' + a'' = 1$$

Since $a'' = s/r$ is the fractional distance from **P′** to **P″**, this equation can serve as a *ratio formula*,

$$\mathbf{P} = (1 - a'')\mathbf{P}' + a''\mathbf{P}''$$

This is a major tool in the application of vectors to plane geometry.

In setting up equations for a straight line, we used the fact that the vector **P′P** is parallel to the vector **E**. As an alternative approach, we may use the criterion for parallelism of Sec. 9.1,

$$(\mathbf{P} - \mathbf{P}') \times \mathbf{E} = \mathbf{O}$$

or in determinant form

$$\begin{vmatrix} x - x' & y - y' & z - z' \\ l & m & n \\ \mathbf{I} & \mathbf{J} & \mathbf{K} \end{vmatrix} = \mathbf{O}$$

If we set the x, y, and z components of the left member equal to zero, we get again the same nonparametric equations for the straight line.

A2.2. EQUATIONS FOR A PLANE

The parametric approach of the preceding section leads to useful equations for a plane. Consider a plane determined by three points whose position vectors are **P′**, **P″**, **P‴**. Let **P** be any point of the plane aside from **P′**. Let the line through **P′** and **P** meet the line through **P″** and **P‴** in the point **Q**. By the results of the preceding section,

$$\mathbf{P} = b\mathbf{Q} + b'\mathbf{P}' \qquad \text{where } b + b' = 1$$

and also

$$\mathbf{Q} = c''\mathbf{P}'' + c'''\mathbf{P}''' \qquad \text{where } c'' + c''' = 1$$

Substituting for **Q**,

$$\mathbf{P} = b(c''\mathbf{P}'' + c'''\mathbf{P}''') + b'\mathbf{P}'$$

or

$$\mathbf{P} = b'\mathbf{P}' + bc''\mathbf{P}'' + bc'''\mathbf{P}'''$$

or changing the names of the scalar multipliers,

$$\mathbf{P} = a'\mathbf{P}' + a''\mathbf{P}'' + a'''\mathbf{P}'''$$

where

$$a' + a'' + a''' = b' + b(c'' + c''') = b' + b = 1$$

The final equation for **P** is a three-parameter equation for the plane, but since the parameters add up to a constant, two parameters will suffice.   Note that the derivation does not hold for the case where **P′P** and **P″P‴** are parallel, but that the result is valid even for this case.

We now write in vector fashion an equation for a plane through **P′** and perpendicular to a unit vector **N**.   Let **P** be any point on the plane (see Fig. A2.2). Then the vector from **P′**, **P** − **P′**, is perpendicular to **N**.   Hence

$$(\mathbf{P} - \mathbf{P'}) \cdot \mathbf{N} = 0$$

This is the desired equation.   It is a scalar equation in terms of vectors.   If **N** has direction cosines l, m, and n, **P** has coordinates (x,y,z), and **P′** (x',y',z'), then the above equation is equivalent to

$$l(x - x') + m(y - y') + n(z - z') = 0$$

Conversely, given an equation of the form $ax + by + cz + d = 0$, suppose that **P′**(x',y',z') is any point on the plane.   Then the equation holds for those coordinates: $ax' + by' + cz' + d = 0$.   Subtracting equations member by member to eliminate d, we have

$$a(x - x') + b(y - y') + c(z - z') = 0$$

which is immediately interpreted as an inner product

$$\mathbf{M} \cdot (\mathbf{P} - \mathbf{P'}) = 0$$

where $\mathbf{M} = a\mathbf{I} + b\mathbf{J} + c\mathbf{K}$ is a vector normal to the plane.   Thus, for instance, given the equation

$$3x - 4y + 5z - 6 = 0$$

we know at once that the vector $3\mathbf{I} - 4\mathbf{J} + 5\mathbf{K}$ is normal to the plane.   From this a unit normal vector may immediately be determined.   The coordinates of a point **P′** on the plane are very easy to find just by assigning arbitrary values to two coordinates and solving for the third (which we pick to have a nonzero coefficient). Thus sample points on the plane $3x - 4y + 5z - 6 = 0$ are $(2,0,0)$, $(0,-1.5,0)$, $(-1,-1,1)$.

A2.3. DISTANCE FROM POINT TO PLANE

Now let **P** be a point not necessarily on the plane described in the preceding section (see Fig. A2.3).   The line through **P** normal to the plane has, using Sec. A2.1, the

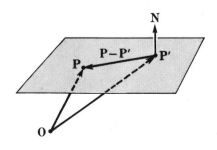

Figure
A2.2

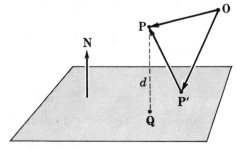

Figure
A2.3

equation
$$R = P + sN$$

for some scalar s.   Denote by Q the point of intersection of line and plane,

$$Q = P + s'N$$

where s' is, except possibly for sign, equal to the distance from P to the plane; that is, $d = |s'|$.   Since Q is a point of the plane, we also have

$$(Q - P') \cdot N = 0$$

Substituting,

$$(P + s'N - P') \cdot N = 0$$

or rearranging,

$$(P - P') \cdot N = -s'$$

but

$$d = |s'| = |-s'| = |(P - P') \cdot N|$$

A2.4. PROJECTIONS ONTO A PLANE

In Chap. 2 we derived an expression for the projection of a vector A onto a plane of normal N.   In terms of this expression it is easy to prove a theorem about projections onto a plane which is analogous to the one proved in Sec. 2.9 about projections onto a line.   The statement is the same as before: The projection of the sum of two (or more) vectors is equal to the sum of their projections.   The proof is as follows.   Let A' and B' denote the projections onto the plane of the vectors A and B.   If N is a unit normal to the plane, then, as just stated above (see Fig. A2.4),

$$A' = A - (A \cdot N)N$$

and

$$B' = B - (B \cdot N)N$$

Using the associative and commutative laws for vector addition, the sum $A' + B'$ may be written

$$A' + B' = A + B - (A \cdot N)N - (B \cdot N)N$$

But by the distributive law for multiplication by a scalar, we may factor out the N from the last two terms.

$$A' + B' = A + B - \{(A \cdot N) + (B \cdot N)\}N$$

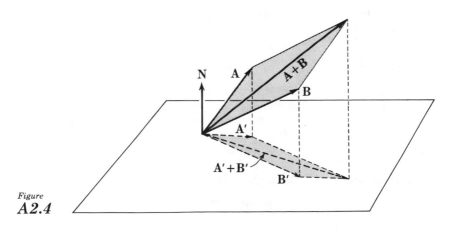

Figure
A2.4

Then, finally, the distributive law for scalar products yields

$$\mathbf{A}' + \mathbf{B}' = \mathbf{A} + \mathbf{B} - \{(\mathbf{A} + \mathbf{B}) \cdot \mathbf{N}\}\mathbf{N}$$

But the right member of this equation is immediately recognizable as the projection onto the plane of the vector $\mathbf{A} + \mathbf{B}$; therefore we have

$$\mathbf{A}' + \mathbf{B}' = (\mathbf{A} + \mathbf{B})'$$

as was to be proved.

Alternatively, using vector products (see Sec. 9.5, Example 1), the projection of a vector $\mathbf{A}$ onto the plane is given by $\mathbf{A}' = \mathbf{N} \times (\mathbf{A} \times \mathbf{N})$, for the expression "projection of $\mathbf{A}$ onto a plane of normal $\mathbf{N}$" is just another way of saying "projection of $\mathbf{A}$ perpendicular to $\mathbf{N}$." In terms of this expression, it is easy to re-prove the foregoing proposition on projections of sums of vectors. All that is needed is two applications of the distributive law for vector multiplication.

$$(\mathbf{A} + \mathbf{B})' = \mathbf{N} \times \{(\mathbf{A} + \mathbf{B}) \times \mathbf{N}\} = \mathbf{N} \times \{(\mathbf{A} \times \mathbf{N}) + (\mathbf{B} \times \mathbf{N})\}$$

$$= \mathbf{N} \times (\mathbf{A} \times \mathbf{N}) + \mathbf{N} \times (\mathbf{B} \times \mathbf{N}) = \mathbf{A}' + \mathbf{B}'$$

A2.5. APPLICATIONS TO PLANE GEOMETRY

In using vectors to prove theorems in plane geometry, three simple tools are particularly useful:

I. Ratio formula: If $\mathbf{P}$ lies on the line determined by $\mathbf{P}'$ and $\mathbf{P}''$, then $\mathbf{P} = a'\mathbf{P}' + a''\mathbf{P}''$, where $a' + a'' = 1$.

II. If $\pm\mathbf{A} \parallel \mathbf{B}$, then $\mathbf{A} = k\mathbf{B}$ for some scalar k.

III. If $\pm\mathbf{A} \nparallel \mathbf{B}$, where $\mathbf{A}$ is not null, then $s\mathbf{A} = t\mathbf{B}$ if and only if $s = t = 0$. (This affirms that $\mathbf{A}$ and $\mathbf{B}$ are linearly independent.) Let us apply these tools to a few specific examples.

Example 1

To show that the diagonals of a parallelogram bisect each other. Take one vertex as origin, as shown in Fig. A2.5. Then the other vertices may be denoted as $\mathbf{A}$, $\mathbf{B}$ and $\mathbf{A} + \mathbf{B}$. The intersection of diagonals is on $\mathbf{A} + \mathbf{B}$, so, by formula II, $\mathbf{M} = t(\mathbf{A} + \mathbf{B})$. Also $\mathbf{M}$ lies on $\mathbf{AB}$, so, by formula I, $\mathbf{M} = (1 - s)\mathbf{A} + s\mathbf{B}$. Equating expressions for $\mathbf{M}$ and rearranging,

$$(1 - s - t)\mathbf{A} = (t - s)\mathbf{B}$$

By formula III,

$$s = t \qquad 1 - 2s = 0 \qquad s = \tfrac{1}{2} = t$$

Example 2

To show that the bisector of an internal angle of a triangle divides the opposite side in the ratio of the adjoining sides. Take the origin at the vertex of the bisected angle (see Fig. A2.6). Then the other vertices are $\mathbf{B} = b\mathbf{E}$ and $\mathbf{C} = c\mathbf{F}$, where $\mathbf{E}$ and $\mathbf{F}$ are unit vectors. $\mathbf{D}$ is the position vector of the point in question on the segment $\mathbf{BC}$.

Now $\mathbf{D} = s\mathbf{B} + t\mathbf{C}$ by formula I. $\mathbf{O}$, $\mathbf{E}$, $\mathbf{E} + \mathbf{F}$, and $\mathbf{F}$ determine a rhombus. Its diagonal also bisects the angle at $\mathbf{O}$, for

$$\mathbf{E} \cdot (\mathbf{E} + \mathbf{F}) = \mathbf{F} \cdot (\mathbf{E} + \mathbf{F})$$

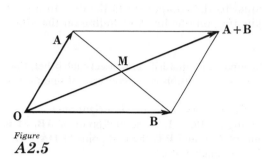

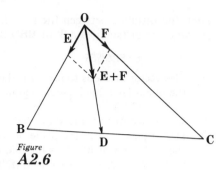

Figure
A2.5

Figure
A2.6

Hence **D** and **E** + **F** are parallel, or, by formula II,

$$\mathbf{D} = u(\mathbf{E} + \mathbf{F})$$

Equating expressions for **D**,

$$sb\mathbf{E} + tc\mathbf{F} = u\mathbf{E} + u\mathbf{F}$$

or

$$(sb - u)\mathbf{E} = (u - tc)\mathbf{F}$$

Then by formula III,

$$sb = u = tc$$

or

$$s:t = c:b$$

Example 3

To write a vector equation for a circle with center at **P'** and radius r. Here the result is immediate.

$$(\mathbf{P} - \mathbf{P}') \cdot (\mathbf{P} - \mathbf{P}') = r^2$$

A2.6. DISTANCE BETWEEN SKEW LINES

An interesting geometrical example of the vector product is found in the computation of the distance between two skew lines in space. Such a distance is measured along a common normal. If the two lines in Fig. A2.7 are **AB** and **A'B'**, respectively (where the letters denote the position vectors of the points so named), the vector product

$$(\mathbf{B} - \mathbf{A}) \times (\mathbf{B}' - \mathbf{A}')$$

gives the direction of such a normal. Let **N** be a unit vector in this direction.

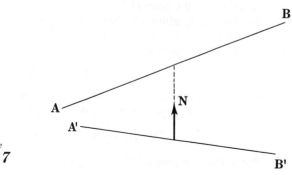

Figure
A2.7

Then the distance between the lines is equal to the component in the direction of **N** of some vector (such as **AB'** or **BB'**) originating on one line and ending on the other.

EXERCISES

1. Use vector methods to prove: If the diagonals of a quadrilateral bisect each other, then the quadrilateral is a parallelogram. (This proposition is the converse of one proved in Sec. A2.5.)

2. Use vector methods to show that an angle inscribed in a circle is a right angle.

3. **D** is a point not in the plane of the triangle **ABC**. **L** is the mid-point of **AB**, **M** is the mid-point of **BC**, **N** is the mid-point of **CD**, and **P** is the mid-point of **DA**. Use vector methods to prove that **LMNP** is a parallelogram.

4. Use vector methods to prove that a line parallel to a side of a triangle divides the other two sides of the triangle in equal ratios.

5. Use vector methods to prove that a segment from a vertex of a parallelogram to the mid-point of an opposite side is trisected by a diagonal.

6. Use vector methods to show that the medians of a triangle meet in a common point, which is a point of trisection for each median.

7. Use vector methods to show that the three segments joining mid-points of opposite edges of a tetrahedron meet in a point. (HINT: Compare Exercise 3.)

8. Let **A** be a fixed position vector. The position vector **P** of any point on a certain locus satisfies the statement: The vector $\mathbf{P} - \mathbf{A}$ is perpendicular to the vector $\mathbf{P} - (-\mathbf{A})$. What is the locus?

9. Find a unit vector perpendicular to the plane parallel to both of the following vectors: $\mathbf{I} + 2\mathbf{K}$ and $\mathbf{I} + \mathbf{J}$.

10. Find direction cosines for a line normal to the plane through the three points $(0,0,0)$, $(1,0,2)$, and $(1,1,0)$.

11. Find the direction cosines for a vector normal to the plane through the three points $(4,2,2)$, $(10,-7,10)$, and $(1,0,-2)$.

12. Compute the distance between the line through the points $(1,2,3)$ and $(3,4,3)$ and the line through the points $(4,6,8)$ and $(4,5,6)$.

13. Given: the line through $(1,1,0)$ parallel to the vector $\mathbf{I} + \mathbf{J} + \mathbf{K}$. How close does this line come to the x axis?

14. For two perpendicular vectors **A** and **B**, prove that the locus of points having position vector **P** such that

$$\mathbf{A} \times \mathbf{P} = \mathbf{B}$$

is a straight line.

15. Use the vector product as a device for obtaining scalar equations for a line perpendicular to the plane

$$x - 8y + 4z + 6 = 0$$

and through the point $(1,2,3)$.

16. Find scalar equations for the line through the origin and perpendicular to both of the following vectors: $3\mathbf{I} - 2\mathbf{K}$, $3\mathbf{I} + 3\mathbf{J}$.

17. Demonstrate that the equation

$$(\mathbf{R} - \mathbf{B}) \cdot (\mathbf{R} - \mathbf{B}) = \mathbf{A} \cdot \mathbf{A}$$

represents a sphere of radius $|\mathbf{A}|$ and center **B**.

18. Prove that the projection of $\mathbf{A} \times \mathbf{B}$ onto a plane of unit normal **N** is given by

$$(\mathbf{A} \times \mathbf{B})' = (\mathbf{B} \cdot \mathbf{N})(\mathbf{A} \times \mathbf{N}) - (\mathbf{A} \cdot \mathbf{N})(\mathbf{B} \times \mathbf{N})$$

19. Prove that the projection onto a plane of the cross product of two vectors plus the

cross product of their projections is equal to their cross product; i.e.,

$$\mathbf{A} \times \mathbf{B} = (\mathbf{A} \times \mathbf{B})' + \mathbf{A}' \times \mathbf{B}'$$

20. The point (x',y',z') lies on the intersection of the two planes

$$ax + by + cz + d = 0 \quad \text{and} \quad a'x + b'y + c'z + d' = 0$$

Show that a set of equations for the line of intersection is the following:

$$\frac{x - x'}{bc' - cb'} = \frac{y - y'}{ca' - ac'} = \frac{z - z'}{ab' - ba'}$$

21. Write an equation for the plane whose normal has direction cosines 0.500, 0.707, −0.500 and which passes through the point $(-2,0,1)$.

22. Use the scalar product as a tool for finding the distance from the point $(1,1,1)$ to the plane through $(4,6,2)$ normal to the unit vector $0.6\mathbf{I} - 0.8\mathbf{J}$.

23. Three noncollinear points $\mathbf{P}_1$, $\mathbf{P}_2$, $\mathbf{P}_3$ determine a plane. Show that the vector

$$\mathbf{P}_1 \times \mathbf{P}_2 + \mathbf{P}_2 \times \mathbf{P}_3 + \mathbf{P}_3 \times \mathbf{P}_1$$

is normal to that plane.

24. Use the result of Exercise 23 to derive the determinantal equation for the plane

$$\begin{vmatrix} x & y & z & 0 \\ x_1 & y_1 & z_1 & 1 \\ x_2 & y_2 & z_2 & 1 \\ x_3 & y_3 & z_3 & 1 \end{vmatrix} = 0$$

25. Describe the locus for each of the following equations. $\mathbf{A}$ and $\mathbf{B}$ are constant non-null and nonparallel vectors.
(a) $\mathbf{R} \cdot \mathbf{R} = \mathbf{A} \cdot \mathbf{A}$.
(b) $\mathbf{R} \cdot \mathbf{A} = \mathbf{R} \cdot \mathbf{B}$.
(c) $(\mathbf{R} - \mathbf{A}) \times \mathbf{B} = \mathbf{O}$.
(d) $\mathbf{R} \times \mathbf{A} \cdot \mathbf{B} = 0$.
(e) $(\mathbf{R} \cdot \mathbf{B})\mathbf{A} = (\mathbf{R} \cdot \mathbf{A})\mathbf{B}$.

26. Use the inner product as a tool for finding the distance from the point $(0,0,0)$ to the line through the points $(5, -7,2)$ and $(-1,1,2)$. (HINT: The altitude of a triangle is equal to the component perpendicular to the base of one of the other sides.)

27. Find the shortest distance from the point $(-1,0,2)$ to the line through the points $(3, -1,3)$ and $(2,2,0)$.

Appendix 3 SUMMARY OF PROPERTIES OF THE OPERATOR ∇

For easy reference, a number of formal properties of the operator ∇ are gathered in this Appendix. Further details may be found in books on vector analysis. A few titles are given in the list of Suggested References.

A3.1. FUNDAMENTAL USES

The operator ∇ has been used in Chaps. 17 and 18 as a device for expressing formulas for gradient, curl, and divergence.

(A3.1) $$\mathbf{grad}\, f = \nabla f$$

(A3.2) $$\mathbf{curl}\, \mathbf{A} = \nabla \times \mathbf{A}$$

(A3.3) $$\mathrm{div}\, \mathbf{A} = \nabla \cdot \mathbf{A}$$

In these equations f is a scalar function of position. $\mathbf{A}$ is a vector function of position. A derived operator $\mathbf{T} \cdot \nabla$, where $\mathbf{T}$ is a unit vector associated with a scalar displacement quantity s, has been used for expressing directional derivatives.

(A3.4) $$\frac{df}{ds} = \mathbf{T} \cdot \nabla f$$

(A3.5) $$\frac{d\mathbf{A}}{ds} = \mathbf{T} \cdot \nabla \mathbf{A}$$

We also have had occasion to use an operator of the form $\mathbf{B} \cdot \nabla$ where $\mathbf{B} = b\mathbf{T}$ is not necessarily a unit vector. This operator is defined by

(A3.6) $$\mathbf{B} \cdot \nabla = b\mathbf{T} \cdot \nabla$$

In Sec. 18.10, for instance, we found use for the operator $\mathbf{V} \cdot \nabla$, where $\mathbf{V}$ is a velocity.

A3.2. ACTION OF ∇ ON PRODUCTS

The use of ∇ on products is analogous to the use of the operator $D = d/dx$ of introductory calculus. Let D_u indicate that the operator D acts only on the function u. Then

(A3.7) $$D(uv) = D_u(uv) + D_v(uv)$$
$$= (Du)v + u(Dv)$$

Analogously, we use ∇_a when we wish to emphasize that ∇ acts only on the vector function of position $\mathbf{A}$. For example,

(A3.8) $$\mathbf{A} \times (\nabla \times \mathbf{B}) = \nabla_b(\mathbf{A} \cdot \mathbf{B}) - (\mathbf{A} \cdot \nabla)\mathbf{B}$$

In the preceding example we have used the algebraic formula for the expansion of a vector triple product without losing sight of the basic circumstance that in the expression $\mathbf{A} \times (\nabla \times \mathbf{B})$, only $\mathbf{B}$ is differentiated by ∇. Formulas concerning products may be checked component by component. Here we proceed to list product formulas using Eq. (A3.7) as a guide and employing various vector identities. Equation (A3.8) will be useful in the form

(A3.9) $$\nabla_b(\mathbf{A} \cdot \mathbf{B}) = \mathbf{A} \times (\nabla \times \mathbf{B}) + (\mathbf{A} \cdot \nabla)\mathbf{B}$$

Other results are listed without comment.

(A3.10) $$\nabla(fg) = f\,\nabla g + g\,\nabla f$$

(A3.11) $$\nabla(\mathbf{A} \cdot \mathbf{B}) = \nabla_a(\mathbf{A} \cdot \mathbf{B}) + \nabla_b(\mathbf{A} \cdot \mathbf{B})$$
$$= \mathbf{B} \times (\nabla \times \mathbf{A}) + (\mathbf{B} \cdot \nabla)\mathbf{A} + \mathbf{A} \times (\nabla \times \mathbf{B}) + (\mathbf{A} \cdot \nabla)\mathbf{B}$$

(A3.12) $$\nabla \cdot (f\mathbf{A}) = f\,\nabla \cdot \mathbf{A} + \mathbf{A} \cdot \nabla f$$

(A3.13) $$\nabla \cdot (\mathbf{A} \times \mathbf{B}) = \nabla_a \cdot (\mathbf{A} \times \mathbf{B}) + \nabla_b \cdot (\mathbf{A} \times \mathbf{B})$$
$$= \mathbf{B} \cdot \nabla \times \mathbf{A} - \mathbf{A} \cdot \nabla \times \mathbf{B}$$

(A3.14) $$\nabla \times f\mathbf{A} = f(\nabla \times \mathbf{A}) + \nabla f \times \mathbf{A}$$

(A3.15) $$\nabla \times (\mathbf{A} \times \mathbf{B}) = \nabla_a \times (\mathbf{A} \times \mathbf{B}) + \nabla_b \times (\mathbf{A} \times \mathbf{B})$$
$$= (\mathbf{B} \cdot \nabla)\mathbf{A} - (\nabla \cdot \mathbf{A})\mathbf{B} - (\mathbf{A} \cdot \nabla)\mathbf{B} + (\nabla \cdot \mathbf{B})\mathbf{A}$$

A3.3. REPEATED USE OF ∇

The following formulas, listed together for convenience, have mostly appeared as exercises earlier in the book.

(A3.16) $$\nabla \times \nabla f = \mathbf{O}$$

(A3.17) $$\nabla \cdot \nabla f = \nabla^2 f$$

(A3.18) $$\nabla \cdot \nabla \times \mathbf{A} = 0$$

(A3.19) $$\nabla \times (\nabla \times \mathbf{A}) = \nabla(\nabla \cdot \mathbf{A}) - \nabla^2\mathbf{A}$$

where $\nabla^2\mathbf{A}$ is the result of acting on $\mathbf{A}$ with the operator $\nabla \cdot \nabla$.

Appendix 4 LINEAR TRANSFORMATIONS AND MATRICES

Since the physicist or engineer is interested in properties which can be divorced from particular reference frames, it is inevitable that he should be concerned with transformations which change coordinates. This concern leads to the study of tensors and, at the algebraic level, to matrices. Furthermore, the algebraic properties of transformations turn out surprisingly to be suitable representations or models for deep physical properties. Hence the future physical scientist needs to become familiar with these branches of mathematics. Since this text is elementary, such mathematical tools are not allowed to assume an indispensable role in the development. But in this Appendix enough about linear transformations and matrices is given to enable a student to appreciate some of their uses.

A4.1. LINEAR TRANSFORMATIONS OF VECTORS

We have talked about vector functions of position. To each position vector $\mathbf{R}$ was assigned a unique vector $\mathbf{V}(\mathbf{R})$. Now, more generally, we say that the vector variable $\mathbf{W}$ is a *function* of the vector variable $\mathbf{V}$ provided that, to every $\mathbf{V}$ in an appropriate set of vectors (the domain of the function), is assigned a unique vector $\mathbf{W}$. For example, the unit radial vector $\mathbf{L}$ may be regarded as a function of the position vector $\mathbf{R}$ for all positions except the origin. Or, given a constant vector $\mathbf{A}$, the vector $\mathbf{W} = \mathbf{A} \times \mathbf{V}$ is a simple function of $\mathbf{V}$ for all $\mathbf{V}$. If $\mathbf{V}$ is a differentiable function of $\mathbf{R}$, then $\mathbf{curl}\ \mathbf{V}$ is another function of $\mathbf{R}$. When $\mathbf{W}$ is a function of $\mathbf{V}$, we may use any of the standard names and nomenclatures for the function. We may write $\mathbf{W} = f(\mathbf{V})$ and say that the function assigns to each $\mathbf{V}$ a particular $\mathbf{W}$. Or we may say that the function is the set of *ordered pairs* of vectors $\{(\mathbf{V},\mathbf{W})\}$ where it is understood that $\mathbf{V}_1 = \mathbf{V}_2$ implies $f(\mathbf{V}_1) = f(\mathbf{V}_2)$ or $\mathbf{W}_1 = \mathbf{W}_2$. In the context of vector algebra, a function is often called a transformation.

    A transformation is said to be *linear* if linear combinations of vectors are preserved; for instance, a transformation $\mathscr{L}$ such that $\mathbf{W} = \mathscr{L}(\mathbf{V})$ is a linear transformation if and only if

(A4.1) $$\mathscr{L}(c_1\mathbf{V}_1 + c_2\mathbf{V}_2) = c_1\mathscr{L}(\mathbf{V}_1) + c_2\mathscr{L}(\mathbf{V}_2)$$

for all scalars c_1, c_2 and all vectors $\mathbf{V}_1$, $\mathbf{V}_2$ in the domain of $\mathscr{L}$. The concept of linearity was mentioned in Sec. 13.3 in connection with the operator $\boldsymbol{\Omega} \times$. Linear transformations are of great importance for several reasons, such as the following: because they occur naturally in connection with change of rectangular coordinates; because the basic operators of calculus d/dx and $\int$ are linear; because more general transformations can be approximated locally by linear transformations.

A4.2. THE MATRIX OF A LINEAR TRANSFORMATION

Let $\mathscr{L}$ be a linear transformation, and denote by $\mathbf{I}'$, $\mathbf{J}'$, $\mathbf{K}'$ the images under the transformation of $\mathbf{I}$, $\mathbf{J}$, $\mathbf{K}$, so that $\mathbf{I}' = \mathscr{L}(\mathbf{I})$, $\mathbf{J}' = \mathscr{L}(\mathbf{J})$, $\mathbf{K}' = \mathscr{L}(\mathbf{K})$. Let us write these new vectors (not necessarily unit vectors) in **IJK** form.

$$\mathbf{I}' = l_{11}\mathbf{I} + l_{21}\mathbf{J} + l_{31}\mathbf{K}$$

(A4.2)
$$\mathbf{J}' = l_{12}\mathbf{I} + l_{22}\mathbf{J} + l_{32}\mathbf{K}$$

$$\mathbf{K}' = l_{13}\mathbf{I} + l_{23}\mathbf{J} + l_{33}\mathbf{K}$$

We can now express in **IJK** form the image under the transformation of any vector $\mathbf{V} = v_x\mathbf{I} + v_y\mathbf{J} + v_z\mathbf{K}$. Suppose that this image is $\mathbf{W} = w_x\mathbf{I} + w_y\mathbf{J} + w_z\mathbf{K}$. Since the transformation is linear, we know that $\mathbf{W}$ can also be written

(A4.3)
$$\mathbf{W} = \mathscr{L}(\mathbf{V}) = v_x\mathbf{I}' + v_y\mathbf{J}' + v_z\mathbf{K}'$$

$$= w_x\mathbf{I} + w_y\mathbf{J} + w_z\mathbf{K}$$

Substituting (A4.2) and equating x, y, and z components, we have

$$w_x = l_{11}v_x + l_{12}v_y + l_{13}v_z$$

(A4.4)
$$w_y = l_{21}v_x + l_{22}v_y + l_{23}v_z$$

$$w_z = l_{31}v_x + l_{32}v_y + l_{33}v_z$$

The square array of coefficients

(A4.5)
$$\|\mathscr{L}\| = \begin{bmatrix} l_{11} & l_{12} & l_{13} \\ l_{21} & l_{22} & l_{23} \\ l_{31} & l_{32} & l_{33} \end{bmatrix} = [l_{ij}]$$

is the coefficient matrix of the transformation $\mathscr{L}$. The symbol L will be used for this matrix, so $\|\mathscr{L}\| = L$. Actually, of course, a transformation has different matrix representations for different sets of reference vectors.

The companion matrix of (A4.2), L^t, given by

(A4.6)
$$[l_{ij}]^t = \begin{bmatrix} l_{11} & l_{21} & l_{31} \\ l_{12} & l_{22} & l_{32} \\ l_{13} & l_{23} & l_{33} \end{bmatrix} = L^t$$

is called the *transpose* of L. It is derived from the matrix L by interchanging rows (horizontal triples) and columns (vertical triples). Thus the first column (l_{11}, l_{12}, l_{13}) of L^t is the first row of L. Either L or L^t could be regarded as the matrix (for the given reference frame) of the linear transformation.

Example

As a familiar illustration of Eq. (A4.2), consider the linear transformation for which $\mathbf{I}'$, $\mathbf{J}'$, $\mathbf{K}'$ are given as follows:

$$\mathbf{I}' = \cos\theta\mathbf{I} + \sin\theta\mathbf{J}$$

$$\mathbf{J}' = -\sin\theta\mathbf{I} + \cos\theta\mathbf{J}$$

$$\mathbf{K}' = \mathbf{K}$$

Under this transformation, the image $\mathbf{W}$ of the vector $\mathbf{V}$ is given by

$$w_x = \cos\theta\, v_x - \sin\theta\, v_y$$

$$w_y = \sin\theta\, v_x + \cos\theta\, v_y$$

$$w_z = v_z$$

The coefficient matrix

$$L = \begin{bmatrix} \cos\theta & -\sin\theta & 0 \\ \sin\theta & \cos\theta & 0 \\ 0 & 0 & 1 \end{bmatrix}$$

is an example of an *orthogonal* matrix: the rows (and columns) represent perpendicular unit vectors. That is, when L is orthogonal, the three vectors $\mathbf{I}'$, $\mathbf{J}'$, $\mathbf{K}'$ are all unit vectors and are mutually perpendicular.

A4.3. VECTORS AND MATRICES

Thus far we have encountered only the square, 3×3, "three by three," matrices L and L^t. It is convenient to call any rectangular array of scalars a matrix. For instance, the **IJK** components v_x, v_y, v_z of the vector $\mathbf{V}$ can be used as a column matrix V or a row matrix V^t:

$$V = \begin{bmatrix} v_x \\ v_y \\ v_z \end{bmatrix} \qquad V^t = [v_x \ v_y \ v_z]$$

Also the rows of L are row matrices:

$$L^{(1)} = [l_{11} \ l_{12} \ l_{13}] \qquad L^{(2)} = [l_{21} \ l_{22} \ l_{23}] \qquad L^{(3)} = [l_{31} \ l_{32} \ l_{33}]$$

so that we can write

$$L = \begin{bmatrix} L^{(1)} \\ L^{(2)} \\ L^{(3)} \end{bmatrix}$$

and similarly, the columns are column matrices:

$$L_{(1)} = \begin{bmatrix} l_{11} \\ l_{21} \\ l_{31} \end{bmatrix} \qquad L_{(2)} = \begin{bmatrix} l_{12} \\ l_{22} \\ l_{32} \end{bmatrix} \qquad L_{(3)} = \begin{bmatrix} l_{13} \\ l_{23} \\ l_{33} \end{bmatrix}$$

so that

$$L = [L_{(1)} L_{(2)} L_{(3)}]$$

In the three-dimensional context of this course, a row matrix is a 1×3, "one by three," matrix, and a column matrix is a 3×1, "three by one," matrix. In general, an $m \times n$, "m by n," matrix has m rows and n columns.

Note that $L^{(1)t} = L_{(1)}$, etc. Two $m \times n$ matrices $L = [l_{ij}]$ and $M = [m_{ij}]$ are said to be *equal* if $l_{ij} = m_{ij}$ for each set of subscripts ij. For instance, a matrix L is said to be *symmetric* if it is *equal* to its transpose:

(A4.7) $L = L^t$

For example, the following matrix is symmetric:

$$\begin{bmatrix} 2 & 6 & 0 \\ 6 & 0 & -2 \\ 0 & -2 & -3 \end{bmatrix}$$

Two operations for matrices are defined just as for vectors in terms of components. These are the operations of addition and of multiplication by a scalar.

The *sum* of two $m \times n$ matrices L and M is defined symbolically by

(A4.8) $$L + M = [l_{ij}] + [m_{ij}] = [l_{ij} + m_{ij}]$$

This means merely that corresponding entries are added. For example,

$$\begin{bmatrix} 1 & 2 & 3 \\ 0 & -1 & 2 \end{bmatrix} + \begin{bmatrix} 0 & -1 & 0 \\ 2 & 1 & 5 \end{bmatrix} = \begin{bmatrix} 1 & 1 & 3 \\ 2 & 0 & 7 \end{bmatrix}$$

This operation, as for vectors, is both commutative and associative:

(A4.9) $$L + M = M + L$$

(A4.10) $$L + (M + N) = (L + M) + N$$

Note that the $m \times n$ *zero matrix*, defined to have each entry equal to zero, behaves like a null vector for $m \times n$ matrices:

(A4.11) $$L + O = L$$

For example,

$$\begin{bmatrix} 1 & 3 \\ -2 & 1 \\ 6 & 0 \end{bmatrix} + \begin{bmatrix} 0 & 0 \\ 0 & 0 \\ 0 & 0 \end{bmatrix} = \begin{bmatrix} 1 & 3 \\ -2 & 1 \\ 6 & 0 \end{bmatrix}$$

$$[-3,2,1] + [3,-2,-1] = [0,0,0]$$

The product of any matrix $L = [l_{ij}]$ by a scalar c is defined by the equation

(A4.12) $$cL = c[l_{ij}] = [cl_{ij}]$$

This means merely that each element of the matrix is multiplied by the scalar factor. For example,

$$3\begin{bmatrix} 2 & -1 \\ 1 & 0 \end{bmatrix} = \begin{bmatrix} 6 & -3 \\ 3 & 0 \end{bmatrix}$$

$$-1\begin{bmatrix} 1 & -2 & 3 \\ 3 & 2 & -1 \end{bmatrix} = \begin{bmatrix} -1 & 2 & -3 \\ -3 & -2 & 1 \end{bmatrix}$$

This operation, as for vectors, satisfies simple desirable rules.

(A4.13) $$c(L + M) = cL + cM$$

(A4.14) $$(c_1 + c_2)L = c_1L + c_2L$$

(A4.15) $$(c_1c_2)L = c_1(c_2L)$$

(A4.16) $$1L = L$$

These properties are valid for any $m \times n$ matrices L and M and for any scalars c_1 and c_2.

Note that the square matrix

$$L = \begin{bmatrix} 0 & -2 & 3 \\ 2 & 0 & 1 \\ -3 & -1 & 0 \end{bmatrix}$$

satisfies the equation

(A4.17) $$L^t = (-1)L$$

This equation is the defining property of *skew-symmetric* matrices. Note also that for any square matrix M one may write:

(A4.18) $$M = 0.5(M + M^t) + 0.5(M - M^t)$$

It is easy to show that the matrix $0.5(M + M^t)$ is symmetric while $0.5(M - M^t)$ is skew-symmetric. Hence any square matrix M can be written as the sum

(A4.19) $$M = S + K$$

where $S^t = S$, $K^t = -K$.

A4.4. PRODUCTS OF MATRICES

Matrix multiplication is defined for an $m \times n$ matrix by an $n \times p$ matrix: it is essential that the first factor have the same number of columns as the second factor has rows. The result of the multiplication is an $m \times p$ matrix. The matrix product is based on the inner product of vectors. Thus, if $\mathbf{A} = a_x\mathbf{I} + a_y\mathbf{J} + a_z\mathbf{K}$ and $\mathbf{B} = b_x\mathbf{I} + b_y\mathbf{J} + b_z\mathbf{K}$, then

(A4.20) $$[a_x\ a_y\ a_z]\begin{bmatrix} b_x \\ b_y \\ b_z \end{bmatrix} = A^tB = \mathbf{A} \cdot \mathbf{B} = a_xb_x + a_yb_y + a_zb_z$$

More generally, to multiply two matrices, consider the first matrix as composed of rows and the second as composed of columns and take the corresponding inner products.

Example I

Evaluate LA.

Solution

$$LA = \begin{bmatrix} L^{(1)} \\ L^{(2)} \\ L^{(3)} \end{bmatrix} A = \begin{bmatrix} L^{(1)}A \\ L^{(2)}A \\ L^{(3)}A \end{bmatrix} = \begin{bmatrix} l_{11}a_x + l_{12}a_y + l_{13}a_z \\ l_{21}a_x + l_{22}a_y + l_{23}a_z \\ l_{31}a_x + l_{32}a_y + l_{33}a_z \end{bmatrix}$$

Example 2

Evaluate A^tL.

Solution

$$A^tL = A^t[L_{(1)}L_{(2)}L_{(3)}] = [A^tL_{(1)} \quad A^tL_{(2)} \quad A^tL_{(3)}]$$
$$= [a_xl_{11} + a_yl_{21} + a_zl_{31} \quad a_xl_{12} + a_yl_{22} + a_zl_{32} \quad a_xl_{13} + a_yl_{23} + a_zl_{33}]$$

Example 3

Evaluate the matrix products LM and ML, where L is as in Eq. (A4.5) and M is the matrix

$$\begin{bmatrix} m_{11} & m_{12} & m_{13} \\ m_{21} & m_{22} & m_{23} \\ m_{31} & m_{32} & m_{33} \end{bmatrix}$$

Solution

   a. To evaluate LM, regard L as composed of rows $L^{(i)}$, and M as composed of columns $M_{(j)}$. Then the ij entry in the product is given by

(A4.21) $(LM)_{ij} = L^{(i)}M_{(j)}$

Thus

$$LM = \begin{bmatrix} L^{(1)} \\ L^{(2)} \\ L^{(3)} \end{bmatrix} [M_{(1)}M_{(2)}M_{(3)}]$$

$$= \begin{bmatrix} L^{(1)}M_{(1)} & L^{(1)}M_{(2)} & L^{(1)}M_{(3)} \\ L^{(2)}M_{(1)} & L^{(2)}M_{(2)} & L^{(2)}M_{(3)} \\ L^{(3)}M_{(1)} & L^{(3)}M_{(2)} & L^{(3)}M_{(3)} \end{bmatrix}$$

Each of the nine entries in the product is a scalar product of a row of L by a column of M. In more detail Eq. (A4.21) becomes

$$(LM)_{ij} = L^{(i)}M_{(j)} = [l_{i1}l_{i2}l_{i3}]\begin{bmatrix} m_{1j} \\ m_{2j} \\ m_{3j} \end{bmatrix}$$

$$= l_{i1}m_{1j} + l_{i2}m_{2j} + l_{i3}m_{3j}$$

   b.

$$ML = \begin{bmatrix} M^{(1)} \\ M^{(2)} \\ M^{(3)} \end{bmatrix}[L_{(1)}L_{(2)}L_{(3)}]$$

$$= \begin{bmatrix} M^{(1)}L_{(1)} & M^{(1)}L_{(2)} & M^{(1)}L_{(3)} \\ M^{(2)}L_{(1)} & M^{(2)}L_{(2)} & M^{(2)}L_{(3)} \\ M^{(3)}L_{(1)} & M^{(3)}L_{(2)} & M^{(3)}L_{(3)} \end{bmatrix}$$

Ordinarily the products LM and ML are unequal.

Example 4

   Evaluate the product LR, where R is the column matrix of the position vector $\mathbf{R} = x\mathbf{I} + y\mathbf{J} + z\mathbf{K}$.

Solution

$$\begin{bmatrix} l_{11} & l_{12} & l_{13} \\ l_{21} & l_{22} & l_{23} \\ l_{31} & l_{32} & l_{33} \end{bmatrix}\begin{bmatrix} x \\ y \\ z \end{bmatrix} = \begin{bmatrix} l_{11}x + l_{12}y + l_{13}z \\ l_{21}x + l_{22}y + l_{23}z \\ l_{31}x + l_{32}y + l_{33}z \end{bmatrix}$$

Note that the set of linear equations (A4.4) is equivalent to the matrix equality.

(A4.22) $W = LV$

   If two linear transformations are performed in succession so that $\mathbf{V} = \mathscr{L}(\mathbf{U})$ and $\mathbf{W} = \mathscr{M}(\mathbf{V})$, then the net result is a linear transformation $\mathbf{W} = \mathscr{P}(\mathbf{U})$. The corresponding matrix equations are $V = LU$, $W = MV$, so that $W = M(LU) = PU$. It can be shown that $M(LU) = (ML)U$ and that $P = ML$. Thus the coefficient matrix of the result of two linear transformations is the matrix product of the coefficient matrices of the given transformations in reverse order. Since $(ML)^t = L^t M^t$, it is often convenient to associate with a transformation L the matrix L^t which appeared in connection with Eq. (A4.2). Then (A4.4) may be written $W^t = V^t L^t$.

Example 5

Express Eq. (15.18) as a matrix equality.

Solution

Write

$$E^t = [l \ m \ n] \qquad M = \begin{bmatrix} i_x & -i_{xy} & -i_{zx} \\ -i_{xy} & i_y & -i_{yz} \\ -i_{zx} & -i_{yz} & i_z \end{bmatrix}$$

Then

$$i = E^t M E$$

The matrix M is called the *inertia matrix*.

Note that the 3×3 unit matrix I, which is defined to have elements equal to 1 on the diagonal where $i = j$ and equal to zero elsewhere, has the desirable properties

(A4.23) $$KI = K \qquad IM = M$$

for every $m \times 3$ matrix K and every $3 \times n$ matrix M.

Furthermore, if the linear transformation given by (A4.4) is one to one, the transformation $\mathscr{L}$ has an inverse. In that case the matrix L is called *nonsingular* and it has an *inverse matrix* L^{-1} such that

(A4.24) $$LL^{-1} = I = L^{-1}L$$

Consider, for example, the two products of the matrices

$$\begin{bmatrix} 2 & 5 \\ 1 & 3 \end{bmatrix} \quad \text{and} \quad \begin{bmatrix} 3 & -5 \\ -1 & 2 \end{bmatrix}$$

A square matrix is nonsingular if and only if its determinant is not zero.

Note also that an *orthogonal* matrix L (see definition at end of Sec. A4.2) must satisfy the equation

$$LL^t = I$$

This follows immediately from the definitions. An alternative definition calls a matrix orthogonal if and only if

$$L^t = L^{-1}$$

A4.5. CHARACTERISTIC VECTORS OF A LINEAR TRANSFORMATION

If $\mathscr{L}$ is a linear transformation, and if $\mathbf{A}$ is a non-null vector whose image under $\mathscr{L}$ is a scalar multiple of $\mathbf{A}$, then $\mathbf{A}$ is called a *characteristic vector* of $\mathscr{L}$. (Synonyms for characteristic vector are proper vector and eigenvector.) Symbolically,

(A4.25) $$\mathscr{L}(\mathbf{A}) = \lambda \mathbf{A}$$

where λ is a scalar called a *characteristic value* (proper value, eigenvalue) of $\mathscr{L}$. Since $\mathscr{L}$ is linear, if $\mathbf{A}$ is a characteristic vector, so is any non-null multiple of $\mathbf{A}$

(with the same characteristic value):

$$\mathscr{L}(c\mathbf{A}) = c\mathscr{L}(\mathbf{A}) = c(\lambda\mathbf{A}) = \lambda(c\mathbf{A})$$

This means that, in the direction of a characteristic vector, a linear transformation is merely a stretching (or compressing) with a multiplication factor constant for that direction. The line determined by $\mathbf{A}$ is an *invariant line* mapped onto itself.

In matrix language Eq. (A4.25) is summarized, for any particular choice of reference frame, by

(A4.26) $$\qquad\qquad LA = \lambda A = \lambda(IA) = (\lambda I)A$$

where I is the unit matrix. This equation may be written

(A4.27) $$\qquad\qquad (L - \lambda I)A = O$$

By our definition of matrix equality Eq. (A4.25) is merely an abbreviation for the linear equations

$$l_{11}a_x + l_{12}a_y + l_{13}a_z = \lambda a_x$$
$$l_{21}a_x + l_{22}a_y + l_{23}a_z = \lambda a_y$$
$$l_{31}a_x + l_{32}a_y + l_{33}a_z = \lambda a_z$$

which have nontrivial solutions only for values of λ such that the determinant of the system vanishes:

$$|L - \lambda I| = 0$$

or

(A4.28) $$\begin{vmatrix} l_{11} - \lambda & l_{12} & l_{13} \\ l_{21} & l_{22} - \lambda & l_{23} \\ l_{31} & l_{32} & l_{33} - \lambda \end{vmatrix} = 0$$

Equation (A4.28) is called the *characteristic equation* or *secular equation* of the matrix L. Its roots are characteristic values of the transformation $\mathscr{L}$. If the transformation is studied in terms of a different reference frame (with the same origin), the characteristic roots are unchanged: they represent intrinsic properties of the transformation. Suppose, for instance, that components are referred to a new frame by means of a linear substitution (details about a change of frame or "basis" may be found in books on linear algebra),

$$V = MV' \qquad W = MW'$$

where the matrix M is nonsingular. Then the transformation (A4.22), $W = LV$, becomes

$$MW' = LMV'$$

or

(A4.29) $$\qquad\qquad W' = (M^{-1}LM)V'$$

In terms of the new reference frame, the transformation $\mathscr{L}$ is represented by the matrix $M^{-1}LM$, which is said to be *similar* to L. Let us consider the characteristic equation of this matrix.

(A4.30) $$\qquad\qquad |M^{-1}{}_1LM - \lambda I| = 0$$

The matrix λI is equal to $\lambda M^{-1}IM$, so the equation may be rewritten

$$|M^{-1}LM - \lambda M^{-1}IM| = 0$$

Factoring and using the fact that the determinant of the product of square matrices equals the product of their determinants, we have

$$|(M^{-1}L - M^{-1}\lambda I)M| = |M^{-1}(L - \lambda I)M| = |M^{-1}|\,|L - \lambda I|\,|M| = 0$$

Since M and M^{-1} are nonsingular, any root of (A4.30) is also a root of (A4.28).

The result just derived may be demonstrated by a more intrinsic argument. If A is a characteristic vector with value λ, we have

$$LA = \lambda A$$

as in (A4.26). Using the new name for A, $M^{-1}A$, and the new matrix representation of $\mathscr{L}$, $M^{-1}LM$, we have

$$(M^{-1}LM)(M^{-1}A) = M^{-1}(LA) = M^{-1}(\lambda A) = \lambda(M^{-1}A)$$

so that λ is still a characteristic root and $M^{-1}A$ is still a characteristic vector.

Example I

A simple transformation $\mathscr{L}$ with equations

$$w_x = 3v_x \qquad w_y = -2v_y$$

has obvious characteristic values 3 and -2. Corresponding characteristic vectors are any multiple of $\mathbf{I} = (1,0)$ and of $\mathbf{J} = (0,1)$. Using the machinery for finding characteristic roots developed in this section,

$$|L - \lambda I| = \begin{vmatrix} 3 - \lambda & 0 \\ 0 & -2 - \lambda \end{vmatrix} = 0$$

which has roots $\lambda = 3$, $\lambda = -2$.

Example 2

Now consider the transformation $\mathscr{M}$ with equations

$$w_x = 28v_x - 50v_y$$
$$w_y = 15v_x - 27v_y$$

Its characteristic roots are given by

$$\begin{vmatrix} 28 - \lambda & -50 \\ 15 & -27 - \lambda \end{vmatrix} = 0$$

or $-(28 - \lambda)(27 + \lambda) + 750 = 0$, which simplifies to $\lambda^2 - \lambda - 6 = 0$.

The roots are again $\lambda = 3$, $\lambda = -2$. The result is not surprising since the matrix of this transformation is similar to that for the preceding example:

$$\begin{bmatrix} 28 & -50 \\ 15 & -27 \end{bmatrix} = \begin{bmatrix} 3 & -5 \\ -1 & 2 \end{bmatrix}^{-1} \begin{bmatrix} 3 & 0 \\ 0 & -2 \end{bmatrix} \begin{bmatrix} 3 & -5 \\ -1 & 2 \end{bmatrix}$$

To find proper vectors for the transformation $\mathscr{M}$, suppose that (a_x, a_y) is a characteristic vector for characteristic value $\lambda = 3$:

$$\begin{bmatrix} 28 & -50 \\ 15 & -27 \end{bmatrix} \begin{bmatrix} a_x \\ a_y \end{bmatrix} = 3 \begin{bmatrix} a_x \\ a_y \end{bmatrix}$$

Carrying out the matrix multiplication and using the definition of matrix equality, we get

$$28a_x - 50a_y = 3a_x \qquad \text{or} \qquad 25a_x = 50a_y$$
$$15a_x - 27a_y = 3a_y \qquad \text{or} \qquad 15a_x = 30a_y$$

From either of these equations we see that the characteristic vectors for $\lambda = 3$ are parallel to $(2,1)$. Similarly, for $\lambda = -2$, from

$$28a_x - 50a_y = -2a_x$$

we find that the characteristic vectors are parallel to $(5,3)$. Note that the characteristic vectors in Example 1 are at right angles while those in Example 2 are not. It is apparent that the change in reference frame was a drastic one, introducing skew axes, but that characteristic values are persistent.

Example 3

Consider the familiar transformation for rotating the xy plane.

$$x' = x \cos \theta - y \sin \theta$$
$$y' = x \sin \theta + y \cos \theta$$

Let us examine its characteristic equation:

$$\begin{vmatrix} \cos \theta - \lambda & -\sin \theta \\ \sin \theta & \cos \theta - \lambda \end{vmatrix} = 1$$

This equation simplifies to

$$\lambda^2 - 2\lambda \cos \theta + 1 = 0$$

By the usual quadratic formula, the characteristic roots are

$$\lambda = \cos \theta \pm \sqrt{\cos^2 \theta - 1}$$

These roots are real only for the cases where θ is an integral multiple of $180°$. This conclusion should agree with your mental picture of a rotation of the xy plane about the z axis. Only when the angle of rotation is $0°$, $180°$, etc., will any position vector map into a vector parallel to itself. When $\theta = 0°$, $360°$, $720°$, etc., $\lambda = +1$ and *every* vector in the plane is a characteristic vector. When $\theta = 180°$, $540°$, etc., $\lambda = -1$, and again every vector is characteristic. If this rotation about the z axis is regarded as a three-dimensional phenomenon, then, regardless of the size of θ, any vector parallel to the z axis is proper, with characteristic value 1.

It is worth observing that *distinct characteristic roots have independent characteristic vectors*. Suppose that roots λ_1, λ_2, λ_3 lead to vectors $\mathbf{A}_1$, $\mathbf{A}_2$, $\mathbf{A}_3$. Suppose that one of the vectors, say, $\mathbf{A}_1$, is equal to a linear combination of $\mathbf{A}_2$, $\mathbf{A}_3$. Then

(A4.31) $$\mathbf{A}_1 = c\mathbf{A}_2 + d\mathbf{A}_3$$

for scalars c, d. First note that $\mathbf{A}_2$ cannot be parallel to $\mathbf{A}_3$. For suppose that $\mathbf{A}_2 = k\mathbf{A}_3$. Then $\mathscr{L}(\mathbf{A}_2) = \lambda_2 \mathbf{A}_2$, but also $\mathscr{L}(\mathbf{A}_2) = \mathscr{L}(k\mathbf{A}_3) = k\mathscr{L}(\mathbf{A}_3) = k\lambda_3\mathbf{A}_3$. Hence $\lambda_2\mathbf{A}_2 = \lambda_2 k\mathbf{A}_3 = k\lambda_3\mathbf{A}_3$, so that $\lambda_2 = \lambda_3$, contrary to the assumption that the characteristic roots are distinct. Similarly, operating with $\mathscr{L}$ on both sides of (A4.31), we get

$$c\lambda_1\mathbf{A}_2 + d\lambda_1\mathbf{A}_3 = c\lambda_2\mathbf{A}_2 + d\lambda_3\mathbf{A}_3$$

This may be rewritten

$$c(\lambda_1 - \lambda_2)\mathbf{A}_2 = d(\lambda_3 - \lambda_1)\mathbf{A}_3$$

Since $\mathbf{A}_2$ and $\mathbf{A}_3$ are not parallel and since the factors $\lambda_1 - \lambda_2$ and $\lambda_3 - \lambda_1$ are not zero, it follows that $c = d = 0$. Hence Eq. (A4.31) and the assumption of dependence are contradicted.

A4.6. APPLICATIONS

Many of the matrices occurring in mechanics are symmetric. Among these are the inertia matrix M of Example 5 in Sec. A4.4, the strain matrix of Eq. (20.10) in Chap. 20, and the stress matrix in Eq. (20.59).

Symmetric matrices have the important property that characteristic vectors corresponding to distinct real characteristic values are perpendicular. (Furthermore, it can be shown that *the characteristic values of a real symmetric matrix are necessarily real*.) Suppose that L is a symmetric matrix, that λ_1 and λ_2 are unequal characteristic values, and that $\mathbf{A}_1$ and $\mathbf{A}_2$ are corresponding characteristic vectors represented by column matrices A_1 and A_2. Then

$$LA_1 = \lambda_1 A_1$$

$$LA_2 = \lambda_2 A_2$$

Using the fact that $(LA_1)^t = A_1^t L^t$, the first of these equations is equivalent to $A_1^t L^t = \lambda_1 A_1^t$. Let us now consider the product $(A_1^t L^t)A_2 = (\lambda_1 A_1^t)A_2$. By the associative law and the symmetry of L (so that $L^t = L$), the same product may be written

$$A_1^t(LA_2) = A_1^t(\lambda_2 A_2) = \lambda_2(A_1^t A_2)$$

Hence

$$\lambda_1(A_1^t A_2) = \lambda_2(A_1^t A_2)$$

or

$$(\lambda_1 - \lambda_2)(A_1^t A_2) = 0$$

Since the factor $\lambda_1 - \lambda_2$ is not zero, we have

$$A_1^t A_2 = 0$$

which is equivalent to

$$\mathbf{A}_1 \cdot \mathbf{A}_2 = 0$$

This equation asserts that the vectors $\mathbf{A}_1$ and $\mathbf{A}_2$ are perpendicular.

If the roots of the characteristic equation are not distinct, we have the same characteristic root for two or more independent vectors. In that case all vectors spanned by these vectors are characteristic, with the same characteristic value. If $\mathbf{A}_1$ and $\mathbf{A}_2$ are independent characteristic vectors with characteristic value λ, then the vector $c_1\mathbf{A}_1 + c_2\mathbf{A}_2$ for any scalars c_1, c_2 is a characteristic vector:

$$\mathscr{L}(c_1\mathbf{A}_1 + c_2\mathbf{A}_2) = c_1\mathscr{L}(\mathbf{A}_1) + c_2\mathscr{L}(\mathbf{A}_2)$$
$$= c_1\lambda\mathbf{A}_1 + c_2\lambda\mathbf{A}_2$$
$$= \lambda(c_1\mathbf{A}_1 + c_2\mathbf{A}_2)$$

In the plane spanned by $\mathbf{A}_1$ and $\mathbf{A}_2$, any pair of perpendicular vectors may be selected. Similar arguments extend to higher dimensions. Our conclusion may be stated thus:

(A4.32) *A real symmetric* 3×3 *matrix has three mutually perpendicular characteristic vectors*.

If characteristic vectors of a symmetric matrix S are allowed to determine coordinate axes as suggested by the preceding proposition, the given matrix may be replaced by a similar matrix D whose nonzero entries lie on the principal diagonal.

These entries are the characteristic values of the original matrix. The matrix equation relating S and D is

$$D = P^{-1}SP$$

Such a change of coordinates may always be effected by a matrix P which is *orthogonal*, i.e., having the property $PP' = I$. An orthogonal matrix corresponds to a transformation where distances and angles are preserved—as we should desire for a simple change of coordinates in mechanics. The possibility of reducing a symmetric matrix to diagonal form has been used informally in the text when inertia, strain, and stress matrices have been simplified by a shift to principal axes.

It is interesting to note that a skew-symmetric matrix [such as occurs in Eq. (20.28)] can have no characteristic roots except zero. Suppose that K is skew-symmetric and that A is a characteristic vector. Then the product $A^t K A$ may be evaluated in two ways:

$$A^t K A = -(A^t K^t)A = -(KA)^t A = -\lambda(A^t A)$$
$$A^t K A = A^t(\lambda A) = \lambda(A^t A)$$

From

$$\lambda(A^t A) = -\lambda(A^t A)$$

we conclude:

$$\lambda = 0 \qquad \text{or} \qquad |A| = 0$$

Example I

Consider the symmetric matrix

$$S = \begin{bmatrix} 19 & -4 & -10 \\ -4 & 7 & -14 \\ -10 & -14 & 10 \end{bmatrix}$$

Its characteristic equation is

$$\begin{vmatrix} 19 - \lambda & -4 & -10 \\ -4 & 7 - \lambda & -14 \\ -10 & -14 & 10 - \lambda \end{vmatrix} = 0$$

or

$$-\lambda^3 + 36\lambda^2 - 81\lambda - 4{,}374 = 0$$

or

$$-(\lambda - 27)(\lambda + 9)(\lambda - 18) = 0$$

so that the characteristic roots are 27, -9, 18. To find characteristic vectors, we look first at the equations corresponding to

$$SA = 27A$$

These equations are

$$19a_x - 4a_y - 10a_z = 27a_x$$
$$-4a_x + 7a_y - 14a_z = 27a_y$$
$$-10a_x - 14a_y + 10a_z = 27a_z$$

Solving, we find that, for $\lambda = 27$, A must be a multiple of $(2,1,-2)$. For example,

$$\begin{bmatrix} 19 & -4 & -10 \\ -4 & 7 & -14 \\ -10 & -14 & 10 \end{bmatrix} \begin{bmatrix} 2 \\ 1 \\ -2 \end{bmatrix} = \begin{bmatrix} 54 \\ 27 \\ -54 \end{bmatrix} = 27 \begin{bmatrix} 2 \\ 1 \\ -2 \end{bmatrix}$$

Similarly, we find that for $\lambda = -9$, A must be a multiple of $(1,2,2)$, and for $\lambda = 18$, A must be a multiple of $(2,-2,1)$. These three characteristic vectors are clearly mutually perpendicular. Unit vectors in the same three orthogonal directions are

$$(\tfrac{2}{3},\tfrac{1}{3},-\tfrac{2}{3}) \qquad (\tfrac{1}{3},\tfrac{2}{3},\tfrac{2}{3}) \qquad (\tfrac{2}{3},-\tfrac{2}{3},\tfrac{1}{3})$$

Taking these unit vectors as columns of a matrix, we have

$$P = \begin{bmatrix} \tfrac{2}{3} & \tfrac{1}{3} & \tfrac{2}{3} \\ \tfrac{1}{3} & \tfrac{2}{3} & -\tfrac{2}{3} \\ -\tfrac{2}{3} & \tfrac{2}{3} & \tfrac{1}{3} \end{bmatrix}$$

It is easy to check the relation $P^t P = I$, so that P is orthogonal. The matrix $P^t SP$, similar to S, may be computed directly as

$$\begin{bmatrix} 27 & 0 & 0 \\ 0 & -9 & 0 \\ 0 & 0 & 18 \end{bmatrix}$$

Note that each element on the diagonal, as should be expected with our new axes parallel to characteristic vectors, is equal to the characteristic roots.

Example 2. Skew-symmetric Matrices and Velocity Patterns

In Chap. 13 we considered velocity patterns for a rigid body with one point **O** taken as origin, at rest. The derivative operator d/dt provides a linear transformation $d/dt : \mathbf{R} \to \mathbf{V}$ for position vectors of points of the body. Relative to a fixed reference frame with origin at **O**, let the matrix of the transformation be $D = [d_{ij}]$. The anticommutative relation (13.18)

$$\mathbf{P} \cdot \mathbf{V}_Q = -\mathbf{Q} \cdot \mathbf{V}_P$$

then becomes, in matrix form,

$$P^t DQ = -Q^t DP$$

Treating the basis vectors **I**, **J**, **K** as position vectors, we get such results as

$$[1,0,0]D\begin{bmatrix} 0 \\ 1 \\ 0 \end{bmatrix} = -[0,1,0]D\begin{bmatrix} 1 \\ 0 \\ 0 \end{bmatrix}$$

or

$$d_{12} = -d_{21}$$

In general, we find that

$$d_{ij} = -d_{ji}$$

or that

$$D^t = -D$$

and that D is skew-symmetric.

Since the characteristic equation of D is a cubic polynomial equation with real coefficients, it must have a real root. But since D is skew-symmetric, the only real characteristic root is zero. Hence there is a line through **O** each of whose vectors **R** satisfies

$$DR = 0R$$

or

$$\mathbf{V}_R = \mathbf{O}$$

Thus we find, as before, that if one point of a rigid body is at rest, then all the points on one line are at rest.

Suppose that D, being skew-symmetric, is written

$$D = \begin{bmatrix} 0 & -c & b \\ c & 0 & -a \\ -b & a & 0 \end{bmatrix}$$

We can then compute the velocity of any point $\mathbf{R}$:

$$V = DR = \begin{bmatrix} 0 & -c & b \\ c & 0 & -a \\ -b & a & 0 \end{bmatrix} \begin{bmatrix} x \\ y \\ z \end{bmatrix} = \begin{bmatrix} -cy + bz \\ cx - az \\ -bx + ay \end{bmatrix}$$

Let us pick a corresponding vector $\mathbf{\Omega} = a\mathbf{I} + b\mathbf{J} + c\mathbf{K}$.   Then

$$\mathbf{\Omega} \times \mathbf{R} = \begin{bmatrix} a & b & c \\ x & y & z \\ \mathbf{I} & \mathbf{J} & \mathbf{K} \end{bmatrix}$$

$$= (bz - cy)\mathbf{I} + (cx - az)\mathbf{J} + (ay - bx)\mathbf{K}$$

But this product is precisely the vector represented by the matrix V.   Hence

$$\mathbf{\Omega} \times \mathbf{R} = \mathbf{V}$$

Again we have shown, as in (13.24), that any velocity pattern for a rigid body with one point at rest is instantaneously a rotation about an axis through that point. The angular velocity vector $\mathbf{\Omega}$ can be used to calculate the velocity for any point of the body.

Students who have studied linear algebra will appreciate the following mathematical summary.   Since the determinant of D is zero, the rank of the transformation d/dt is at most 2.   Hence the dimension of the kernel (null space) is at least 1.   But the kernel of the mapping d/dt consists of precisely the points of zero velocity.

SUGGESTED REFERENCES

A useful list of references for a broad field like mechanics is necessarily arbitrary. The following are books to which the author currently refers his own students.

INTRODUCTORY TEXTBOOKS ON MECHANICS

Beer, F. P., and E. R. Johnston, Jr.: "Vector Mechanics for Engineers," McGraw-Hill Book Company, Inc., New York, in press.

Brand, L.: "Vectorial Mechanics," John Wiley & Sons, Inc., New York, 1930.
Emphasizes the postulational approach to mechanics. Considerable detail is given on engineering structures and mechanisms, cables, and belts.

Langhaar, H. L., and A. P. Boresi: "Engineering Mechanics," McGraw-Hill Book Company, Inc., New York, 1959.

Lindsay, R. B.: "Physical Mechanics," 2d ed., D. Van Nostrand Company, Inc., Princeton, N.J., 1950.
A treatment of the mechanical aspects of physics, including kinetic theory of gases, acoustic resonators, surface phenomena and viscosity, and an introduction to advanced mechanics.

Osgood, W. F.: "Mechanics," The Macmillan Company, New York, 1937.
A critical approach with good examples.

Symon, K. R.: "Mechanics," 2d ed., Addison-Wesley Publishing Company, Inc., Reading, Mass., 1960.
A useful development of physical mechanics.

Synge, J. L., and B. A. Griffith: "Principles of Mechanics," 3d ed., McGraw-Hill Book Company, Inc., New York, 1959.
For supplemental reading on the foundations of mechanics, and on advanced methods, the motion of a charged particle, and the special theory of relativity.

PROBLEM COLLECTIONS

Karelitz, G. B., J. Ormondroyd, and J. M. Garrelts: "Problems in Mechanics," The Macmillan Company, New York, 1939.

McLean, W. G., and E. W. Nelson: "Theory and Problems of Engineering Mechanics," Schaum Publishing Company, Inc., New York, 1952.

Spiegel, M. R.: "Theory and Problems of Vector Analysis," Schaum Publishing Company, Inc., New York, 1959.

ADVANCED OR SPECIALIZED REFERENCES

Appell, P.: "Traité de mécanique rationnelle," 5th ed., Gauthier-Villars, Paris, 1926.
A singularly lucid treatise of which the first volume especially is a suitable reference for intermediate students.

Aris, R.: "Vectors, Tensors, and the Basic Equations of Fluid Mechanics," Prentice-Hall, Inc., Englewood Cliffs, N.J., 1962.
A modern introduction to tensors applied to fluid mechanics.

Becker, R. A.: "Introduction to Theoretical Mechanics," McGraw-Hill Book Company, Inc., New York, 1954.

Birkhoff, G.: "Hydromechanics," 2d ed., Princeton University Press, Princeton, N.J., 1960.
Contains an account of dimensional analysis applied to modeling.

Coe, C. J.: "Theoretical Mechanics," The Macmillan Company, New York, 1938.
A treatise on vectorial mechanics emphasizing mathematical niceties.

Constant, F. W.: "Theoretical Physics—Mechanics," Addison-Wesley Publishing Company, Inc., Reading, Mass., 1954.
An introduction to theoretical mechanics at an intermediate level.

Corben, H. C., and P. Stehle: "Classical Mechanics," 2d ed., John Wiley & Sons, Inc., New York, 1960.
A modern sophisticated treatment of mechanics.

Coulson, C. A.: "Waves," 7th ed., Oliver & Boyd Ltd., London, 1955.
A concise treatment of mechanical, acoustical, and electrical waves.

Crandall, S. H., and N. C. Dahl (eds.): "An Introduction to the Mechanics of Solids," McGraw-Hill Book Company, Inc., New York, 1959.
The equilibrium of deformable bodies is approached from the viewpoint of engineering science.

Geiringer, H.: "Geometrical Foundations of Mechanics," mimeographed notes, Brown University, 1942.
An advanced treatment, unusual in its perspective as well as its methods.

Goldstein, H.: "Classical Mechanics," Addison-Wesley Publishing Company, Inc., Reading, Mass., 1950.
A modern treatment of advanced dynamics.   Contains an excellent bibliography.

Jeans, Sir James: "An Introduction to the Kinetic Theory of Gases," The Macmillan Company, New York, 1940.
For further reading concerning the statistical use of mechanics in the theory of heat.

Johnson, W. C.: "Mathematical and Physical Principles of Engineering Analysis," McGraw-Hill Book Company, Inc., New York, 1944.
A systematic approach to the setting up of practical problems.   Use is made of electrical analogues of mechanical systems.

Kaplan, W.: "Advanced Calculus," Addison-Wesley Publishing Company, Inc., Reading, Mass., 1952.
This book contains a development of classical vector analysis.

Kinsley, L. E., and A. R. Frey: "Fundamentals of Acoustics," John Wiley & Sons, Inc., New York, 1950.
For a more extensive treatment of waves in elastic media.

Landau, L. D., and E. M. Lifshitz: "Mechanics," Addison-Wesley Publishing Company, Inc., Reading, Mass., 1960.
An English translation of an outstanding advanced treatise.

Langhaar, H. L.: "Dimensional Analysis and the Theory of Models," John Wiley & Sons, Inc., New York, 1951.
For theory and applications of dimensional analysis.

Lass, H.: "Vector and Tensor Analysis," McGraw-Hill Book Company, Inc., New York, 1950.
A source for further information on the theory and use of vectors.

McCuskey, S. W.: "An Introduction to Advanced Dynamics," Addison-Wesley Publishing Company, Inc., Reading, Mass., 1959.

Milne-Thomson, L. M.: "Theoretical Hydrodynamics," 4th ed., The Macmillan Company, New York, 1960.
A standard text using vector methods.

Morse, P. M.: "Vibration and Sound," 2d ed., McGraw-Hill Book Company, Inc., New York, 1948.
A source for material on mechanical oscillations and waves.

Munroe, M. E.: "Modern Multidimensional Calculus" Addison-Wesley Publishing Company, Inc., Reading, Mass., 1963.

This singular textbook contains a modern introduction to vector calculus.

Olson, H. F.: "Dynamical Analogies," D. Van Nostrand Company, Inc., Princeton, N.J., 1943.

Prager, W.: "Introduction to Mechanics of Continua," Ginn and Company, Boston, 1961.

An austere basic course on deformable media.

Schwartz, M., S. Green, and W. A. Rutledge: "Vector Analysis with Applications to Geometry and Physics," Harper & Row, Publishers, Incorporated, New York, 1960.

A detailed treatment of classical vector analysis and its applications.

Slater, J. C., and N. H. Frank: "Mechanics," McGraw-Hill Book Company, Inc., New York, 1947.

A good reference for advanced mechanics including oscillating systems.

Sokolnikoff, I. S.: "Mathematical Theory of Elasticity," 2d ed., McGraw-Hill Book Company, Inc., New York, 1956.

Springer, C. E.: "Tensor and Vector Analysis," The Ronald Press Company, New York, 1962.

An intermediate introduction to tensors, showing the relationships with vector analysis and with differential geometry.

Timoshenko, S. P., and D. H. Young: "Advanced Dynamics," McGraw-Hill Book Company, Inc., New York, 1948.

For a more detailed account of small vibrations and of gyrostatic phenomena.

Webster, A. G.: "The Dynamics of Particles and of Rigid, Elastic, and Fluid Bodies," Dover Publications, Inc., New York, 1959.

LIST OF ANSWERS TO SOME EXERCISES

(Generally to slide-rule accuracy)

CHAPTER 2

3. 911 ft. **5.** 0.663, 0.500, 0.557. **7.** $\gamma = 60°$ or $120°$. **21.** $5\underline{/135°}$, $5\underline{/-30°}$.
29. (a) $13\underline{/67.4°}$, (b) $29\underline{/313.6°} = 29\underline{/-46.4°}$. **33.** (a) 5, (c) 7.33, (e) -2.70.
37. (a) $-11.49\mathbf{I} + 9.64\mathbf{J}$, (b) $-5\mathbf{J}$, (c) $80\mathbf{J} - 60\mathbf{K}$, (d) $20\mathbf{I} + 30\mathbf{J} - 60\mathbf{K}$,
(e) $25\mathbf{I} + 35.3\mathbf{J} - 25\mathbf{K}$. **39.** (a) 1.7, $0.577\mathbf{I} + 0.577\mathbf{J} + 0.577\mathbf{K}$;
(b) 1.4, $0.707\mathbf{I} + 0.707\mathbf{K}$; (c) 9, $0.333\mathbf{I} + 0.667\mathbf{J} - 0.667\mathbf{K}$; (d) 15.9, $0.130\mathbf{I} + 0.99\mathbf{J}$;
(e) 7, $\mathbf{J}$. **41.** $(-3.86, 3.92, 0.06)$. **43.** (a) 7.07; 0.707, 0, -0.707;
(b) 13.9; 0.502, 0.574, 0.646. **47.** (a) $70.5°$, (b) $119.7°$, (c) $143.2°$, (d) $90°$.
49. $|\mathbf{A}| = |\mathbf{B}|$. **51.** (a) $-6\mathbf{J}$, (b) $5.52\mathbf{I} - 7.36\mathbf{K}$. **53.** -5.0, 7.0.
57. (a) $(984; 2,780; 2,700)$; (b) $(-1,530; 2,570; 2,660)$; (c) $(-2,810; -2,290; -1,690)$.
59. $(-0.49, -0.65, -0.57)$. **63.** $-0.470\mathbf{I} + 0.706\mathbf{J} - 0.529\mathbf{K}$.
65. $1\underline{/115.6°}$, $1\underline{/176.6°}$, $1\underline{/-64.4°}$, $1\underline{/-3.4°}$. **71.** (a) $5.0\mathbf{I} + 8.7\mathbf{J} - 6.0\mathbf{K}$,
(b) $(3.0, 8.5, -45°)$. **75.** The angle between $\mathbf{E}$ and $\mathbf{F}$ must be $75.5°$. **81.** 3.61.
83. $x - 2y - 3z = 0$.

CHAPTER 3

7. $9.3\underline{/38°}$. **9.** 10.6 lb; 0.48, 0.62, 0.61. **17.** $133.4°$. **19.** 2.0 lb, 1.7 lb.
21. 44.1 lb, $21.8°$ above plane. **27.** (a) $-3.6°$, $63.6°$; (b) 598 lb, 267 lb.
29. 981 newtons; 1,690 newtons. **35.** $35.1°$ with vertical; 2,050 lb; 1,224 lb.
37. $\frac{1}{3}$. **39.** $w'' \leq \mu(w + 3w')$.

CHAPTER 4

1. $20°$, 240 lb. **3.** $\theta = \phi$. **5.** 14.1 newtons. **7.** 173 lb.
9. 1,000 lb; 4,000 lb; both tensions. **11.** $b \geq h(2 \tan \phi - \tan \theta)$.
21. $p_{max} = w(\sin \theta + \mu \cos \theta)/(\cos \theta - \mu \sin \theta)$,
$p_{min} = w(\sin \theta - \mu \cos \theta)/(\cos \theta + \mu \sin \theta)$. **23.** 307 lb. **25.** ab: $-2,000$;
bc: $-2,000$; ad: 1,730; de: 580; ce: $-1,150$; bd: 0; cd: 2,310
(compressions indicated by "$-$"). **27.** Reading left to right, top to bottom:
1,000; 707; -707; 1,410; 1,000; $-2,120$; $-2,120$. **29.** 353 lb.

CHAPTER 5

1. A straight line. **3.** $-0.898\mathbf{J}$ ft/sec. **5.** $(2t + \Delta t)\mathbf{I} + (1 - 4t - 2\Delta t)\mathbf{J}$.
11. (a) $4t\mathbf{I} + 4\mathbf{J}$, (b) $4 \cos t\mathbf{I} - 4 \sin t\mathbf{J} + 2t\mathbf{K}$. **13.** $10/\underline{36.9°}$. **17.** 12.8°, 44.1 mph.
19. 480 ft. **21.** 149 mph, 30.2° E of N. **23.** 11.47 mph, from 67.5° W of S.
25. 20.7° E of N, 35.5 min. **27.** From 18.5° E of S. **29.** For example, $t = \pi/3$ sec,
$\mathbf{V} = 30\mathbf{I}$ ft/sec. **31.** 2. **33.** $0.815\mathbf{I} + 0.533\mathbf{J} - 0.228\mathbf{K}$; 4.44 m/sec.
35. $v = 10$ m/sec, $\mathbf{T} = -0.8\mathbf{I} + 0.6\mathbf{K}$, $a_N = 16$ m/sec², $a_T = 0$, $\rho = 6.25$ m.
37. 0.314 m/sec², 8.88 m/sec². **39.** 1, 0. **41.** 0, 2, 4. **43.** 5.29 ft/sec. **45.** 5.6 ft/sec.
49. 6 sec, 0. **51.** 0.511 sec, 5 ft/sec². **53.** 20, 0.221 sec. **55.** 9.43 ft/sec, 29.6 ft/sec².
59. (b) $18\mathbf{I} + 18\mathbf{J}$. **61.** (a) 642 ft/sec; (b) 1,284 ft/sec. **65.** $(\frac{1}{3})(\mathbf{\bar{R}}_1 + \mathbf{\bar{R}}_2 + \mathbf{\bar{R}}_3)$.
67. 1.5 ft and 1.0 ft from the perpendicular sides of the triangle.
69. $3\mathbf{I} - \mathbf{J} + 4\mathbf{K}$ ft/sec, $-3\mathbf{J} + 4\mathbf{K}$ ft/sec², $0.59\mathbf{I} - 0.20\mathbf{J} + 0.78\mathbf{K}$.
71. 103.9 mph. **73.** 10.53 miles, 15° E of S. **75.** 28.1° E of N, 1.3 hr. **79.** 2.63 sec.
81. 136.5, 182.2, 228 cm/sec²; 0.33 sec. **83.** 6,000; 3,600 cm/sec².
85. 1.25 ft/sec, $-0.8\mathbf{J} + 0.6\mathbf{K}$, 0.90 ft/sec², 1.20 ft/sec², 1.30 ft. **89.** 3.63, 3.58 ft/sec;
-1.42, 0.64 ft/sec². **91.** 0.326 sec. **93.** 12.5 miles. **95.** 628 mph²; 2,513 mph².
97. 0.8 cm/sec², 20 cm. **99.** 853 cm, 3.39 cm/sec². **103.** (a) $r[1 - (2/\pi)^2]^{\frac{1}{2}}$.
105. 58,500 ft; 12.9°; 3,100 ft.

CHAPTER 6

1. 9.81 newtons. **3.** 8.05 ft/sec². **5.** 32.2 ft/sec². **7.** 4.45×10^5 dynes.
9. 10^5 dynes. **11.** 7,200 lb. **13.** $2\mathbf{I} - 6\mathbf{K}$ ft/sec². **15.** 151.9 lb.
17. 3.5 ft, 111.7 ft/sec². **19.** 1,437 lb. **21.** 14.8 m/sec. **23.** 17.9 ft/sec.
27. (a) 0.712 sec, (b) 32.1 ft. **31.** 0.193 lb, 14.2 ft/sec².
33. 18.4 ft/sec², 13.8 ft/sec², 23.0 ft/sec². **35.** 8.05 ft/sec², 11.25 lb, 3.75 lb.
39. (a) $\mathbf{\bar{R}} = 0.2\mathbf{I} + 0.6\mathbf{J}$ m, (b) $\mathbf{\bar{A}} = 0.2\mathbf{I} + 0.6\mathbf{J}$ m/sec². **41.** 262, 200 lb.
43. 5.55 sec. **45.** (a) 153 lb, 385 lb; (b) 192 lb, 319 lb. **47.** 0.015. **49.** 0.59.
51. $4\pi^2/9g$. **53.** 9.8 lb. **57.** (a) 4.99 mph, (b) 89.5 ft. **59.** 10 rad/sec.
61. 3.27 m/sec², 9.81 newtons. **63.** 3.27 m/sec². **65.** $k = \rho(1 + \mu)/\mu(1 + \rho)$.
67. 5.5 ft (1.67 m).

CHAPTER 7

1. 28.8 lb-sec. **3.** 0.8 lb-sec. **5.** $2.58\mathbf{I} + 5\mathbf{J} - 4.51\mathbf{K}$ ft/sec. **7.** $0.99/\underline{105°}$ lb-sec.
9. $2mv \cos \theta$. **11.** 32 m/sec. **13.** 69 lb. **15.** 1.33 ft/sec. **17.** 51.3°.
21. (a) $(1/e) \tan \theta_1$, (b) $(1/e)(\tan \theta_1 - \mu - \mu e)$. **25.** 0.25. **27.** -41 ft-lb. **29.** 0.
31. 12 ft-lb. **33.** 0.0114 ft-lb. **35.** 0.101 joule. **37.** 18.4 ft/sec.
39. 9.75×10^3 ft-lb. **41.** 0.032. **43.** 41.8°.
47. (a) $v = [2gs (w_2 - w_1 \sin 20°)/(w_1 + w_2)]^{\frac{1}{2}}$, (b) 4.38 newtons. **49.** 28.1 ft/sec.
57. $2\pi \sqrt{\dfrac{r}{g}}$. **59.** 346 lb. **61.** 289 lb. **63.** Roughly 120, 50 lb. **65.** 5,190 lb.
67. 25.7°, unstable. **69.** $19\mathbf{I} - 30\mathbf{J} + 5\mathbf{K}$ ft/sec.
71. (a) $1.987\mathbf{I} + 3.48\mathbf{J}$ lb-sec ($64\mathbf{I} + 112\mathbf{J}$ poundal-sec), (b) 0 ft-lb. **73.** 20 ft.
77. $\pi(m/k)^{\frac{1}{2}}$, $v_0(mk)^{\frac{1}{2}}$, $-2mv_0$. **79.** 1.33 m/sec. **83.** $(h'/h)^{\frac{1}{2}}$.
87. 0.498 sec, 1.2 lb. **89.** 0.32, -3.2 lb-sec. **91.** $50\mathbf{I} + 20\mathbf{J}$, $10\mathbf{J}$ cm/sec.

93. 24.8 slug-ft/sec, 24.1 ft/sec, 241 ft-lb.   **95.** 72 newtons.   **97.** $wd(1 - s)^2/2s$.
99. 1 ft (i.e., compressed to length 1.5 ft).   **101.** $k^{\frac{1}{2}}r_1(mr_1^2 V_0 \cdot V_0 + k)^{-\frac{1}{2}}$.
105. 1.2 ft/sec.   **107.** $(\frac{2}{3})(mg/k)^{\frac{1}{2}}$.

CHAPTER 8

1. $[lf^{-1}]$.   **3.** $c'c''/(2c'' + c')$.   **5.** $\frac{1}{2}c'c''/(c' + c'')$.   **9.** 3.14 sec, 13 cm.
11. (a) 0.703 sec, (b) 4.47 ft/sec.   **13.** 14.4 sec^{-1}.   **21.** (a) 0.016, (b) 22 oscillations.
25. (a) 0.0309 m/newton, (b) 6.00 newton-sec/m, (c) 11.4 newton-sec/m.
27. (a) 1 ft, (b) 1.01 ft.   **29.** $\pi/2\lambda$.   **31.** (a) 76.6 rev/min, (b) 0.0166.   **33.** $l + \frac{1}{2} mgc$.
35. 0.0405 m/newton, 15.7 cm/sec, 1.0 newton-sec/m, 63 newton-sec/m.
37. 0.569 m, 0.184 m/sec.   **39.** 0.003 ft/lb; 1.6 lb-sec/ft; 50; 1,600 lb-sec/ft.
41. (a) 0.625 ft-lb, (b) 0.625 ft-lb, (c) 0.261 sec.   **43.** 1.39 sec.
49. (a) 0.079 sec, 0.13 ft; (b) 0.050 sec, 0.056 ft.

CHAPTER 9

1. (a) -19.8K, (b) **O**, (c) -17.1K, (d) **O**, (e) **I** − **J** + **K**.
3. **R** = x**I** + **J** (i.e., the locus is the line $y = 1$).   **7.** (a) 2**I** − 2**K**, (b) −4**I** + 8**J** − 4**K**,
(c) **O**.   **17.** (a) 0.35**I** − 0.94**J**, (b) 5.0 ft/sec, (c) 0.6**I** − 0.8**J**, (d) 3.6 ft/sec^2,
(e) 4.8 ft/sec^2, (f) $\rho = 5.2$ ft, (g) 0.65 rad/sec.   **19.** 15.   **23.** 18.3.
39. (a) joule, (b) newton-sec, (c) ft-lb-sec^2, (d) lb-ft-sec^{-1}.   **41.** 7.37 ft-lb-sec^2.
43. $[f^{-1}l^4t^{-4}]$.   **45.** Const $(\beta/\rho)^{\frac{1}{2}}$.   **47.** Const $\gamma^{-\frac{1}{2}}m^{-\frac{1}{2}}a^{\frac{3}{2}}$.
53. -0.385**I** + 0.077**K**.

CHAPTER 10

1. 2.60 ft.   **5.** 20.8 ft-lb; -0.481, 0.144, 0.865.   **9.** (a) -5**K** ft-lb, (b) -20**K** ft-lb.
11. 728 ft-lb.   **13.** -100**K** ft-lb, $\gamma_x = 0$, $\gamma_y = 0$, $\gamma_z = -100$ ft-lb.
15. (a) -16**I** + 12**J** + 18**K** ft-lb; (b) -16**I** + 12**J** + 6**K** ft-lb;
(c) -16**I** + 12**J** + 12**K** ft-lb; (d) 18**K** ft-lb; (e) -12**I** + 9**J** + 17**K** ft-lb;
(f) $\gamma_x = -16$ ft-lb, $\gamma_y = 12$ ft-lb, $\gamma_z = 18$ ft-lb.   **17.** 165.4 ft-lb.   **19.** -47.5.
23. Couple: 2.45d (where d is length of cube); 0.408, -0.817, 0.408.   Force: 5.39;
0.371, 0.557, 0.743.
25. $\bar{\Gamma} = -6$**I** + 40**J** − 72**K** ft-lb, $\bar{F} = 10$**I** + 2**J** lb.
27. CA (compression): 10,400 lb; BA (tension): 8,200 lb.
29. 25 lb.   **31.** (a) 74**I** − 144**J** + 39**K** ft-lb; (b) $-46.7, 0, 69.3$ ft-lb.   **35.** -300 ft-lb.
37. (a) 100**I** + 75**J** + 50**K** lb, (b) 500**J** − 750**K** ft-lb.   **39.** (a) 20**I** − 30**J** newton,
(b) 2.8 m.   **41.** **F** = 2**I** + 14**J**, **G** = 1**I** lb.

CHAPTER 11

3. A force 16**I** lb acting at (0, 9.5, 0) ft.
5. A force 8**J** lb acting at ($-23.75, 0, -3.75$) ft.   **9.** $b = 1,000$; $c = 1,500$ lb.
11. 66.7 lb, 66.7 lb.   **13.** (a) 393 lb; (b) 314, 364 lb.   **15.** 13.3 lb, 13.3 lb.
17. 1,000; 866; 0; 1,000; 0; 866; 1,000; 1,000; 0; 866; 0; 1,000; 866 lb.
19. $f_s = \frac{1}{24} \mu l^2$.   **21.** -75 ft-lb, 15 lb.   **25.** 10**I** lb, **O** ft-lb.

27. (*a*) 675 lb, (*b*) 428 lb.   **29.** $144\mathbf{I} + 100\mathbf{J}$ lb.   **33.** $(wr/2l)\,\csc^2(\theta/2)$.
35. (*a*) $130\mathbf{I} - 160\mathbf{J}$ lb; (*b*) $-1{,}300\mathbf{K}$ lb; (*c*) $x = 23.1$ ft.   **37.** $w/2$.   **41.** 39°.
43. 292 lb, 527 lb, 667 lb.   **45.** 93.8, 93.8, 100 lb.   **47.** (*a*) 3.19 tons, (*b*) 1.88 tons,
(*c*) 3.13 tons.   **49.** 195, 71.5, 128.5 lb.   **51.** (*a*) 160 lb;
(*b*) $-213\mathbf{I} + 150\mathbf{J}$, $53\mathbf{I} + 150\mathbf{J}$ lb.   **53.** (*a*) 3,543 lb; (*b*) 30°; (*c*) 3,380 lb;
(*d*) 3,384 tension; (*e*) 3,543 compression; (*f*) 0; (*g*) 3,384 tension;
(*h*) 3,543 compression; (*i*) 0; (*j*) 0.   **55.** (*a*) 31,700 lb; $5{,}810\mathbf{I} - 29{,}200\mathbf{J}$ lb;
(*b*) 3,535 tension; 3,535 compression; 7,070 compression; 6,170 tension;
4,000 compression.

CHAPTER 12

1. (*a*) $fr\,\theta/\omega$, (*b*) $(fr/\omega)\sin\theta$.   **3.** 710 m/sec.
9. 100 percent (assuming circular lunar orbit), 90 percent for $e = 0.0549$.   **11.** 1.034.
13. 184.5.   **15.** Hyperbolic.   **27.** (*a*) 6,500 A; (*b*) 1,200 A.
29. $f/v = (2/n)(n - 1)^2(2n - 1)^{-1}$, $\lim = 1$.
35. 1.414.   **37.** 258 days.   **47.** 0.21.   **53.** 100 percent.
55. 162,700 miles; 0.82; 36,200 miles²/sec; 8,820 mph; 295,900 miles; 870 mph.

CHAPTER 13

1. $\omega = \omega_0 + \alpha t$, $\theta = \theta_0 + \omega_0 t + \frac{1}{2}\alpha t^2$.   **3.** -0.167 rad/sec², $\omega_{\text{eff}} = 0$.
5. 5.33 rad.   **9.** 2.2×10^4 ft/sec².
13. 0.577, -0.577, 0.577; 1.732 rad/sec; $(0, 2, -2)$ ft.
15. $40\mathbf{I} + 20\mathbf{J}$ ft/sec, $-400\mathbf{I} + 800\mathbf{J}$ ft/sec².   **23.** $(0, 8)$.   **29.** 533 ft/sec.
31. 14.36 rad/sec.   **33.** One diameter below lowest point of wheel.
35. 8 in. vertically below center of wheel.   **37.** $3\mathbf{J}$.   **39.** 138.2 rad/sec.
41. 50 ft/sec², 53.1°.   **43.** (*a*) 2 rad/sec, (*b*) $7\mathbf{I}$ ft/sec, (*c*) $5\mathbf{I} - 2\mathbf{J}$ ft/sec.
45. $80\mathbf{I} - 32\mathbf{J} + 80\mathbf{K}$ ft/sec.   **47.** 1.5 ft below wheel.
51. 2.90 ft vertically above *B*.

CHAPTER 14

1. $100\mathbf{J} - 1{,}050\mathbf{K}$, $-1{,}150\mathbf{K}$, $-100\mathbf{J} - 1{,}050\mathbf{K}$, $-950\mathbf{K}$ mph.
13. 15 ft/sec, 20 ft/sec, 125 ft/sec², 200 ft/sec².   **15.** 1.57 sec.
17. (*a*) 1.28 sec, (*c*) 1.32 sec.   **19.** 4.01 rad/sec.   **21.** $2m\omega v'$, $m\omega^2 r$.
25. 45°, 0.00174 rad.   **27.** 6,000; 250 in./sec².
29. $\mathbf{V} = (b + 2ct)\mathbf{I}' + \omega(a + bt + ct^2)\mathbf{J}'$,
$\mathbf{A} = [2c - \omega^2(a + bt + ct^2)]\mathbf{I}' + [2\omega(b + 2ct)]\mathbf{J}'$.
31. (*a*) $60\mathbf{I} - 40\mathbf{J}$ cm/sec; (*b*) $15\mathbf{J}$ cm/sec; (*c*) $60\mathbf{I} - 25\mathbf{J}$ cm/sec;
(*d*) $-800\mathbf{I} - 1{,}200\mathbf{J}$ cm/sec²; (*e*) $600\mathbf{I}$ cm/sec²; (*f*) $-112.5\mathbf{I}$ cm/sec²;
(*g*) $-312.5\mathbf{I} - 1{,}200\mathbf{J}$ cm/sec².   **33.** 29.2 lb.   **41.** 192 ft, West.   **43.** 271°/day.

CHAPTER 15

1. 0.533 m from lightest end.   **3.** 1.5 ft and 5.0 ft from the perpendicular rods.
5. 0.5 in. and 1.5 in. from inside edges.   **7.** $3(5\delta_0 + 4kh)h/5(4\delta_0 + 3kh)$.

9. 0.636 r from center of curvature.   **11.** 0.70 ft from bottom of square.
13. (a) 45 lb_m-ft² or 1.40 slug-ft², (b) 90 lb_m-ft², (c) 90 lb_m-ft², (d) 180 lb_m-ft².
15. $\bar{p}^2 = 3(5\delta_0 + 4kr)r^2/10(3\delta_0 + 2kr)$.   **17.** $(\tfrac{7}{3})mr^2$.
19. 0.90 kg-m², 2.70 kg-m².   **21.** 0.5 r.   **23.** 0.548 r.   **25.** 1.118 a.
29. $\bar{p}^2 = 2a^2b^2/[3(a^2 + b^2)]$.   **31.** 2.4I + 1.3J − 0.8K cm.   **33.** 0.85 in.
37. $0.41b = b/\sqrt{6}$.   **39.** 13.7 in.   **41.** 0.375 a.   **43.** $\bar{p}^2 = (\tfrac{2}{3})r^2$.

CHAPTER 16

1. 5.47, 4.53 lb.   **3.** 0.504, 0.74 newton.   **5.** 143.4 lb (vertical), 12.8° with vertical.
7. r/h.   **9.** 56 lb, 74.1 ft/sec².   **11.** 310 sec.   **13.** 150.5 rev, 60.2 sec.   **15.** 2.828 sec.
17. 120 ft-lb-sec².   **19.** 1.33 ft.   **21.** 2.675 kg-m².   **23.** 0.74 per sec.
25. 1.33; 13.3 ft.   **27.** 2.60 sec.   **29.** 0.571 sec, 4.28 ft.   **31.** 2.24 ft/sec², 22.2 lb.
33. 0.917 sec.   **35.** 3.12 m joule (m mass in kg).   **39.** 0.6 joule.   **41.** 66.7 ft-lb.
43. 2.48 ft/sec.   **45.** 7.22 ft/sec.   **47.** $[(2\gamma rs)/m(\bar{p}^2 + r^2)]^{\frac{1}{2}}$, $\mu mgr1 + (\bar{p}^2/r^2)$.
49. 361, 216 lb.   **51.** 0.889 ft from B'.
53. $\pi[(2r/g)(9\pi − 16)(r' − r)]^{\frac{1}{2}}[(3\pi − 4)r + 4r']^{-\frac{1}{2}}$.   **55.** 1.18 sec.   **57.** 2.25 sec.
61. 0.894 ft.   **63.** 149 ft/sec.   **65.** 12.5 ft/sec, 10 rad/sec, −10 ft/sec, 0.5.
69. 82 rad/sec.   **73.** 0.707 g.   **75.** 77.3 ft/sec².   **77.** 30 ft/sec².
79. 2.95, 2.09, 3.61 sec.   **81.** 2.16 sec, 0.507 rad/sec.   **85.** 7.38 $(r/g)^{\frac{1}{2}}$.
87. 1.565 sec; 29.2, 70.8 cm.   **89.** 0.98 sec.   **91.** 10 in., 4 ft, 30 in.   **93.** $4s/gt^2$.
95. 11.8 ft/sec.   **97.** (a) 8.05 ft/sec², 32.2 rad/sec²; (b) 13.1 ft/sec².
99. (a) $g[\sin \theta − \mu \cos \theta(1 + r/r')]$; (b) $\mu rmg \cos \theta/r'(\bar{a} + g)$.   **101.** 1 ft/sec².
105. $\phi\mathbf{H} \cdot (\mathbf{D_1} − \mathbf{D_0})$.   **107.** 36.6 ft/sec.   **109.** $w/4$, $3w/2$.   **111.** 2.2 percent.
113. 17.9, 11.1 lb.   **115.** 9.27 rad/sec, 13.7 lb at 12.7° with horizontal.   **117.** 0.205.
119. 41.8°, 19.5°.   **121.** 0.32 rad/sec.   **123.** $2\pi(d/6g)^{\frac{1}{2}}$, $2\pi(2d/3g)^{\frac{1}{2}}$.
125. $2r/\pi$, r, $(8g/\pi r)^{\frac{1}{2}}$.   **127.** $\tan \theta = \frac{1}{2}(\text{ctn } \beta − \text{ctn } \alpha)$.   **129.** $2(gr \cos \theta/l)^{\frac{1}{2}}$.
131. $2mgr(1 − \cos \theta)$, $1.5 mr^2\omega^2$, $2\pi(3r/2g)^{\frac{1}{2}}$, unstable.
133. 60°, unstable; 180°, stable.   **135.** $\frac{5}{9}g \sin \beta$.   **137.** $(e/\mu)(8h/g)^{\frac{1}{2}}$.   **141.** 21.9 in.
147. 727 rad/sec.   **149.** 42.8 rad/sec.   **153.** $s^2\Delta\theta^2/c$, $2\pi(7mc/6)^{\frac{1}{2}}$.   **155.** 60°.
157. 141, 181 lb.   **159.** $i = (r^2/a)\{m_2[g − a] − m_1[a + g(\mu \cos \theta + \sin \theta)]\}$.

CHAPTER 17

3. $0.577(1 − x + y + yz − xz − xy)$.   **9.** (a) $(−\gamma m'm/r^2)\mathbf{L}$, (b) **L**, (c) **L**.   **11.** 8.
17. 9.81 newtons/kg.   **19.** (a) $−3x + 7z$, (b) 10.02 ft/sec.   **21.** 9.81×10^3 joules/kg.
25. 2.23.   **27.** 1,640 miles.   **29.** 6.95 mps.   **31.** About 40 miles.
33. (a) 6.0×10^{24} kg, (b) 5.5.   **35.** $a_x(\partial b_x/\partial x) + a_y(\partial b_x/\partial y) + a_z(\partial b_x/\partial z)$.   **37.** **A**.
39. (a) 0, (b) 5.74, (c) 1.6.   **45.** 1.38.   **51.** $(2\gamma mm'/r^3)\mathbf{L}$.

CHAPTER 18

3. 6.75×10^6 lb.   **5.** $h/2$.   **9.** −2.   **15.** (a) $−\mathbf{I} − \mathbf{J} − x^2\mathbf{K}$, (b) **O**.   **17.** **O**.
19. **O** (except at origin).   **21.** (b) and (c) are irrotational.   **23.** (a) $(n + 3)r^n$, (b) 0.
25. 14.6 percent.   **29.** $[(2p_0/\delta_0) \ln (p_1/p_0)]^{\frac{1}{2}}$.   **33.** (a) −2, (b) **O**,
(c) $−0.6\mathbf{I} + 0.8\mathbf{J} − 2.4\mathbf{K}$, (d) 0.   **35.** (a) $2ax\mathbf{I} − b\mathbf{J} + 2cz\mathbf{K}$.   **49.** $−2q\mathbf{L}/4\pi\epsilon_0 r^3$.

CHAPTER 19

1. $2\sigma e_l$.   **3.** 0.004 rad.   **5.** $(f\cos\theta - g\sin\theta)/2rh$, $(f\sin\theta + g\cos\theta)/2rh$.
9. 3.8×10^8 newtons/m².   **11.** 1.38 in., 3.42×10^3 ft-lb/rad.   **12.** $wl^3/4\psi bd^4$.
14. $y = (w/24i'\psi l)(6x^2 l^2 - 4lx^3 + x^4)$.   **17.** 0.0212 percent, 0.0085 percent.
19. $\psi a\epsilon^2/l$.   **21.** 21,800 lb.   **23.** $8.94b$ newtons (for b the thickness in mm).

CHAPTER 20

1. (a) $-\theta(m_1\mathbf{I} - l_1\mathbf{J})$, (b) 0.
5. $e_{xx} = a_{11} - 1$, $e_{yy} = a_{22} - 1$, $e_{xy} = 0.5(a_{12} + a_{21})$, others are zero.
17. 0.032, 0.026, -0.012, 0.040, -0.004, 0.015.   **19.** 22.5°, 112.5°.
21. Greatest: $\theta = 45°$, 135°.   **23.** 5.3×10^{-3} rad (max).
25. $\cos^2\theta\, x_x + \sin 2\theta\, x_y + \sin^2\theta\, y_y$, $\sin\theta\cos\theta(y_y - x_x) + x_y\cos 2\theta$.
27. $-1,000$ lb/in.²; 3,000 lb/in.²   **29.** 3,640 lb/in.²
33. 0.286, 1.40×10^{11} newtons/m².   **35.** Arctan $(e' + e)/(e' - e + 2)$.
41. (a) e, $-0.3e$, $-0.3e$, 0, 0, 0; (b) $0.532e$; (c) $-0.18e$.

CHAPTER 21

6. 426 per sec.   **8.** 156.3 per sec.   **17.** 18.3, 54.8 per sec.   **19.** 5,030 m/sec.
21. $\xi = 2\xi_m \sin[(2n - 1)\pi ct/2l] \sin[(2n - 1)\pi x/2l]$.
23. $\xi = 2\xi_m \sin(\pi cnt/l) \cos(\pi nx/l)$.   **24.** (a) 291 m/sec, (b) 344 m/sec.
33. $\frac{1}{2}\beta(\partial\xi/\partial x)^2$, $\frac{1}{2}\delta(\partial\xi/\partial t)^2$.

CHAPTER 22

1. 1,840 m/sec.   **4.** (a) 5×10^{-21} joule at each point;
(b) 0, 0, 10×10^{-21}, 10×10^{-21} joule; (c) 5×10^{-21} joule.   **6.** 1,300 m/sec.   **7.** p.
8. 7.6×10^6 joules.   **13.** 2,150 m/sec.   **16.** $-46°$C.
19. $3n/4\pi$, $37n/64$, $\frac{3}{10}nmv_0^2$.   **24.** 4 percent.   **25.** $(\pi k\theta/2m)^{\frac{1}{2}}$.
27. 1.0×10^{-7}, 1.0×10^{-5}, 7.7×10^{-4} m.   **33.** $(\frac{3}{5})^{\frac{1}{2}}v_0$, $0.75v_0$, $(\frac{2}{3})v_0$.
37. (a) $(\pi k\theta/2m)^{\frac{1}{2}}$; (b) $v_m = 2v_0/\pi^{\frac{1}{2}}$, $\bar{v} = (6/\pi)^{\frac{1}{2}}v_0$, $v_{av} = 4v_0/\pi$, $v_{imi} = v_0$.

INDEX